Conversion Factors

Mass

$1\ \text{g} = 10^{-3}\ \text{kg}$
$1\ \text{kg} = 10^{3}\ \text{g}$
$1\ \text{u} = 1.66 \times 10^{-24}\ \text{g} = 1.66 \times 10^{-27}\ \text{kg}$
$1\ \text{metric ton} = 1000\ \text{kg}$

Length

$1\ \text{nm} = 10^{-9}\ \text{m}$
$1\ \text{cm} = 10^{-2}\ \text{m} = 0.394\ \text{in.}$
$1\ \text{m} = 10^{-3}\ \text{km} = 3.28\ \text{ft} = 39.4\ \text{in.}$
$1\ \text{km} = 10^{3}\ \text{m} = 0.621\ \text{mi}$
$1\ \text{in.} = 2.54\ \text{cm} = 2.54 \times 10^{-2}\ \text{m}$
$1\ \text{ft} = 0.305\ \text{m} = 30.5\ \text{cm}$
$1\ \text{mi} = 5280\ \text{ft} = 1609\ \text{m} = 1.609\ \text{km}$

Area

$1\ \text{cm}^2 = 10^{-4}\ \text{m}^2 = 0.1550\ \text{in}^2 = 1.08 \times 10^{-3}\ \text{ft}^2$
$1\ \text{m}^2 = 10^{4}\ \text{cm}^2 = 10.76\ \text{ft}^2 = 1550\ \text{in}^2$
$1\ \text{in}^2 = 6.94 \times 10^{-3}\ \text{ft}^2 = 6.45\ \text{cm}^2 = 6.45 \times 10^{-4}\ \text{m}^2$
$1\ \text{ft}^2 = 144\ \text{in}^2 = 9.29 \times 10^{-2}\ \text{m}^2 = 929\ \text{cm}^2$

Volume

$1\ \text{cm}^3 = 10^{-6}\ \text{m}^3 = 3.35 \times 10^{-5}\ \text{ft}^3 = 6.10 \times 10^{-2}\ \text{in}^3$
$1\ \text{m}^3 = 10^{6}\ \text{cm}^3 = 10^{3}\ \text{L} = 35.3\ \text{ft}^3 = 6.10 \times 10^{4}\ \text{in}^3 = 264\ \text{gal}$
$1\ \text{liter} = 10^{3}\ \text{cm}^3 = 10^{-3}\ \text{m}^3 = 1.056\ \text{qt} = 0.264\ \text{gal} = 0.0353\ \text{ft}^3$
$1\ \text{in}^3 = 5.79 \times 10^{-4}\ \text{ft}^3 = 16.4\ \text{cm}^3 = 1.64 \times 10^{-5}\ \text{m}^3$
$1\ \text{ft}^3 = 1728\ \text{in}^3 = 7.48\ \text{gal} = 0.0283\ \text{m}^3 = 28.3\ \text{L}$
$1\ \text{qt} = 2\ \text{pt} = 946\ \text{cm}^3 = 0.946\ \text{L}$
$1\ \text{gal} = 4\ \text{qt} = 231\ \text{in}^3 = 0.134\ \text{ft}^3 = 3.785\ \text{L}$

Time

$1\ \text{h} = 60\ \text{min} = 3600\ \text{s}$
$1\ \text{day} = 24\ \text{h} = 1440\ \text{min} = 8.64 \times 10^{4}\ \text{s}$
$1\ \text{y} = 365\ \text{days} = 8.76 \times 10^{3}\ \text{h} = 5.26 \times 10^{5}\ \text{min} = 3.16 \times 10^{7}\ \text{s}$

Angle

$1\ \text{rad} = 57.3°$

$1° = 0.0175\ \text{rad}$	$60° = \pi/3\ \text{rad}$
$15° = \pi/12\ \text{rad}$	$90° = \pi/2\ \text{rad}$
$30° = \pi/6\ \text{rad}$	$180° = \pi\ \text{rad}$
$45° = \pi/4\ \text{rad}$	$360° = 2\pi\ \text{rad}$

$1\ \text{rev/min} = (\pi/30)\ \text{rad/s} = 0.1047\ \text{rad/s}$

Speed

$1\ \text{m/s} = 3.60\ \text{km/h} = 3.28\ \text{ft/s} = 2.24\ \text{mi/h}$
$1\ \text{km/h} = 0.278\ \text{m/s} = 0.621\ \text{mi/h} = 0.911\ \text{ft/s}$
$1\ \text{ft/s} = 0.682\ \text{mi/h} = 0.305\ \text{m/s} = 1.10\ \text{km/h}$
$1\ \text{mi/h} = 1.467\ \text{ft/s} = 1.609\ \text{km/h} = 0.447\ \text{m/s}$
$60\ \text{mi/h} = 88\ \text{ft/s}$

Force

$1\ \text{N} = 0.225\ \text{lb}$
$1\ \text{lb} = 4.45\ \text{N}$
Equivalent weight of a mass of 1 kg on Earth's surface = 2.2 lb = 9.8 N

Pressure

$1\ \text{Pa}\ (\text{N/m}^2) = 1.45 \times 10^{-4}\ \text{lb/in}^2 = 7.5 \times 10^{-3}\ \text{torr (mm Hg)}$
$1\ \text{torr (mm Hg)} = 133\ \text{Pa}\ (\text{N/m}^2) = 0.02\ \text{lb/in}^2$
$1\ \text{atm} = 14.7\ \text{lb/in}^2 = 1.013 \times 10^{5}\ \text{N/m}^2 = 30\ \text{in. Hg} = 76\ \text{cm Hg}$
$1\ \text{lb/in}^2 = 6.90 \times 10^{3}\ \text{Pa}\ (\text{N/m}^2)$
$1\ \text{bar} = 10^{5}\ \text{Pa}$
$1\ \text{millibar} = 10^{2}\ \text{Pa}$

Energy

$1\ \text{J} = 0.738\ \text{ft}\cdot\text{lb} = 0.239\ \text{cal} = 9.48 \times 10^{-4}\ \text{Btu} = 6.24 \times 10^{18}\ \text{eV}$
$1\ \text{kcal} = 4186\ \text{J} = 3.968\ \text{Btu}$
$1\text{Btu} = 1055\ \text{J} = 778\ \text{ft}\cdot\text{lb} = 0.252\ \text{kcal}$
$1\ \text{cal} = 4.186\ \text{J} = 3.97 \times 10^{-3}\ \text{Btu} = 3.09\ \text{ft}\cdot\text{lb}$
$1\ \text{ft}\cdot\text{lb} = 1.36\ \text{J} = 1.29 \times 10^{-3}\ \text{Btu}$
$1\ \text{eV} = 1.60 \times 10^{-19}\ \text{J}$
$1\ \text{kWh} = 3.6 \times 10^{6}\ \text{J}$

Power

$1\ \text{W} = 0.738\ \text{ft}\cdot\text{lb/s} = 1.34 \times 10^{-3}\ \text{hp} = 3.41\ \text{Btu/h}$
$1\ \text{ft}\cdot\text{lb/s} = 1.36\ \text{W} = 1.82 \times 10^{-3}\ \text{hp}$
$1\ \text{hp} = 550\ \text{ft}\cdot\text{lb/s} = 745.7\ \text{W} = 2545\ \text{Btu/h}$

Mass–Energy Equivalents

$1\ \text{u} = 1.66 \times 10^{-27}\ \text{kg} \leftrightarrow 931.5\ \text{MeV}$
$1\ \text{electron mass} = 9.11 \times 10^{-31}\ \text{kg} = 5.49 \times 10^{-4}\ \text{u} \leftrightarrow 0.511\ \text{MeV}$
$1\ \text{proton mass} = 1.67262 \times 10^{-27}\ \text{kg} = 1.007\,276\ \text{u} \leftrightarrow 938.27\ \text{MeV}$
$1\ \text{neutron mass} = 1.67493 \times 10^{-27}\ \text{kg} = 1.008\,665\ \text{u} \leftrightarrow 939.57\ \text{MeV}$

Temperature

$T_F = \frac{9}{5} T_C + 32$
$T_C = \frac{5}{9}(T_F - 32)$
$T_K = T_C + 273$

cgs Force

$1\ \text{dyne} = 10^{-5}\ \text{N} = 2.25 \times 10^{-6}\ \text{lb}$

cgs Energy

$1\ \text{erg} = 10^{-7}\ \text{J} = 7.38 \times 10^{-6}\ \text{ft}\cdot\text{lb}$

COLLEGE PHYSICS

JERRY D. WILSON · ANTHONY J. BUFFA
WITH BO LOU

Taken from:
College Physics, Fifth Edition
by Jerry D. Wilson and Anthony J. Buffa

Cover image courtesy of Photodisc/Getty Images.

Taken from:

College Physics, Fifth Edition
by Jerry D. Wilson and Anthony J. Buffa

Published by Prentice Hall
Upper Saddle River, New Jersey 07458

This special edition published in cooperation with Pearson Custom Publishing.

Printed in the United States of America

10 9 8 7 6 5 4 3 2 1

ISBN 0-536-91679-9

2005360237

EM

Please visit our web site at *www.pearsoncustom.com*

PEARSON CUSTOM PUBLISHING
75 Arlington Street, Suite 300, Boston, MA 02116
A Pearson Education Company

About the Authors

Jerry D. Wilson, a native of Ohio, is Emeritus Professor of Physics and former Chair of the Division of Biological and Physical Sciences at Lander University in Greenwood, South Carolina. He received his B.S. degree from Ohio University, M.S. degree from Union College, and, in 1970, a Ph.D. from Ohio University. He earned his M.S. degree while employed as a Materials Behavior Physicist by the General Electric Co.

As a doctoral graduate student, Professor Wilson held the faculty rank of Instructor and began teaching physical-science courses. During this time, he coauthored a physical-science text that is now in its 10th edition. In conjunction with his teaching career, Professor Wilson continued his writing and has authored or coauthored six titles. Having retired from full-time teaching, he continues to write, producing, among other works, *The Curiosity Corner*, a weekly column for local newspapers that can also be found on the Internet.

With several competitive books available, one may wonder why I chose to cowrite another algebra-based physics text. Having taught introductory physics many times, I was well aware of the needs of students and the difficulties they have in mastering the subject. I decided to write a text that presents the basic physics principles in a clear and concise manner, with illustrative examples that help resolve the major difficulty in learning physics: problem solving. Also, I wanted to write a text that is relevant to real-life situations, so as to show students how physics applies in their everyday world, how things work, and why things happen. Once the basics are learned, an understanding of such applications follows naturally.

—Jerry Wilson

Anthony J. Buffa received his B.S. degree in physics from Rensselaer Polytechnic Institute and both his M.S. and Ph.D. degrees in physics from the University of Illinois, Urbana–Champaign. In 1970, Professor Buffa joined the faculty at California Polytechnic State University, San Luis Obispo, where he is currently Professor of Physics, and has been a research associate with the Radioanalytical Facility of the department of physics since 1980.

Professor Buffa's main interest continues to be teaching. He has taught courses at Cal Poly ranging from introductory physical science to quantum mechanics, has developed and revised many laboratory experiments, and has taught elementary physics to local teachers in an NSF-sponsored workshop. Combining physics with his interests in art and architecture, Dr. Buffa develops his own artwork and sketches, which he uses to increase his effectiveness in teaching physics.

I try to teach my students the crucial role physics plays in understanding all aspects of the world around them—whether it be technology, biology, astronomy, or any other field. In that regard, I emphasize conceptual understanding before number crunching. To this end, I rely heavily on visual methods. I hope the artwork and other pedagogical features in this book assist you in achieving your own teaching goals for your students.

—Tony Buffa

Brief Contents

Contents

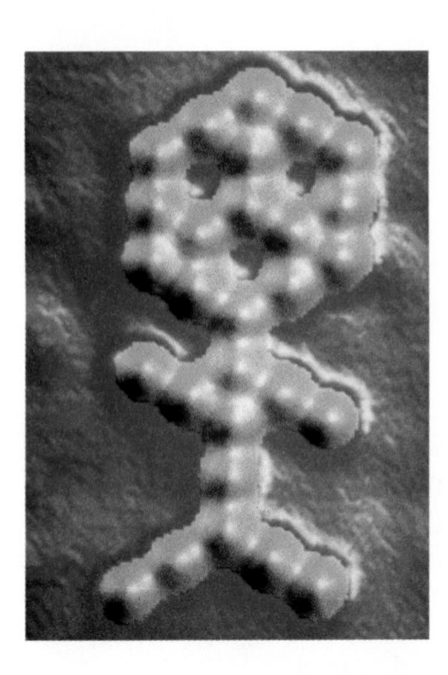

6 Linear Momentum and Collisions *179*

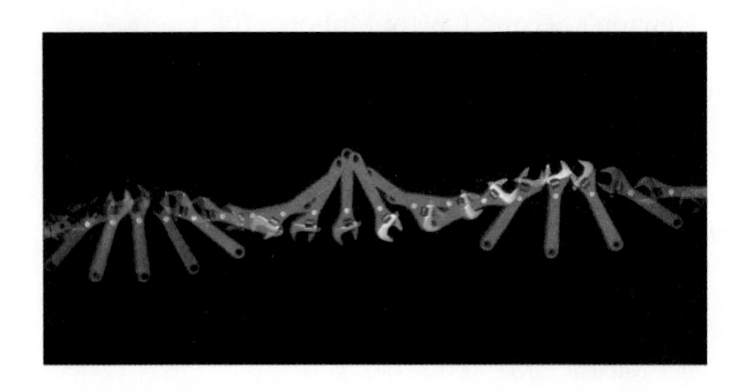

7 Solids and Fluids *219*

8 Temperature and Kinetic Theory *259*

9 Sound *287*

10 Reflection and Refraction of Light *322*

Learn by Drawing

Applications (Insights appear in **boldface**, and "(bio)" indicates a biomedical application)

Physlet® Illustrations

Preface

We believe that there are two basic goals in any introductory physics course: (1) to impart an understanding of the basic concepts of physics and (2) to enable students to use these concepts to solve a variety of problems.

These goals are linked. We want students to apply concepts to the problems that they are trying to solve. However, they often begin the problem-solving process by searching for an equation. There is the temptation to try and plug numbers into equations before visualizing the situation or considering the physical concepts that could be used to solve the problem.

Research in physics education has shown that a surprising number of students who learn to solve typical problems well enough to pass examinations do so without ever arriving at a real understanding of the most elementary physical concepts. Simply put, they can solve quantitative problems and get the right answer, but they do not know why it is right. In addition, students often do not check their numerical answer to see if it matches their understanding of the relevant physical concept.

Our Goals—Features of This Edition

Our goals for this text are simple, yet challenging. With the goals of the course in mind, we identified areas in need of improvement and made efforts to further enhance the strengths of the book.

First, we asked a trusted colleague to contribute to our efforts. Bo Lou, of Ferris State University, has been an important part of *College Physics* since the Third Edition. He has authored the *Instructor's Solutions Manual* and the *Student Study Guide* and has played an important role as a member of AZTEC (Absolutely Zero Tolerance for Errors Club). In this edition, his expertise in optics has been used to update the chapter dealing with that topic (Chapter 10). Also, Professor Lou was responsible for updating the end-of-chapter exercises. His Ph.D., in condensed-matter physics, is from Emory University.

We feel, and many users have agreed, that the strengths of this textbook are as follows:

Conceptual Basis. We believe that giving students a secure grasp of physical principles will almost invariably enhance their problem-solving abilities. Central to this belief is an approach to the development of problem-solving skills that stresses an understanding of basic concepts, rather than the mechanical and rote use of equations, as the essential foundation. Throughout the writing of *College Physics*, we have organized discussions and incorporated pedagogical tools to ensure that conceptual insight drives the development of practical skills.

Concise Coverage. To maintain a sharp focus on essential concepts, a textbook should emphasize the basics and minimize superfluous material. In this text, topics of marginal interest have been avoided, as have those that present formal or mathematical difficulties for students. Similarly, we have not wasted space on deriving relationships when they shed no additional light on the principle involved. It is usually more important for students in a course such as this book is geared toward to understand what a relationship means and how it can be used, rather than the mathematical or analytical techniques employed to derive it.

INSIGHT

Nanotechnology

A prefix for metric units refers to the order of the dimension of measurement used. The prefix *micro-* (10^{-6}) has been in common use for some time—e.g., in microscope, microchip, microbiology, microchemistry, and so on. Now the prefix *nano-* is coming into use, and you will probably be hearing a great deal about it with respect to nanotechnology (*nanotech* for short).

In general, nanotechnology is any technology done on the nanometer scale. A nanometer is one billionth (10^{-9}) of a meter, about the width of three to four atoms. Basically, nanotechnology involves the manufacture or building of things one atom or molecule at a time, so the nanometer is the appropriate scale. One atom or molecule at a time? That may sound a bit farfetched, but it's not. This possibility was advanced by physicist Richard Feynman in 1956: "The principles of physics, as far as I can see, do not speak against the possibility of maneuvering things atom by atom." This has been accomplished by using a special microscope at very low temperatures and "pushing around" single atoms (Fig. 1).

In a sense, nanotechnology occurs naturally in the cells of our bodies. Ribosomes (tiny particles in all living cells) are the sites at which information carried by the genetic code is converted into protein molecules. Ribosomes are like tiny "machines," no larger then a few nanometers long, that read DNA instructions on how to build enzymes and other proteins molecule by molecule.

Perhaps you can now see the potential of nanotechnology. The chemical properties of atoms and molecules are well understood. For example, rearranging the atoms in coal can produce a diamond. (We can already do this task without nanotechnology, using heat and pressure.) Nanotechnology presents the possibility of constructing novel molecular devices or "machines" with extraordinary properties and

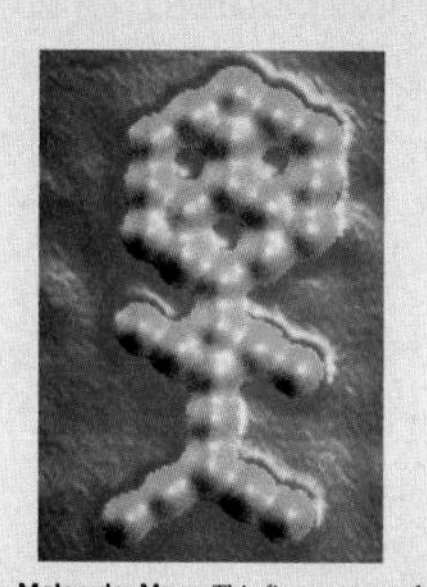

FIGURE 1 Molecular Man This figure was crafted by moving 28 molecules, one at a time. Each of the gold-colored peaks is the image of a carbon monoxide molecule. The molecules rest on a single crystal platinum surface. "Molecular Man" measures 5 nm tall and 2.5 nm wide (hand-to-hand). More than 20000 figures, linked hand-to-hand, would be needed to span a single human hair. The molecules in the figure were positioned using a special microscope at very low temperatures.

Scanning tunneling microscope

Applications. *College Physics* is known for the strong mix of applications related to medicine, science, technology, architecture, and everyday life in its text narrative and Insight boxes. While this edition continues to have a wider range of applications than do most texts, we have also increased the number of biological applications, in recognition of the high percentage of premed and allied health majors who take the course for which it is used. Some examples of topics discussed in biology-oriented Insights are nanotechnology, weightlessness and its effects on the human body, the physics of ear popping, desirable and undesirable resonance, body-fat analysis, cornea surgery, and bioengineering. A complete list of applications discussed, with page references, is found on page viii.

Learn by Drawing

A Lens Ray Diagram (See Example 23.5.)

1 Parallel ray — Object, ①, F, F, d_o

2 Chief (central) ray — Object, ①, ②, F, F, d_o

3 Locating image — Object, ①, ②, F, F, Real image, d_o, d_i

4 Can also use focal ray — Object, ①, ②, ③, F, F, Real image, d_o, d_i

The following pedagogical features have been enhanced in this edition:

Learn by Drawing Boxes. Visualization is one of the most important problem-solving tools in physics. In many cases, if students can make a sketch of a problem, they can solve it. "Learn by Drawing" features offer students specific help on making certain types of sketches and graphs that will provide key insights into a variety of physical situations.

Integrated Learning Objectives. Specific learning objectives, located at the beginning of each chapter section, help students structure their reading and facilitate review of the material.

Suggested Problem-Solving Procedure. An extensive section (Section 1.7) provides a framework for thinking about problem solving. This section includes

- An overview of problem-solving strategies;
- A seven-step procedure that is general enough to apply to most problems in physics, but is easily used in specific situations;
- Three Examples that illustrate the detailed problem-solving process, showing how the general procedure is applied in practice.

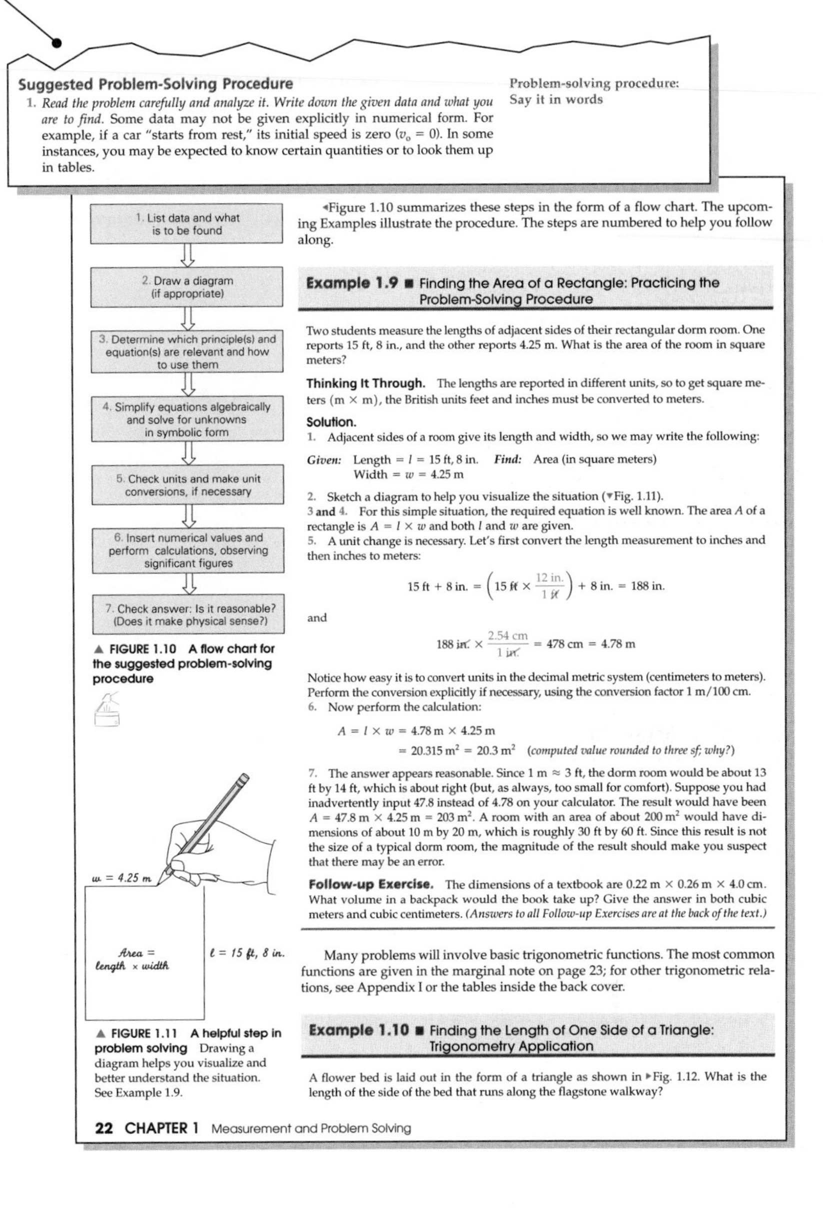

Suggested Problem-Solving Procedure

1. *Read the problem carefully and analyze it. Write down the given data and what you are to find.* Some data may not be given explicitly in numerical form. For example, if a car "starts from rest," its initial speed is zero ($v_o = 0$). In some instances, you may be expected to know certain quantities or to look them up in tables.

Problem-solving procedure: Say it in words

◂Figure 1.10 summarizes these steps in the form of a flow chart. The upcoming Examples illustrate the procedure. The steps are numbered to help you follow along.

▲ **FIGURE 1.10 A flow chart for the suggested problem-solving procedure**

Example 1.9 ■ Finding the Area of a Rectangle: Practicing the Problem-Solving Procedure

Two students measure the lengths of adjacent sides of their rectangular dorm room. One reports 15 ft, 8 in., and the other reports 4.25 m. What is the area of the room in square meters?

Thinking It Through. The lengths are reported in different units, so to get square meters (m × m), the British units feet and inches must be converted to meters.

Solution.

1. Adjacent sides of a room give its length and width, so we may write the following:

Given: Length $= l = 15$ ft, 8 in. *Find:* Area (in square meters)
Width $= w = 4.25$ m

2. Sketch a diagram to help you visualize the situation (▾Fig. 1.11).

3 and 4. For this simple situation, the required equation is well known. The area A of a rectangle is $A = l \times w$ and both l and w are given.

5. A unit change is necessary. Let's first convert the length measurement to inches and then inches to meters:

$$15\text{ ft} + 8\text{ in.} = \left(15\text{ ft} \times \frac{12\text{ in.}}{1\text{ ft}}\right) + 8\text{ in.} = 188\text{ in.}$$

and

$$188\text{ in.} \times \frac{2.54\text{ cm}}{1\text{ in.}} = 478\text{ cm} = 4.78\text{ m}$$

Notice how easy it is to convert units in the decimal metric system (centimeters to meters). Perform the conversion explicitly if necessary, using the conversion factor 1 m/100 cm.

6. Now perform the calculation:

$$A = l \times w = 4.78\text{ m} \times 4.25\text{ m}$$
$$= 20.315\text{ m}^2 = 20.3\text{ m}^2 \quad (\textit{computed value rounded to three sf; why?})$$

7. The answer appears reasonable. Since 1 m ≈ 3 ft, the dorm room would be about 13 ft by 14 ft, which is about right (but, as always, too small for comfort). Suppose you had inadvertently input 47.8 instead of 4.78 on your calculator. The result would have been $A = 47.8\text{ m} \times 4.25\text{ m} = 203\text{ m}^2$. A room with an area of about 200 m^2 would have dimensions of about 10 m by 20 m, which is roughly 30 ft by 60 ft. Since this result is not the size of a typical dorm room, the magnitude of the result should make you suspect that there may be an error.

Follow-up Exercise. The dimensions of a textbook are 0.22 m × 0.26 m × 4.0 cm. What volume in a backpack would the book take up? Give the answer in both cubic meters and cubic centimeters. (*Answers to all Follow-up Exercises are at the back of the text.*)

▲ **FIGURE 1.11 A helpful step in problem solving** Drawing a diagram helps you visualize and better understand the situation. See Example 1.9.

Many problems will involve basic trigonometric functions. The most common functions are given in the marginal note on page 23; for other trigonometric relations, see Appendix I or the tables inside the back cover.

Example 1.10 ■ Finding the Length of One Side of a Triangle: Trigonometry Application

A flower bed is laid out in the form of a triangle as shown in ▸Fig. 1.12. What is the length of the side of the bed that runs along the flagstone walkway?

22 CHAPTER 1 Measurement and Problem Solving

Problem-Solving Strategies and Hints. The initial treatment of problem solving is followed up throughout *College Physics* with an abundance of suggestions, tips, cautions, shortcuts, and useful techniques for solving specific kinds of problems. These strategies and hints help students apply general principles to specific contexts, as well as avoid common pitfalls and misunderstandings.

Conceptual Examples. *College Physics* was among the first physics texts to include examples that are conceptual in nature, in addition to quantitative ones. Our Conceptual Examples ask students to think about a physical situation and choose the correct prediction out of a set of possible outcomes, on the basis of an understanding of relevant principles. The discussion that follows ("Reasoning and Answer") explains clearly how the correct answer can be identified, as well as why the other answers are wrong.

Worked Examples. We have tried to make the solutions to in-text Examples as clear and detailed as possible. The aim is not merely to show students which equations to use, but to explain the strategy being employed and the role of each step in the overall plan. Students are encouraged to learn the "why" of each step along with the "how." This technique will make it easier for students to apply the demonstrated techniques to other problems that are not identical in structure. Each worked Example also includes the following:

- ***Thinking It Through.*** This section, which follows the statement of the problem and precedes the solution, focuses students on the critical thinking and analysis they should undertake before beginning to use equations.
- ***Follow-up Exercise.*** The Follow-up Exercise at the end of each Conceptual Example and each regular worked Example further reinforces the importance of conceptual understanding and offers additional practice. (Answers to Follow-up Exercises are given at the back of the text.)

Integration of Conceptual and Quantitative Exercises. To help break down the artificial barrier between conceptual questions and quantitative problems, we do not separate these categories in the end-of-chapter exercises. Instead, each section begins with a series of multiple-choice and short-answer questions that provide review of the chapter's content, test students' conceptual understanding, and ask students to reason from principles. The aim is to show students that the same kind of conceptual insight is required regardless of whether the desired answer involves words, equations, or numbers. The conceptual questions are marked by a bold CQ in the text for easy reference when assigning questions. *College Physics* offers short answers to all odd-numbered conceptual questions (as well as to all odd-numbered quantitative problems) at the back of the text, so that students can check their understanding of those problems.

($\mathbf{F}_{net} = m\mathbf{a}$) and inserting the expression for centripetal acceleration from Eq. 7.9, we can write

$$F_c = ma_c = \frac{mv^2}{r} \quad \textit{magnitude of centripetal force} \quad (7.11)$$

Centripetal Force

The centripetal force, like the centripetal acceleration, is directed radially toward the center of the circular path.

Keep in mind that, in general, a net force applied at an angle to the direction of motion of an object produces changes in the magnitude *and* direction of the velocity. However, when a net force of constant magnitude is continuously applied at an angle of 90° to the direction of motion (as is centripetal force), only the direction of the velocity changes. Also notice that because the centripetal force is always perpendicular to the direction of motion, this force does no work. (Why?) Therefore, by the work–energy theorem, a centripetal force does not change the kinetic energy or speed of the object.

Note that the centripetal force in the form $F = mv^2/r$ is not really a new individual force, but rather the cause of the centripetal acceleration supplied by a real force or forces. In Example 7.5, the force supplying the centripetal acceleration was gravity. In Conceptual Example 7.7, it was the tension in the string. Another force that often supplies centripetal acceleration is friction. Suppose that an automobile moves into a level, circular curve. To negotiate the curve, the car must have a centripetal acceleration, which is supplied by the force of friction between the tires and the road.

However, this (static; why?) friction has a maximum limiting value. If the speed of the car is high enough, the friction will not be sufficient to supply the necessary centripetal acceleration, and the car will skid outward from the center of the curve. If the car moves onto a wet or icy spot, the friction between the tires and the road may be reduced, allowing the car to skid at an even lower speed. (Banking a curve also helps vehicles negotiate the curve. See Exercises 45 and 59.)

230 CHAPTER 7 Circular Motion and Gravitation

Paired Exercises. Most numbered sections include at least one set of paired Exercises that deal with similar situations. The first problem in a pair is solved in the *Student Study Guide and Solutions Manual;* the second problem, which explores a similar situation to that presented in the first problem, has only an answer at the back of the book, thereby encouraging students to work out the problem on their own.

Additional Exercises. Each chapter includes a supplemental section of Additional Exercises drawn from all sections of the chapter, to ensure that students can synthesize concepts.

New features to this edition include the following:

Physlet® Illustrations. Physlet® Illustrations are short Java applets that clearly illustrate, through animation, a concept from the text. Available on the Wilson/Buffa Companion Web site, Physlet® Illustrations are followed by a series of questions that ask students to think critically about the concept at hand. Physlet® Illustrations are denoted by an icon in the margin of the text.

Integrated Examples. In order to further emphasize the connection between conceptual understanding and quantitative problem-solving, we have developed Integrated Examples for each chapter. These Examples work through a physical situation both qualitatively and quantitatively. Integrated Examples demonstrate how conceptual understanding and numerical calculations go hand in hand in understanding and solving problems.

Integrated Example 11.3 ■ Cooking Class 101: Studying Specific Heats While Boiling Water

To prepare pasta, you bring a pot of water from room temperature (20°C) to its boiling point (100°C). The pot has a mass of 0.900 kg, is made of steel, and holds 3.00 L of water. (a) Which of the following is true? (1) The pot requires more heat, (2) the water requires more heat, or (3) they require the same amount of heat. (b) Determine the required heat for both the water and the pot, and the ratio Q_w/Q_{pot}.

(a) Conceptual Reasoning. The temperature increase is the same for the water and the pot. Thus, the only factors that determine the difference in required heat are mass and specific heat. Since a liter of water has a mass of 1.0 kg, we have 3.0 kg of water to heat. This mass is more than three times the mass of the pot. From Table 11.1, the specific heat of water is about nine times larger than that of steel. Thus, both factors indicate that the water will require significantly more heat than the pot, so the answer is (2).

(b) Thinking It Through. The heats can be found using Eq. 11.1, after looking up the specific heats and converting the volume of water to mass. The temperature change is easily determined from the initial and final values.

We list the data given and find the water's mass from its volume and density:

Given: $m_{pot} = 0.900$ kg
$m_w = 3.00$ kg
$c_{pot} = 460$ J/kg·C° (From Table 11.1)
$c_w = 4186$ J/kg·C° (From Table 11.1)

Find: The heat for the water and the pot and the heat ratio Q_w/Q_{pot}

In general, the amount of heat required is given by $Q = mc\Delta T$. The temperature increase for both objects is 80 C°. Thus, the heat required for the water is

$$\begin{aligned} Q_w &= m_w c_w \Delta T_w \\ &= (3.00\ \text{kg})(4186\ \text{J/kg}\cdot\text{C}°)(80\ \text{C}°) = 1.00 \times 10^6\ \text{J} \end{aligned}$$

and the heat required for the pot is

$$\begin{aligned} Q_{pot} &= m_{pot} c_{pot} \Delta T_{pot} \\ &= (0.900\ \text{kg})(460\ \text{J/kg}\cdot\text{C}°)(80\ \text{C}°) = 3.31 \times 10^4\ \text{J} \end{aligned}$$

The water requires over 30 times the heat, since

$$\frac{Q_w}{Q_{pot}} = \frac{1.00 \times 10^6\ \text{J}}{3.31 \times 10^4\ \text{J}} = 30.2$$

Follow-up Exercise. (a) In this Example, if the pot were made of the same mass of aluminum, would you expect the ratio of heat (water to pot) to be smaller or larger than the answer for the steel pot? Explain. (b) Verify your choice by calculating this ratio for the case of the aluminum pot.

Integrated Exercises. Like the Integrated Examples in the chapter, Integrated Exercises ask students to solve a problem quantitatively as well as answer a conceptual question dealing with the

Exercise. By answering both parts, students can see if their numerical answer matches their conceptual understanding.

Figure Reference Icon. In this edition, we have placed an arrow next to each in-text figure reference as well as next to each figure caption. These "placeholders" point the student in the direction of the appropriate figure and are easily located when the student returns to the sentence.

Chapter Review. The Important Concepts and Equations section is integrated into the new Chapter Review section of each chapter. Key concepts are in bold and defined in words as well as symbolically. This new format provides a quick study reference for students.

We have continued to ensure accuracy through the Absolutely Zero Tolerance for Errors Club (The AZTECs). Bo Lou of Ferris State University, the author of our *Instructor's Solutions Manual*, headed the AZTEC team and was supported by the text's authors and two other accuracy checkers, Bill McCorkle of West Liberty State University and Dave Curott of the University of North Alabama. Each member of the team individually and independently worked all end-of-chapter Exercises. The results were then collected, and any discrepancies were resolved by a team discussion. All data in the chapters, as well as the answers at the back of the book, were checked and rechecked in first- and second-page proofs. In addition, five other physics teachers—Xiaochun He of Georgia State University, Jerry Shi of Pasadena City College, John Walkup of California Polytechnic State University at San Luis Obispo, William Dabby of Edison Community College, and Donald Elliott of Carroll College—read pages in detail, checking for errors in the chapter narrative, worked Examples, and text art. Although it is almost certainly not humanly possible to produce a physics text with absolutely no errors, that was our goal; we worked very hard to make the book as error free as possible.

This edition is supplemented by a state-of-the-art Media and Print Ancillary package developed to address the needs of both students and instructors.

Companion Web Site. Our Web site (http://www.pearsoncustom.com/itt/GE253_Physics), which hosts contributions from leaders in physics education research, provides students with a variety of interactive explorations of each chapter's topics, easily accommodating differences in learning styles. Student tools provided on the Web site include Physlet® Illustrations by Steve Mellema and Chuck Niederriter (Gustavus Adolphus College); Warm-Ups, Puzzles, and "What Is Physics Good For?" applications by Gregor Novak and Andy Gavrin (Indiana University– Purdue University, Indianapolis); award-winning Java-based Physlet® problems by Wolfgang Christian (Davidson College); algorithmically generated numerical Practice Problems, multiple-choice Practice Questions, and on-line destinations by Carl Adler (East Carolina University); Ranking Task Exercises edited by Tom O'Kuma (Lee College), David Maloney (Indiana University–Purdue University, Fort Wayne), and Curtis Hieggelke (Joliet Junior College); Chapter Objectives and Solutions to Select Exercises by Bo Lou (Ferris State University); and MCAT Questions by Glen Terrell (University of Texas at Arlington) and from ARCO's MCAT Supercourse. Using the Preferences module on the opening page of the site or the tool in the "Results reporter" part of each module, students can, at a professor's request, have the results of their work on the Companion Web site e-mailed to the professor or teaching assistant. Instructor tools include on-line grading capabilities and a Syllabus Manager. See pp. **xxii–xxiii** for further information about the modules in this site.

For the Instructor

Annotated Instructor's Edition (0-13-047193-3). The margins of the *Annotated Instructor's Edition* (*AIE*) contain an abundance of suggestions for classroom demonstrations and activities, along with teaching tips (points to emphasize, discussion suggestions, and common misunderstandings to avoid). In addition, the *AIE* contains

- Icons that identify each illustration reproduced as a transparency in the *Transparency Pack* and
- Answers to end-of-chapter Exercises (following each Exercise).

Instructor's Resource Manual (0-13-047180-1). Written by Kathy Whatley and Judy Beck (both of University of North Carolina–Asheville), the IRM, new to this edition, provides teaching suggestions, lecture outlines, notes, demonstrations, sample syllabi, and additional references and resources.

Instructor's Solutions Manual (0-13-047194-1). Prepared by Bo Lou of Ferris State University, the *Instructor's Solutions Manual* supplies answers with complete, worked-out solutions to all end-of-chapter exercises. Each solution has been checked for accuracy by a minimum of five instructors. This manual is also available electronically on both Windows (***0-13-047203-4***) and Macintosh (***0-13-047202-6***) platforms.

Test Item File (0-13-047196-8). Fully revised by Dave Curott of the University of North Alabama, the *Test Item File* now offers more than 2600 Multiple-Choice, Essay, True/False, and Fill-in-the-Blank questions. The questions are organized and referenced by chapter section and by question type.

Test Generator EQ (0-13-047778-8). New to this edition, TestGenEQ is an easy-to-use, fully networkable software program for creating tests ranging from short quizzes to long exams. Questions from the *Test Item File,* including algorithmic versions, are supplied, and professors can use the Question Editor to modify existing questions or create new questions.

Transparency Pack (0-13-047199-2). The *Transparency Pack* contains more than 300 full-color acetates of text illustrations useful for class lectures. It is available upon adoption of the text.

Media Portfolio CD-ROM (0-13-047190-9). Prepared by Sue Willis (Northern Illinois University), this CD-ROM, new to this edition, contains all the art from the text in JPEG format, for easy incorporation into presentation software. It is also available as a password-protected module on the Companion Web site.

"Physics You Can See" Video Demonstrations (0-205-12393-7). Each segment, 2–5 minutes long, demonstrates a classical physics experiment. Eleven segments are included, such as "Coin & Feather" (acceleration due to gravity), "Monkey & Gun" (rate of vertical free fall), "Swivel Hips" (force pairs), and "Collapse a Can" (atmospheric pressure).

Peer Instruction (0-13-656441-6). Authored by Eric Mazur (Harvard University), this manual explains peer instruction, an interactive teaching style that actively involves students in the learning process by focusing their attention on underlying concepts through interactive "ConcepTests," reading quizzes, and conceptual exam questions. Results are assessed though scores on the Force Concept Inventory and final exams, showing that students better understand concepts and perform more highly on conventional problems in this environment. Peer instruction can be easily adapted to fit individual lecture styles and used in a variety of settings.

Just-in-Time Teaching: Blending Active Learning with Web Technology (0-13-085034-9). Just-in-Time Teaching (JiTT) is an exciting teaching and learning methodology designed to engage students. Using feedback from preclass Web assignments, instructors can adjust classroom lessons so that students receive rapid response to the specific questions and problems they are having—instead of more generic lectures that may or may not address topics with which students actually need help. Many teachers have found that this process makes students become active and interested learners. In this resource book for educators, authors Gregor Novak (Indiana University–Purdue University, Indianapolis), Evelyn Patterson (United States Air Force Academy), Andrew Gavrin (Indiana University–Purdue University, Indianapolis), and Wolfgang Christian (Davidson College) more fully explain what Just-in-Time Teaching is, its underlying goals and philosophies, and how to implement it. They also provide an extensive section of tested resource materials that can be used in introductory physics courses with the JiTT approach.

Ranking Task Exercises in Physics (0-13-022355-7). This book, by Thomas L. O'Kuma (Lee College), David P. Maloney (Indiana University–Purdue University, Fort Wayne), and Curtis J. Hieggelke (Joliet Junior College), describes ranking tasks, which are an innovative type of conceptual exercise that asks students to make comparative judgments about a set of variations on a particular physical situation. This text is a unique resource for physics instructors who are looking for tools to incorporate more conceptual analysis in their courses. This supplement contains approximately 200 Ranking Task Exercises that cover all classical physics topics (with the exception of optics).

Physlets®: Teaching Physics with Interactive Curricular Material (0-13-029341-5). Authored by Wolfgang Christian and Mario Belloni (both of Davidson College), this text is a teacher's resource book with an accompanying CD for instructors who are interested in incorporating Physlets® into their physics courses. The book and CD discuss the pedagogy behind the use of Physlets® and provide instructors with information on how to author their own interactive curricular material, using Physlets®.

For the Student

Student Study Guide and Solutions Manual (0-536-91986-0). Updated by Bo Lou of Ferris State University, the *Student Study Guide and Solutions Manual* presents chapter-by chapter reviews, chapter summaries, additional worked examples, and solutions to paired and selected exercises.

Student Pocket Guide (0-13-047192-5). Written by Biman Das (State University of New York–Potsdam), this easy-to-carry 5" × 7" paperback contains a summary of the entire text, including all key concepts and equations, as well as tips and hints. Perfect for carrying to lectures and taking notes in.

MCAT Physics Study Guide (0-13-627951-1). This study resource, by Joseph Boone of California Polytechnic State University–San Luis Obispo, references all of the physics topics on the MCAT to the appropriate sections in the text.

Since most MCAT questions require more thought and reasoning than simply plugging numbers into an equation, this study guide is designed to refresh students' memory about the topics they've covered in class. Additional review, practice problems, and review questions are included.

***Tutorials in Introductory Physics* (0-13-097069-7).** Authored by Lillian C. McDermott, Peter S. Schaffer, and the Physics Education Group at the University of Washington, this landmark book presents a series of physics tutorials designed by a leading physics education research group. Emphasizing the development of concepts and scientific reasoning skills, the tutorials focus on the specific conceptual and reasoning difficulties that students tend to encounter. The tutorials cover a range of topics in Mechanics, E & M, and Waves and Optics.

***Interactive Physics Player Workbook* (0-13-067108-8).** Written by Cindy Schwarz of Vassar College, this highly interactive workbook and software package contains simulation projects of varying difficulty. Each includes a physics review, simulation details, hints, an explanation of results, math help, and a self-test.

Acknowledgments

We would like to acknowledge the generous assistance we received from many people during the preparation of this edition. First, our sincere thanks go to Bo Lou of Ferris State University for his vital contributions to the chapters on optics. His meticulous, conscientious help with checking solutions and answers to problems, as well as preparing the *Instructor's Solutions Manual*, the answer keys for the back of the book, and the *Student Study Guide and Solutions Manual* are greatly appreciated. We are similarly grateful to Dave Curott of the University of North Alabama for preparing the *Test Item File* as well as for his participation as an accuracy checker for all solutions to end-of-chapter exercises.

Indeed, all the members of AZTEC—Bo Lou, Dave Curott, and Bill McCorkle (West Liberty State University)—as well as the reviewers of first-and second-page proofs—William Dabby (Edison Community College), Donald Elliott (Carroll College), Xiaochun He (Georgia State University), Jerry Shi (Pasadena City College), John Walkup (California Polytechnic State University at San Luis Obispo)—deserve more than a special thanks for their tireless, timely, and extremely thorough review of all materials in the book for scientific accuracy.

Dozens of other colleagues, listed in the upcoming section, helped us with reviews of the previous edition to help us plan this edition, as well as with reviews of manuscript as it was developed. We are indebted to them, as their thoughtful and constructive suggestions benefited the book greatly.

The editorial staff of Prentice Hall continued to be particularly helpful. First, we would like to extend a heartfelt thanks to our former editor, Alison Reeves, for initiating this revision and providing insightful direction. We are grateful to Mary Catherine Hager, Development Editor; Patrick Burt, Project Manager for the book; and Beth Sturla Sweeten, Assistant Managing Editor, who kept the whole complex endeavor moving forward, while designer Jonathan Boylan made sure that the ultimate physical presentation would be both visually engaging and clean and easy to use. We also thank Mark Pfaltzgraff, Executive Marketing Manager; Christian Botting, Assistant Editor, for his extensive work on the supplements, media program, and review program; Erik Fahlgren, Acquisitions Editor, and Eileen Nee, Editorial Assistant, for their help in coordinating all of these facets; and John Challice, Editor in Chief, for his support and encouragement.

In addition, I (Tony Buffa) once again extend many thanks to my coauthor, Professor Jerry Wilson, for his cheerful helpfulness and professional approach to the work on this edition. I am also indebted to Professor Bo Lou, who contributed many good comments and ideas that helped enormously. As always, several colleagues of mine at Cal Poly gave of their time for fruitful discussions. Among them are Professors Joseph Boone, Ronald Brown, Theodore Foster, Richard Frankel, and John Walkup. My family—my wife, Connie, and daughters, Jeanne and Julie—was, as always, a continuous and welcomed source of support. I also acknowledge the support from my father, Anthony Buffa, Sr., and my aunt, Dorothy Abbott. Last, I thank the students in my classes who contributed excellent ideas over the past few years.

Finally, both of us would like to urge anyone using the book—student or instructor—to pass on to us any suggestions that you have for its improvement. We look forward to hearing from you.

—Jerry D. Wilson
jwilson@ais-gwd.com
—Anthony J. Buffa
abuffa@calpoly.edu

Reviewers of Previous Editions

William Achor
Western Maryland College

Alice Hawthorne Allen
Virginia Tech

Arthur Alt
College of Great Falls

Zaven Altounian
McGill University

Frederick Anderson
University of Vermont

Charles Bacon
Ferris State College

Ali Badakhshan
University of Northern Iowa

Anand Batra
Howard University

Michael Berger
Indiana University

William Berres
Wayne State University

James Borgardt
Juniata College

Hugo Borja
Macomb Community College

Bennet Brabson
Indiana University

Jeffrey Braun
University of Evansville

Michael Browne
University of Idaho

Mike Broyles
Collin County Community College

David Bushnell
Northern Illinois University

Lyle Campbell
Oklahoma Christian University

James Carroll
Eastern Michigan State University

Aaron Chesir
Lucent Technologies

Lowell Christensen
American River College

Philip A. Chute
University of Wisconsin–Eau Claire

Robert Coakley
University of Southern Maine

Lawrence Coleman
University of California–Davis

Lattie F. Collins
East Tennessee State University

Sergio Conetti
University of Virginia, Charlottesville

James Cook
Middle Tennessee State University

David M. Cordes
Belleville Area Community College

James R. Crawford
Southwest Texas State University

William Dabby
Edison Community College

Purna Das
Purdue University

J. P. Davidson
University of Kansas

Donald Day
Montgomery College

Richard Delaney
College of Aeronautics

James Ellingson
College of DuPage

Donald Elliott
Carroll College

Arnold Feldman
University of Hawaii

John Flaherty
Yuba College

Rober J. Foley
University of Wisconsin–Stout

Lewis Ford
Texas A&M University

Donald Foster
Wichita State University

Donald R. Franceschetti
Memphis State University

Frank Gaev
ITT Technical Institute–Ft. Lauderdale

Rex Gandy
Auburn University

Simon George
California State–Long Beach

Barry Gilbert
Rhode Island College

Richard Grahm
Ricks College

Tom J. Gray
University of Nebraska

Douglas Al Harrington
Northeastern State University

Gary Hastings
Georgia State University

Xiaochun He
Georgia State University

J. Erik Hendrickson
University of Wisconsin–Eau Claire

Al Hilgendorf
University of Wisconsin–Stout

Joseph M. Hoffman
Frostburg State University

Andy Hollerman
University of Louisiana, Layfayette

Jacob W. Huang
Towson University

Randall Jones
Loyola University

Omar Ahmad Karim
University of North Carolina–Wilmington

S. D. Kaviani
El Camino College

Victor Keh
ITT Technical Institute–Norwalk, California

John Kenny
Bradley University

James Kettler
Ohio University, Eastern Campus

Dana Klinck
Hillsborough Community College

Chantana Lane
University of Tennessee–Chattanooga

Phillip Laroe
Carroll College

Rubin Laudan
Oregon State University

Bruce A. Layton
Mississippi Gulf Coast Community College

R. Gary Layton
Northern Arizona University

Kevin Lee
University of Nebraska

Paul Lee
California State University, Northridge

Federic Liebrand
Walla Walla College

Mark Lindsay
University of Louisville

Bryan Long
Columbia State Community College

Michael LoPresto
Henry Ford Community College

Dan MacIsaac
Northern Arizona University

Robert March
University of Wisconsin

Trecia Markes
University of Nebraska–Kearney

Aaron McAlexander
Central Piedmont Community College

William McCorkle
West Liberty State University

John D. McCullen
University of Arizona

Michael McGie
California State University–Chico

Paul Morris
Abilene Christian University

Gary Motta
Lassen College

J. Ronald Mowrey
Harrisburg Area Community College

Gerhard Muller
University of Rhode Island

K. W. Nicholson
Central Alabama Community College

Erin O'Connor
Allan Hancock College

R. Daryl Pedigo
Austin Community College

T. A. K. Pillai
University of Wisconsin–La Crosse

Anthony Pitucco
Glendale Community College

William Pollard
Valdosta State University

Darden Powers
Baylor University

Donald S. Presel
University of Massachusetts–Dartmouth

E. W. Prohofsky
Purdue University

Dan R. Quisenberry
Mercer University

W. Steve Quon
Ventura College

David Rafaelle
Glendale Community College

George Rainey
California State Polytechnic University

Michael Ram
SUNY–Buffalo

William Riley
Ohio State University

William Rolnick
Wayne State University

Robert Ross
University of Detroit–Mercy

Craig Rottman
North Dakota State University

Gerald Royce
Mary Washington College

Roy Rubins
University of Texas, Arlington

Sid Rudolph
University of Utah

Om Rustgi
Buffalo State College

Anne Schmiedekamp
Pennsylvania State University–Ogontz

Cindy Schwarz
Vassar College

Ray Sears
University of North Texas

Mark Semon
Bates College

Bartlett Sheinberg
Houston Community College

Jerry Shi
Pasadena City College

Peter Shull
Oklahoma State University

Thomas Sills
Wilbur Wright College

Larry Silva
Appalachian State University

Michael Simon
Housatonic Community Technical College

Christopher Sirola
Tri-County Technical College

Gene Skluzacek
St. Petersburg College

Soren P. Sorensen
University of Tennessee–Knoxville

Ross Spencer
Brigham Young University

Mark Sprague
East Carolina University

Dennis W. Suchecki
San Diego Mesa College

Frederick J. Thomas
Sinclair Community College

Jacqueline Thornton
St. Petersburg Junior College

Anthony Trippe
ITT Technical Institute–San Diego

Gabriel Umerah
Florida Community College–Jacksonville

Lorin Vant-Hull
University of Houston

Pieter B. Visscher
University of Alabama

Karl Vogler
Northern Kentucky University

John Walkup
California Polytechnic State University

Arthur J. Ward
Nashville State Technical Institute

Larry Weinstein
Old Dominion University

John C. Wells
Tennessee Technical University

Arthur Wiggins
Oakland Community College

Kevin Williams
ITT Technical Institute–Earth City

Linda Winkler
Appalachian State University

Jeffery Wragg
College of Charleston

Rob Wylie
Carl Albert State University

John Zelinsky
Southern Illinois University

Dean Zollman
Kansas State University

Multimedia Explorations of Physics

Companion Website www.pearsoncustom.com/itt/GE253_Physics

This text-specific Website for introductory physics provides students and instructors with a wealth of innovative on-line materials for use with *College Physics*.

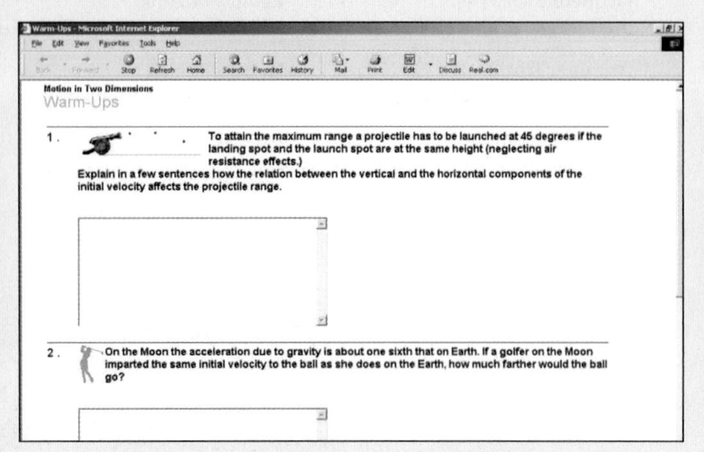

Warm-Ups & Puzzles

by Gregor Novak and Andrew Gavrin (Indiana University–Purdue University, Indianapolis)

Warm-Up and Puzzle questions are real-world short-answer questions based on important concepts in the text chapters. Both types of questions get students' attention, often refer to current events, and are good discussion starters. The **Warm-Ups** are designed to help introduce a topic, whereas the **Puzzles** are more complex and often require the integration of more than one concept. Thus, professors can assign Warm-Up questions after students have read a chapter but before the class lecture on that topic, and Puzzle questions as follow-up assignments submitted after class.

Physlet® Illustrations

by Steve Mellema and Chuck Niederritter (Gustavus Adolphus College)

New to this edition, **Physlet® Illustrations** are short interactive Java applets that clearly illustrate, through animation, a concept from the text. Available on the Wilson/Buffa Companion Website, Physlet® Illustrations are often followed by a series of questions that ask students to think critically about the concept at hand. Physlet® Illustrations are denoted by an icon in the margin of the text:

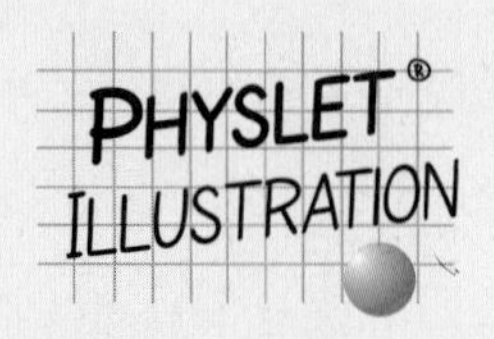

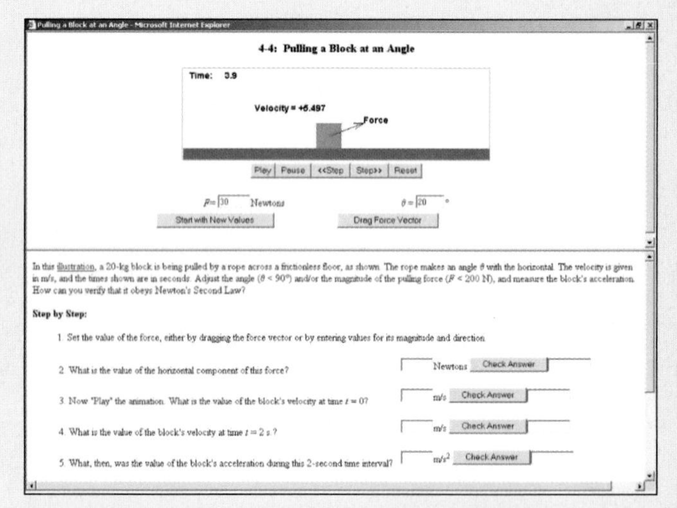

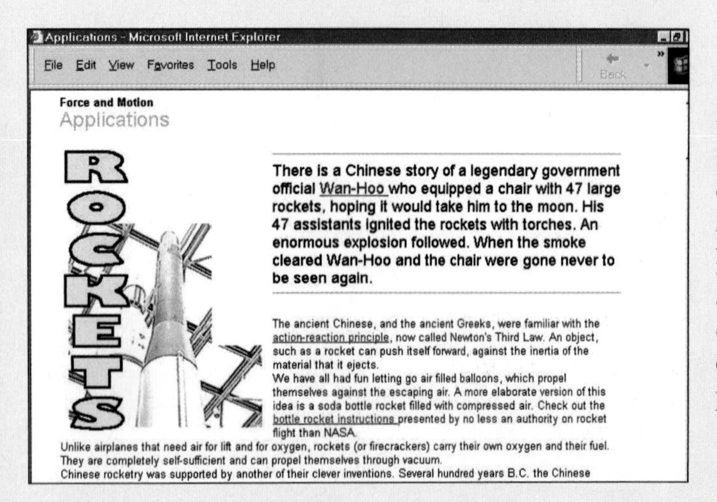

Applications

by Gregor Novak and Andrew Gavrin (Indiana University–Purdue University, Indianapolis)

The **Applications** modules answer the question "What is physics good for?" by connecting physics concepts to real-world phenomena and new developments in science and technology. These illustrated essays include embedded Web links to related sites, one for each chapter. Each essay is followed by short-answer/essay questions, which professors can assign for extra credit.

Physlet® Problems

by Wolfgang Christian (Davidson College)

Physlet® Problems are multimedia-focused problems based on Wolfgang Christian's award-winning Java applets for physics, called Physlets®. With these problems, students use multimedia elements to help solve a problem by observing, applying appropriate physics concepts, and making measurements of parameters they deem important. No numbers are given, so students are required to consider a problem qualitatively instead of plugging numbers into formulas.

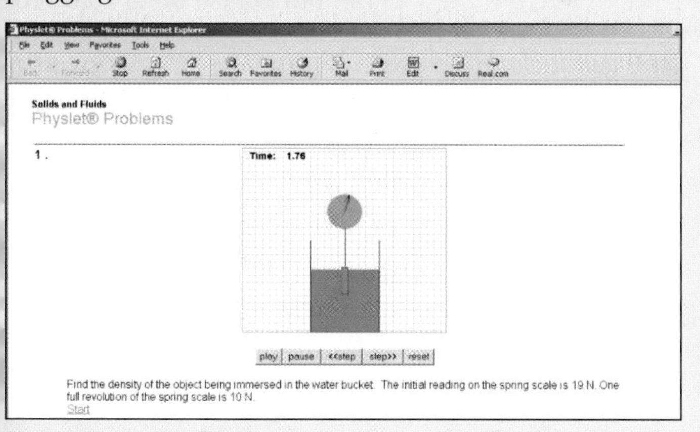

Practice Questions

by Carl Adler (East Carolina University)

Two modules of 10 to15 multiple-choice **Practice Questions** are available for review with each chapter.

MCAT Study Guide

by Glen Terrell (University of Texas at Arlington) and ARCO's MCAT Supercourse

For all relevant chapters, the MCAT Study Guide module provides students with an average of 25 multiple-choice questions on topics and concepts covered on the MCAT exam. As with all multiple-choice modules, the computer automatically grades and scores student responses and provides cross-references to corresponding text sections.

Practice Problems

by Carl Adler (East Carolina University)

Ten algorithmically generated numerical **Practice Problems** per chapter allow students to get multiple iterations of each problem set for practice.

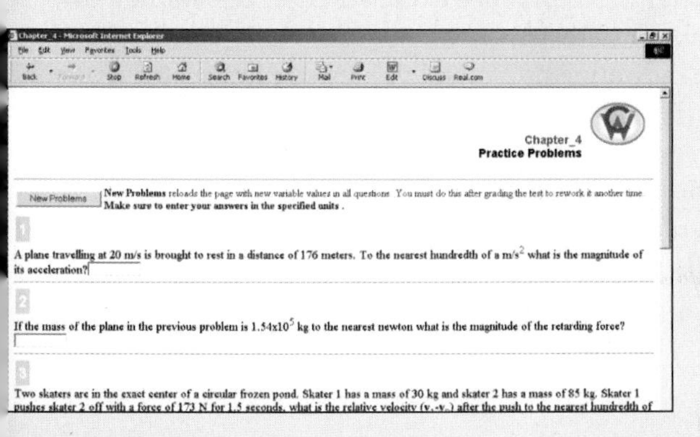

Destinations

Destinations are links to relevant Websites for each chapter, either about the physics topic in the chapter or about related applications.

Solutions to Selected Exercises

by Bo Lou (Ferris State University)

Solutions to six selected exercises per chapter from Bo Lou's *Student Study Guide and Solutions Manual.*

Syllabus Manager

Wilson/Buffa's **Syllabus Manager** provides instructors with an easy, step-by-step process for creating and revising a class syllabus with direct links to the text's Companion Website and other on-line content. Through this on-line syllabus, instructors can add assignments and send announcements to the class with the click of a button. The completed syllabus is hosted on Prentice Hall's servers, allowing the syllabus to be updated from any computer with Internet access.

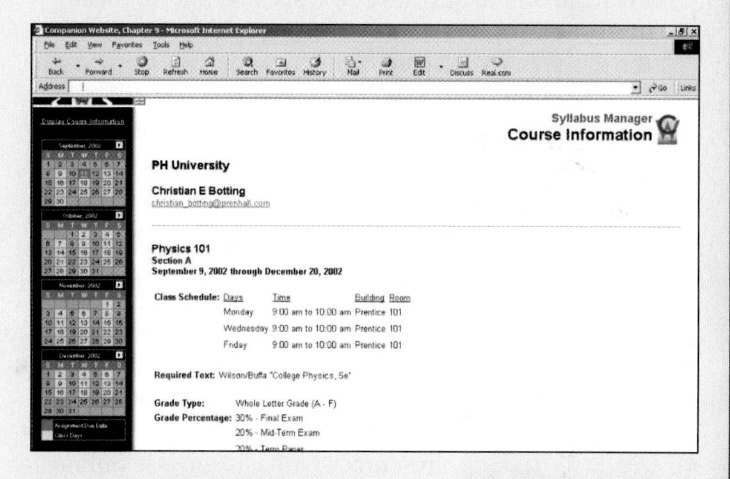

Ranking Task Exercises

edited by Thomas O'Kuma (Lee College), David Maloney (Indiana University–Purdue University, Fort Wayne), and Curtis Hieggelke (Joliet Junior College)

Available for most text chapters as PDF files downloadable from the Wilson/Buffa Website, **Ranking Tasks** are conceptual exercises that require students to rank a number of situations or variations of a situation. Engaging in this process of making comparative judgments helps students reason about physical situations and often gives them new insights into relationships among various concepts and principles.

On-line Grading

Scoring for all objective questions and problems, as well as responses to essay questions, can be e-mailed back to the instructor.

Course and Homework Management Tools for *College Physics*

Blackboard

Blackboard ™ is a comprehensive and flexible e-Learning software platform that delivers a course management system, customizable institution-wide portals, online communities, and an advanced architecture that allows for Web-based integration of multiple administrative systems.

Features:

- Course Management System including progress tracking, class and student management, grade book, communication, assignments, and reporting tools.
- Testing programs with the capability for instructors to create online quizzes and tests, and automatically grade and track results. All tests can be entered into the grade book for easy course management.
- Communications Tools such as the Virtual Classroom™ (chat rooms, Whiteboard, slides), document sharing, and bulletin boards.

CourseCompass

Powered by **Blackboard**

With the highest level of service, support, and training available today, CourseCompass combines tested, quality online course resources with easy-to-use online course management tools. CourseCompass is designed to address the individual needs of instructors, who will be able to create an online course without any special technical skills or training.

Features:

- Greater ease of use—you will be able to create an online course in 15 minutes or less.
- Higher flexibility—Professors can adapt Prentice Hall content to match their own teaching goals, with little or no outside assistance needed.
- Assessment, customization, class administration, and communication tools.
- Point-and-click access—Prentice Hall's vast educational resources are available to instructors at a click of the mouse.
- A nationally hosted and fully supported system that relieves individuals and institutions of the burdens of trouble shooting and maintenance.

WebCT—WebCT offers a powerful set of tools that enables you to create practical Web-based educational programs—the ideal resources to enhance a campus course or to construct one entirely online. The WebCT shell and tools, integrated with the *College Physics* content, results in a versatile, course-enhancing teaching and learning system.

Features:

- Page tracking, progress tracking, class and student management, grade book, communication, calendar, reporting tools, and more.
- Communication tools including chat rooms, bulletin boards, private e-mail, and WhiteBoard.
- Testing tools that help create and administer timed online quizzes and tests, and automatically grade and track all results.

WebAssign

WebAssign unlocks the door to a new way of teaching—to a classroom without walls, where time isn't a boundary and record keeping is no longer a constraint. WebAssign's unparalleled homework delivery service harnesses the power of the Internet and puts it to work for you. Collecting and grading homework becomes the province of the WebAssign service, which gives you the freedom to get back to teaching. Create assignments from a database of exercises from *College Physics*, or write and customize your own exercises. You have complete control over the homework your students receive, including due date, content, feedback, and question formats.

Features:

- Create, post, and review assignments 24 hours a day, 7 days a week.
- Deliver, collect, grade, and record assignments instantly.
- Offer more practice exercises, quizzes, homework, labs, and tests.
- Randomize numerical values or phrases to create unique questions.
- Assess student performance to keep abreast of individual progress.
- Grade algebraic formulas with enhanced math-type display.
- Capture the attention of your online, distance learning students.

Measurement and Problem Solving

Is it first and 10? A measurement is needed, as with many other things in our lives. Length measurements tell us how far it is between cities, how tall you are, and as in the photo, if it's first and 10. Time measurements tell you how long it is until the class ends, when the semester or quarter begins, and how old you are. Drugs taken because of illnesses are given in measured doses. Lives depend on various measurements made by doctors, medical technologists, and pharmacists in the diagnosis and treatment of disease.

Measurements allow us to compute quantities and solve problems. For example, suppose you were asked to find the volume of a cylindrical container. How would you do it? By measuring the diameter (d) and height (h) of the container, and computing the volume from the standard equation $V = \pi r^2 h$, where r, the radius, is one-half the measured diameter. Your problem is solved. Units also come into such problem solving. If you had measured the cylinder's dimensions in inches, the volume would be in in.^{3} (cubic inches); if in centimeters, then cm^3 (cubic centimeters).

Measurement and problem solving are part of our lives. They play a particularly central role in our attempts to describe and understand the physical world, as we shall see in this chapter.

1.1 Why and How We Measure

OBJECTIVE: **To distinguish standard units and systems of units.**

Imagine that someone is giving you directions to her house. Would you find it helpful to be told, "Drive along Elm Street for a little while, and turn right at one of the lights. Then keep going for quite a long way."? Or would you want to deal with a bank that sent you a statement at the end of the month saying, "You still have some money left in your account. Not a great deal, though."?

Measurement is important to all of us. It is one of the concrete ways in which we deal with our world. This concept is particularly true in physics. *Physics is concerned with the description and understanding of nature*, and measurement is one of its most important tools.

There certainly are ways of describing the physical world that do not involve measurement. For instance, we might talk about the color of a flower or a dress. But perception of color is subjective: It may vary from one person to another. Indeed, many people are color-blind and cannot tell certain colors apart. Light can also be described in terms of wavelengths and frequencies. Different wavelengths are associated with different colors because of the physiological response of our eyes to light. But unlike the sensations or perceptions of color, the wavelengths can be measured. They are the same for everyone. In other words, they are *objective. Physics attempts to describe nature in an objective way through measurements.*

Standard Units

Measurements are expressed in unit values, or units. As you are probably aware, a large variety of units is used to express measured values. Some of the earliest units of measurement, such as the foot, were originally referenced to parts of the human body. (Even today, the hand is still used as a unit to measure the height of horses.) If a unit becomes officially accepted, it is called a **standard unit.** Traditionally, a government or international body establishes standard units.

A group of standard units and their combinations is called a **system of units**. Two major systems of units are in use today—the metric system and the British system. The latter is still widely used in the United States, but has virtually disappeared in the rest of the world, having been replaced by the metric system.

Different units in the same system or units from different systems can be used to describe the same thing. For example, your height can be expressed in inches, feet, centimeters, meters—or even miles, for that matter (although this unit would not be very convenient). It is always possible to convert from one unit to another, and such conversion is sometimes necessary. It is best, however, and certainly most practical, to work consistently within the same system of units, as you will see.

1.2 SI Units of Length, Mass, and Time

OBJECTIVES: **To (a) describe the SI and (b) specify the references for the three main base quantities of this system.**

Length, mass, and time are fundamental physical quantities that describe a great many objects and phenomena. In fact, the topics of mechanics (the study of motion and force) covered in the first part of this book require *only* these physical quantities. The system of units used by scientists to represent these and other quantities is based on the metric system

Historically, the metric system was the outgrowth of proposals for a more uniform system of weights and measures in France during the 17th and 18th centuries. The modern version of the metric system is called the **International System of Units,** officially abbreviated as **SI** (from the French *Système International des Unités*).

The SI includes *base quantities* and *derived quantities*, which are described by base units and derived units, respectively. **Base units,** such as the meter and the kilogram, are represented by standards. Other quantities that may be expressed in terms of combinations of base units are called **derived units.** (Think of how we commonly measure the length of a trip in miles and the amount of time the trip takes in hours. To express how fast we travel, we use the derived unit of miles per hour, which represents distance per unit of time, or length per time.)

One of the refinements of the SI was the adoption of new standard references for some base units, including those of length and of time.

Length

Length is the base quantity used to measure distances or dimensions in space. We commonly say that length is the distance between two points. But the distance between any two points depends on how the space between them is traversed, which may be in a straight or a curved path.

The SI unit of length is the **meter (m).** The meter was originally defined as 1/10 000 000 of the distance from the North Pole to the equator along a meridian running through Paris (▼Fig. 1.1a).* A portion of this meridian between Dunkirk, France, and Barcelona, Spain, was surveyed to establish the standard length, which was assigned the name *metre*, from the Greek word *metron*, meaning "a measure." (The American spelling is *meter*.) A meter is 39.37 inches—slightly longer than a yard.

The length of the meter was initially preserved in the form of a material standard: the distance between two marks on a metal bar (made of a platinum–iridium alloy) that was stored under controlled conditions and called the Meter of the Archives. However, it is not desirable to have a reference standard that changes with external conditions, such as temperature. In 1983, the meter was redefined in terms of a more accurate standard, an unvarying property of light: the length of the path traveled by light in a vacuum during an interval of 1/299 792 458 of a second (Fig. 1.1b). In other words, light travels 299 792 458 meters in a second, and the speed of light in a vacuum is defined to be 299 792 458 meters per second. Note that the length standard is referenced to time, which can be measured with great accuracy.

▼ **FIGURE 1.1 The SI length standard: the meter** **(a)** The meter was originally defined as 1/10 000 000 of the distance from the North Pole to the Equator along a meridian running through Paris, of which a portion was measured between Dunkirk and Barcelona. A metal bar (called the Meter of the Archives) was constructed as a standard. **(b)** The meter is currently defined in terms of the speed of light.

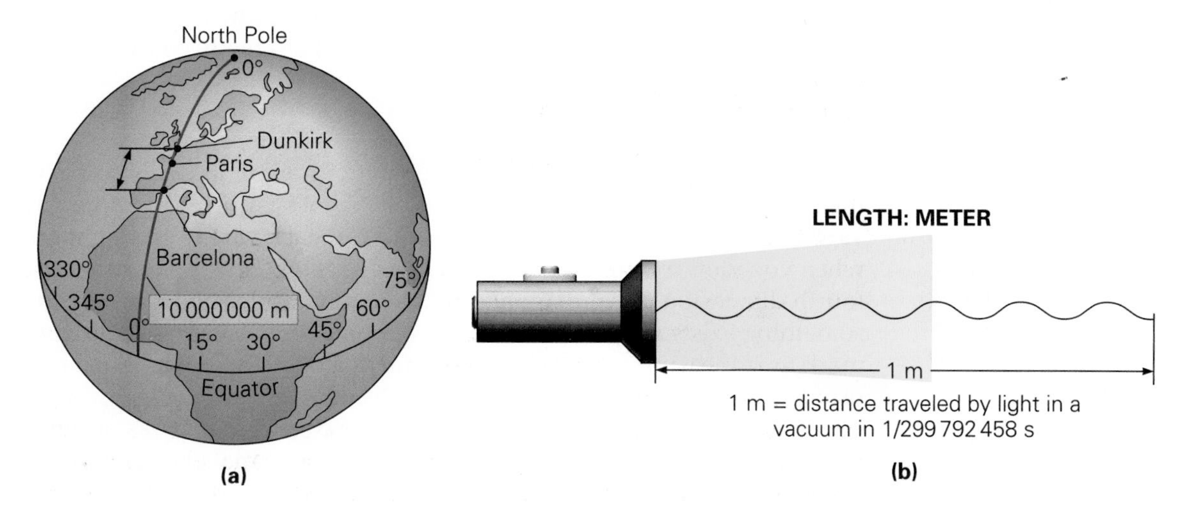

*Note that this book and most physicists have adopted the practice of writing large numbers with a thin space for three-digit groups—for example, 10 000 000 (not 10,000,000). This is done to avoid confusion with the European practice of using a comma as a decimal point. For instance, 3.141 in the United States would be written as 3,141 in Europe. Large decimal numbers, such as 0.537 84, may also be separated, for consistency. Spaces are generally used for numbers with more than four digits on either side of the decimal point.

MASS: KILOGRAM

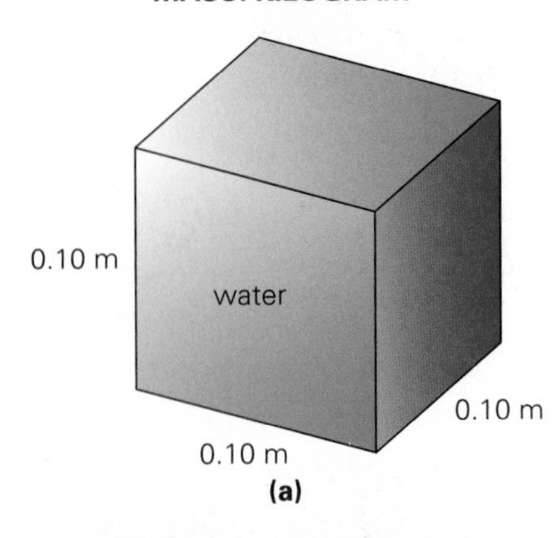

(b)

▲ **FIGURE 1.2 The SI mass standard: the kilogram** **(a)** The kilogram was originally defined in terms of a specific volume of water, that of a cube 0.10 m on a side, thereby associating the mass standard with the length standard. The standard kilogram is now defined by a metal cylinder. **(b)** The international prototype of the kilogram is kept at the French Bureau of Weights and Measures. It was manufactured in the 1880s of an alloy of 90% platinum and 10% iridium. Copies have been made for use as 1 kg national prototypes, one of which is the mass standard for the United States. It is kept at the National Institute of Standards and Technology (NIST) in Washington, D.C.

Mass

Mass is the base quantity used to describe amounts of matter. The more massive an object, the more matter it contains. (We will encounter more precise definitions of mass in Chapter 4.)

The SI unit of mass is the **kilogram (kg).** The kilogram was originally defined in terms of a specific volume of water, but is now referenced to a specific material standard: the mass of a prototype platinum–iridium cylinder kept at the International Bureau of Weights and Measures in Sèvres, France (◂Fig. 1.2). The United States has a duplicate of the prototype cylinder. The duplicate serves as a reference for secondary standards that are used in everyday life and commerce. (The kilogram may eventually be referenced to something less subject to time and chance than a piece of metal.)

You may have noticed that the phrase "weights and measures" is generally used instead of "masses and measures." In the SI, mass is a base quantity, but in the more familiar British system, weight is used instead to describe amounts of mass—for example, weight in pounds instead of mass in kilograms. The weight of an object is the gravitational attraction that the Earth exerts on the object. For example, when you weigh yourself on a scale, your weight is a measure of the downward gravitational force exerted on you by the Earth. We can use weight in this way because near the Earth's surface, mass and weight are directly proportional to each other: They differ only by a particular constant.

But treating weight as a base quantity creates some problems. A base quantity is naturally most useful if its value is the same everywhere. This is the case with mass—an object has the same mass, or amount of matter, regardless of its location. *But it is not true of weight.* For example, the weight of an object on the Moon is less than its weight on the Earth. This is because the Moon is less massive than the Earth, and the gravitational attraction exerted on an object by the Moon (i.e., the object's weight) is less than that exerted by the Earth. That is, an object with a given amount of mass has a particular weight on the Earth, but on the Moon, the same amount of mass will weigh only about one sixth as much. Similarly, the weight of an object would vary on the surfaces of different planets.

For now, keep in mind that *weight is related to mass, but they are not the same.* Since the weight of an object of a certain mass can vary with location, it is much more useful to take mass as the base quantity, as the SI does. Base quantities should remain the same regardless of where they are measured, under normal or standard conditions. The distinction between mass and weight will be more fully explained in a later chapter. Our discussion until then will be chiefly concerned with mass.

Time

Time is a difficult concept to define. (Try it.) A common definition is that time is the forward flow of events. This statement is not so much a definition as an observation that time has never been known to run backward, as it might appear to do when you view a film run backward in a projector. Time is sometimes said to be a fourth dimension, accompanying the three dimensions of space (x, y, z, t). Thus, if something exists in space, it also exists in time. In any case, events can be used to mark time measurements. The events are analogous to the marks on a meterstick used for measurements of length.

The SI unit of time is the **second (s).** The solar "clock" was originally used to define the second. A solar day is the interval of time that elapses between two successive crossings of the same longitude line (meridian) by the Sun at its highest point in the sky at that longitude. A second was fixed as 1/86 400 of this apparent solar day $(1 \text{ day} = 24 \text{ h} = 1440 \text{ min} = 86\,400 \text{ s})$. However, the elliptical path of the Earth's motion around the Sun causes apparent solar days to vary in length.

As a more precise standard, an average, or mean, solar day was computed from the lengths of the apparent solar days during a solar year. In 1956, the second

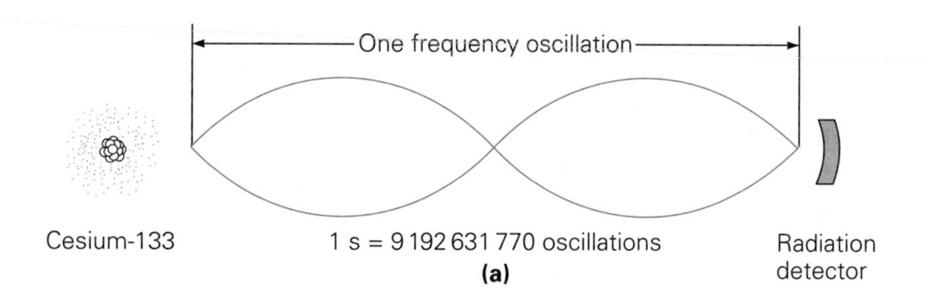

(b)

▲ **FIGURE 1.3 The SI time standard: the second** The second was once defined in terms of the average solar day. **(a)** It is now defined by the frequency of the radiation associated with an atomic transition. **(b)** The atomic fountain "clock" shown here, at NIST, is the time standard for the United States. The variation of this "timepiece" is less than one second per 20 million years.

was referenced to this mean solar day. But the mean solar day is not exactly the same for each yearly period, because of minor variations in the Earth's motions and a steady slowing of its rate of rotation, due to tidal friction. So scientists kept looking for something better.

In 1967, an atomic standard was adopted as a better reference. The second was defined by the radiation frequency of the cesium-133 atom. This "atomic clock" used a beam of cesium atoms to maintain our time standard, with a variation of about one second in 300 years. In 1999, another cesium-133 atomic clock was adopted, the atomic fountain clock, which, as the name implies, is based on the radiation frequency of a fountain of cesium atoms rather than a beam (▲Fig. 1.3). The variation of this timepiece is less than one second per 20 million years!*

SI Base Units

The complete SI has seven base quantities and base units. In addition to the meter, kilogram, and second for (1) length, (2) mass, and (3) time, respectively, we measure (4) electric current (charge/second) in amperes (A), (5) temperature in kelvins (K), (6) amount of substance in moles (mol), and (7) luminous intensity in candelas (cd). See Table 1.1.

The foregoing quantities are thought to compose the smallest number of base quantities needed for a full description of everything observed or measured in nature. There are also two supplemental units for angular measure: the two-dimensional plane angle and the three-dimensional solid angle. Scientists have not reached general agreement about whether these geometric units are base or derived units.

TABLE 1.1 The Seven Base Units of the SI

Name of Unit (abbreviation)	*Property Measured*
meter (m)	length
kilogram (kg)	mass
second (s)	time
ampere (A)	electric current
kelvin (K)	temperature
mole (mol)	amount of substance
candela (cd)	luminous intensity

*An even more precise clock, the all-optical atomic clock, is under development. It is so named because it uses laser technology and measures the shortest time interval ever recorded—100 000 times shorter than that of the best current clocks. The new clock does not use cesium atoms, but rather a single cooled ion of liquid mercury linked to a laser oscillator. The frequency of the mercury ion is 100 000 times higher than the frequency of cesium atoms, hence the shorter, more precise time interval.

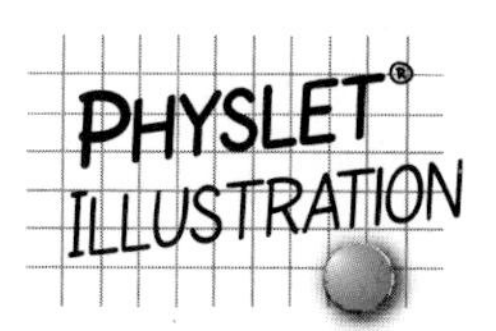

Introduction to Physlet Illustrations

1.3 More about the Metric System

OBJECTIVES: To use common (a) metric prefixes and (b) nonstandard metric units.

The metric system involving the standard units of length, mass, and time, now incorporated in the SI was once called the **mks system** (for *m*eter–*k*ilogram–*s*econd). Another metric system that has been used in dealing with relatively small quantities is the **cgs system** (for *c*entimeter–*g*ram–*s*econd). In the United States, the system still generally in use is the British (or English) engineering system, in which the standard units of length, mass, and time are foot, slug, and second, respectively. You may not have heard of the slug, because, as we mentioned earlier, gravitational force (weight) is commonly used instead of mass—pounds instead of slugs—to describe quantities of matter. As a result, the British system is sometimes called the **fps system** (for *f*oot–*p*ound–*s*econd).

The metric system is predominant throughout the world and is coming into increasing use in the United States. Primarily because it is simple mathematically, it is the preferred system of units for science and technology. SI units are used throughout most of this book. All quantities can be expressed in SI units. However, some units from other systems are accepted for limited use as a matter of practicality—for example, the time unit of hour and the temperature unit of degree Celsius. British units will sometimes be used in the early chapters for comparison purposes, since these units are still employed in everyday activities and for many practical applications.

The increasing worldwide use of the metric system means that you should be familiar with it. One of the greatest advantages of the metric system is that it is a decimal, or base-10, system. This means that larger or smaller units are obtained by multiplying or dividing, respectively, a base unit by powers of 10. A list of some multiples and corresponding prefixes for metric units is given in Table 1.2. In decimal measurements, the prefixes milli-, centi-, and kilo- are the ones most commonly used. The decimal characteristic makes it convenient to change measurements from one size of metric unit to another. With the familiar British system, different conversion factors must be used, such as 16 for converting pounds to ounces and 12 for converting feet to inches. The British system developed historically and not very scientifically.

TABLE 1.2 Some Multiples and Prefixes for Metric Units*

Multiple†	*Prefix (and abbreviation)*	*Pronunciation*	*Multiple*†	*Prefix (and abbreviation)*	*Pronunciation*
10^{12}	tera- (T)	ter′a (as in *terr*ace)	10^{-2}	centi- (c)	sen′ti (as in *senti*mental)
10^{9}	giga- (G)	jig′a (*jig* as in *jig*gle, *a* as in *a*bout)	10^{-3}	milli- (m)	mil′li (as in *mili*tary)
10^{6}	mega- (M)	meg′a (as in *mega*phone)	10^{-6}	micro- (μ)	mi′kro (as in *micro*phone)
10^{3}	kilo- (k)	kil′o (as in *kilo*watt)	10^{-9}	nano- (n)	nan′oh (*an* as in *an*nual)
10^{2}	hecto- (h)	hek′to (*heck-toe*)	10^{-12}	pico- (p)	pe′ko (*peek-oh*)
10	deka- (da)	dek′a (*deck* plus *a* as in *a*bout)	10^{-15}	femto- (f)	fem′toe (*fem* as in *fem*inine)
10^{-1}	deci- (d)	des′i (as in *deci*mal)			

*For example, 1 gram (g) multiplied by 1000, or 10^3, is 1 kilogram (kg); 1 gram multiplied by 1/1000, or 10^{-3}, is 1 milligram (mg).

†The most commonly used prefixes are printed in blue. Note that the abbreviations for the multiples 10^6 and greater are capitalized, whereas the abbreviations for the smaller multiples are lowercased.

You are already familiar with one base-10 system—U.S. currency. Just as a meter can be divided into 10 decimeters, 100 centimeters, or 1000 millimeters, the "base unit" of the dollar can be broken down into 10 "decidollars" (dimes), 100 "centidollars" (cents), or 1000 "millidollars" (tenths of a cent, or mills, used in figuring property taxes and bond levies). Since all the metric prefixes are powers of 10, there are no metric analogues for quarters or nickels.

The official metric prefixes can help eliminate confusion. In the United States, a billion is a thousand million (10^9); in Great Britain, a billion is a million million (10^{12}). The use of metric prefixes eliminates any confusion, since giga- indicates 10^9 and tera- stands for 10^{12}. You may be hearing more about nano, a prefix that indicates 10^{-9}, and the nanometer. See the Insight on *nano*technology.

Volume

In the SI, the standard unit of volume is the cubic meter (m^3)—the three-dimensional derived unit of the meter base unit. Because this unit is rather large, it is often more convenient to use the nonstandard unit of volume (or capacity) of a cube 10 cm (centimeters) on a side. This volume was given the name *litre*, which is spelled **liter**, and abbreviated as L in the United States. The volume of a liter is $1000\ cm^3 (10\ cm \times 10\ cm \times 10\ cm)$. Since $1\ L = 1000\ mL$ (milliliters), it follows that $1\ mL = 1\ cm^3$. (The cubic centimeter is sometimes abbreviated as cc, particularly in chemistry and biology.) See ▸Fig. 1.4a.

Note: Liter is sometimes abbreviated as a lowercase "ell" (l), but a capital "ell" (L) is preferred in the United States so that the abbreviation is less likely to be confused with the numeral one. (Isn't 1 L clearer than 1 l ?)

Example 1.1 ■ The Metric Ton (or Tonne): Another Unit of Mass

As we have seen, the metric unit of mass was originally related to the length standard, with a liter ($1000\ cm^3$) of water having a mass of 1 kg. The standard metric unit of volume is the cubic meter (m^3) and this volume of water was used to define a larger unit of mass called the *metric ton* (or *tonne*, as it is sometimes spelled). A metric ton is equivalent to how many kilograms?

Thinking It Through. A cubic meter is a relatively large volume and holds a large amount of water (more than a cubic yard; why?). The key is to find how many cubic volumes measuring 10 cm on a side (liters) are in a cubic meter. We expect, therefore, a large number.

Solution. Each liter of water has a mass of 1 kg, so we must find out how many liters there are in $1\ m^3$. Since there are 100 cm in a meter, we can visualize a cubic meter as simply a cube with sides 100 cm in length. Therefore, a cubic meter ($1\ m^3$) has a volume of $10^2\ cm \times 10^2\ cm \times 10^2\ cm = 10^6\ cm^3$. Since $1\ L = 10^3\ cm^3$, there must be $(10^6\ cm^3)/(10^3\ cm^3/L) = 1000\ L$ in $1\ m^3$. Thus, 1 metric ton is equivalent to 1000 kg.

Note that this entire line of reasoning can be expressed very concisely in a single calculation:

$$\frac{1\ m^3}{1\ L} = \frac{100\ cm \times 100\ cm \times 100\ cm}{10\ cm \times 10\ cm \times 10\ cm} = 1000 \quad \text{or} \quad 1\ m^3 = 1000\ L$$

Follow-up Exercise. One kilogram has an equivalent weight of 2.2 lb. Using this relationship, how does the metric ton compare with the British ton? *(Answers to all Follow-up Exercises are at the back of the text.)**

Recall that the standard unit of mass, the kilogram, was originally defined to be the mass of a cubic volume of water 10 cm, or 0.10 m, on a side, or the volume of one liter of water (at its maximum density, at about 4°C). The density of water

*The Answers to Follow-up Exercises section after the appendices contains the answers—and, for Conceptual Exercises, the reasoning—for all Follow-up Exercises in this book.

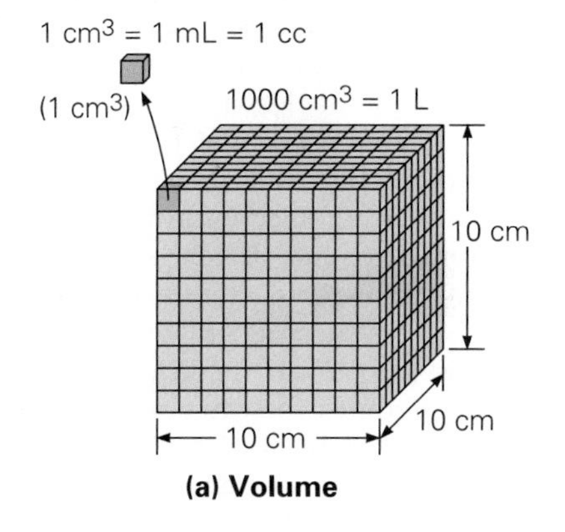

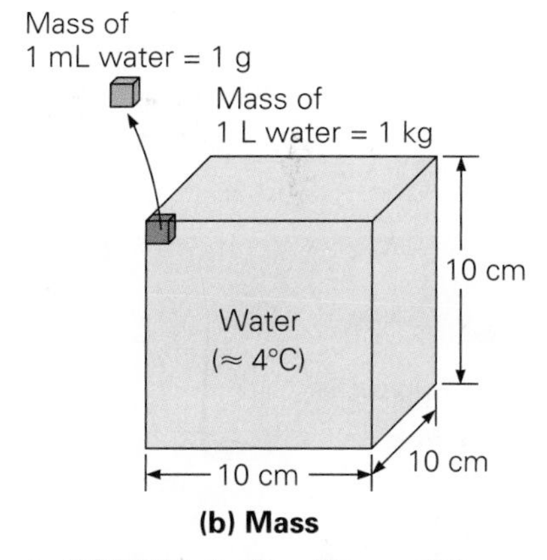

▲ **FIGURE 1.4 The liter and the kilogram** Other metric units are derived from the meter. **(a)** A unit of volume (capacity) was taken to be the volume of a cube 10 cm, or 0.01 m, on a side and was given the name *liter* (L). **(b)** The mass of a liter of water (at its maximum density) was defined to be 1 kg. Note that the decimeter cube contains $1000\ cm^3$, or 1000 mL. Thus, $1\ cm^3$, or 1 mL, of water has a mass of 1 g.

INSIGHT

Nanotechnology

A prefix for metric units refers to the order of the dimension of measurement used. The prefix *micro-* (10^{-6}) has been in common use for some time—e.g., in microscope, microchip, microbiology, microchemistry, and so on. Now the prefix *nano-* is coming into use, and you will probably be hearing a great deal about it with respect to nanotechnology (*nanotech* for short).

In general, nanotechnology is any technology done on the nanometer scale. A nanometer is one billionth (10^{-9}) of a meter, about the width of three to four atoms. Basically, nanotechnology involves the manufacture or building of things one atom or molecule at a time, so the nanometer is the appropriate scale. One atom or molecule at a time? That may sound a bit farfetched, but it's not. This possibility was advanced by physicist Richard Feynman in 1956: "The principles of physics, as far as I can see, do not speak against the possibility of maneuvering things atom by atom." This has been accomplished by using a special microscope at very low temperatures and "pushing around" single atoms (Fig. 1).

In a sense, nanotechnology occurs naturally in the cells of our bodies. Ribosomes (tiny particles in all living cells) are the sites at which information carried by the genetic code is converted into protein molecules. Ribosomes are like tiny "machines," no larger then a few nanometers long, that read DNA instructions on how to build enzymes and other proteins molecule by molecule.

Perhaps you can now see the potential of nanotechnology. The chemical properties of atoms and molecules are well understood. For example, rearranging the atoms in coal can produce a diamond. (We can already do this task without nanotechnology, using heat and pressure.) Nanotechnology presents the possibility of constructing novel molecular devices or "machines" with extraordinary properties and

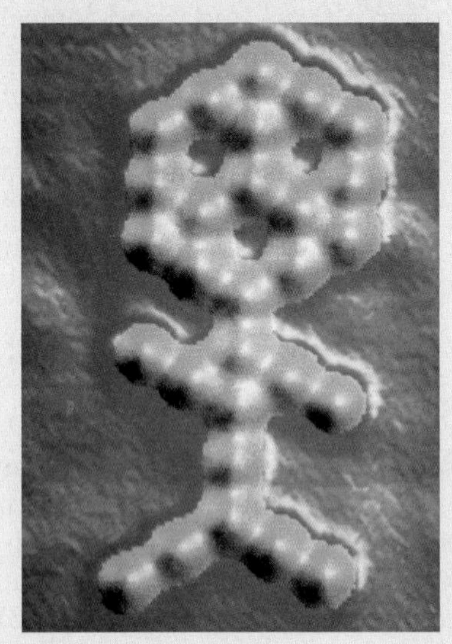

FIGURE 1 Molecular Man This figure was crafted by moving 28 molecules, one at a time. Each of the gold-colored peaks is the image of a carbon monoxide molecule. The molecules rest on a single crystal platinum surface. "Molecular Man" measures 5 nm tall and 2.5 nm wide (hand-to-hand). More than 20 000 figures, linked hand-to-hand, would be needed to span a single human hair. The molecules in the figure were positioned using a special microscope at very low temperatures.

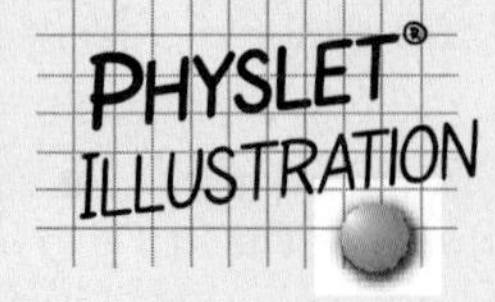

Scanning tunneling microscope

does not vary greatly with temperature, so we can say with fairly good accuracy that *1 L of water has a mass of 1 kg*, an approximation that we will use throughout this book (Fig. 1.4b). Also, since 1 kg = 1000 g and 1 L = 1000 cm^3, then *1 cm^3 (or 1 mL) of water has a mass of 1 g*.

You are probably more familiar with the liter than you think. The use of the liter is becoming quite common in the United States, as ◂Fig. 1.5 indicates.

Because the metric system is coming into increasing use in the United States, you may find it helpful to have an idea of how metric and British units compare. The relative sizes of some units are illustrated in ▸Fig. 1.6. The mathematical conversion from one unit to another will be discussed shortly.

▲ **FIGURE 1.5 Two, three, one, and one-half liters** The liter is now a common volume unit for soft drinks.

1.4 Dimensional Analysis and Unit Analysis

OBJECTIVES: **To explain the advantages of and apply (a) dimensional analysis and (b) unit analysis.**

The fundamental, or base, quantities used in physical descriptions are called *dimensions*. For example, length, mass, and time are dimensions. You could measure the distance between two points and express it in units of meters, centimeters, or feet, but the quantity would still have the dimension of length.

abilities. Here are a few potential applications that scientists hope to develop:

- *Medical delivery*. Nanostructures might be injected into the body to go to a particular site, such as a cancerous growth, and deliver a drug directly. Other organs of the body would then be spared any effects of the drug. (This process might be considered nanochemotherapy.)
- *Nanocomputing*. A new technology will soon be needed to make smaller or faster computer chips. As more and more transistors are packed onto a chip, the microscopic "wires" that connect the transistors must be made smaller and thinner. (They are currently down to a thickness of a few hundred atoms.) When down to a thickness of several atoms, the wires explode when electrical signals are passed through them. To save the day, enter the "nanotube," a nanostructure composed of carbon atoms and shaped like a hollow tube, which can carry the electrical signals without being destroyed. Nanotubes have already been developed, and research on their application is underway.
- *Fabric improvement*. A research company is now developing nanostructures that can be attached to fibers. One type, when attached to cotton fibers, causes spilled liquids to bead up on the surface so they can be quickly wiped off, making the fabric both water-repellent and resistant to stains. Another type applies to synthetic fibers, such as polyester. The nanostructure allows the fabric to act as natural fibers in clothing do, moving moisture away from a person's body to the surface for quick evaporation and more comfort.

To illustrate the new technology, scientists have made a "nanoguitar" (Fig. 2). The world's smallest guitar has been carved out of crystalline silicon. How is this procedure done? The key is electron-beam technology. Electron-beam lithography is a technique for creating extremely fine patterns, much smaller than can be seen with the unaided eye. It was developed from early electron-beam microscope technology. The nanoguitar was made for fun and illustration—it doesn't play. (Perhaps the scientists haven't been able to fashion a "nanopick" to use on the strings.) Actually, the strings, which are only 50 nanometers (nm) wide, or the width of about 100 atoms, could be plucked by special microscope techniques and would vibrate, but at inaudible frequencies. (See Chapter 9.)

It is difficult for us to grasp or visualize the new concept of nanotechnolgy. Even so, keep in mind that a nanometer is one billionth of a meter. The diameter of a human hair is about 200 000 nanometers—huge compared with the new nanoapplications. The future should be an exciting nanotime.

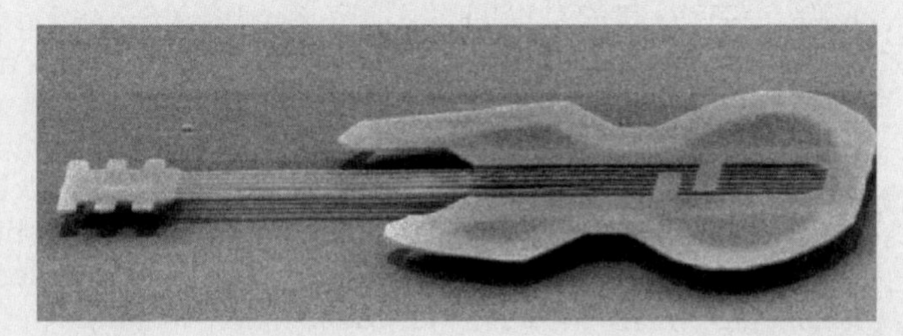

FIGURE 2 Nanoguitar The world's smallest guitar is 10 μm long—about the size of a single cell—with six strings, each about 50 nm (or 100 atoms) wide. The guitar was formed from crystalline silicone.

▼ FIGURE 1.6 Comparison of some SI and British units The bars illustrate the relative magnitudes of each pair of units. (*Note*: The comparison scales are different in each case.)

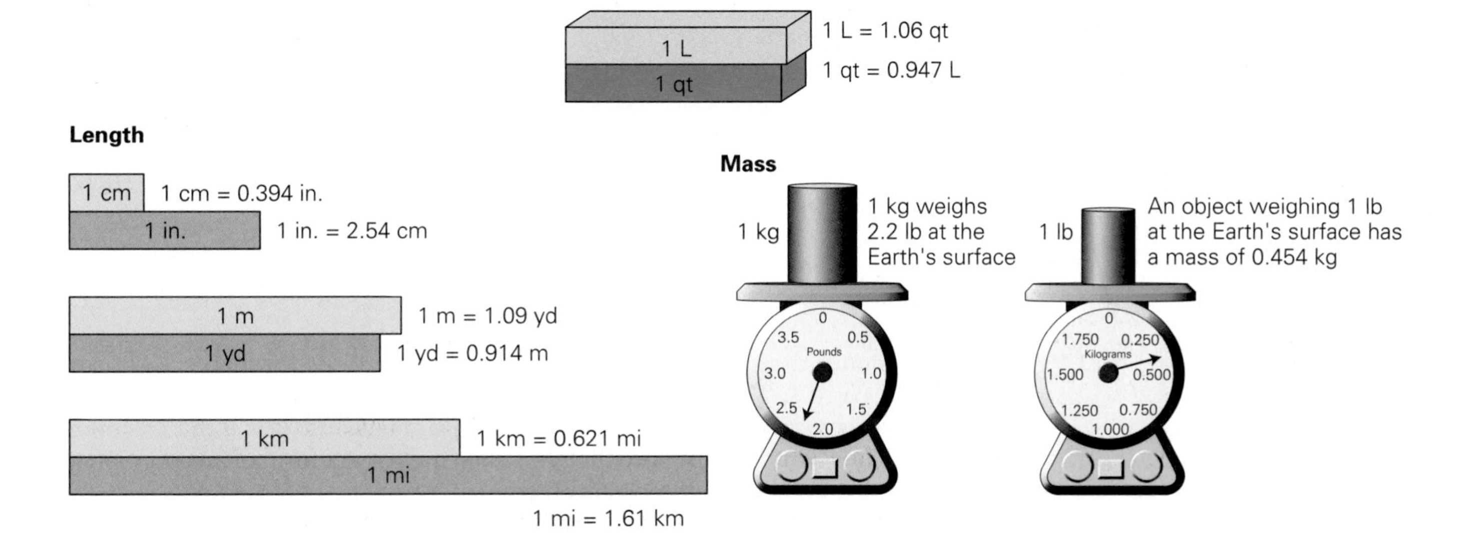

It is common to express dimensional quantities by bracketed symbols, such as [L], [M], and [T] for length, mass, and time, respectively. (The dimensions and units of some common quantities are given in Table 1.3.) Derived quantities are combinations of dimensions; for example, velocity (v) has the dimensions [L]/[T] (think of miles/hour or meters/second), and volume (V) has the dimensions [L] × [L] × [L], or [L^3]. Addition and subtraction can be done only with quantities that have the same dimensions; for example, 10 s + 20 s = 30 s, or [T] + [T] = [T].

Dimensional analysis is a procedure by which the dimensional consistency of any equation may be checked. You have used equations and know that an equation is a mathematical equality. Since physical quantities used in equations have dimensions, *the two sides of an equation must be equal not only in numerical value, but also in dimensions*. For example, suppose you had the length quantities $a = 3.0\text{ m}$ and $b = 4.0\text{ m}$. Inserting these values into the equation $a \times b = c$, gives $3.0\text{ m} \times 4.0\text{ m} = 12\text{ m}^2$. Both sides of the equation are numerically equal ($3 \times 4 = 12$), and both sides are dimensionally equal ([L] × [L] = [L^2]). Notice that we are not algebraically manipulating the dimension symbol [L] in the same way you normally would a variable, such as L. (Note also that variables are italicized.)

TABLE 1.3 Some Dimensions and Units of Common Quantities

Quantity	Dimension	Unit
mass	[M]	kg
time	[T]	s
length	[L]	m
area	[L^2]	m^2
volume	[L^3]	m^3
velocity (v)	$\frac{[L]}{[T]}$	$\frac{m}{s}$
acceleration (a or g)	$\frac{[L]}{[T^2]}$	$\frac{m}{s^2}$

The expression [L] × [L] = [L^2] is read, "when you take a length dimension and multiply it by a length dimension, the result has the dimension of length squared." A second example will help clarify the point: If a and b are inserted into the equation $a + b = c$, we get 3.0 m + 4.0 m = 7.0 m. Comparing both sides of the equation dimensionally, we would say [L] + [L] = [L], or a length plus a length gives another length, but *not* [L] + [L] = 2[L].

One of the major advantages of dimensional analysis is its usefulness in checking an equation to see if it has the correct form. For example, suppose that you think you can solve a problem about the distance an object travels by using the equation $x = at$, where x represents distance, or length, and has the dimension [L]; a represents acceleration, which, as we will see in Chapter 2, has the dimensions [L]/[T^2]; and t represents time and has the dimension [T]. First, before trying to use numbers with the equation, you can check to see if it is dimensionally correct:

$$x = at$$

is expressed dimensionally as

$$[L] = \frac{[L]}{[T^2]} \times [T] \qquad \text{or} \qquad [L] = \frac{[L]}{[T]}$$

which is not true. Thus, $x = at$ cannot be a correct equation.

Dimensional analysis will tell you if an equation is dimensionally incorrect, but a dimensionally consistent equation does not necessarily express correctly the real relationship of quantities. For example, in terms of dimensions,

$$x = at^2$$

is

$$[L] = \frac{[L]}{[T^2]} \times [T^2] \qquad \text{or} \qquad [L] = [L]$$

This equation is dimensionally correct. But, as you will see in Chapter 2, it is not physically correct. The correct form of the equation—both dimensionally and physically—is $x = \frac{1}{2}at^2$. (The fraction $\frac{1}{2}$ has no dimensions; it is a dimensionless number.) Thus, you must be sure that you have the correct form of an equation before you use it to find solutions to problems.

Doing dimensional analysis with the symbols [L], [T], and [M] is fine, but in practice, it is often more convenient to use specific units, such as m, s, and kg. Units can also be treated as algebraic quantities and, like symbols, can be canceled. Using units instead of symbols in dimensional analysis is called **unit analysis.** If an equation is correct by unit analysis, it must be dimensionally correct. Example 1.2 demonstrates the use of unit analysis.

Example 1.2 ■ Checking Dimensions: Unit Analysis

A professor puts two equations on the board: (a) $v = v_o + at$ and (b) $x = v/2a$, where x is a distance in meters (m); v and v_o are velocities in meters/second (m/s); a is acceleration in (meters/second)/second, or meters/second^2 (m/s^2); and t is time in seconds (s). Are the equations dimensionally correct? Use unit analysis to find out.

Thinking It Through. Simply insert the units for the quantities in each equation, cancel, and check the units on both sides.

Solution.

(a) The equation is

$$v = v_o + at$$

Inserting units for the physical quantities gives

$$\frac{\text{m}}{\text{s}} = \frac{\text{m}}{\text{s}} + \left(\frac{\text{m}}{\text{s}^2} \times \text{s}\right) \quad \text{or} \quad \frac{\text{m}}{\text{s}} = \frac{\text{m}}{\text{s}} + \left(\frac{\text{m}}{\text{s} \times \cancel{\text{s}}} \times \cancel{\text{s}}\right)$$

Notice that units cancel like numbers in a fraction. Then, we have

$$\frac{\text{m}}{\text{s}} = \frac{\text{m}}{\text{s}} + \frac{\text{m}}{\text{s}} \quad \left[\begin{matrix}\textit{dimensionally} \\ \textit{correct}\end{matrix}\right]$$

The equation is dimensionally correct, since the units on each side are meters per second. (The equation is also a correct relationship, as we shall see in Chapter 2.)

(b) By unit analysis, the equation

$$x = \frac{v}{2a}$$

is

$$\text{m} = \frac{\left(\frac{\text{m}}{\text{s}}\right)}{\left(\frac{\text{m}}{\text{s}^2}\right)} = \frac{\cancel{\text{m}}}{\cancel{\text{s}}} \times \frac{\text{s}^{\cancel{2}}}{\cancel{\text{m}}} \quad \text{or} \quad \text{m} = \text{s} \quad \left[\begin{matrix}\textit{not dimensionally} \\ \textit{correct}\end{matrix}\right]$$

Meters (m) cannot equal seconds (s), so in this case, the equation is dimensionally incorrect and therefore not physically correct.

Follow-up Exercise. Is the equation $x = v^2/a$ dimensionally correct? *(Answers to all Follow-up Exercises are at the back of the text.)*

Another useful application of unit analysis is to determine the units of a quantity from a correct equation. For example, $x = \frac{1}{2}at^2$ is a correct expression relating distance (x), acceleration (a), and time (t), and say you want to know the units of a. Then,

$$a = \frac{2x}{t^2} \quad \text{or} \quad a = 2\left(\frac{\text{m}}{\text{s}^2}\right)$$

Thus, we find that the units of a are m/s^2. (The 2 is a numerical factor and is not associated with units.)

Mixed Units

Unit analysis also allows you to check for mixed units. In general, when working problems, you should always use the same unit for a given dimension throughout a problem. For example, suppose that you wanted to buy a new carpet to fit a rectangular room. To compute the area of the floor, you would measure the lengths of two adjacent sides of the room and multiply them. Would you measure the sides in different units, such as 10 ft × 3.0 m, and express the area as 30 ft · m? Probably not. Such mixed units are not usually very useful.

Let's look at mixed units in an equation. Suppose that you used centimeters as the unit for x in the equation

$$v^2 = v_o^2 + 2ax$$

and the units for the other quantities as in Example 1.2. In terms of units, this equation would give

$$\left(\frac{\text{m}}{\text{s}}\right)^2 = \left(\frac{\text{m}}{\text{s}}\right)^2 + \left(\frac{\text{m} \times \text{cm}}{\text{s}^2}\right)$$

or

$$\frac{\text{m}^2}{\text{s}^2} = \frac{\text{m}^2}{\text{s}^2} + \frac{\text{m} \times \text{cm}}{\text{s}^2}$$

which is dimensionally correct. That is, it is dimensionally equivalent to

$$\frac{[\text{L}^2]}{[\text{T}^2]} = \frac{[\text{L}^2]}{[\text{T}^2]} + \frac{[\text{L}^2]}{[\text{T}^2]}$$

But the units are mixed (m and cm). The terms on the right-hand side should not be added together without centimeters first being converted to meters.

Determining the Units of Quantities

Another aspect of unit analysis that is very important in physics is the determination of the units of quantities from defining equations. For example, **density** (represented by the Greek letter rho, ρ) is defined by the equation

$$\rho = \frac{m}{V} \tag{1.1}$$

where m is mass and V is volume. (Density is the mass of an object or substance per unit volume and is a measure of the compactness of the mass of that object or substance.) What are the units of density? In SI units, mass is measured in kilograms and volume in cubic meters. Hence, the defining equation

$$\rho = \frac{m}{V} \left(\frac{\text{kg}}{\text{m}^3}\right)$$

gives the derived SI unit for density as kilograms per cubic meter (kg/m^3).

What are the units of π? The relationship between the circumference (c) and the diameter (d) of a circle is given by the equation $c = \pi d$, so $\pi = c/d$. If length is measured in meters, then

$$\pi = \frac{c}{d} \left(\frac{\cancel{\text{m}}}{\cancel{\text{m}}}\right)$$

Thus, the constant π has no units, because they cancel out. It is unitless, or a dimensionless, constant.

1.5 Unit Conversions

OBJECTIVES: **To (a) explain conversion-factor relationships and (b) apply them in converting units within a system or from one system of units to another.**

Because units in different systems, or even different units in the same system, can express the same quantity, it is sometimes necessary to convert the units of a quantity from one unit to another. For example, we may need to convert feet to yards or inches to centimeters. You already know how to do many unit conversions. If a room is 12 ft long, what is its length in yards? Your immediate answer is 4 yd.

How did you do this conversion? Well, you must have known a relationship between the units of foot and yard. That is, you know that 1 yd = 3 ft. This is what we call an *equivalence statement*. As we saw in Section 1.4, the numerical values and units on both sides of an equation must be the same. In equivalence statements, we commonly use an equal sign to indicate that 1 yd and 3 ft stand for the *same*, or *equivalent, length*. The numbers are different because they stand for different *units* of length.

Mathematically, to change units, we use **conversion factors**, which are simply equivalence statements expressed in the form of ratios—for example, 1 yd/3 ft or 3 ft/1 yd. (The "1" is often omitted in the denominators of such ratios for convenience—for example, 3 ft/yd.) To understand why such ratios are useful, note that dividing the expression 1 yd = 3 ft by 3 ft (or 3 ft = 1 yd by 1 yd) on both sides gives, respectively,

$$\frac{(1\text{ yd} = 3\text{ ft})}{3\text{ ft}} = \frac{1\text{ yd}}{3\text{ ft}} = \frac{3\text{ ft}}{3\text{ ft}} = 1 \quad \text{or} \quad \frac{(3\text{ ft} = 1\text{ yd})}{1\text{ yd}} = \frac{3\text{ ft}}{1\text{ yd}} = \frac{1\text{ yd}}{1\text{ yd}} = 1$$

As you can see from these examples, a conversion factor always has an actual value of unity—and you can multiply any quantity by one without changing its value or size. Thus, *a conversion factor simply lets you express a quantity in terms of other units without changing its physical value or size.*

The manner in which 12 feet is converted to yards may be expressed mathematically as follows:

$$12\ \cancel{\text{ft}} \times \frac{1\text{ yd}}{3\ \cancel{\text{ft}}} = 4\text{ yd} \quad (\textit{units cancel})$$

Using the appropriate conversion-factor form, the units cancel, as shown by the slash marks, giving the correct unit analysis, yd = yd.

Suppose you are asked to convert 12.0 inches to centimeters. You may not know the conversion factor in this case, but you can get it from a table (such as the one that appears inside the front cover of this book) that gives the needed relationships: 1 in. = 2.54 cm or 1 cm = 0.394 in. It makes no difference which of these equivalence statements is used. The question, once you have expressed the equivalence statement as a conversion factor, is whether to divide or multiply by that factor to make the conversion. *In doing unit conversions, take advantage of unit analysis*—that is, let the units determine the appropriate form of conversion factor, so to speak.

Note that the equivalence statement 1 in. = 2.54 cm can give rise to two forms of the conversion factor: 1 in./2.54 cm or 2.54 cm/1 in. When changing in. to cm, the appropriate form for multiplying is 2.54 cm/in. When changing cm to in. use the form 1 in./2.54 cm. (The inverse forms could be used in each case, but the quantities would have to be *divided* by the conversion factors for proper unit cancellation.) In general, the multiplication form of conversion factors will be used throughout this book.

A few commonly used equivalence statements are not dimensionally correct; for example, consider 1 kg = 2.2 lb, which is used for conversions. The kilogram is a unit of mass, and the pound is a unit of weight. This means that 1 kilogram is *equivalent* to 2.2 pounds; that is, a 1-kg *mass* has a *weight* of 2.2 lb, but only on the Earth's surface. Since mass and weight are directly proportional, differing only by

Note: 1 kg of mass has an equivalent weight of 2.2 lb near the surface of the Earth.

a particular constant, we can use the dimensionally incorrect conversion factor 1 kg/2.2 lb (but *only* near the Earth's surface).

▲ **FIGURE 1.7 Unit conversion** Signs sometimes list both the British and metric units, as shown here for elevation and distance.

Example 1.3 ■ Converting Units: Use of Conversion Factors

(a) A basketball player is 6.5 ft tall. What is the player's height in meters? (b) How many seconds are there in a 30-day month? (c) What is 50 mi/h in meters per second? (See table of conversion factors inside front cover of this book.)

Thinking It Through. If we use the correct conversion factors, the rest is arithmetic.

Solution.

(a) From the conversion table, we have 1 ft = 0.305 m, so

$$6.5\ \cancel{\text{ft}} \times \frac{0.305\ \text{m}}{1\ \cancel{\text{ft}}} = 2.0\ \text{m}$$

Another foot–meter conversion is shown in ◂Fig. 1.7. Is it correct? You should be able to do this one in your head.

(b) The conversion factor for days and seconds is available from the table (1 day = 86 400 s), but you may not always have a table handy. You can always use several better known conversion factors to get the result:

$$30\ \frac{\cancel{\text{days}}}{\text{month}} \times \frac{24\ \cancel{\text{h}}}{\cancel{\text{day}}} \times \frac{60\ \cancel{\text{min}}}{\cancel{\text{h}}} \times \frac{60\ \text{s}}{\cancel{\text{min}}} = \frac{2.6 \times 10^6\ \text{s}}{\text{month}}$$

Note how unit analysis checks the conversion factors for you. The rest is simple arithmetic.

(c) In this case, from the conversion table, we have 1 mi = 1609 m and 1 h = 3600 s. (The latter is easily computed.) These ratios are used to cancel the units that are to be changed, leaving behind the ones that are wanted:

$$\frac{50\ \cancel{\text{mi}}}{1\ \cancel{\text{h}}} \times \frac{1609\ \text{m}}{1\ \cancel{\text{mi}}} \times \frac{1\ \cancel{\text{h}}}{3600\ \text{s}} = 22\ \text{m/s}$$

Follow-up Exercise. (a) Convert 50 mi/h directly to meters per second by using a single conversion factor, and (b) show that this single conversion factor can be derived from those in part (c) of this Example. *(Answers to all Follow-up Exercises are at the back of the text.)*

Example 1.4 ■ More Conversions: A Really Long Capillary System

Capillaries, the smallest blood vessels of the body, connect the arterial system with the venous system and supply our tissues with oxygen and nutrients (▾Fig. 1.8). It is estimated that if all of the capillaries of an average adult were unwound and spread out end

▸ **FIGURE 1.8 Capillary system** Capillaries connect the arterial and venous systems in our bodies. They are the smallest blood vessels, but their total length is impressive.

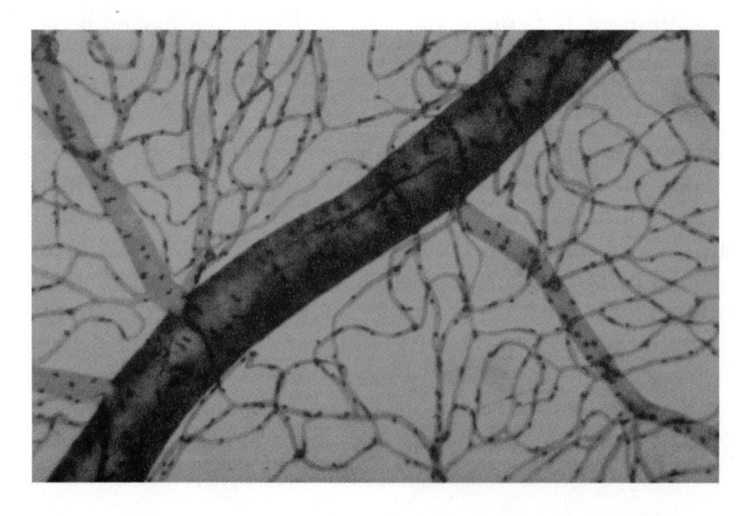

to end, they would extend to a length of about 64 000 km. (a) How many miles is this length? (b) Compare this length with the circumference of the Earth.

Thinking It Through. (a) This conversion is straightforward—just use the appropriate conversion factor. (b) How do we calculate the circumference of a circle or sphere? There is an equation to do so, and you must know the radius or diameter of the Earth. (If you do not remember one of these values, see the solar system data table inside the back cover of this book.)

Solution.

(a) We see in the conversion table that 1 km = 0.621 mi, so

$$64\,000 \text{ km} \times \frac{0.621 \text{ mi}}{1 \text{ km}} = 40\,000 \text{ mi} \quad \textit{(rounded off)}$$

(b) A length of 40 000 mi is substantial. To see how this length compares with the circumference (c) of the Earth, recall that the radius of the Earth is about 4000 mi, so the diameter (d) is 8000 mi. The circumference of a circle is given by $c = \pi d$, as we saw in Section 1.4. Therefore, we have

$$c = \pi d \approx 3 \times 8000 \text{ mi} = 24\,000 \text{ mi}$$

[To make a general comparison, we round π (=3.14...) off to 3.] So,

$$\frac{\text{capillary length}}{\text{Earth's circumference}} = \frac{40\,000 \text{ mi}}{24\,000 \text{ mi}} = 1.7$$

The capillaries of your body have a total length that would extend 1.7 times around the world. Wow!

Follow-up Exercise. Taking the average distance between the east and west coasts of the continental United States to be 4800 km, how many times would the total length of your body's capillaries cross the country? *(Answers to all Follow-up Exercises are at the back of the text.)*

Example 1.5 ■ Converting Units of Area: Choosing the Correct Conversion Factor

A hall bulletin board has an area of 2.5 m^2. What is this area in square centimeters (cm^2)?

Thinking It Through. This problem is a conversion of area units, and we know that 1 m = 100 cm. So, some squaring must be done to get square meters and square centimeters.

Solution. A common error in such conversions is the use of incorrect conversion factors. Because 1 m = 100 cm, it is sometimes assumed that 1 m^2 = 100 cm^2, which is wrong. The correct area conversion factor may be obtained directly from the correct linear conversion factor, 100 cm/1 m, or 10^2 cm/1 m, by squaring the linear conversion factor:

$$\left(\frac{10^2 \text{ cm}}{1 \text{ m}}\right)^2 = \frac{10^4 \text{ cm}^2}{1 \text{ m}^2}$$

Hence, 1 m^2 = 10^4 cm^2(= 10 000 cm^2). We can therefore write the following:

$$2.5 \text{ m}^2 \times \left(\frac{10^2 \text{ cm}}{1 \text{ m}}\right)^2 = 2.5 \text{ m}^2 \times \frac{10^4 \text{ cm}^2}{1 \text{ m}^2} = 2.5 \times 10^4 \text{ cm}^2$$

Follow-up Exercise. How many cubic centimeters are there in one cubic meter? *(Answers to all Follow-up Exercises are at the back of the text.)*

Throughout this textbook, you will be presented with various Conceptual Examples. These examples show the reasoning used in applying particular concepts, often with little or no mathematics.

Conceptual Example 1.6 ■ Which Is Faster? Comparison Using Unit Conversions

Two students disagree on which speed is faster, (a) 1 km/h or (b) 1 m/s. Which would you choose? *Clearly establish the reasoning used in determining your answer before you check it below. That is,* **why** *did you select your answer?*

Reasoning and Answer. To answer this, the quantities should be compared in the same units, so unit conversion is involved, and one looks for the easiest conversions. Observing the prefix *kilo-*, we know that 1 km is 1000 m, so that conversion is easy. Also, one hour is quickly expressed as 3600 s. (Why?) Then we have 1 km/h = 1000 m/3600 s, which is less than 1 m/s, so the answer is (b).

Follow-up Exercise. An American and a European are comparing the gas mileage they get with their RVs. The American calculates that he gets 10 mi/gal, and the European gives his as 10 km/L. Who is getting the better gas mileage? *(Answers to all Follow-up Exercises are at the back of the text.)*

Some examples of the importance of unit conversion are given in the accompanying Insight.

1.6 Significant Figures

OBJECTIVES: To (a) determine the number of significant figures in a numerical value and (b) report the proper number of significant figures after performing simple calculations.

▲ **FIGURE 1.9 Significant figures and insignificant figures** For the division operation 5.3/1.67, a calculator with a floating decimal point gives many digits. A calculated quantity can be no more accurate than the least accurate quantity involved in the calculation, so this result should be rounded off to two significant figures—that is, 3.2.

Most of the time, you will be given numerical data when asked to solve a problem. In general, such data are either exact numbers or measured numbers (quantities). **Exact numbers** are numbers without any uncertainty or error. This category includes numbers such as the "100" used to calculate a percentage and the "2" in the equation $r = d/2$ relating the radius and diameter of a circle. **Measured numbers** are numbers obtained from measurement processes and thus generally have some degree of uncertainty or error.

When calculations are done with measured numbers, the error of measurement is propagated, or carried along, by the mathematical operations. A question of how to report a result arises. For example, suppose that you are asked to find time (t) from the formula $x = vt$ and are given that $x = 5.3$ m and $v = 1.67$ m/s. Then

$$t = \frac{x}{v} = \frac{5.3\text{ m}}{1.67\text{ m/s}} = ?$$

Doing the division operation on a calculator yields a result such as 3.173 652 695 (◂Fig. 1.9). How many figures, or digits, should you report in the answer?

The error or uncertainty of the result of a mathematical operation may be computed by statistical methods. A simpler, widely used procedure for estimating this uncertainty involves the use of **significant figures (sf)**, sometimes called *significant digits*. The degree of accuracy of a measured quantity depends on how finely divided the measuring scale of the instrument is. For example, you might measure the length of an object as 2.5 cm with one instrument and 2.54 cm with another; the second instrument provides more significant figures and a greater degree of accuracy.

INSIGHT

Is Unit Conversion Important? You Be the Judge

The answer to this question is, you bet! Here are a couple of cases in point. In 1999, the $125 million Mars Climate Orbiter was making a trip to the Red Planet to investigate its atmosphere (Fig. 1). The spacecraft approached the planet in September, but suddenly contact between the Orbiter and personnel on Earth was lost, and the Orbiter was never heard from again.

Investigations showed that the Orbiter had approached Mars at a far lower altitude than planned. Instead of passing 147 km (87 mi) above the Martian surface, tracking data showed that the Orbiter was on a trajectory that would have taken it as close as 57 km (35 mi) to the surface—some 80 km (50 mi) closer to the planet than intended. As a result, the spacecraft either burned up in the Martian atmosphere or crashed into the surface.

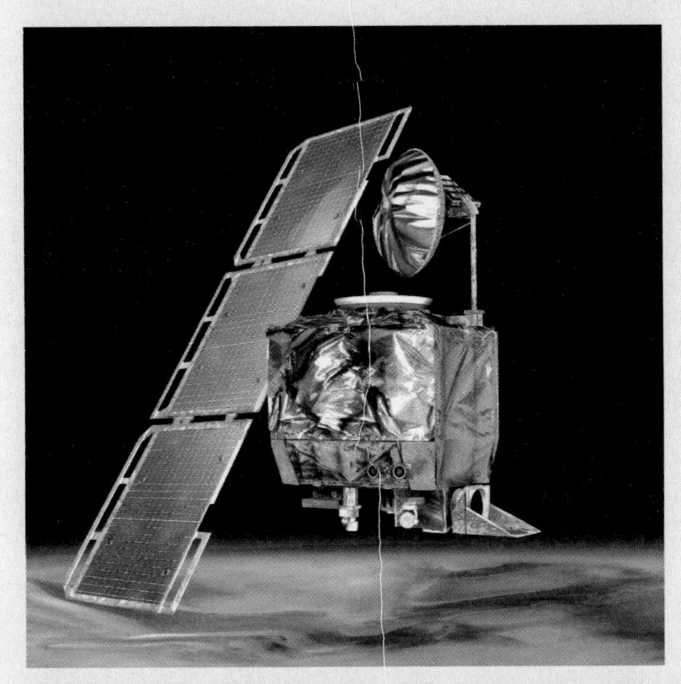

FIGURE 1 Mars Climate Orbiter An artist's conception of the Orbiter near the surface of Mars. The actual Orbiter either burned up in the Martian atmosphere or crashed into the surface. The cause was attributed to a mix-up in units, and a $125 million spacecraft was lost.

How could this have happened? Investigations showed that the failure of the Orbiter was primarily a problem of unit conversions, or a lack thereof. At Lockheed Martin Astronautics, which built the spacecraft, the engineers calculated the navigational information in British units. When scientists at NASA's Jet Propulsion Laboratory received the data they assumed that the information was in metric units, as called for in the mission specifications. These unit conversions weren't made, and a $125 million spacecraft was lost on the Red Planet—causing a few red faces.

A less well-remembered flight closer to Earth is that of the "Gimli Glider" in 1983. Air Canada Flight 143 was on course from Montréal to Edmonton, Canada, with 61 passengers in a new Boeing 767, at the time the most advanced jetliner in the world. But, almost halfway into the flight, a warning light came on for a fuel pump, then for another, and finally for all four pumps. The engines quit, and this advanced plane was now a glider, about 100 miles from the nearest major airport, at Winnipeg.

Without engines, Flight 143's descent would bring it down 10 miles short of the airport, so it was diverted to an old Royal Canadian Air Force landing field at Gimli, which had been converted into an auto racetrack with end barriers. The pilot maneuvered the powerless plane to a landing, stopping just short of the barrier, hence the name Gimli Glider. Did the plane have bad fuel pumps? No, the plane had run out of fuel!

This near-disaster was caused by another conversion problem. It seems that the fuel computers weren't working properly in the first place, so the mechanics had used the old procedure of measuring the fuel in the tanks with a dipstick. The length of the stick that is wet gives the mechanics information with which to determine the volume of fuel by using conversion values in tables. Air Canada had for years computed the amount of fuel in pounds, whereas the new 767's fuel consumption was expressed in kilograms. Even worse, the dipstick procedure gave the amount of fuel onboard in liters instead of pounds or kilograms.

These incidents underscore the importance of using appropriate units, making correct unit conversions, and working consistently in the same system of units. Several problems at the end of the chapter will challenge you to develop your skills in accurate unit conversions (See Exercises, Section 1.5 Unit Conversions).

Basically, *the significant figures in any measurement are the digits that are known with certainty, plus one digit that is uncertain.* This set of digits is usually defined as all of the digits that can be read directly from the instrument used in making the measurement, plus one uncertain digit that is obtained by estimating the fraction of the smallest division of the instrument's scale.

The quantities 2.5 cm and 2.54 cm have two and three significant figures, respectively. This information is rather evident. However, some confusion may arise when a quantity contains one or more zeros. For example, how many significant figures does the quantity 0.0254 m have? What about 104.6 m? 2705.0 m? In such cases, we will use the following rules:

1. Zeros at the beginning of a number are not significant. They merely locate the decimal point. For example,

   0.0254 m has three significant figures (2, 5, 4)

2. Zeros within a number are significant. For example,

   104.6 m has four significant figures (1, 0, 4, 6)

3. Zeros at the end of a number after the decimal point are significant. For example,

   2705.0 m has five significant figures (2, 7, 0, 5, 0).

4. In whole numbers without a decimal point that end in one or more zeros (trailing zeros)—for example, 500 kg—the zeros may or may not be significant. In such cases, it is not clear which zeros serve only to locate the decimal point and which are actually part of the measurement. That is, if the first zero from the left (5<u>0</u>0 kg) is the estimated digit in the measurement, then only two digits are reliably known, and there are only two significant figures. Similarly, if the last zero is the estimated digit (50<u>0</u> kg), then there are three significant figures. This ambiguity may be removed by using scientific (powers-of-ten) notation:

   5.0×10^2 kg has two significant figures
   5.00×10^2 kg has three significant figures

   This notation is helpful in expressing the results of calculations with the proper numbers of significant figures, as we shall see shortly. (Appendix I includes a review of scientific notation.)

   Note: To avoid confusion regarding numbers having trailing zeroes used as given quantities in text examples and exercises, we will consider the trailing zeroes to be significant. For example, assume that a time of 20 s has two significant figures, even if it is not written out as 2.0×10^1 s.

It is important to report the results of mathematical operations with the proper number of significant figures. This is accomplished by using rules for (1) multiplication and division, and (2) addition and subtraction. To obtain the proper number of significant figures, the results are rounded off. Here are some general rules that will be used for mathematical operations and rounding.

Significant Figures in Calculations

1. When multiplying and dividing quantities, leave as many significant figures in the answer as there are in the quantity with the least number of significant figures.
2. When adding or subtracting quantities, leave the same number of decimal places (rounded) in the answer as there are in the quantity with the least number of decimal places.

Rules for Rounding*

1. If the first digit to be dropped is less than 5, leave the preceding digit as is.
2. If the first digit to be dropped is 5 or greater, increase the preceding digit by one.

What the rules for significant figures mean is that the result of a calculation can be no more accurate than the least accurate quantity used. That is, you cannot gain

*It should be noted that these rounding rules give an approximation of accuracy, as opposed to the results provided by more advanced statistical methods.

accuracy in performing mathematical operations. Thus, the result that should be reported for the division operation discussed at the beginning of this section is

$$\underset{(3\ sf)}{\overset{(2\ sf)}{\frac{5.3\ \text{m}}{1.67\ \text{m/s}}}} = 3.2\ \text{s}\ \ (2\ sf)$$

The result is rounded off to two significant figures. (See Fig. 1.9.)

Applications of these rules are shown in the following Examples.

Example 1.7 ■ Using Significant Figures in Multiplication and Division: Rounding Applications

The following operations are performed and the results rounded off to the proper number of significant figures:

Multiplication

$$\underset{(2\ sf)}{2.4\ \text{m}} \times \underset{(3\ sf)}{3.65\ \text{m}} = 8.76\ \text{m}^2 = 8.8\ \text{m}^2 \quad \textit{(rounded to two sf)}$$

Division

$$\underset{(3\ sf)}{\overset{(4\ sf)}{\frac{725.0\ \text{m}}{0.125\ \text{s}}}} = 5800\ \text{m/s} = 5.80 \times 10^3\ \text{m/s} \quad \textit{(represented with three sf; why?)}$$

Follow-up Exercise. Perform the following operations, and express the answers in the standard powers-of-ten notation (one digit to the left of the decimal point) with the proper number of significant figures: (a) $(2.0 \times 10^5\ \text{kg})(0.035 \times 10^2\ \text{kg})$ and (b) $(148 \times 10^{-6}\ \text{m})/(0.4906 \times 10^{-6}\ \text{m})$. *(Answers to all Follow-up Exercises are at the back of the text.)*

Example 1.8 ■ Using Significant Figures in Addition and Subtraction: Application of Rules

The following operations are performed by finding the number that has the least number of decimal places. (Units have been omitted for convenience.)

Addition

In the numbers to be added, note that 23.1 has the least number of decimal places:

$$\begin{array}{r} 23.1 \\ 0.546 \\ \underline{1.45} \\ 25.096 \end{array} \xrightarrow{\textit{(rounding off)}} 25.1$$

Subtraction

The same rounding procedure is used. Here, the "157" has the least number of decimal places (none).

$$\begin{array}{r} 157 \\ \underline{-\ 5.5} \\ 151.5 \end{array} \xrightarrow{\textit{(rounding off)}} 152$$

Follow-up Exercise. Given the numbers 23.15, 0.546, and 1.058, (a) add the first two numbers and (b) subtract the last number from the first. *(Answers to all Follow-up Exercises are at the back of the text.)*

Suppose that you must deal with mixed operations—multiplication and/or division *and* addition and/or subtraction. What do you do in this case? Just follow your regular rules for order of algebraic operations, and observe significant figures as you go.

The number of digits reported in a result depends on the number of digits in the given data. The rules for rounding will generally be observed for examples in this book. However, there will be exceptions that may make a difference, as explained in the following hint.

Problem-Solving Hint: The "Correct" Answer

When working problems, you naturally strive to get the correct answer and will probably want to check your answers against those listed in the Answers to Odd-Numbered Exercises section in the back of the book. However, on occasion, you may find that your answer differs slightly from that given, even though you have solved the problem correctly. There are several reasons why this could happen.

As stated previously, it is best to round off only the final result of a multipart calculation, but this practice is not always convenient in elaborate calculations. Sometimes, the results of intermediate steps are important in themselves and need to be rounded off to the appropriate number of digits as if each were a final answer. Similarly, Examples in this book are often worked in steps to show the stages in the *reasoning* of the solution. The results obtained when the results of intermediate steps are rounded off may differ slightly from those obtained when only the final answer is rounded.

Rounding differences may also occur when using conversion factors. For example, in changing 5.0 mi to kilometers using the conversion factor listed in the front of the book in different forms,

$$5.0\ \cancel{\text{mi}}\left(\frac{1.609\ \text{km}}{1\ \cancel{\text{mi}}}\right) = (8.045\ \text{km}) = 8.0\ \text{km} \quad \textit{(two significant figures)}$$

and

$$5.0\ \cancel{\text{mi}}\left(\frac{1\ \text{km}}{0.621\ \cancel{\text{mi}}}\right) = (8.051\ \text{km}) = 8.1\ \text{km} \quad \textit{(two significant figures)}$$

The difference arises because of rounding of the conversion factors. Actually, $1\ \text{km} = 0.6214\ \text{mi}$, so $1\ \text{mi} = (1/0.6214)\ \text{km} = 1.609\,269\ \text{km} \approx 1.609\ \text{km}$. (Try repeating these conversions with the unrounded factors, and see what you get.) To avoid rounding differences in conversions, we will generally use the multiplication form of a conversion factor, as in the first of the foregoing equations, unless there is a convenient exact factor, such as 1 min/60 s.

Slight differences in answers may occur when different methods are used to solve a problem, because of rounding differences. Keep in mind that when solving a problem (a general procedure for which is given in Section 1.7), *if your answer differs from that in the text in only the last digit, the disparity is most likely the result of a rounding difference for an alternative method of solution being used.*

1.7 Problem Solving

OBJECTIVES: **To (a) establish a problem-solving procedure and (b) apply it to typical problems.**

An important aspect of physics is problem solving. In general, problem solving involves the application of physical principles and equations to data from a particular situation in order to find some unknown or wanted quantity. There is no universal method for approaching a problem that will automatically produce a solution.

A few general points, though, are worth keeping in mind:

- *Make sure you understand the problem.* The foundation of successful problem solving is having a thorough grasp of the problem. Before starting to work a problem, make it a habit to list everything that is given or known (as we will do for most of the Examples in this text). It's all too easy to overlook a critical piece of information.
- To proceed from the given data to the solution, you may have to *devise a strategy or plan.* Many problems cannot be solved merely by finding one equation and "plugging in" the given quantities to get the solution. Often, you will need to perform intermediate steps, each of which will bring you closer to the final answer.
- *Remember that equations are expressions of physical principles.* Solving problems involves translating principles into the "language" of equations, but you should also be able to look at an equation and determine what physical relationship it embodies.
- *A common cause of failure in problem solving is the misapplication of physical principles or equations.* Principles and equations are generally subject to certain conditions or are limited in their applicability to physical situations.
- *Many problems can be solved by more than one method.* If you understand the problem and the relevant principles well, you can probably figure out how to solve the problem in the fastest and easiest way.

Although there is no magic formula for problem solving, there are some sound practices that can be very useful. The steps in the following procedure are intended to provide you with a framework that can be applied to solving most of the problems that you will encounter in this text. We generally will use these steps in dealing with the Example problems throughout this text. Additional helpful problem-solving hints will be given where appropriate in subsequent chapters.

Suggested Problem-Solving Procedure

1. *Read the problem carefully, and analyze it. Write down the given data and what you are to find.* Some data may not be given explicitly in numerical form. For example, if a car "starts from rest," its initial speed is zero ($v_o = 0$). In some instances, you may be expected to know certain quantities or to look them up in tables.
2. *Draw a diagram as an aid in visualizing and analyzing the physical situation of the problem where appropriate.* This step may not be necessary in every case, but it is usually helpful.
3. *Determine which principle(s) and equation(s) are applicable to this situation and how they can be used to get from the information given to what is to be found.* You may have to devise a strategy that involves several steps.
4. *Simplify mathematical expressions as much as possible through algebraic manipulation before inserting actual values.* Trigonometric relationships (summarized in Appendix I) can sometimes be used to simplify equations. The less calculation you do, the less likely you are to make a mistake—so *don't put the numbers in until you have to.*
5. *Check units before doing calculations.* Make unit conversions if necessary so that all units are in the same system (preferably standard units). This practice avoids mixed units and is helpful in unit analysis. (Unit checking and conversions are often done when writing the data in Step 1.)
6. *Substitute given quantities into equation(s), and perform calculations. Report the result with the proper units and the proper number of significant figures.*
7. *Consider whether the result is reasonable.* Does the answer have an appropriate magnitude? (This means, is it in the right ballpark?) For example, if a person's calculated mass turns out to be 4.60×10^2 kg, the result should be questioned, since 460 kg corresponds to a weight of 1010 lb.

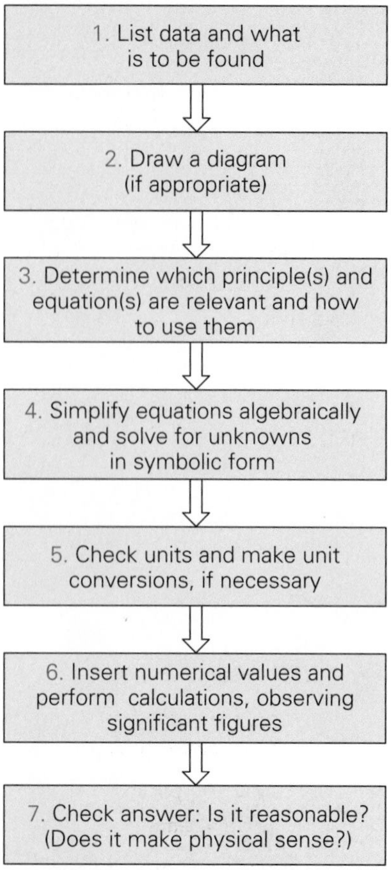

1. List data and what is to be found

⇩

2. Draw a diagram (if appropriate)

⇩

3. Determine which principle(s) and equation(s) are relevant and how to use them

⇩

4. Simplify equations algebraically and solve for unknowns in symbolic form

⇩

5. Check units and make unit conversions, if necessary

⇩

6. Insert numerical values and perform calculations, observing significant figures

⇩

7. Check answer: Is it reasonable? (Does it make physical sense?)

▲ FIGURE 1.10 A flow chart for the suggested problem-solving procedure

◂Figure 1.10 summarizes these steps in the form of a flow chart. The upcoming Examples illustrate the procedure. The steps are numbered to help you follow along.

Example 1.9 ■ Finding the Area of a Rectangle: Practicing the Problem-Solving Procedure

Two students measure the lengths of adjacent sides of their rectangular dorm room. One reports 15 ft, 8 in., and the other reports 4.25 m. What is the area of the room in square meters?

Thinking It Through. The lengths are reported in different units, so to get square meters ($\text{m} \times \text{m}$), the British units feet and inches must be converted to meters.

Solution.

1. Adjacent sides of a room give its length and width, so we may write the following:

Given: Length $= l = 15$ ft, 8 in. *Find:* Area (in square meters)
Width $= w = 4.25$ m

2. Sketch a diagram to help you visualize the situation (▾Fig. 1.11).

3 and 4. For this simple situation, the required equation is well known. The area A of a rectangle is $A = l \times w$ and both l and w are given.

5. A unit change is necessary. Let's first convert the length measurement to inches and then inches to meters:

$$15\text{ ft} + 8\text{ in.} = \left(15\text{ ft} \times \frac{12\text{ in.}}{1\text{ ft}}\right) + 8\text{ in.} = 188\text{ in.}$$

and

$$188\text{ in.} \times \frac{2.54\text{ cm}}{1\text{ in.}} = 478\text{ cm} = 4.78\text{ m}$$

Notice how easy it is to convert units in the decimal metric system (centimeters to meters). Perform the conversion explicitly if necessary, using the conversion factor 1 m/100 cm.

6. Now perform the calculation:

$$A = l \times w = 4.78\text{ m} \times 4.25\text{ m}$$
$$= 20.315\text{ m}^2 = 20.3\text{ m}^2 \quad \textit{(computed value rounded to three sf; why?)}$$

7. The answer appears reasonable. Since $1\text{ m} \approx 3$ ft, the dorm room would be about 13 ft by 14 ft, which is about right (but, as always, too small for comfort). Suppose you had inadvertently input 47.8 instead of 4.78 on your calculator. The result would have been $A = 47.8\text{ m} \times 4.25\text{ m} = 203\text{ m}^2$. A room with an area of about 200 m^2 would have dimensions of about 10 m by 20 m, which is roughly 30 ft by 60 ft. Since this result is not the size of a typical dorm room, the magnitude of the result should make you suspect that there may be an error.

Follow-up Exercise. The dimensions of a textbook are $0.22\text{ m} \times 0.26\text{ m} \times 4.0\text{ cm}$. What volume in a backpack would the book take up? Give the answer in both cubic meters and cubic centimeters. *(Answers to all Follow-up Exercises are at the back of the text.)*

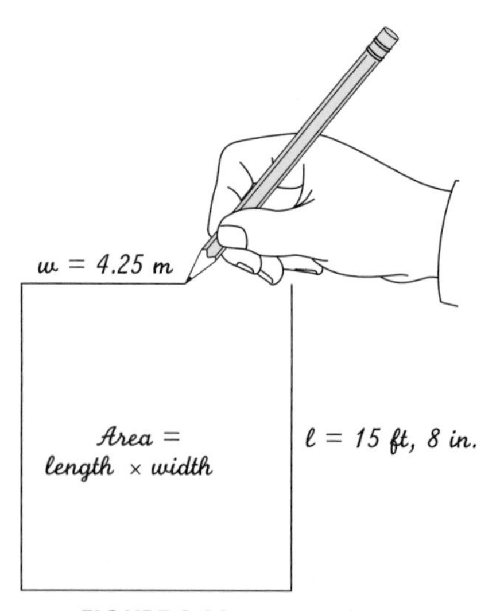

▲ FIGURE 1.11 A helpful step in problem solving Drawing a diagram helps you visualize and better understand the situation. See Example 1.9.

Many problems will involve basic trigonometric functions. The most common functions are given in the marginal note on page 23; for other trigonometric relations, see Appendix I or the tables inside the back cover.

Example 1.10 ■ Finding the Length of One Side of a Triangle: Trigonometry Application

A flower bed is laid out in the form of a triangle as shown in ▸Fig. 1.12. What is the length of the side of the bed that runs along the flagstone walkway?

Thinking It Through. The length of one side of a right triangle and an angle are given. Basic trigonometry applies.

Solution.

1 **and** 2. In some problems, we are given diagrams that contain data. Here, we have the following information:

Given: $x = 5.4$ m *Find:* r (long side of triangle)
$\theta = 40°$

3 **and** 4. Noting in the figure that the flower bed is a right triangle (as indicated by the right-angle symbol at the large angle), we can use a trigonometric function to find the hypotenuse r. Recalling that x and r are associated with the cosine for a standard right triangle, we can write

$$\cos\theta = \frac{x}{r} \quad \text{or} \quad r = \frac{x}{\cos\theta}$$

5 **and** 6. The units are fine. (Since x is in meters and $\cos\theta$ is dimensionless, r will be in meters.) So putting in the data:

$$r = \frac{x}{\cos\theta} = \frac{5.4\text{ m}}{\cos 40°} = \frac{5.4\text{ m}}{0.766} = 7.0\text{ m}$$

7. The magnitude of r seems reasonable compared with the value of x. Note that r must be greater than x (why?), and it is.

Follow-up Exercise. To keep animals out of the flower bed in Fig. 1.12, the owner decides to fence in the perimeter of the bed. What will be the total length of the fence? *(Answers to all Follow-up Exercises are at the back of the text.)*

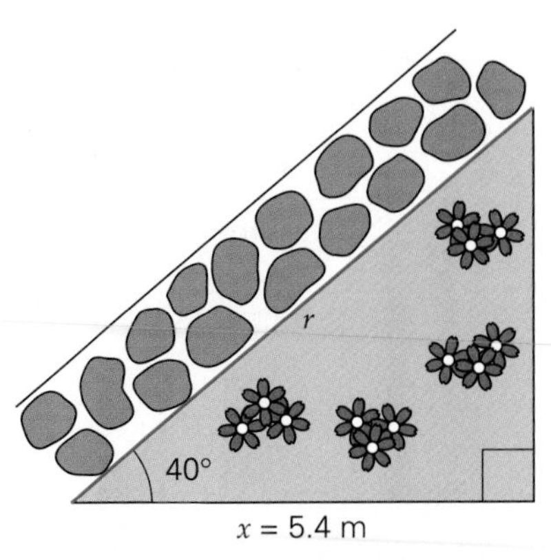

▲ **FIGURE 1.12 The length of a triangle's side** See Example 1.10.

Trigonometric functions:

$$\cos\theta = \frac{x}{r}\left(\frac{\text{side adjacent}}{\text{hypotenuse}}\right)$$

$$\sin\theta = \frac{y}{r}\left(\frac{\text{side opposite}}{\text{hypotenuse}}\right)$$

$$\tan\theta = \frac{\sin\theta}{\cos\theta} = \frac{y}{x}\left(\frac{\text{side opposite}}{\text{side adjacent}}\right)$$

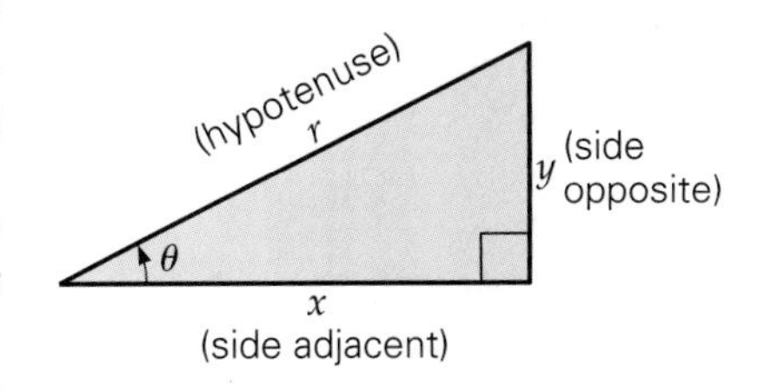

It is understood that you do not need to write out the steps of your problem-solving procedure each time. However, it is good practice to run through them mentally when working a problem. In the examples in upcoming chapters, the problem-solving steps will not always be listed as was done here for illustration. Even so, you should be able to see the general pattern outlined in the foregoing examples.

The main point of this section is that in solving problems, you should have some systematic procedure for analyzing the situation and extracting the information wanted. The suggested problem-solving procedure given here is one option.

In short, this procedure is (1) a pictorial representation, (2) a physical representation, (3) a mathematical representation, and (4) an evaluation of the results. To emphasize the aspects of problem solving, an occasional Integrated Example will be presented, in which a sketch or reasoning of the situation is specifically called for as part of the exercise. Integrated Exercises are also given in the end-of-chapter exercises.) Here is an Integrated Example.

Integrated Example 1.11 ■ Around the World—at Different Latitudes

If we consider the Earth to be a sphere with a radius of $R_E = 4000$ mi, it is easy to find the distance around the Earth at the equator (0° latitude), or the equatorial circumference ($c = 2\pi R_E$). However, a student wants to know the distance around the Earth at her latitude of 40° N (about the midlatitude of the conterminous 48 states). (a) Is the circumference radius at this latitude given by (1) $R_{40} = R_E \cos 40°$, (2) $R_{40} = R_E \sin 40°$, (3) $R_{40} = R_E \cos 50°$, or (4) $R_{40} = R_E \sin 50°$? (b) What is the distance around the Earth at 40° N latitude in km?

(a) Conceptual Reasoning. Recalling (or looking up) that the latitude angle is measured from the center of the Earth relative to the equator, we observe that the distance around the Earth at 40° N latitude is that along a circular path (called a *parallel*) at this latitude. The radius of this circle (R_{40}) involves a cosine or sine function, but it is difficult to visualize which and whether the angle would be the latitude angle (40°) or its complementary angle ($50° = 90° - 40°$). A quick sketch as in ◀Fig. 1.13 helps, and it is seen that the answer is (1).

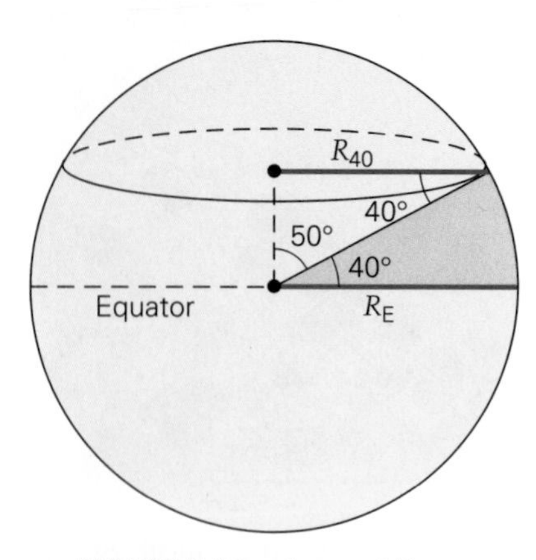

▲ **FIGURE 1.13 Around the World** Not so far around at 40° latitude as at the equator (0°). See Integrated Example 1.11.

(b) Thinking It Through. The distance around the parallel at 40° N (the circumference) is given by $c = 2\pi R_{40}$, which can be readily computed.

Given: $R_E = 4000 \text{ mi } (1.61 \text{ km/mi}) = 6440 \text{ km}$, $\theta = 40°$ *Find:* Distance around the Earth at latitude 40° N

[*Note*: After reading in part (b) of the question that the distance is to be in km, we do the conversion prior to working the rest of the problem.] Then,

$$c = 2\pi R_{40} = 2\pi R_E \cos 40°$$
$$= 2\pi(6440 \text{ km})(0.766) = 3.10 \times 10^4 \text{ km}$$

Follow-up Exercise. At what latitude would the distance around a parallel be 3.71×10^4 km? *Hint*: Should you have two answers? *(Answers to all Follow-up Exercises are at the back of the text.)*

Approximation and Order-of-Magnitude Calculations

At times when solving a problem, you may not be interested in an exact answer, but want only an estimate, or a "ballpark" figure. Approximations can be made by rounding off quantities so as to make the calculations easier and, perhaps, obtainable without the use of a calculator. For example, suppose you want to get an idea of the area of a circle with a radius $r = 9.5$ cm. Then rounding $9.5 \text{ cm} \approx 10$ cm, and $\pi \approx 3$ instead of 3.14. And,

$$A = \pi r^2 \approx 3(10 \text{ cm})^2 = 300 \text{ cm}^2$$

(Note that significant figures are not a concern in calculations involving approximations.) The answer is not exact, but it is a good approximation. Compute the exact answer and see.

Powers-of-ten, or scientific, notation is particularly convenient in making estimates or approximations in what are called **order-of-magnitude calculations**. *Order of magnitude* means that we express a quantity to the power of 10 closest to the actual value. For example, in the foregoing calculation, approximating $9.5 \text{ cm} \approx 10$ cm is expressing 9.5 as 10^1, and we say that the radius is *on the order of* 10 cm. Expressing a distance of $75 \text{ km} \approx 10^2$ km indicates that the distance is on the order of 10^2 km. The radius of the Earth is $6.4 \times 10^3 \text{ km} \approx 10^4$ km, or on the order of 10^4 km. A nanostructure with a width of 8.2×10^{-9} m is on the order of 10^{-8} m, or 10 nm. (Why a -8 exponent?)

An order-of-magnitude calculation gives only an estimate, of course. But this estimate may be enough to provide you with a better grasp or understanding of a physical situation. Usually, the result of an order-of-magnitude calculation is precise within a power of 10, or *within an order of magnitude*. That is, the prefix to the power of 10 is somewhere between 1 and 10. For example, if we got a time result of 10^5 s, we would expect the exact answer to be somewhere between 1×10^5 s and 10×10^5 s.

Example 1.12 ■ Order-of-Magnitude Calculation: Drawing Blood

A medical technologist draws 15 cc of blood from a patient's vein. Back in the lab, it is determined that this volume of blood has a mass of 16 g. Estimate the density of the blood, in standard units.

Thinking It Through. The data are given in cgs (centimeter–gram–second) units, which are often used for practicality when dealing with small, whole-number quantities in some situations. The cc abbreviation is commonly used in the medical and chemistry fields for cm^3. Density (ρ) is mass per unit volume, where $\rho = m/V$ (Section 1.4).

Solution.

Given: $m = 16\text{ g}\left(\dfrac{1\text{ kg}}{1000\text{ g}}\right) = 1.6 \times 10^{-2}\text{ kg} \approx 10^{-2}\text{ kg}$ *Find:* ρ (density)

$$V = 15\text{ cm}^3\left(\frac{1\text{ m}}{10^2\text{ cm}}\right)^3 = 1.5 \times 10^{-5}\text{ m}^3 \approx 10^{-5}\text{ m}^3$$

So, we have

$$\rho = \frac{m}{V} \approx \frac{10^{-2}\text{ kg}}{10^{-5}\text{ m}^3} = 10^3\text{ kg/m}^3$$

This result is quite close to the average density of whole blood, $1.05 \times 10^3\text{ kg/m}^3$.

Follow-up Exercise. A patient receives 750 cc of whole blood. Estimate the mass of the blood, in standard units. *(Answers to all Follow-up Exercises are at the back of the text.)*

Example 1.13 ■ How Many Cells in Your Blood?

The blood volume in the human body varies with a person's age, body size, and sex. On average, this volume is about 5 L. A typical value of red blood cells (erythrocytes) per volume is 5 000 000 per mm^3. Estimate how many "red cells" you have in your body.

Thinking It Through. The red blood cell count in cells/mm^3 is sort of a red blood cell "density." Multiplying this figure by the total volume of blood [(cells/volume) × total volume] will give the total number of cells. But note that we must have the volumes in the same units.

Solution.

Given: $V = 5\text{ L}$ *Find:* the approximate number of red cells in the body

$$= 5\text{ L}\left(10^{-3}\,\frac{\text{m}^3}{\text{L}}\right)$$

$$= 5 \times 10^{-3}\text{ m}^3 \approx 10^{-2}\text{ m}^3$$

$$\text{cells/volume} = 5 \times 10^6\,\frac{\text{cells}}{\text{mm}^3} \approx 10^7\,\frac{\text{cells}}{\text{mm}^3}$$

Then, changing to m^3,

$$\frac{\text{cells}}{\text{volume}} \approx 10^7\,\frac{\text{cells}}{\text{mm}^3}\left(\frac{10^3\text{ mm}}{1\text{ m}}\right)^3 = 10^{16}\,\frac{\text{cells}}{\text{m}^3}$$

Note: The conversion factor for L to m^3 was obtained directly from the conversion tables, but there is no conversion factor given for converting mm^3 to m^3, so we just use a conversion we know and cube it. So, we have

$$\left(\frac{\text{cells}}{\text{volume}}\right)(\text{total volume}) \approx \left(10^{16}\,\frac{\text{cells}}{\text{m}^3}\right)(10^{-2}\text{ m}^3) = 10^{14}\text{ red cells}$$

Follow-up Exercise. The average number of white cells (leukocytes) in human blood is normally 5000 to 10 000 cells per mm^3. Estimate the number of white blood cells you have in your body. *(Answers to all Follow-up Exercises are at the back of the text.)*

Chapter Review

Important Concepts and Equations

- **SI units of length, mass, and time.** The meter (m), the kilogram (kg), and the second (s), respectively.
- **Liter (L).** A volume of 1000 mL, or 1000 cm^3. To a good approximation, a liter of water has a mass of 1 kg.
- **Dimensional analysis and/or unit analysis.** Either can be used to determine if an equation has the correct form. Unit analysis can be used to find the unit of a quantity.
- **Significant figures (digits).** The digits that are known with certainty, plus one digit that is uncertain, in a measured value.
- **Problem solving.** Problems should be worked using a consistent procedure. Order-of-magnitude calculations may be done when only an estimated value is desired.
- **Density (ρ).** The mass per unit volume of an object or substance, which is a measure of the compactness of the material it contains:

$$\rho = \frac{m}{V} \quad \left(\frac{\text{mass}}{\text{volume}}\right) \tag{1.1}$$

Exercises*

Exercises designated CQ *are Conceptual Questions; those designated* IE *are Integrated Exercises, which involve conceptual reasoning and calculations. Throughout the text, many exercise sections will include "paired" exercises. These exercise pairs, identified with red numbers, are intended to assist you in problem solving and learning. In a pair, the first exercise (even numbered) is worked out in the Study Guide so that you can consult it should you need assistance in solving it. The second exercise (odd numbered) is similar in nature, and its answer is given at the back of the book.*

1.2 SI Units of Length, Mass, and Time *and* 1.3 More about the Metric System

1. The only SI standard represented by an artifact is the (a) meter, (b) kilogram, (c) second, or (d) electric charge.

2. Which of the following is *not* an SI base unit? (a) length, (b) mass, (c) weight, or (d) time.

3. Which one of the following is the SI unit of mass? (a) pound, (b) gram, (c) kilogram, or (d) ton.

4. CQ Is each of the following statements reasonable? (Justify your answers.) (a) It took 300 L of gasoline to fill up the car's tank. (b) The center on the basketball team is 225 cm tall. (c) The area of a dorm room is 120 m^2.

5. The prefix micro- (μ) means (a) 10^6, (b) 10^{-6}, (c) 10^3, or (d) 10^{-3}.

6. CQ If a fellow student tells you that he saw a 3-cm-long ladybug in his vegetable garden, would you believe him? How about if another student says she caught a 10-kg salmon?

*Keep in mind here and throughout the text that your answer to an odd-number exercise may differ slightly from that given at the back of the book because of rounding. See Problem-Solving Hint: The "Correct Answer" in this chapter.

7. ■ The metric system is a decimal (base-10) system, and the British system is, in part, a duodecimal (base-12) system. Discuss the ramifications if our monetary system had a duodecimal base. What would be the possible values of our coins if this were the case?

8. ■ (a) In the British system, 16 oz = 1 pt and 16 oz = 1 lb. Is there something wrong here? Explain. (b) Here's an old one: A pound of feathers weighs more than a pound of gold. How can that be? (*Hint*: Look up *ounce* in the dictionary.)

9. ■■ A sailor tells you that if his ship is traveling at 25 knots (nautical miles per hour), it is moving faster than the 25 miles per hour your car travels. How can that be?

1.4 Dimensional Analysis and Unit Analysis**

10. Both sides of an equation are equal in (a) numerical value, (b) units, (c) dimensions, or (d) all of the preceding.

11. Unit analysis of an equation cannot tell you if (a) the equation is dimensionally correct, (b) the equation is physically correct, (c) the numerical value is correct, or (d) both (b) and (c).

**Dimensions and/or units of velocity and acceleration are given in the chapter.

12. CQ Can dimensional analysis tell you whether you have used the correct equation in solving a problem? Explain.

13. If an equation has the same numerical value on both sides, the equation (a) is dimensionally correct, (b) is correct, (c) may be correct, or (d) both (a) and (c).

14. If meters/second (m/s) is divided by second (s), what is the resulting unit?

15. CQ Discuss the differences between dimensional analysis and unit analysis.

16. ■ Show that the equation $x = x_o + vt$, where v is velocity and x and x_o are lengths, is dimensionally correct.

17. ■ If x refers to distance, v_o and v to speeds, a to acceleration, and t to time, which of the following equations is dimensionally correct? (a) $x = v_o t + at^3$, (b) $v^2 = v_o^2 + 2at$, (c) $x = at + vt^2$, or (d) $v^2 = v_o^2 + 2ax$.

18. ■ Show that $t = \sqrt{2x/a}$ is dimensionally correct. (a is acceleration, t is time, and x is length.)

19. ■■ Use SI unit analysis to show that the equation $A = 4\pi r^2$, where A is the area and r is the radius of a sphere, is dimensionally correct.

20. ■■ You are told that the volume of a sphere is given by $V = \pi d^3/4$, where V is the volume and d is the diameter of the sphere. Is this equation dimensionally correct? (Use SI unit analysis to find out.)

21. ■■ The correct equation for the volume of a sphere is $V = 4\pi r^3/3$, where r is the radius of the sphere. Is the equation in Exercise 20 correct? If not, what should it be when expressed in terms of d?

22. ■■ If $x = gt^2/2$, where x is length and t is time, is dimensionally correct, what are the SI units of the constant g?

23. ■■ Is the equation $v = v_o \sin\theta - gt^2$ dimensionally correct? Use SI unit analysis to find out. (v and v_o are velocities, θ is an angle, t is time, and g is acceleration.)

24. ■■ Density is defined as the mass of an object divided by the volume of the object. Using SI unit analysis, determine the SI unit for density. (See Section 1.4 for units of mass and volume.)

25. ■■ Is the equation for the area of a trapezoid, $A = \frac{1}{2}a(b_1 + b_2)$, where a is the height and b_1 and b_2 are the bases, dimensionally correct? (▶Fig. 1.14) If not, what should be changed to correct it?

26. ■■ One student, using unit analysis, says that the equation $v = \sqrt{2ax}$ is dimensionally correct. Another says it isn't. With whom do you agree, and why?

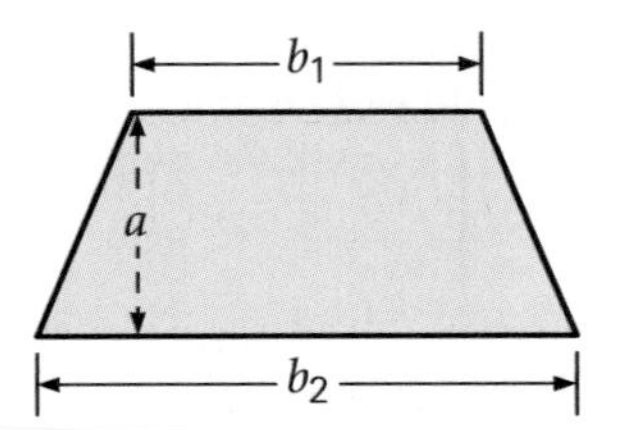

◀ **FIGURE 1.14 The area of a trapezoid** See Exercise 25.

27. ■■ The equation for the frequency f of oscillation of a simple pendulum is

$$f = \frac{1}{2\pi}\sqrt{\frac{g}{L}}$$

where L is the length of the pendulum string and g is the acceleration due to gravity. Frequency is commonly expressed in units of hertz (Hz). What is a hertz unit in terms of SI base units?

28. ■■■ Newton's second law of motion (Chapter 4) is expressed by the equation $F = ma$, where F represents force, m is mass, and a is acceleration. (a) The SI unit of force is, appropriately, called the newton (N). What are the units of the newton in terms of base quantities? (b) An equation for force associated with uniform circular motion is $F = mv^2/r$, where v is speed and r is the radius of the circular path. Does this equation give the same units for the newton?

29. ■■■ Einstein's famous mass–energy equivalence is expressed by the equation $E = mc^2$, where E is energy, m is mass, and c is the speed of light. (a) What are the SI base units of energy? (b) Another equation for energy is $E = mgh$, where m is mass, g is the acceleration due to gravity, and h is height. Does this equation give the same units as in (a)?

1.5 Unit Conversions*

30. A good way to ensure proper unit conversion is to (a) use another measurement instrument, (b) always work in one system of units, (c) use unit analysis, or (d) use dimensional analysis.

31. You often see 1 kg = 2.2 lb. This expression means that (a) 1 kg is equivalent to 2.2 lb, (b) this is a true equation, (c) 1 lb = 2.2 kg, or (d) none of the preceding.

32. ■ Figure 1.7 (top) shows the elevation of a location in both feet and meters. If a town is 130 ft above sea level, what is the elevation in meters?

33. IE ■ (a) If you wanted to express your height with the largest number, you would use (1) meters, (2) feet, (3) inches, or (4) centimeters? Why? (b) If you are 6.00 ft tall, what is your height in centimeters?

34. ■ What is the length in feet of (a) a 100-m dash and (b) a 2.4-m high jump?

*Conversion factors are listed inside the front cover of the text.

35. ■ If the capillaries of an average adult were unwound and spread out end to end, they would extend to a length over 40 000 mi (Fig. 1.8). If you are 1.75 m tall, how many times your height would the capillary length equal?

36. ■ Standing at 452 m, the Petronas Twin Towers in Malaysia is one of the tallest buildings in the world. What is its height in feet?

37. ■ The largest airplane, the Airbus A380, has a length of 239 ft, 6 in.; a wingspan of 261 ft, 10 in.; and a height of 79 ft, 1 in. What are these dimensions in meters?

38. IE ■ (a) Compared with a two-liter soda bottle, a half-gallon soda bottle holds (1) more, (2) the same amount of, or (3) less soda? Why? (b) Verify your answer for (a).

39. ■ A commuting student wants to buy 18 gal of gas, but the gas station has installed new pumps that are measured in liters. How many liters of gas (rounded off to a whole number) should he ask for?

40. ■ (a) A football field is 300 ft long and 160 ft wide. What are the field's dimensions in meters? (b) A football is 11.0 to $11\frac{1}{4}$ in. long. What is its length in centimeters?

41. ■ Suppose that when the United States goes completely metric, the dimensions of a football field are established as 100 m by 54 m. Which would be larger, the metric football field or a current football field (see Exercise 40a), and what would be the difference between the areas?

42. ■■ If blood flows with an average speed of 0.35 m/s in the human circulatory system, how many miles does a blood cell travel in 1 h?

43. ■■ Driving a jet-powered car, Royal Air Force pilot Andy Green broke the sound barrier on land for the first time and achieved a record land speed of more than 763 mi/h in Black Rock Desert, NV, on Oct. 15, 1997 (▼Fig. 1.15). (a) What is this speed expressed in m/s? (b) How long would it take the jet-powered car to travel the length of a 300-ft football field at this speed?

▲ **FIGURE 1.15 Record run** See Exercise 43.

44. IE ■■ (a) Which one of the following represents the greatest speed? (1) 1 m/s, (2) 1 km/h, (3) 1 ft/s, or (4) 1 mi/h. (b) Express the speed 15.0 m/s in mi/h.

45. ■■ An automobile speedometer is shown in ▼Fig. 1.16. (a) What would be the equivalent scale readings (for each empty box) in kilometers per hour? (b) What would be the 70-mi/h speed limit in kilometers per hour?

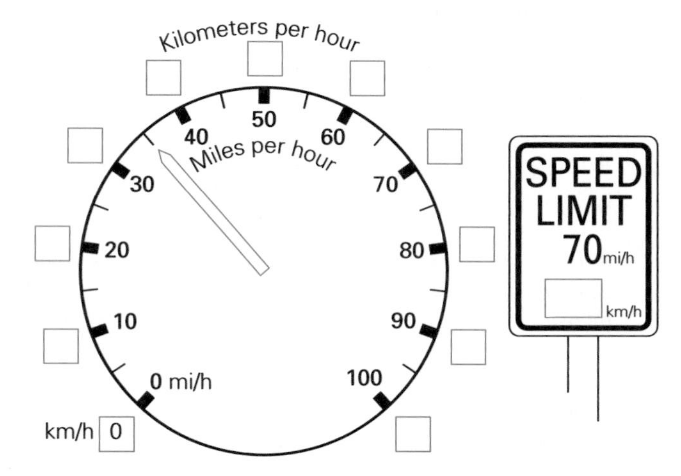

▲ **FIGURE 1.16 Speedometer readings** See Exercise 45.

46. ■■ A student has a car that gets, on average, 25.0 mi/gal of gasoline. She plans to spend a year in Europe and take the car with her. (a) What should she expect the car's average gas mileage to be in kilometers per liter? (b) During the year there, she drove 6000 km. Assuming that gas costs $5.00/gal in Europe, how much did she spend on fuel? (Compute to the nearest dollar.)

47. ■■ Some common product labels are shown in ▼Fig. 1.17. From the units on the labels, find (a) the number of milliliters in 2 fl. oz and (b) the number of ounces in 100 g.

▲ **FIGURE 1.17 Conversion factors** See Exercise 47.

48. ■■ ▸Fig. 1.18 is a picture of red blood cells seen under a scanning electron microscope. Normally, women possess about 4.5 million of these cells in each cubic millimeter of blood. If the blood flow through the heart is 250 milliliters per minute, how many red blood cells flow through a woman's heart each second?

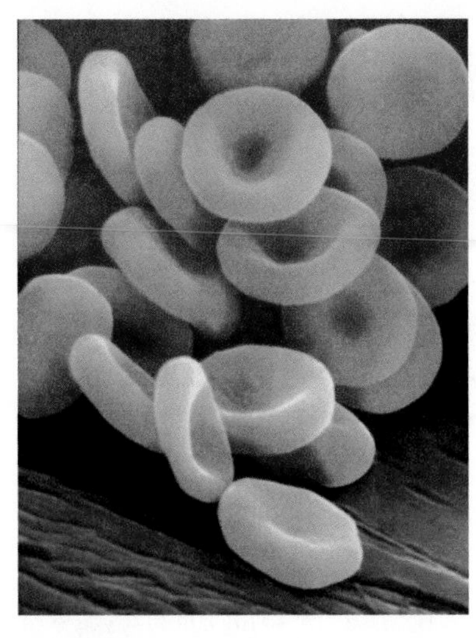

◀ **FIGURE 1.18 Red blood cells** See Exercise 48.

▲ **FIGURE 1.19 Noah and his ark** See Exercise 54.

49. ■■ A student was 18 in. long when she was born. She is now 5 ft 6 in. tall and 20 years old. How many centimeters a year did she grow on average?

50. ■■ A 19-in. TV has a diagonal length of the TV tube of 19 inches. Assuming that the face of the tube is flat and rectangular and that the diagonal makes a 37° angle with the base of the tube, what is the area of the tube face in (a) square inches and (b) square centimeters? (*Hint*: A diagram, as suggested in the problem-solving procedure, is helpful here.)

51. ■■ The width and length of a room are 3.2 yd and 4.0 yd, respectively. If the height of the room is 8.0 ft, what is the volume of the room in (a) cubic meters and (b) cubic feet?

52. ■■■ The density of metal mercury is 13.6 g/cm^3. (a) What is this density as expressed in kg/m^3? (b) How many kilograms of mercury would be required to fill a 0.250-L container?

53. ■■■ Engineers often express the density of a substance as a weight density, for example, in pounds per cubic foot. (a) What is the weight density of water? (b) What is the weight of one gallon of water?

54. ■■■ In the Bible, Noah is instructed to build an ark 300 cubits long, 50.0 cubits wide, and 30.0 cubits high (▶Fig. 1.19). Historical records indicate a cubit is equal to half of a yard. (a) What would the dimensions of the ark be in meters? (b) What would the ark's volume be in cubic meters? To approximate, assume that the ark is to be rectangular.

1.6 Significant Figures

55. Which of the following has the greatest number of significant figures? (a) 103.07, (b) 124.5, (c) 0.099 16, or (d) 5.408×10^5.

56. In a multiplication and/or division operation involving the numbers 15 437, 201.08, and 408.0×10^5, the result should be rounded to how many significant figures? (a) 3, (b) 4, (c) 5, or (d) any number.

57. ■ Express the length 50 500 μm (micrometers) in centimeters, decimeters, and meters, to three significant figures.

58. ■ Using a meterstick, a student measures a length and reports it to be 0.8755 m. What is the smallest division on the meterstick scale?

59. ■ If a measured length is reported as 25.483 cm, could this length have been measured with an ordinary meterstick whose smallest division is millimeters? Discuss in terms of significant figures.

60. ■ Determine the number of significant figures in the following measured numbers: (a) 1.007 m; (b) 8.03 cm; (c) 16.272 kg; (d) 0.015 μs (microseconds).

61. ■ Express each of the numbers in Exercise 60 with two significant figures.

62. ■ Which of the following quantities has three significant figures? (a) 305.0 cm, (b) 0.0500 mm, (c) 1.000 81 kg, or (d) 8.06×10^4 m^2.

63. ■ Express each of the following numbers to only three significant figures: (a) 10.072 m; (b) 775.4 km; (c) 0.002 549 kg; (d) 93 000 000 mi.

64. ■■ The cover of your physics book measures 0.274 m long and 0.222 m wide. What is its area in m^2?

65. ■■ A compact disc (CD) has a diameter of approximately 12 cm. What is its area in m^2?

66. ■■ The side of a cube is measured, and its volume is reported to be 2.5×10^2 cm^3. What was the measured length of the side of the cube?

67. IE ■■ The outside dimensions of a cylindrical soda can are reported as 12.559 cm for the diameter and 5.62 cm for the height. (a) How many significant figures will the total outside area have, (1) two, (2) three, (3) four, or (4) five? Why? (b) What is the total outside surface area of the can in cm^2?

68. IE ■■■ In doing a problem, a student adds 46.9 m and 5.72 m and then subtracts 38 m from the result. (a) How many decimal places will the final answer have, (1) zero, (2) one, or (3) two? Why? (b) What is the final answer?

69. ■■■ Work this exercise by the two given procedures as directed, commenting on and explaining any difference in the answers. Use your calculator for the calculations. Compute $p = mv$, where $v = x/t$. Given: $x = 8.5$ m, $t = 2.7$ s, and $m = 0.66$ kg. (a) First compute v and then p. (b) Compute $p = mx/t$ without an intermediate step. (c) Are the results the same? If not, why?

1.7 Problem Solving

70. An important step in problem solving before mathematically solving an equation is (a) checking units, (b) checking significant figures, (c) consulting with a friend, or (d) checking to see if the result is reasonable.

71. An important final step in problem solving before reporting an answer is (a) reading the problem again, (b) saving your calculations, (c) seeing if the answer is reasonable, or (d) checking your results with another student.

72. CQ When you do order-of-magnitude calculations, should you be concerned about significant figures? Explain.

73. ■ A corner construction lot has the shape of a right triangle. If the two sides perpendicular to each other are 37 m long and 42.3 m long, respectively, what is the length of the hypotenuse?

74. ■ The Earth has a mass of 6.0×10^{24} kg and a volume of 1.1×10^{21} m^3. What is the Earth's average density?

75. ■ The lightest solid material is silica aerogel, which has a typical density of only about 0.10 g/cm^3. The molecular structure of silica aerogel is typically 95% empty space. What is the mass of 1 m^3 of silica aerogel?

76. ■ Estimate the area of a circle if its radius is 3.1×10^{-4} m.

77. ■■ Nutrition Facts labels now appear on most foods. An abbreviated label concerned with fat is shown in ▶Fig. 1.20. When burned in the body, each gram of fat supplies 9 Calories. (a) What percentage of the Calories in one serving is supplied by fat? (b) You may notice that our answer doesn't agree with the listed Total Fat percentage in Fig. 1.20. This is because the given Percent Daily Values are the percentages of the maximum recommended amounts of nutrients (in grams) contained in a 2000-Calorie diet. What are the maximum recommended amounts of total fat and saturated fat for a 2000-Calorie diet?

Nutrition Facts
Serving Size: 1 can
Calories: 310

Amount Per Serving	% Daily Value*
Total Fat 18 g	28%
Saturated Fat 7g	35%

* Percent Daily Values are based on a 2,000 Calorie diet.

◀ **FIGURE 1.20 Nutrition Facts** See Exercise 77.

78. ■■ The thickness of the total of numbered pages of a textbook is measured to be 3.75 cm. (a) If the last page of the book is numbered 860, what is the average thickness of a page? (b) Repeat the calculation by using order-of-magnitude calculations.

79. ■■ A light-year is a unit of distance corresponding to the distance light travels in a vacuum in 1 year. If the speed of light is 3.00×10^8 m/s, what is the length of a light-year in meters?

80. IE ■■ To go to a football stadium from your house, you first drive 1000 m north, then 500 m west, and finally 1500 m south. (a) Relative to your home, the football stadium is (1) north of west, (2) south of east, (3) north of east, or (4) south of west. (b) What is the straight-line distance from your house to the stadium?

81. ■■ Two chains of length 1.0 m are used to support a lamp, as shown in ▼Fig. 1.21. The distance between the two chains is 1.0 m along the ceiling. What is the vertical distance from the lamp to the ceiling?

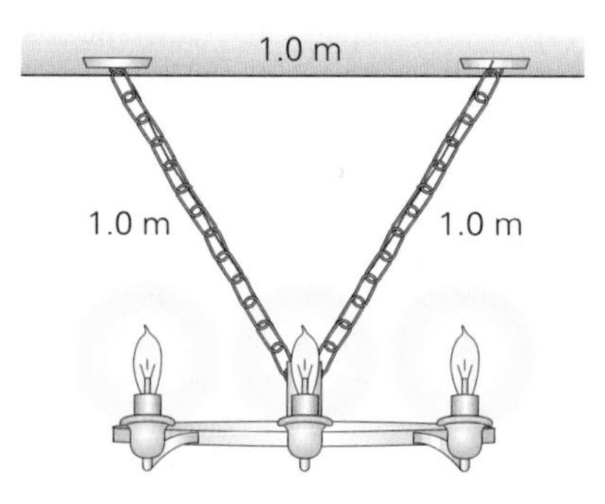

◀ **FIGURE 1.21 Support the lamp** See Exercise 81.

82. ■■ Tony's Pizza Palace sells a medium 9.0-in. (diameter) pizza for $7.95, and a large 12-in. pizza for $13.50. Which pizza is the better buy?

83. ■■ In ▶Fig. 1.22 which black region has the greater area, the center circle or the outer ring?

84. ■■ The shortest distance between the bases in a baseball field is 90 ft. What is the straight-line distance in meters between first base and third base?

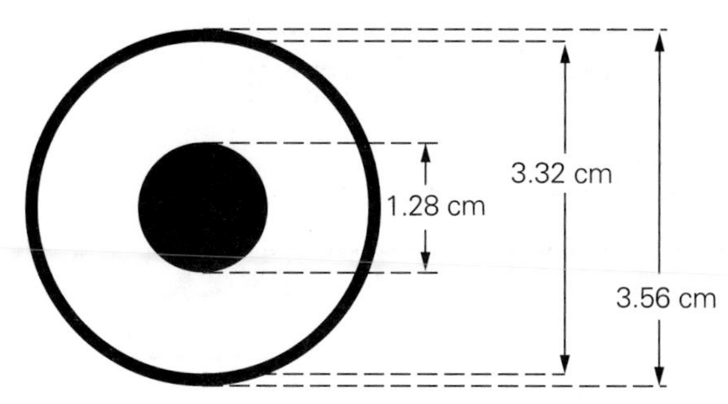

▲ **FIGURE 1.22 Which black area is greater?** See Exercise 83.

85. ■■ The Channel Tunnel, or "Chunnel" which runs under the English Channel between Great Britain and France, is 31 mi long. (There are actually three separate tunnels.) A shuttle train that carries passengers through the tunnel travels with an average speed of 75 mi/h. On average, how long, in minutes, does it take the shuttle to make a one-way trip through the Chunnel?

86. ■■■ Approximately 118 mi wide and 307 mi long and averaging 279 ft in depth, Lake Michigan is the second-largest Great Lake by volume. Estimate its volume of water in m^3.

87. ■■■ A student wants to determine the distance of a small island from the lakeshore (▼Fig. 1.23). He first draws a 50-m line parallel to the shore. Then, he goes to the ends of the line and measures the angles of the lines of sight from the island relative to the line he has drawn. The angles are 30° and 40°. How far is the island from the shore?

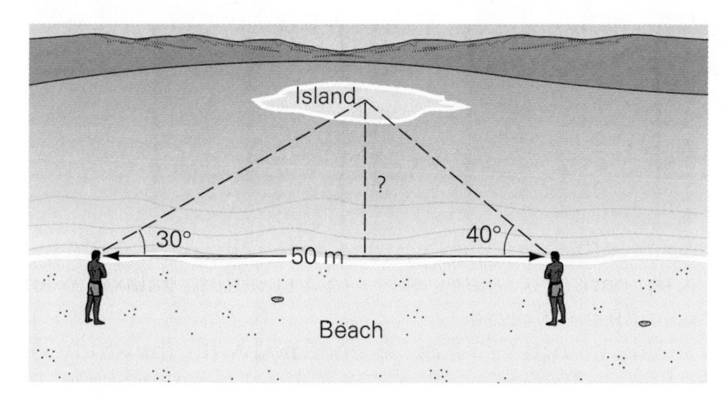

▲ **FIGURE 1.23 Measuring with lines of sight** See Exercise 87.

Additional Exercises

88. Express the following calculations to the proper number of significant figures: (a) $12.634 + 2.1$; (b) $13.5 - 2.134$; (c) $\pi(0.25\text{ m})^2$; (d) $\sqrt{2.37/3.5}$.

89. Suppose you are paying $1.20 for 1 gal of gas. Then the United States switches to SI units, and you find that gas costs $0.32/L. Which is the greater cost for gas?

90. On average, the human heart beats 70 times a minute (called the *pulse rate*). On average, how many times does the heart beat in a 70-year lifetime?

91. The base and the height of a right triangle are 11.2 cm long and 7.5 cm high, respectively. What is the area of the triangle?

92. The general equation for a parabola is $y = ax^2 + bx + c$, where a, b, and c are constants. What are the units of each constant if y and x are in meters?

93. A rectangular block has the dimensions 2.8 cm, 9.5 cm, and 8.7 cm. Estimate the volume of the block in cubic centimeters.

94. The radius of a solid sphere is 12 cm. What is the surface area of the sphere in (a) square centimeters and (b) square meters? (c) If the mass of the sphere is 9.0 kg, what is the sphere's density in kilograms per cubic meter?

95. A cylindrical drinking glass has an inside diameter of 8.0 cm and a depth of 12 cm. If a person drinks a completely full glass of water, how much water (in liters) will be consumed?

96. **IE** The top of a rectangular table measures 1.245 m by 0.760 m. (a) The smallest division on the scale of the measurement instrument is (1) m, (2) cm, or (3) mm. Why? (b) What is the area of the tabletop?

97. When computing the average speed of a cross-country runner, a student gets 25 m/s. Is this result reasonable? Justify your answer.

98. The average density of the Moon is $3.36\,\text{g/cm}^3$, and the Moon's diameter is 2160 mi. What is the total mass of the Moon in kilograms? (Compare your answer with the value given inside the back cover of this text.)

99. **IE** A car is driven 13 miles east and then a certain distance due north and ends up at a position of 25 degrees north of east. (a) The distance traveled by the car due north is (1) less then, (2) equal to, or (3) greater than 13 miles. Why? (b) What distance does the car go due north?

100. An airplane flies 100 mi south from city A to city B, 200 mi east from city B to city C, and then 300 mi north from city C to city D. (a) What is the straight-line distance from city A to city D? (b) What is the direction of city D relative to city A?

101. A hollow spherical ball of radius 12 cm is filled with water. What is the mass of water inside the sphere, in kilograms?

102. Tampa, Florida, is at a latitude of about 28° North. What is the distance traveled by a building in Tampa in one day (in space) as a result of the Earth's rotation? The equatorial radius of the Earth is 6.38×10^6 m.

CHAPTER 2

Kinematics: Description of Motion

The cheetah is running at full stride. This fastest of all land animals is capable of attaining speeds up to 113 km/h, or 70 mi/h. The sense of motion in this photograph is so strong that you can almost feel the air rushing by you. And yet, this sense of motion is an illusion. Motion takes place in time, but the photo can only "freeze" a single instant. You'll find that, without the dimension of time, you can hardly describe motion at all.

The description of motion involves the representation of a restless world. Nothing is ever perfectly still. You may sit, apparently at rest, but your blood flows, and air moves into and out of your lungs. The air is composed of gas molecules moving at different speeds and in different directions. And, while you experience stillness, you, your chair, the building you are in, and the air you breathe are all revolving through space with the Earth, part of a solar system in a spiraling galaxy in an expanding universe.

The branch of physics concerned with the study of motion and what produces and affects motion is called **mechanics**. The roots of mechanics and of human interest in motion go back to early civilizations. The study of the motions of heavenly bodies, or *celestial mechanics*, grew out of the need to measure time and location. Several early Greek scientists, notably Aristotle, put forth theories of motion that were useful descriptions, but were later proved to be incomplete or incorrect. Our currently accepted concepts of motion were formulated in large part by Galileo (1564–1642) and Isaac Newton (1642–1727).

Mechanics is usually divided into two parts: (1) kinematics and (2) dynamics. **Kinematics** deals with the *description* of the motion of objects, without consideration of what causes the motion. **Dynamics** analyzes the *causes* of motion. This chapter covers kinematics and reduces the description of motion to its simplest terms by considering motion in a straight line. We'll learn to analyze changes in motion—speeding up, slowing down, stopping. Along the way, we'll deal with a particularly interesting case of accelerated motion: free fall under the influence only of gravity. Chapter 3 focuses on motion in two dimensions (which can easily be extended to three dimensions). Chapter 4 investigates dynamics to show what causes changes in motion.

▲ **FIGURE 2.1 Distance—total path length** In driving to State University from Hometown, one student may take the shortest route and travel a distance of 81 km (50 mi). Another student takes a longer route in order to visit a friend in Podunk before returning to school. The longer trip is in two segments, but the distance traveled is the total length, 97 km + 48 km = 145 km (90 mi).

2.1 Distance and Speed: Scalar Quantities

OBJECTIVES: **To (a) define distance and calculate speed and (b) explain what is meant by a scalar quantity.**

Distance

We can observe motion in many instances around us. What is motion? This question seems simple but you might have some difficulty giving an immediate answer (and it's not fair to use forms of the verb "to move" to describe motion). After a little thought, you should be able to conclude that **motion** (or moving) involves the changing of position. Motion can be described in part by specifying *how far* something travels in changing position—that is, the distance it travels. **Distance** is simply the *total path length* traversed in moving from one location to another. For example, you may drive to school from your hometown and express the distance traveled in miles or kilometers. In general, the distance between two points depends on the path traveled (▸ Fig. 2.1).

Along with many other quantities in physics, distance is a scalar quantity. A **scalar quantity** is a quantity with only magnitude, or size. That is, a *scalar* has only a numerical value, such as 160 km or 100 mi. (Note that the magnitude includes units.) Distance is a scalar quantity; it tells you the magnitude only—how far, but not how far in any direction. Other examples of scalars are quantities such as 10 s (time), 3.0 kg (mass), and 20°C (temperature).

Note: A scalar quantity has magnitude, but no direction.

Speed

When something is in motion, its position changes with time. That is, it moves a certain distance in a given amount of time. Both length and time are therefore important quantities in describing motion. For example, imagine a car and a pedestrian moving down a street and traveling a distance (length) of one block. You would expect the car to travel faster, and thus to cover the distance in a shorter time, than the person does. This relation can be expressed by using length and time to give the rate at which distance is traveled, or the **speed**, for each.

Definition of: Average Speed

Average speed ($\bar{s}$) is the distance d traveled, i.e., the actual length of the path, divided by the total time Δt elapsed in traveling that distance:

$$\text{average speed} = \frac{\text{distance traveled}}{\text{total time to travel that distance}} \tag{2.1}$$

$$\bar{s} = \frac{d}{\Delta t} = \frac{d}{t_2 - t_1}$$

SI unit of speed: meters per second (m/s)

Note: A symbol with a bar over it is often used to denote an average. The Greek letter Δ is used to represent a change or difference in a quantity, in this case the change in time between the beginning (t_1) and end (t_2) of a trip, or the elapsed time.

The SI standard unit of speed is meters per second (length/time), although kilometers per hour is used in many everyday applications. The British standard unit is feet per second, but we often use miles per hour.

Since distance is a scalar (as is time), speed is also a scalar. The distance does not have to be in a straight line. (See Fig. 2.1.) For example, you probably have computed the average speed of an automobile trip by using the distance obtained from the starting and ending odometer readings. Suppose these readings were 17 455 km and 17 775 km, respectively, for a four-hour trip. (We'll assume that you have a car with odometer readings in kilometers.) Subtracting the readings gives a traveled distance d of 320 km, so the average speed of the trip is $d/t = 320\text{ km}/4.0\text{ h} = 80\text{ km/h}$ (or about 50 mi/h).

Average speed gives a general description of motion over a time interval Δt. In the case of the auto trip with an average speed of 80 km/h, the car's speed wasn't *always* 80 km/h. With various stops and starts on the trip, the car must have been moving more slowly than the average speed part of the time. It therefore had to be moving more rapidly than the average speed another part of the time. With an average speed, you really don't know how fast the car was moving at any particular time during the trip. Similarly, the average test score of a class doesn't tell you the score of any particular student.

▲ **FIGURE 2.2 Instantaneous speed** The speedometer of a car gives the speed over a very short interval of time, so its reading approaches the instantaneous speed.

If the time interval Δt considered becomes smaller and smaller and approaches zero, the speed calculation gives an **instantaneous speed**. This quantity is how fast something is moving *at a particular instant of time*. The speedometer of a car gives an approximate instantaneous speed. For example, the speedometer shown in ◀Fig. 2.2 indicates a speed of about 44 mi/h, or 70 km/h. If the car travels with constant speed (so the speedometer reading does not change), then the average and instantaneous speeds will be equal. (Do you agree? Think of the average test score analogy.)

Example 2.1 ■ Slow Motion: *Sojourner* Moves Along

▲ **FIGURE 2.3 Away we go!** Sojourner speeding at 0.60 m/min (0.010 m/s) along the Martian surface. See Example 2.1.

On July 4, 1997, the *Pathfinder Lander* touched down on the surface of Mars. Out rolled the rover named *Sojourner* (◀Fig. 2.3).

Sojourner could move at a maximum speed of 0.60 m/min. At this speed, what is the shortest time it takes the rover to travel 3.0 m to get to another rock to analyze?

Thinking It Through. Knowing the average speed and distance, we can compute the time from the equation for average speed.

Solution. Listing the data and what is to be found in symbol form:

Given: $\bar{s} = 0.60\,\dfrac{\text{m}}{\cancel{\text{min}}}\left(\dfrac{1\,\cancel{\text{min}}}{60\text{ s}}\right) = 0.010\text{ m/s}$, $d = 3.0\text{ m}$

Find: Δt (time to travel distance d)

In the given data, the unit meters per minute was converted to the standard meters per second.

From Eq. 2.1, we have

$$\bar{s} = \frac{d}{\Delta t}$$

Rearranging,

$$\Delta t = \frac{d}{\bar{s}} = \frac{3.0\text{ m}}{0.010\text{ m/s}} = 3.0 \times 10^2\text{ s } (= 5.0\text{ min})$$

Follow-up Exercise. (a) Was it necessary to convert meters per minute to meters per second? Explain. (b) Suppose *Sojourner* took 15.0 min to travel the 3.00 m. What would be the rover's average speed in this case? (*Answers to all Follow-up Exercises are at the back of the text.*)

Determination of Average Speed

2.2 One-Dimensional Displacement and Velocity: Vector Quantities

OBJECTIVES: To (a) define displacement and calculate velocity, and (b) explain the difference between scalar and vector quantities.

Displacement

For straight-line, or linear, motion, it is convenient to specify position by using the familiar two-dimensional Cartesian coordinate system, with x- and y-axes at right angles. A straight-line path can be in any direction, but for convenience, we usually orient the coordinate axes so that the motion is along one of them. (See Learn by Drawing (LBD).)

As we have seen, distance is a scalar quantity with only magnitude (and units). However, often when we describe motion, more information can be given by adding a *direction*. This information is particularly convenient for a change of position in a straight line. We define **displacement** as the straight-line distance between two points, along with the *direction* from the starting point to the final position. Unlike distance (a scalar), displacement can have either positive or negative values, with the signs indicating the directions along a coordinate axis.

As such, displacement is a **vector quantity**. A *vector* has both magnitude and direction. For example, when we describe the displacement of an airplane as 25 km north, we are giving a *vector* description (magnitude and direction). Other vector quantities include velocity and acceleration.

Algebra applies to vectors, but we have to know how to specify and deal with the direction part of the vector. This process is relatively simple in one dimension. To illustrate this with respect to finding displacements, consider the situation shown in ▼Fig. 2.4, where x_1 and x_2 indicate positions on the x-axis. A student moves in a straight line from the lockers to the physics lab. As can be seen in Fig. 2.4a, the scalar distance between the two points is 8.0 m. To specify displacement (a vector) between x_1 and x_2, we use the expression

$$\Delta x = x_2 - x_1 \tag{2.2}$$

Learn by Drawing

Cartesian Coordinates and One-dimensional Displacement

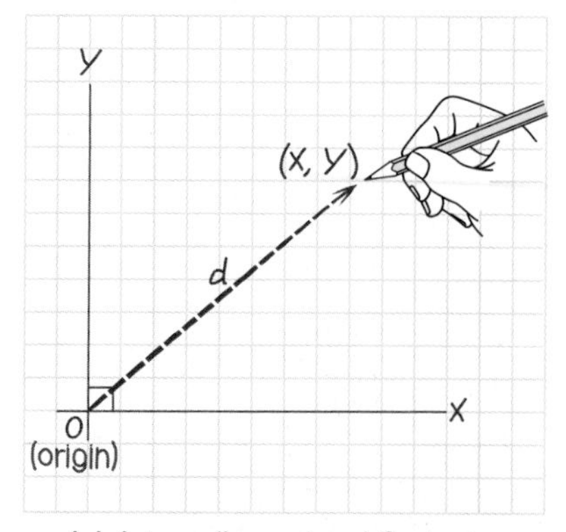

(a) A two-dimensional Cartesian coordinate system. A displacement vector **d** locates a point (x, y).

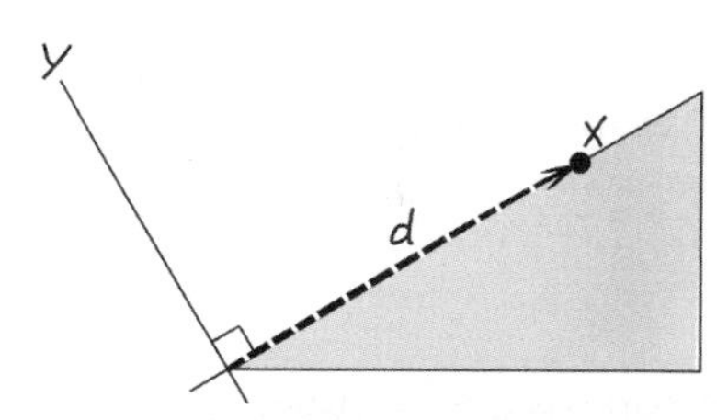

(b) For one-dimensional, or straight-line, motion, it is convenient to orient one of the coordinate axes along the direction of motion.

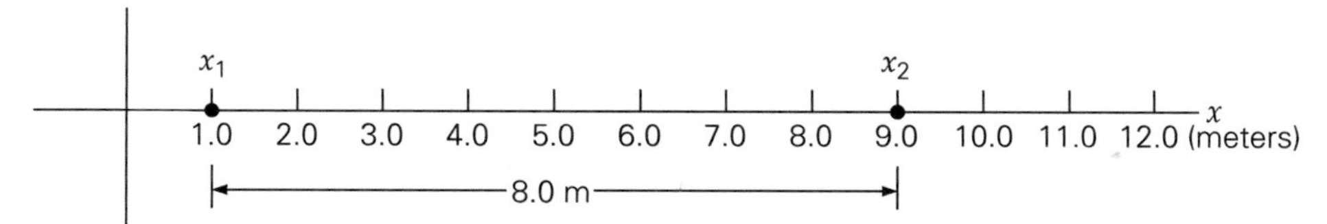

(a) Distance (magnitude or numerical value)

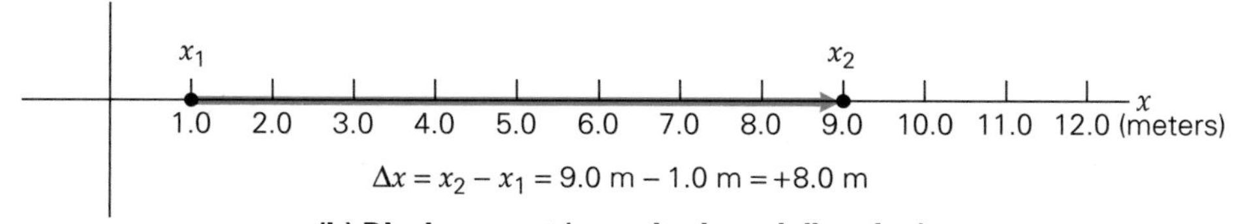

(b) Displacement (magnitude and direction)

◀ **FIGURE 2.4 Distance (scalar) and displacement (vector)** **(a)** The distance (straight-line path) between the student and the physics lab is 8.0 m and is a scalar quantity. **(b)** To indicate displacement, x_1 and x_2 specify the initial and final positions, respectively. The displacement is then $\Delta x = x_2 - x_1 = 9.0\text{ m} - 1.0\text{ m} = +8.0\text{ m}$—that is, 8.0 m in the $+x$-direction.

Note: Δ always means *final minus initial*, just as a *change* in your bank account is the final balance minus the initial balance.

where Δ is again used to represent a change or difference in a quantity. Then, as in Fig. 2.4b, we have

$$\Delta x = x_2 - x_1 = 9.0\text{ m} - 1.0\text{ m} = +8.0\text{ m}$$

Hence, the student's displacement (magnitude and direction) is 8.0 m in the positive x-direction, as indicated by the positive (+) result in Fig. 2.4b. (As in "regular" mathematics, the plus sign is often omitted, as it is understood, so this displacement can be written as $\Delta x = 8.0$ m instead of $\Delta x = +8.0$ m.)

Note: For displacement in *one direction*, the distance is the magnitude of the displacement.

Vector quantities in this book are usually indicated by boldface type; for example, a velocity vector is indicated by **v**. However, when working in one dimension, this notation is not needed and can be simplified by using plus and minus signs to indicate the only two possible directions. The x-axis is commonly used for horizontal motions, and a plus (+) sign is taken to indicate the direction to the right, or in the "positive x-direction," and a minus (−) sign indicates the direction to the left, or in the "negative x-direction." Keep in mind that these signs only "point" in *particular directions*. An object moving along the negative x-axis toward the origin would be moving in the + direction, even though its x-position is negative. How about an object moving along the $+x$-axis toward the origin? If you said the minus (−) direction, you are correct.

Suppose the other student in Fig. 2.4 walks from the physics lab (the initial position is different and $x_1 = 9.0$ m) to the end of the lockers (the final position is now $x_2 = 1.0$ m). Her displacement would be

$$\Delta x = x_2 - x_1 = 1.0\text{ m} - 9.0\text{ m} = -8.0\text{ m}$$

The minus sign indicates that the direction of the displacement was in the negative x-direction. In this case, we say that the two students' displacements are equal (in magnitude) and opposite (in direction).

Velocity

Note: Don't confuse velocity (a vector) with speed (a scalar).

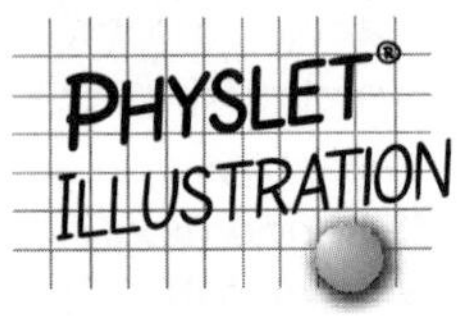

Velocity and Speed

As we have seen, speed, like the distance it incorporates, is a scalar quantity—it has magnitude only. Another quantity used to describe motion is *velocity*. Speed and velocity are often used synonymously in everyday conversation, but the terms have different meanings in physics. Speed is a scalar, and velocity is a vector—it has both magnitude and direction. Unlike speed (but like displacement) velocity can have both positive and negative values, indicating directions.

Velocity tells you how fast something is moving *and* in which direction it is moving. And just as we can speak of average and instantaneous speeds, we have average and instantaneous velocities involving vector displacements. The **average velocity** is the displacement divided by the total travel time.

Definition of: Average velocity

$$\text{average velocity} = \frac{\text{displacement}}{\text{total travel time}} \qquad (2.3)^*$$

$$\bar{v} = \frac{\Delta x}{\Delta t} = \frac{x_2 - x_1}{t_2 - t_1}$$

SI unit of velocity: meters per second (m/s),

*Another common form of this equation is

$$\bar{v} = \frac{\Delta x}{\Delta t} = \frac{(x_2 - x_1)}{(t_2 - t_1)} = \frac{(x - x_o)}{(t - t_o)} = \frac{(x - x_o)}{t},$$

or, after rearranging

$$x = x_o + \bar{v}t, \qquad (2.3)$$

where x_o is the initial position, x is the final position, and $\Delta t = t$ with $t_o = 0$. See Section 2.3 for more on this notation.

In this equation, Δx is the displacement and Δt is the time interval, where t_1 is the initial time and t_2 is the final time.

In the case of more than one displacement (successive displacements), the average velocity for all the displacements is equal to the total or net displacement divided by the total time. The total displacement is found by adding the displacements algebraically according to the directional signs.

You might be wondering whether there is a relationship between average speed and average velocity. A quick look at Fig. 2.4 will show you that if all the motion is in one direction, that is, no reversal of direction, the distance is equal to the magnitude of the displacement, and the average speed is equal to the magnitude of the average velocity. However, be careful. This set of relationships is not true if there is a reversal of direction, as Example 2.2 shows.

Example 2.2 ■ There and Back: Average Velocities

A jogger jogs from one end to the other of a straight 300-m track in 2.50 min and then jogs back to the starting point in 3.30 min. What was the jogger's average velocity (a) in jogging to the far end of the track, (b) coming back to the starting point, and (c) for the total jog?

Thinking It Through. The average velocities are computed from the defining equation. Note that the times given are the Δt's associated with the particular displacements.

Solution. From the problem, we have:

Given: $\Delta x_1 = 300$ m (taking the initial direction as positive)
$\Delta x_2 = -300$ m (taking the direction of the return trip as negative)
$\Delta t_1 = 2.50\ \text{min}\,(60\ \text{s/min}) = 150\ \text{s}$
$\Delta t_2 = 3.30\ \text{min}\,(60\ \text{s/min}) = 198\ \text{s}$ } (conversion to standard units)

Find: Average velocities for (a) the first leg of the jog, (b) the return jog, and (c) the total jog

(a) The jogger's average velocity for the trip down the track is found from Eq. 2.3:

$$\bar{v}_1 = \frac{\Delta x_1}{\Delta t_1} = \frac{300\ \text{m}}{150\ \text{s}} = +2.00\ \text{m/s}$$

(b) Similarly, for the return trip, we have

$$\bar{v}_2 = \frac{\Delta x_2}{\Delta t_2} = \frac{-300\ \text{m}}{198\ \text{s}} = -1.52\ \text{m/s}$$

(c) For the total trip, there are two displacements to consider, down and back, so these are added together to get the total displacement, and then divided by the total time;

$$\bar{v}_3 = \frac{\Delta x_1 + \Delta x_2}{\Delta t_1 + \Delta t_2} = \frac{300\ \text{m} + (-300\ \text{m})}{150\ \text{s} + 198\ \text{s}} = 0\ \text{m/s}$$

The average velocity for the total trip is zero! Do you see why? Recall from the definition of displacement that the magnitude of displacement is the straight-line distance between two points. The displacement from one point back to the same point is zero, hence the average velocity is zero. (See ▸ Fig. 2.5.)

The total displacement could have been found by simply taking $\Delta x = x_{\text{final}} - x_{\text{initial}} = 0 - 0 = 0$, but it was done in parts here for illustration purposes.

Follow-up Exercise. Find the jogger's average speed for each of the cases in this Example, and compare it with the respective average velocities. [Will the average speed for (c) be zero?] *(Answers to all Follow-up Exercises are at the back of the text.)*

▲ **FIGURE 2.5 Back home again!** Despite having covered nearly 110 m on the base paths, at the moment the runner slides through the batter's box (his original position) into home plate, his displacement is zero—at least, if he is a right-handed batter. No matter how fast he ran the bases, his average velocity for the round trip is also zero.

As Example 2.2 shows, average velocity provides only a very general description of motion. One way to take a closer look at motion is to take smaller time intervals, that is, to let the observation time (Δt) become smaller and smaller. As with speed, when Δt approaches zero, we obtain the **instantaneous velocity**, which describes how fast something is moving and in which direction at a particular instant of time.

Note: for displacements in both the + and − directions (reversal of direction), the distance is *not* the magnitude of the total displacement.

Instantaneous velocity is defined mathematically as

$$v = \lim_{\Delta t \to 0} \frac{\Delta x}{\Delta t} \tag{2.4}$$

This expression is read as "the instantaneous velocity is equal to the limit of $\Delta x/\Delta t$ as Δt goes to zero." The time interval does not ever equal zero (why?), but *approaches* zero. Instantaneous velocity is an average velocity, but over such a small Δt that it is essentially an average "at an instant in time," which is why we call it the instantaneous velocity.

Note: The word *uniform* means constant.

In one dimension, **uniform motion** means motion with a constant velocity (constant magnitude *and* constant direction). For example, the car in ▼Fig. 2.6 has a uniform velocity (as well as a uniform speed). It travels the same distance in equal time intervals (50 km each hour), and the direction of its motion does not change.

Graphical Analysis

Graphical analysis is often helpful in understanding motion and its related quantities. For example, the motion of the car in Fig. 2.6a may be represented on a plot of position versus time, or x versus t. As can be seen from Fig. 2.6b, a straight line is obtained for a uniform, or constant, velocity on such a graph.

Recall from Cartesian graphs of y versus x that the slope of a straight line is given by $\Delta y/\Delta x$. Here, with a plot of x versus t, the slope of the line, $\Delta x/\Delta t$, is

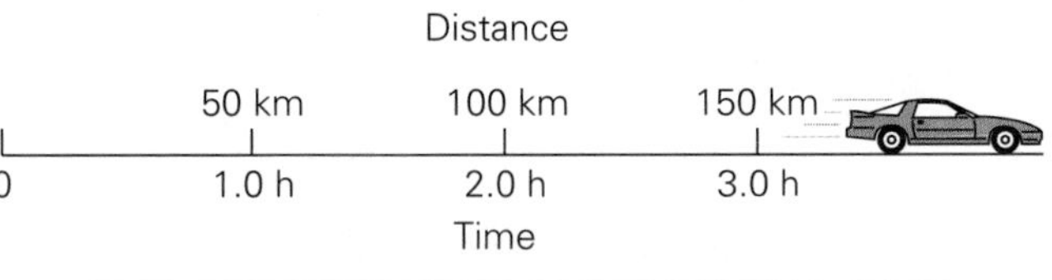

Δx (km)	Δt (h)	$\Delta x/\Delta t$
50	1.0	50 km/1.0 h = 50 km/h
100	2.0	100 km/2.0 h = 50 km/h
150	3.0	150 km/3.0 h = 50 km/h

(a)

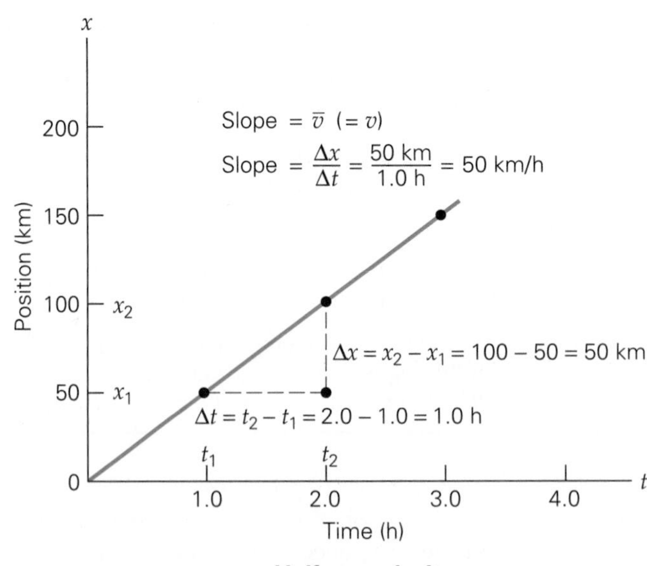

▶ **FIGURE 2.6 Uniform linear motion—constant velocity** In uniform linear motion, an object travels at a constant velocity, covering the same distance in equal time intervals. **(a)** Here, a car travels 50 km each hour. **(b)** An x-versus-t plot is a straight line, since equal displacements are covered in equal times. The numerical value of the slope of the line is equal to the magnitude of the velocity, and the sign of the slope gives its direction. (The average velocity equals the instantaneous velocity in this case. Why?)

equal to the average velocity $\bar{v} = \Delta x/\Delta t$. For uniform motion, this value is equal to the instantaneous velocity. That is, $\bar{v} = v$. (Why?) The numerical value of the slope is the magnitude of the velocity, and the sign of the slope gives the direction. A positive slope indicates that x increases with time, so the motion is in the positive x-direction. (The plus sign is often omitted, as being understood.)

Suppose that a plot of position versus time for a car's motion was a straight line with a negative slope, as in ▾Fig. 2.7. What does this slope indicate? As the figure shows, the position (x) values get smaller with time at a constant rate, indicating that the car was traveling in uniform motion in the negative x-direction.

In most instances, the motion of an object is nonuniform, meaning that different distances are covered in equal intervals of time. An x-versus-t plot for such motion in one dimension is a curved line, as illustrated in ▾Fig. 2.8. The average velocity of the object at a particular interval of time is the slope of a straight line between the two points on the curve that correspond to the starting and ending times of the interval. In the figure, the average velocity of the total trip is the slope of the straight line joining the beginning and ending points of the curve (t_1 and t_2).

The instantaneous velocity is equal to the slope of a straight line tangent to the curve at a specific point. Five tangent lines are shown in Fig. 2.8. At (1), the slope is positive, and the motion is in the positive x-direction. At (2), the slope of a horizontal tangent line is zero, so there is no motion. That is, the object has instantaneously stopped ($v = 0$). At (3), the slope is negative, so the object is moving in the negative x-direction. Thus, the object stopped and changed direction at point (2). What is happening at points (4) and (5)?

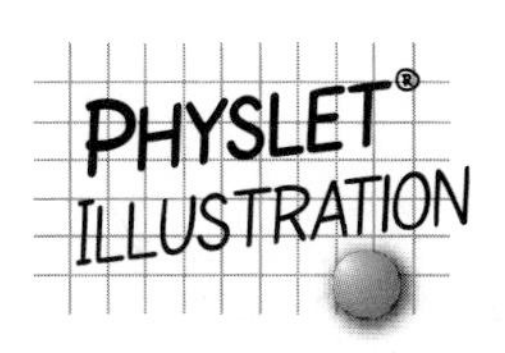

Graphical Determination of Velocity

Drawing various tangent lines along the curve, we see that their slopes vary, indicating that the instantaneous velocity is changing with time. An object in

▾ FIGURE 2.7 Position-versus-time graph for an object in uniform motion in the $-x$-direction A straight line on an x-versus-t plot with a negative slope indicates uniform motion in the $-x$-direction. Note that the object's location changes at a constant rate. At $t = 4.0$ h, the object is at $x = 0$. How would the graph look if the motion continues for $t > 4.0$ h?

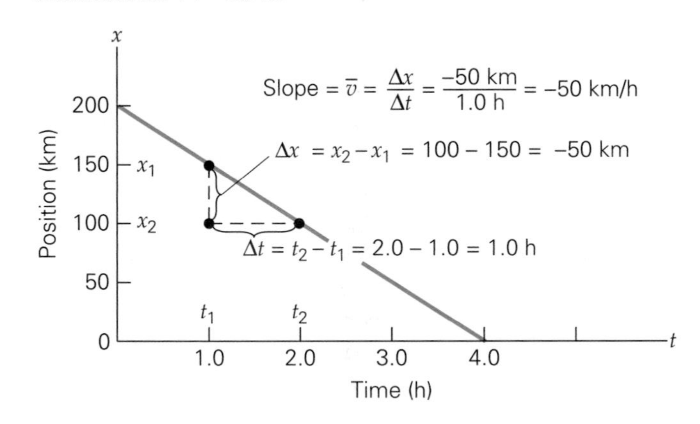

▾ FIGURE 2.8 Position-versus-time graph for an object in nonuniform linear motion For a nonuniform velocity, an x-versus-t plot is a curved line. The slope of the line between two points is the average velocity between those positions, and the instantaneous velocity is the slope of a line tangent to the curve at any point. Five tangent lines are shown, with the value of $\Delta x/\Delta t$ given for the fifth. Can you describe the object's motion in words?

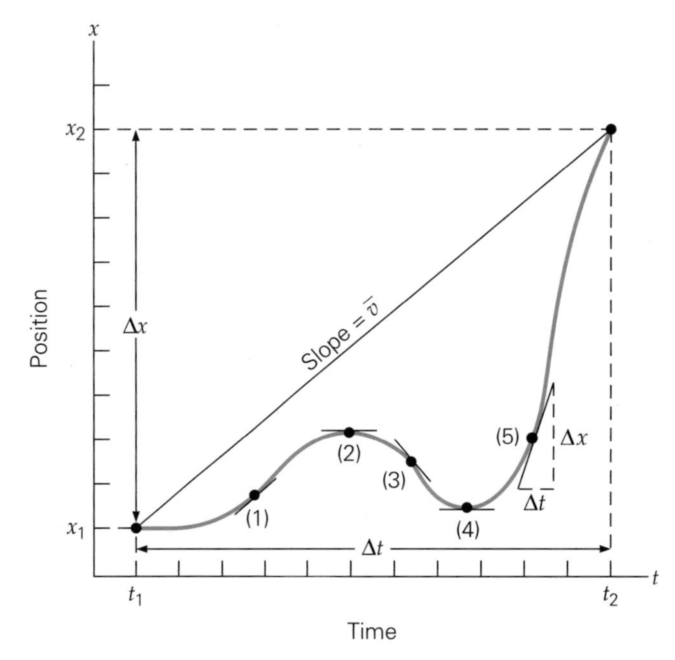

nonuniform motion can speed up, slow down, or change direction. How we describe motion with changing velocity is the topic of Section 2.3.

2.3 Acceleration

OBJECTIVES: **To (a) explain the relationship between velocity and acceleration and (b) perform graphical analyses of acceleration.**

The basic description of motion involves the time rate of change of position, which we call *velocity*. Going one step further, we can consider how this *rate of change* changes. Suppose that something is moving at a constant velocity and then the velocity changes. Such a change in velocity is called an *acceleration*. The gas pedal on an automobile is commonly called the *accelerator*. When you press down on the accelerator, the car speeds up; when you let up on the accelerator, the car slows down. In either case, there is a change in velocity with time. We define **acceleration** as the time rate of change of velocity.

Analogous to average velocity is the **average acceleration**, or the change in velocity divided by the time taken to make the change:

Definition of: Average acceleration

$$\text{average acceleration} = \frac{\text{change in velocity}}{\text{time to make the change}} \tag{2.5}$$

$$\bar{a} = \frac{\Delta v}{\Delta t}$$

$$= \frac{v_2 - v_1}{t_2 - t_1} = \frac{v - v_o}{t - t_o}$$

SI unit of acceleration: meters per second squared (m/s^2).

Note that we have changed the initial and final variables to a more commonly used notation. v_o and t_o are the initial or original velocity and time, respectively, and v and t are the general velocity and time at some time in the future, such as when you want to know the velocity v at a particular time t.

The dimensions of acceleration are ([L]/[T])/[T], from $\Delta v/\Delta t$. The SI units of acceleration are therefore meters per second per second, that is, (m/s)/s, or $m/s \cdot s$, commonly expressed as meters per second squared (m/s^2). In the British system, the units are feet per second squared (ft/s^2).

Note: In compound units, multiplication is indicated by a dot.

Because velocity is a vector quantity, so is acceleration, since acceleration represents a change in velocity. Being a vector quantity, velocity has both magnitude and direction, and a change in velocity may thus involve either or both of these factors. An acceleration, therefore, may result from a change in *speed* (magnitude), a change in *direction*, or a change in *both*, as illustrated in ▸Fig. 2.9.

For straight-line, linear motion, plus and minus signs will be used to indicate the directions of velocity and acceleration, as was done for linear displacements. Eq. 2.5 is commonly simplified and written as

$$\bar{a} = \frac{v - v_o}{t} \tag{2.6}$$

where t_o is taken to be zero. (v_o may not be zero, so it cannot generally be omitted.)

Analogous to instantaneous velocity, **instantaneous acceleration** is the acceleration at a particular instant of time. This quantity is expressed mathematically as

$$a = \lim_{\Delta t \to 0} \frac{\Delta v}{\Delta t} \tag{2.7}$$

The conditions of the time interval approaching zero are the same here as described for instantaneous velocity.

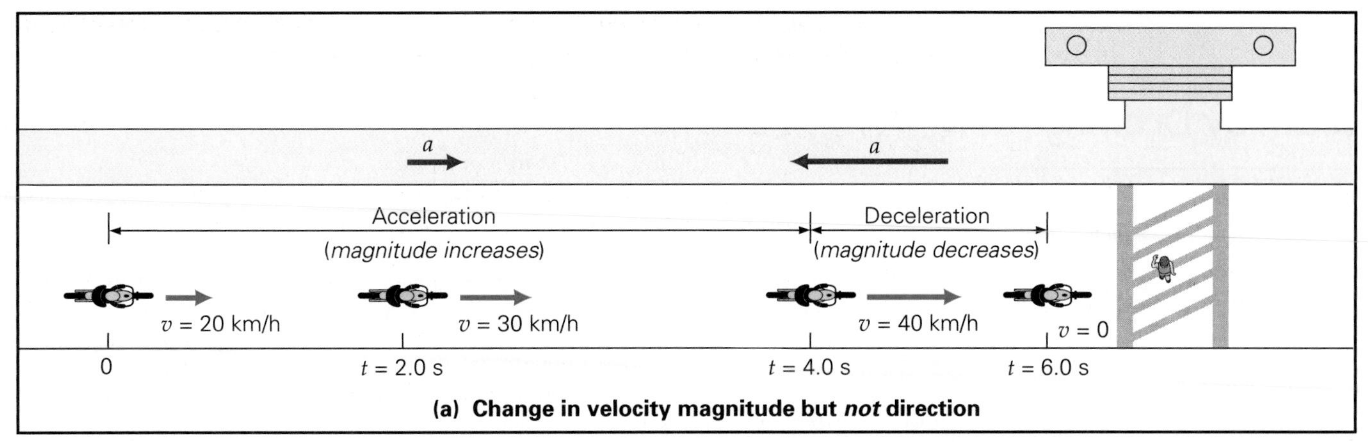

(a) Change in velocity magnitude but *not* direction

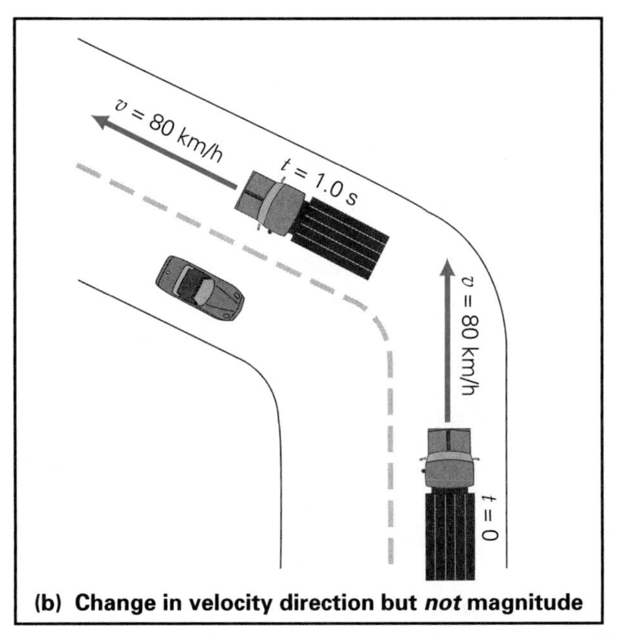

(b) Change in velocity direction but *not* magnitude

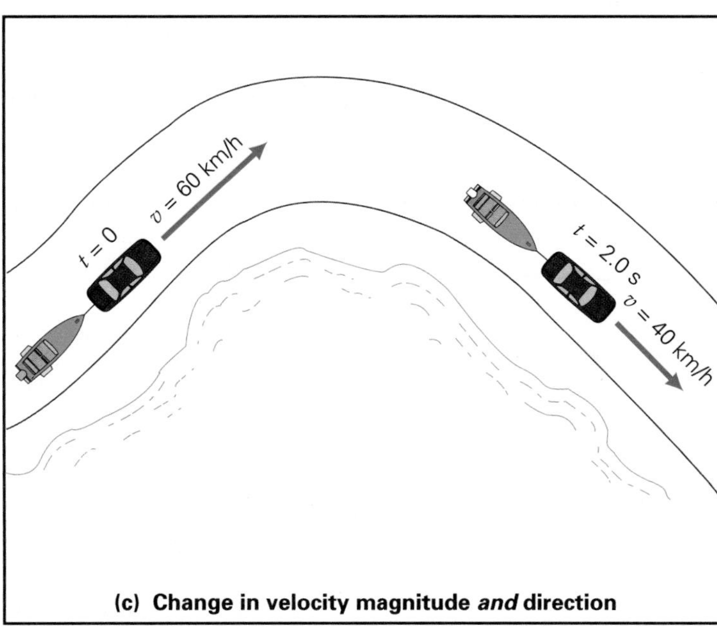

(c) Change in velocity magnitude *and* direction

▲ **FIGURE 2.9 Acceleration—the time rate of change of velocity** Since velocity is a vector quantity, with magnitude and direction, an acceleration can occur when there is **(a)** a change in magnitude, but not direction, **(b)** a change in direction, but not magnitude, or **(c)** a change in both magnitude and direction.

Example 2.3 ■ Slowing It Down: Average Acceleration

A couple in their sport utility vehicle (SUV) is traveling 90 km/h down a straight highway. They see an accident in the distance, so the driver slows down to 40 km/h in 5.0 s. What is the average acceleration of the SUV?

Thinking It Through. To find the average acceleration, the variables as defined in Eq. 2.6 must be given, and they are.

Solution. From the statement of the problem, we have the following data:

Given: $v_o = (90\ \text{km/h})\left(\frac{0.278\ \text{m/s}}{1\ \text{km/h}}\right) = 25\ \text{m/s}$ *Find:* $\bar{a}$ (average acceleration)

$v = (40\ \text{km/h})\left(\frac{0.278\ \text{m/s}}{1\ \text{km/h}}\right) = 11\ \text{m/s}$

$t = 5.0\ \text{s}$

[With the motion in a straight line, the instantaneous velocities are assumed to be in the positive direction, and conversions to standard units (kilometers per second to meters per second) are made right away, since it is noted that the time is given in seconds. In general, we always work with acceleration in standard units.]

Given the initial and final velocities and the time interval, the average acceleration can be found by using Eq. 2.6:

$$\bar{a} = \frac{v - v_o}{t} = \frac{11\ \text{m/s} - 25\ \text{m/s}}{5.0\ \text{s}} = -2.8\ \text{m/s}^2$$

The minus sign indicates the direction of the (vector) acceleration. In this case, the acceleration is opposite to the direction of the motion ($+v$), and the car slows. Such an acceleration is sometimes called a *deceleration*, since the car is slowing.

Follow-up Exercise. Does a negative acceleration necessarily mean that a moving object is slowing down (decelerating) or that its speed is decreasing? *Hint*: see LBD. *(Answers to all Follow-up Exercises are at the back of the text.)*

Learn by Drawing

Signs of Velocity and Acceleration

a positive / v positive — Result: Faster in +x direction (−x … +x)

a negative / v positive — Result: Slower in +x direction (−x … +x)

a positive / v negative — Result: Slower in −x direction (−x … +x)

a negative / v negative — Result: Faster in −x direction (−x … +x)

Constant Acceleration

Although acceleration can vary with time, our study of motion will generally be restricted to constant accelerations for simplicity. (An important constant acceleration is the acceleration due to gravity near the Earth's surface, which will be considered in the next section.) Since for a constant acceleration, the average is equal to the constant value ($\bar{a} = a$), the bar over the acceleration in Eq. 2.6 may be omitted. Thus, for a constant acceleration, the equation relating velocity, acceleration, and time is commonly written (rearranging Eq. 2.6) as follows:

$$v = v_o + at \qquad (\textit{constant acceleration only}) \qquad (2.8)$$

(Note that the term at represents the *change* in velocity that occurs, since $at = v - v_o = \Delta v$.)

Example 2.4 ■ Fast Start, Slow Stop: Motion with Constant Acceleration

A drag racer starting from rest accelerates in a straight line at a constant rate of 5.5 m/s^2 for 6.0 s. (a) What is the racer's velocity at the end of this period of time? (b) If a parachute deployed at this time causes the racer to slow down uniformly at a rate of 2.4 m/s^2, how long will it take the racer to come to a stop?

Thinking It Through. The racer first speeds up and then slows down, so close attention must be given to the directional signs of the vector quantities. Choose a coordinate system with the positive direction in the direction of the initial velocity. (Draw a sketch of the situation for yourself.) The answers can then be found by using the appropriate equations.

Solution. Taking the initial motion to be in the positive direction, we have the following data:

Given: (a) $v_o = 0$ (at rest)
$a = 5.5\ \text{m/s}^2$
$t = 6.0\ \text{s}$
(b) $v_o = v$ [from part (a)]
$v = 0$ (comes to stop)
$a = -2.4\ \text{m/s}^2$ (opposite direction of v_o).

Find: (a) v (final velocity)
(b) t (time)

The data have been listed in two parts. This practice helps avoid confusion with symbols. Note that the final velocity v that is to be found in part (a) becomes the initial velocity v_o for part (b).

(a) To find the final velocity v, we use Eq. 2.8 directly:

$$v = v_o + at = 0 + (5.5\ \text{m/s}^2)(6.0\ \text{s}) = 33\ \text{m/s}$$

(b) Here, we want to find time, so solving Eq. 2.6 for t and using $v_o = 33$ m/s from part (a), we have

$$t = \frac{v - v_o}{a} = \frac{0 - 33\ \text{m/s}}{-2.4\ \text{m/s}^2} = 14\ \text{s}$$

Note that the time comes out positive, as it should. We start implicitly at zero time (taking $t_o = 0$ when the parachute is deployed), and time goes forward, or in a "positive direction."

Follow-up Exercise. What is the racer's instantaneous velocity 10 seconds after the parachute is deployed? *(Answers to all Follow-up Exercises are at the back of the text.)*

Motions with constant accelerations are easy to represent graphically by plotting instantaneous velocity versus time. A v-versus-t plot is a straight line whose slope is equal to the acceleration, as illustrated in ▼Fig. 2.10. Note that Eq. 2.8 can be written as $v = at + v_o$, which, as you may recognize, has the form of an equation of a straight line, $y = mx + b$ (slope m and intercept b). In Fig. 2.10a, the motion is in the positive direction, and the acceleration adds to the velocity

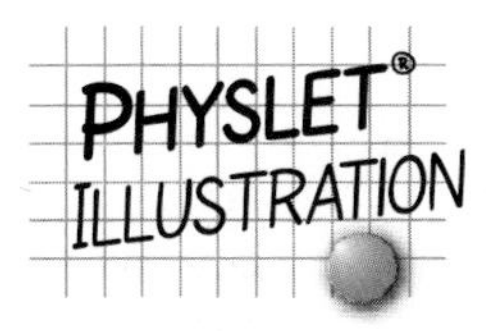

Graphical Determination of Acceleration

▼ **FIGURE 2.10 Velocity-versus-time graphs for motions with constant accelerations** The slope of a v-versus-t plot is the acceleration. **(a)** A positive slope indicates an increase in the velocity in the positive direction. The vertical arrows to the right indicate how the acceleration adds velocity to the initial velocity v_o. **(b)** A negative slope indicates a decrease in the initial velocity v_o, or a deceleration. **(c)** Here a negative slope indicates a negative acceleration, but the initial velocity is in the negative direction, $-v_o$, so the speed of the object increases in that direction. **(d)** The situation here is initially similar to that of (b) but ends up resembling that in (c). Can you explain what happened at time t_1?

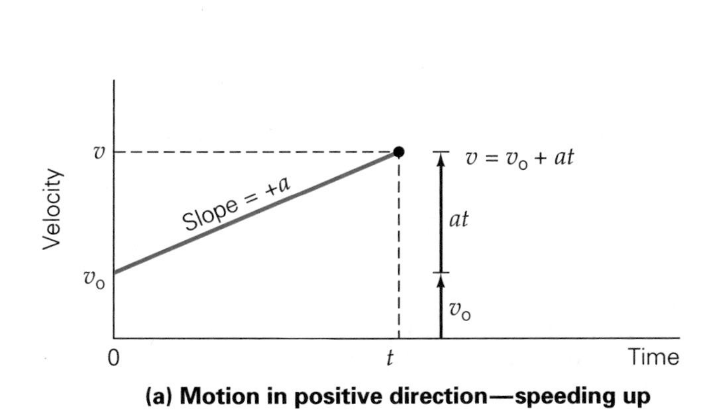

(a) Motion in positive direction—speeding up

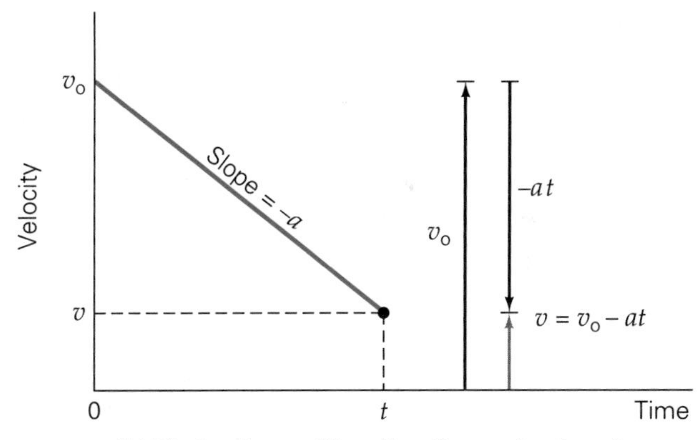

(b) Motion in positive direction—slowing down

(c) Motion in negative direction—speeding up

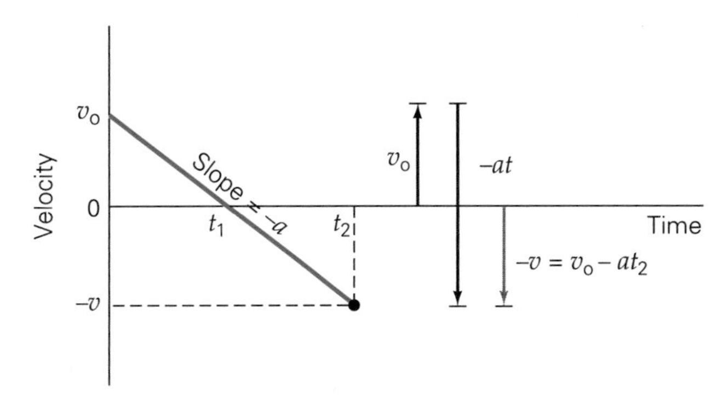

(d) Changing direction

for a time t, as illustrated by the vertical arrows at the right of the graph. Here, the slope is positive, $+a$. In Fig. 2.10b, the negative slope $(-a)$ indicates a negative acceleration that produces a slowing down, or deceleration. However, Fig. 2.10c illustrates how a negative acceleration can speed things up (for motion in the negative direction). The situation in Fig. 2.10d is slightly more complex. Can you explain what is happening there?

When an object moves at a constant acceleration, its velocity changes by the same amount in each time unit. For example, if the acceleration is 10 m/s^2 in the same direction as that of the initial velocity, the object's velocity increases by 10 m/s in each second. Suppose that the object has an initial velocity v_o of 20 m/s at $t_o = 0$. Then, for $t = 0$, 1.0, 2.0, 3.0, and 4.0 s, the velocities are 20, 30, 40, 50, and 60 m/s, respectively. The average velocity over the four-second interval is $\bar{v} = 40$ m/s.

This average velocity may be computed in the regular manner (Eq. 2.3), or you may immediately recognize that the uniformly increasing series of numbers 20, 30, 40, 50, and 60 has an average value of 40 (the midway value of the series). Note that the average of the extreme (initial and final) values also gives the average of the series—that is, $(20 + 60)/2 = 40$. When the velocity changes at a uniform rate because of a constant acceleration, $\bar{v}$ is the average of the initial and final velocities:

$$\bar{v} = \frac{v + v_o}{2} \qquad \textit{(constant acceleration only)} \qquad (2.9)$$

Example 2.5 ■ On the Water: Using Multiple Equations

A motorboat starting from rest on a lake accelerates in a straight line at a constant rate of 3.0 m/s^2 for 8.0 s. How far does the boat travel during this time?

Thinking It Through. We have only one equation for distance (Eq. 2.3, $x = x_o + \bar{v}t$), but this equation cannot be used directly. The average velocity must first be found, so multiple equations are involved.

Solution. Reading the problem and summarizing the given data and what is to be found, we have the following:

Given: $x_o = 0$
$v_o = 0$
$a = 3.0\ m/s^2$
$t = 8.0$ s

Find: x (distance)

(Note that all of the units are standard.)

In analyzing the problem, we might reason as follows: To find x, we will need to use Eq. 2.3, $x_o + \bar{v}t$. (The average velocity $\bar{v}$ must be used because the velocity is changing and thus not constant.) With time t given, the solution to the problem then involves finding $\bar{v}$. By Eq. 2.9, $\bar{v} = (v + v_o)/2$, and with $v_o = 0$, we need only find the final velocity v to solve the problem. Equation 2.8, $v = v_o + at$, enables us to calculate v from the given data. So, we have the following:

The velocity of the boat at the end of 8.0 s is

$$v = v_o + at = 0 + (3.0\ m/s^2)(8.0\ s) = 24\ m/s$$

The average velocity over that time interval is

$$\bar{v} = \frac{v + v_o}{2} = \frac{24\ m/s + 0}{2} = 12\ m/s$$

Finally, the magnitude of the displacement, which in this case is the same as the distance traveled, is given by Eq. 2.3 (with $x_o = 0$):

$$x = \bar{v}t = (12\ m/s)(8.0\ s) = 96\ m$$

Follow-up Exercise. (Sneak preview.) In Section 2.4, the following equation will be derived, $x = v_o t + \frac{1}{2}at^2$. Use the data in this Example to see if this equation gives the distance traveled. *(Answers to all Follow-up Exercises are at the back of the text.)*

2.4 Kinematic Equations (Constant Acceleration)

OBJECTIVES: **To (a) explain the kinematic equations of constant acceleration and (b) apply them to physical situations.**

The description of motion in one dimension with constant acceleration requires only three basic equations. From previous sections, these equations are

$$x = x_o + \bar{v}t \qquad (2.3)$$

$$\bar{v} = \frac{v + v_o}{2} \qquad \textit{(constant acceleration only)} \qquad (2.9)$$

$$v = v_o + at \qquad \textit{(constant acceleration only)} \qquad (2.8)$$

(Keep in mind that the first equation, Eq. 2.3, is general and is not limited to situations in which there is constant acceleration, as the latter two equations are.)

However, as Example 2.5 showed, the description of motion in some instances requires multiple applications of these equations, which may not be obvious at first. It would be helpful if there were a way to reduce the number of operations in solving kinematic problems, and there is—by combining equations algebraically.

For instance, suppose we want an expression that gives location x in terms of time and acceleration rather than in terms of time and average velocity (as in Eq. 2.3). We can eliminate $\bar{v}$ from Eq. 2.3 by substituting for $\bar{v}$ from Eq. 2.9 into Eq. 2.3:

$$x = x_o + \bar{v}t = x_o + \left(\frac{v + v_o}{2}\right)t$$

and

$$x = x_o + \tfrac{1}{2}(v + v_o)t \qquad \textit{(constant acceleration only)} \qquad (2.10)$$

Then, substituting for v from Eq. 2.8 gives

$$x = x_o + \tfrac{1}{2}(v_o + at + v_o)t$$

Simplifying,

$$x = x_o + v_o t + \tfrac{1}{2}at^2 \qquad \textit{(constant acceleration only)} \qquad (2.11)$$

Essentially, this series of steps was done in Example 2.5. The combined equation allows the distance traveled by the motorboat in that Example to be computed directly:

$$x - x_o = \Delta x = v_o t + \tfrac{1}{2}at^2 = 0 + \tfrac{1}{2}(3.0\ \text{m/s}^2)(8.0\ \text{s})^2 = 96\ \text{m}$$

Much easier, isn't it?

Perhaps we want an expression that gives velocity as a function of position x rather than time (as in Eq. 2.8). We can eliminate t from Eq. 2.8 by using Eq. 2.3 in the form $t = (x - x_o)/\bar{v}$:

$$v = v_o + a\left(\frac{x - x_o}{\bar{v}}\right)$$

Note: $\Delta x = x - x_o$ is displacement, but with $x_o = 0$, as it often is, then $\Delta x = x$, and the value of the x position is the same as that of the displacement, which saves writing $\Delta x = x - x_o$ every time.

Then we replace $\bar{v}$, using Eq. 2.9:

$$v = v_o + \frac{a(x - x_o)}{\left(\frac{v + v_o}{2}\right)} \quad \text{or} \quad v - v_o = \frac{2a(x - x_o)}{v + v} \quad \text{or} \quad (v + v_o)(v - v_o) = 2a(x - x_o)$$

Simplifying by using the algebraic relationship $(v + v_o)(v - v_o) = v^2 - v_o^2$, we have

$$v^2 = v_o^2 + 2a(x - x_o) \quad \textit{(constant acceleration only)} \quad (2.12)$$

Problem-Solving Hint

Students in introductory physics courses are sometimes overwhelmed by the various kinematic equations. Keep in mind that equations and mathematics are the tools of physics. As any mechanic or carpenter will tell you, tools make your work easier so long as you are familiar with them and know how to use them. The same is true for physics tools.

In Sections 2.3 and 2.4, we here presented the kinematic equations. The following set of equations for linear motion with *constant* acceleration is used to solve the majority of kinematic problems:

$$v = v_o + at \quad (2.8)$$

$$x = x_o + \tfrac{1}{2}(v + v_o)t \quad (2.10)$$

$$x = x_o + v_o t + \tfrac{1}{2}at^2 \quad (2.11)$$

$$v^2 = v_o^2 + 2a(x - x_o) \quad (2.12)$$

(Occasionally, we are interested in average speed or velocity, but, as noted earlier, averages generally don't tell you a great deal.) Note that each of the equations in the list has four or five variables. All but one of the variables in an equation must be known in order to be able to solve for what you are trying to find. That is, for Eq. 2.8, three variables must be known to be able to solve for the fourth, unknown variable, and, for the rest of the equations, four variables must be known to be able to solve for a fifth, unknown variable.

Always try to understand and visualize a problem. Listing the data as described in the Suggested Problem-Solving Procedure in Chapter 1 may help you decide which equation to use, by determining the known and unknown variables. Remember this approach as you work through the remaining Examples in the chapter. Also, don't overlook any *implied data*, an error illustrated by Example 2.6.

Integrated Example 2.6 ■ Moving Apart: Where Are They Now?

Two riders on dune buggies sit 10 m apart on a long, straight track, facing in opposite directions. Starting at the same time, both riders accelerate at a constant rate of $2.0\ \text{m/s}^2$. (a) Make a problem-solving sketch of the situation. (b) How far apart will the dune buggies be at the end of 3.0 s?

(a) Conceptual Reasoning. We know only that the dune buggies are initially 10 m apart, so they can be positioned anywhere on the x-axis. It is convenient to place one at the origin so that one initial position (x_o) is zero. A sketch of the situation is shown in ▶Fig. 2.11.

(b) Thinking It Through. Referring to the sketch, we have the following data:

Given: $x_{o_A} = 0$
$a_A = -2.0\ \text{m/s}^2$
$t = 3.0\ \text{s}$
$x_{o_B} = 10\ \text{m}$
$a_B = 2.0\ \text{m/s}^2$

Find: separation distance at $t = 3.0\ \text{s}$

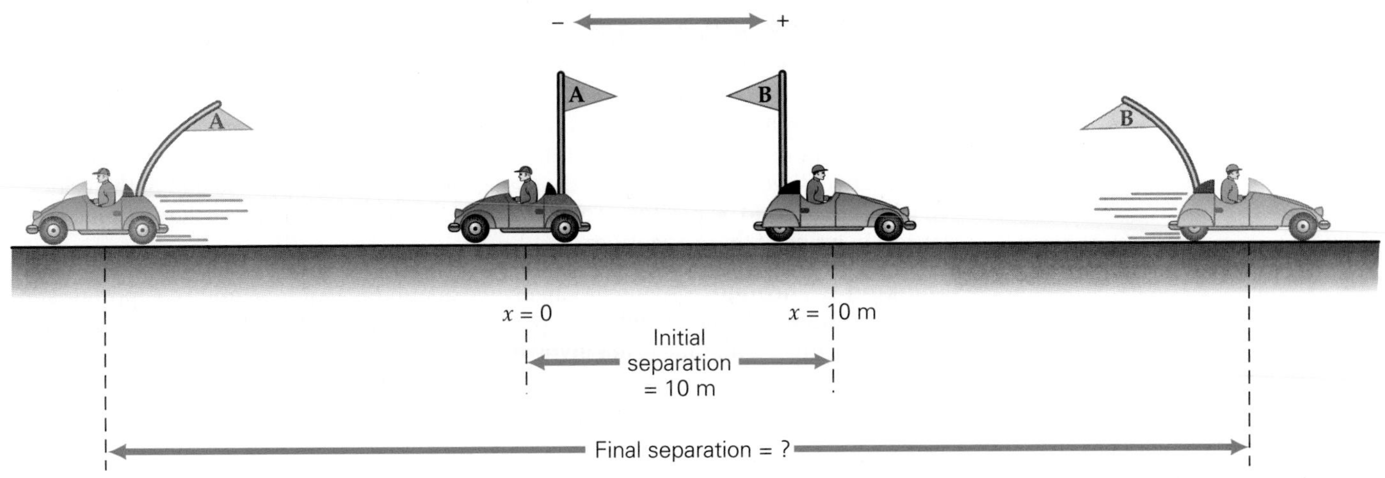

▲ **FIGURE 2.11 Away they go!** Two dune buggies accelerate away from each other. How far are they apart at a later time? See Integrated Example 2.6.

The distance each vehicle travels is given by Eq. 2.11 [the only displacement (x) equation with acceleration (a)]: $x = x_o + v_o t + \frac{1}{2}at^2$. But wait, we don't have v_o in the Given list. Some implied data may have been missed. We quickly note that $v_o = 0$ for both vehicles, so

$$x_A = x_{o_A} + v_{o_A}t + \tfrac{1}{2}a_A t^2 = 0 + 0 + \tfrac{1}{2}(-2.0\ \text{m/s}^2)(3.0\ \text{s})^2 = -9\ \text{m}$$

and

$$x_B = x_{o_B} + v_{o_A}t + \tfrac{1}{2}a_B t^2 = 10\ \text{m} + 0 + \tfrac{1}{2}(2.0\ \text{m/s}^2)(3.0\ \text{s})^2 = 19\ \text{m}$$

What does $x_A = -9$ m tell us? That vehicle A is at the -9 m position from the origin on the $-x$-axis, whereas vehicle B is at a position of 19 m on the $+x$-axis. Hence, the separation distance between the two dune buggies is 28 m.

Follow-up Exercise. Would it make any difference in the separation distance if vehicle B had been initially put at the origin instead of vehicle A? *(Answers to all Follow-up Exercises are at the back of the text.)*

Conceptual Example 2.7 ■ Two Race Cars: The Effect of Squared Quantities

During some time trials, race car A, starting from rest, accelerates uniformly along a straight, level track for a particular interval of time. Race car B, also starting from rest, accelerates at the same rate, but for twice the time. At the ends of their respective acceleration periods, which of these statements is true: (a) Car A has traveled a greater distance; (b) car B has traveled twice as far as car A; (c) car B has traveled four times as far as car A; (d) both cars have traveled the same distance? *Clearly establish the reasoning and physical principle(s) used in determining your answer before checking it below. That is,* ***why*** *did you select your answer?*

Reasoning and Answer. It is given that $v_o = 0$, and the acceleration is the same for both cars. To find the distances traveled in a time t, you would use Eq. 2.11, which, with $v_o = 0$ and taking $x_o = 0$, becomes $x = \frac{1}{2}at^2$. The important thing to note here is that the distance increases as t^2. That is, if you double the amount of time, the distance quadruples (i.e., increases by a factor of four).

In this example, car B accelerates for twice as long as car A, or $t_B = 2t_A$, so car B travels four times as far as car A, and the answer is (c). Expressed mathematically, the solution is

$$x_A = \tfrac{1}{2}at_A^2 \quad \text{and} \quad x_B = \tfrac{1}{2}at_B^2 = \tfrac{1}{2}a(2t_A)^2 = \tfrac{1}{2}a(4t_A^2) = 4(\tfrac{1}{2}at_A^2) = 4x_A$$

How do the cars' distances compare if $t_B = 3t_A$?

Follow-up Exercise. In this Example, how do the speeds of the cars compare at the ends of the acceleration periods? *(Answers to all Follow-up Exercises are at the back of the text.)*

Example 2.8 ■ Putting on the Brakes: Vehicle Stopping Distance

The stopping distance of a vehicle is an important factor in road safety. This distance depends on the initial speed $(+v_o)$ and the braking capacity, or deceleration, $-a$, which is assumed to be constant. (Recall that the minus sign indicates that the acceleration is in the negative direction. In this case, the sign of acceleration is opposite that of the velocity, which is taken to be positive. Thus, the car slows to a stop.) Express the stopping distance x in terms of these quantities.

Thinking It Through. Again, a kinematic equation is required, and the appropriate one is determined by listing what is given and what is to be found. Notice that the distance x is wanted, and time is not involved.

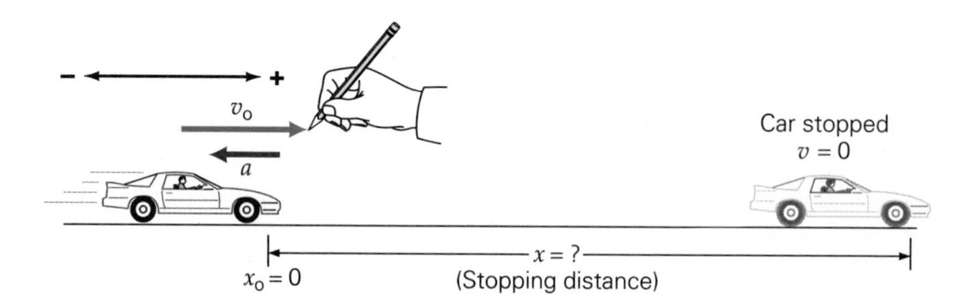

▶ **FIGURE 2.12 Vehicle stopping distance** A sketch to help visualize the situation in Example 2.8.

Solution. Here, we are working with variables, so we can represent quantities only in symbolic form.

Given: v_o (positive direction)
$-a$ (opposite direction of v_o)
$v = 0$ (car comes to stop)
$x_o = 0$ (car taken to be initially at the origin)

Find: x (in terms of the given variables)

Again, it is helpful to make a sketch of the situation, particularly when directional vector quantities are involved (▲Fig. 2.12). (Since Eq. 2.12 has the variables we want, it should allow us to find the stopping distance x. Expressing the negative acceleration explicitly and assuming $x_o = 0$ gives

$$v^2 = v_o^2 + 2(-a)x = v_o^2 - 2ax$$

Since the vehicle comes to a stop $(v = 0)$, we can solve for x:

$$x = \frac{v_o^2}{2a}$$

This equation gives us x expressed in terms of the vehicle's initial speed and stopping acceleration.

Notice that the stopping distance x is proportional to the *square* of the initial speed. Doubling the initial speed therefore increases the stopping distance by a factor of 4 (for the same deceleration). That is, if the stopping distance is x_1 for an initial speed of v_1, then for a twofold increase in the initial speed $(v_2 = 2v_1)$, the stopping distance would increase fourfold:

$$x_1 = \frac{v_1^2}{2a}$$

$$x_2 = \frac{v_2^2}{2a} = \frac{(2v_1)^2}{2a} = 4\left(\frac{v_1^2}{2a}\right) = 4x_1$$

We can get the same result by directly using ratios:

$$\frac{x_2}{x_1} = \frac{v_2^2}{v_1^2} = \left(\frac{v_2}{v_1}\right)^2 = 2^2 = 4$$

Do you think this consideration is important in setting speed limits, for example, in school zones? (The driver's reaction time should also be considered. A method for approximating a person's reaction time is given in Section 2.5.)

Follow-up Exercise. Tests have shown that the Chevy Blazer has an average braking deceleration of 7.5 m/s^2, while that of a Toyota Celica is 9.2 m/s^2. Suppose two of these vehicles are being driven down a straight, level road at 97 km/h (60 mi/h), with the Celica in front of the Blazer. A cat runs across the road ahead of them, and both drivers apply their brakes at the same time and come to safe stops (not hitting the cat). Assuming the same reaction times for both drivers, what is the minimum safe tailgating distance for the Blazer so that there won't be a rear-end collision with the Celica when the two vehicles came to a stop? *(Answers to all Follow-up Exercises are at the back of the text.)*

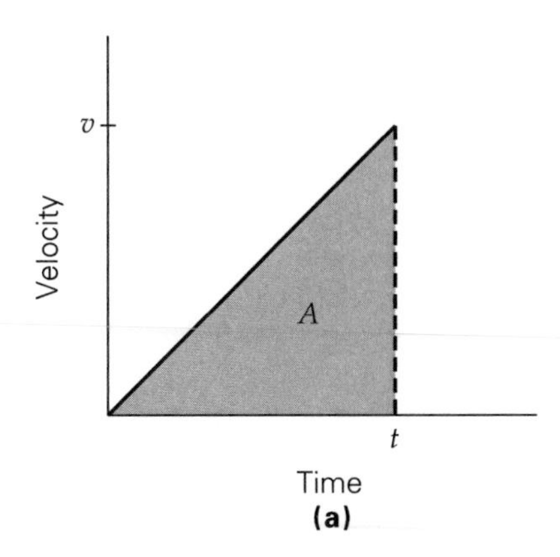

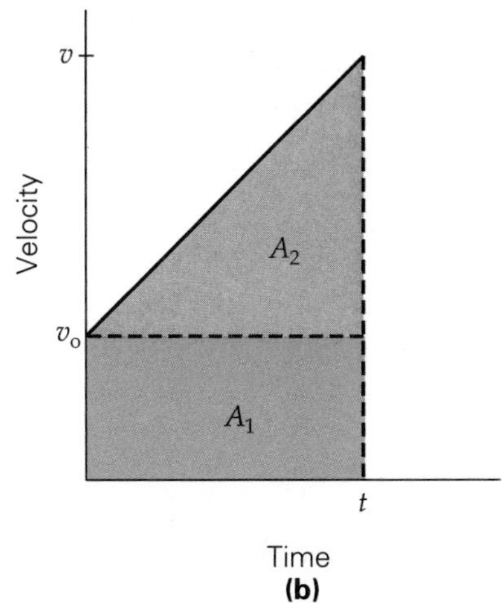

▲ **FIGURE 2.13** ***v*-versus-*t* graphs, one more time** **(a)** In the straight-line plot for a constant acceleration, the area under the curve is equal to x, the distance covered. **(b)** If v_o is not zero, the distance is still given by the area under the curve, here divided into two parts, areas A_1 and A_2.

Graphical Analysis of Kinematic Equations

As was shown in Fig. 2.10, plots of v versus t gave straight-line graphs where the slopes were constant accelerations. There is another interesting aspect of v-versus-t graphs. Consider the one shown in ▸Fig. 2.13a, particularly the shaded area under the curve. Suppose we calculate the area of the shaded triangle, where, in general, $A = \frac{1}{2}ab$ [Area $= \frac{1}{2}$(altitude)(base)].

For the graph in Fig. 2.13a, the altitude is v and the base is t, so $A = \frac{1}{2}vt$. But, from the equation $v = v_o + at$, we have $v = at$, where $v_o = 0$ (zero intercept on graph). Therefore,

$$A = \tfrac{1}{2}vt = \tfrac{1}{2}(at)t = \tfrac{1}{2}at^2 = \Delta x = x$$

(The equation $x = \frac{1}{2}at^2$ arises from Eq. 2.11 with $v_o = 0$ and $x_o = 0$, with the object initially at the origin.) Hence, x, the distance covered, is equal to the area under a v-versus-t curve.

Now take a look at Fig. 2.13b. Here, there is a nonzero value of v_o at $t = 0$, so the object is initially moving. Consider the shaded areas. We know that the area of the triangle is $A_2 = \frac{1}{2}at^2$, and the area of the rectangle can be seen (with $x_o = 0$) to be $A_1 = v_o t$. Adding these areas to get the total area yields

$$A_1 + A_2 = v_o t + \tfrac{1}{2}at^2 = x$$

Eq. 2.11 is on the right, and again x, the distance covered, is equal to the area under the v-versus-t curve.

2.5 Free Fall

OBJECTIVE: **To use the kinematic equations to analyze free fall.**

One of the more common cases of constant acceleration is the acceleration due to gravity near the Earth's surface. When an object is dropped, its initial velocity (at the instant it is released) is zero. At a later time while falling, it has a nonzero velocity. There has been a change in velocity and thus, by definition, an acceleration. This **acceleration due to gravity** (g) has an approximate magnitude of

$$g = 9.80 \text{ m/s}^2, \quad \textit{acceleration due to gravity}$$

(or 980 cm/s^2) and is directed downward (toward the center of the Earth). In British units, the value of g is about 32.2 ft/s^2.

The values given here for g are only approximate because the acceleration due to gravity varies slightly at different locations as a result of differences in elevation and regional average mass density of the Earth. These small variations will be ignored in this book unless otherwise noted. Air resistance is another factor that affects the acceleration of a falling object, but it, too, will be ignored here for simplicity. (The frictional effect of air resistance will be considered in Chapter 4.)

Objects in motion solely under the influence of gravity are said to be in ***free fall.*** The words "free fall" bring to mind dropped objects that are moving downward under the influence of gravity ($g = 9.80 \text{ m/s}^2$ in the absence of air resistance). However, the term can be applied in general to any vertical motion under the sole influence of gravity. Objects released from rest or thrown upward or downward are in free fall once they are released. That is, after $t = 0$ (the time of release), only gravity is acting and influencing the motion. (Even when an object projected upward is traveling upward, *it is still accelerating downward.*) Thus, the set of equations for motion in one dimension can be used to describe generalized free fall.

The acceleration due to gravity, g, is the *constant* acceleration for all free-falling objects, regardless of their mass or weight. It was once thought that heavier bodies fall faster than lighter bodies. This concept was part of Aristotle's theory of motion. You can easily observe that a coin falls faster than a sheet of paper when dropped simultaneously from the same height. But in this case, air resistance plays a noticeable role. If the paper is crumpled into a compact ball, it gives the coin a better race. Similarly, a feather "floats" down much more slowly than a coin falls. However, in a near-vacuum, where there is negligible air resistance, the feather and the coin fall with the same acceleration—the acceleration due to gravity (▼Fig. 2.14).

Astronaut David Scott performed a similar experiment on the Moon in 1971 by simultaneously dropping a feather and a hammer from the same height. He did not need a vacuum pump: The Moon has no atmosphere and therefore no air resistance. The hammer and the feather reached the lunar surface together, but both fell at a slower rate than on Earth. The acceleration due to gravity near the Moon's surface is about one sixth of that near the Earth's surface ($g_M \approx g/6$).

Currently accepted ideas about the motion of falling bodies are due in large part to Galileo. He challenged Aristotle's theory and experimentally investigated the motion of objects. Legend has it that Galileo studied the accelerations of falling bodies by dropping objects of different weights from the top of the Leaning Tower of Pisa. (See the accompanying Insight on Galileo.)

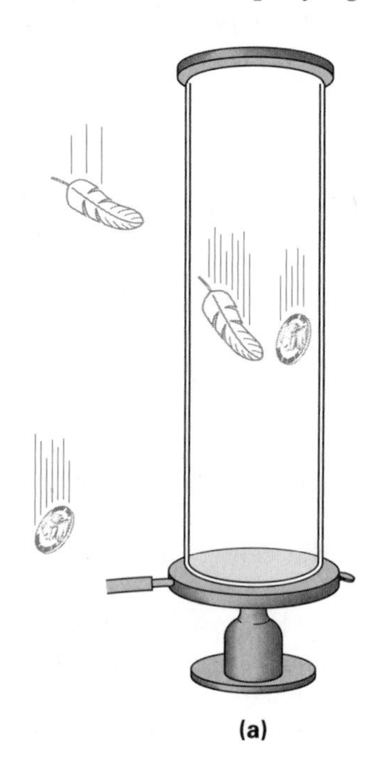

(a)

(b)

▶ **FIGURE 2.14 Free fall and air resistance** **(a)** When dropped simultaneously from the same height, a feather falls more slowly than a coin, because of air resistance. But when both objects are dropped in an evacuated container with a good partial vacuum, where air resistance is negligible, the feather and the coin fall together with a constant acceleration. **(b)** An actual demonstration with multiflash photography: An apple and a feather are released simultaneously through a trap door into a large vacuum chamber, and they fall together—almost. Because the chamber has a partial vacuum, there is still some air resistance. (How can you tell?)

INSIGHT

Galileo Galilei and the Leaning Tower of Pisa

Galileo Galilei (Fig. 1) was born in Pisa, Italy, in 1564 during the Renaissance. Today, he is known throughout the world by his first name and is often referred to as the father of modern science or the father of modern mechanics and experimental physics, which attests to the magnitude of his scientific contributions.

One of Galileo's greatest contributions to science was the establishment of the scientific method—that is, investigation through experiment. In contrast, Aristotle's approach was based on logical deduction. By the scientific method, for a theory to be valid, it must predict or agree with experimental results. If it doesn't, it is invalid or requires modification. Galileo said, "I think that in the discussion of natural problems we ought not to begin at the authority of places of Scripture, but at sensible experiments and necessary demonstrations."*

Probably the most popular and well-known legend about Galileo is that he performed experiments with falling bodies by dropping objects from the Leaning Tower of Pisa (Fig. 2). There is some debate as to whether Galileo actually did this, but there is little doubt that he questioned Aristotle's view on the motion of falling objects. In 1638, Galileo wrote,

> Aristotle says that an iron ball of one hundred pounds falling from a height of one hundred cubits reaches the ground before a one-pound ball has fallen a single cubit. I say that they arrive at the same time. You find, on making the experiment, that the larger outstrips the smaller by two finger-breadths, that is, when the larger has reached the ground, the other is short of it by two finger-breadths; now you would not hide behind these two fingers the ninety-nine cubits of Aristotle.†

This and other writings show that Galileo was aware of the effect of air resistance.

The experiments at the Tower of Pisa were supposed to have taken place around 1590. In this writings of about that time, Galileo mentions dropping objects from a high tower, but never specifically names the Tower of Pisa. A letter written to Galileo from another scientist in 1641 describes the dropping of a cannon ball and a musket ball from the Tower of Pisa. The first account of Galileo doing a similar experiment was written a dozen years after his death by Vincenzo Viviani, his last pupil and first biographer. It is not known whether Galileo told this story to Viviani in his declining years or Viviani created this picture of his former teacher.

The important point is that Galileo recognized (and probably experimentally showed) that free-falling objects fall with the same acceleration regardless of their mass or weight. (See Fig. 2.14.) Galileo gave no reason as to why all objects in free fall have the same acceleration, but Newton did, as you will learn in a later chapter.

*From *Growth of Biological Thought: Diversity, Evolution & Inheritance*, by F. Meyr (Cambridge, MA: Harvard University Press, 1982).

†From *Aristotle, Galileo, and the Tower of Pisa*, by L. Cooper (Ithaca, NY: Cornell University Press, 1935).

FIGURE 1 Galileo Galileo is alleged to have performed free-fall experiments by dropping objects off the Leaning Tower of Pisa.

FIGURE 2 The Leaning Tower of Pisa The tower, constructed as a belfry for a nearby cathedral, was built on shifting subsoil. Construction began in 1173, and the tower started to shift one way and then the other, before inclining to its present direction. Today, the tower leans about 5 m (16 ft) from the vertical at the top. It was closed in 1990, and efforts were made to stabilize the leaning.

Note: While traveling upward ($+v$), a projected object is accelerating downward, or has an acceleration in the downward direction ($-g$).

It is customary to use y to represent the vertical direction and to take upward as positive (as with the vertical y-axis of Cartesian coordinates). Because the acceleration due to gravity is always downward, then it is in the negative y-direction. This negative acceleration, $a = -g = -9.80\ \text{m/s}^2$, should be substituted into the equations of motion. However, the relationship $a = -g$ may be expressed explicitly in the equations for linear motion for convenience:

$$v = v_o - gt \tag{2.8'}$$

$$y = y_o + v_o t - \tfrac{1}{2}gt^2 \tag{2.11'}$$

Free-fall equations with $-g$ expressed explicitly

$$v^2 = v_o^2 - 2g(y - y_o) \tag{2.12'}$$

Equation 2.9 applies as well, but it does not contain g:

$$y = y_o + \tfrac{1}{2}(v + v_o)t \tag{2.10'}$$

The origin ($y = 0$) of the frame of reference is usually taken to be at the initial position of the object. Since upward is generally taken to be in the positive direction ($+y$-axis on a graph), writing $-g$ explicitly in the equations reminds you of directional differences, and the value of g is inserted as $9.80\ \text{m/s}^2$. However, the choice is arbitrary. The equations can be written with $a = g$, for example, $v = v_o + gt$, with the directional minus sign associated directly with g. In this case, a value of $-9.80\ \text{m/s}^2$ must be substituted for g each time.

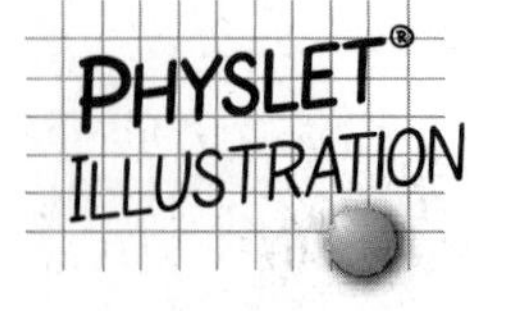

Free Fall

Note that you have to be explicit about the directions of vector quantities. The location y and the velocities v and v_o may be positive or negative, depending on the direction of motion. The use of these equations and the sign convention are illustrated in the following Examples.

Example 2.9 ■ A Stone Thrown Downward: The Kinematic Equations Revisited

A boy on a bridge throws a stone vertically downward with an initial velocity of 14.7 m/s toward the river below. If the stone hits the water 2.00 s later, what is the height of the bridge above the water?

Thinking It Through. This is a free-fall problem, but note that the initial velocity is downward, or negative. It is important to express this factor explicitly.

Solution. As usual, we first write down what is given and what is to be found:

Given: $v_o = -14.7\ \text{m/s}$ (downward taken as the negative direction)
$t = 2.00\ \text{s}$
$g\ (= 9.80\ \text{m/s}^2)$

Find: y (height)

Notice that g is taken as a positive number, since the directional minus sign has already been put into the previous equations of motion. After a while, you will probably just write down the symbol g, since you will be familiar with its numerical value. This time, draw a sketch of your own to help you analyze the situation.

Which equation(s) will provide the solution using the given data? It should be evident that the distance the stone travels in an amount of time t is given directly by Eq. 2.11′ (taking $y_o = 0$):

$$y = v_o t - \tfrac{1}{2}gt^2 = (-14.7\ \text{m/s})(2.00\ \text{s}) - \tfrac{1}{2}(9.80\ \text{m/s}^2)(2.00\ \text{s})^2$$
$$= -29.4\ \text{m} - 19.6\ \text{m} = -49.0\ \text{m}$$

The minus sign indicates that the displacement is downward, which agrees with what you know from the statement of the problem. Thus the height is 49.0 m.

Follow-up Exercise. How much longer would it take for the stone to reach the river if the boy in this Example had dropped the ball rather than thrown it? *(Answers to all Follow-up Exercises are at the back of the text.)*

Example 2.10 ■ Measuring Reaction Time: Free Fall

Reaction time is the time it takes a person to notice, think, and act in response to a situation—for example, the time between first observing and then responding to an obstruction on the road ahead while you are driving an automobile. Reaction time varies with the complexity of the situation (and with the individual). In general, the largest part of a person's reaction time is spent thinking, but practice in dealing with a given situation can reduce this time.

A person's reaction time can be measured by having another person drop a ruler (without warning) even with and through the first person's thumb and forefinger, as shown in ▸Fig. 2.15. The first person grasps the falling ruler as quickly as possible, and the length of the ruler below the top of the finger is noted. If, on average, the ruler descends 18.0 cm before it is caught, what is the person's average reaction time?

Thinking It Through. Both distance and time are involved. This observation indicates which kinematic equation should be used.

Solution. Notice that only the distance of fall is given. However, we know a couple of other things, such as v_o and g, so, taking $y_o = 0$:

Given: $y = -18.0\text{ cm} = -0.180\text{ m}$ *Find:* t (reaction time)
$v_o = 0$
$g\ (= 9.80\text{ m/s}^2)$

(Note that the distance y has been converted directly to meters.) We can see that Eq. 2.11′ applies here, giving us

$$y = v_o t - \tfrac{1}{2}gt^2$$

or

$$y = -\tfrac{1}{2}gt^2 \quad (\text{with } v_o = 0)$$

Solving for t gives

$$t = \sqrt{\frac{2y}{-g}} = \sqrt{\frac{2(-0.180\text{ m})}{-9.80\text{ m/s}^2}} = 0.192\text{ s}$$

Try this experiment with a fellow student, and measure your reaction time. Why do you think another person besides you should drop the ruler?

Follow-up Exercise. A popular trick is to substitute a crisp dollar bill lengthwise for the ruler in Fig. 2.15, telling the person that he or she can have the dollar if able to catch it. Is this proposal a good deal? (The length of a dollar is 15.7 cm.) *(Answers to all Follow-up Exercises are at the back of the text.)*

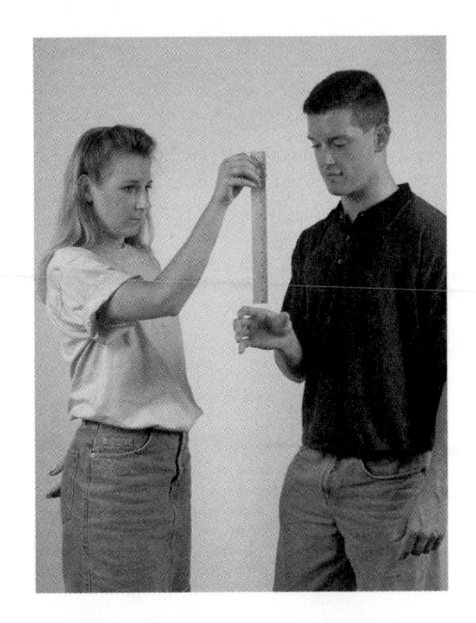

▲ **FIGURE 2.15 Reaction time**
A person's reaction time can be measured by having the person grasp a dropped ruler. See Example 2.10.

Example 2.11 ■ Free Fall Up and Down: Using Implicit Data

A worker on a scaffold on a billboard throws a ball straight up. The ball has an initial velocity of 11.2 m/s when it leaves the worker's hand at the top of the billboard (▸Fig. 2.16). (a) What is the maximum height the ball reaches relative to the top of the billboard? (b) How long does it take the ball to reach this height? (c) What is the position of the ball at $t = 2.00$ s?

Thinking It Through. In (a), only the upward part of the motion has to be considered. Note that the ball stops (zero velocity) at the maximum height, which allows us to determine this height. (b) Knowing the maximum height, we can determine the upward time of flight. In (c), the distance–time equation (Eq. 2.11′) applies for any time and gives the position (y) of the ball relative to the launch point.

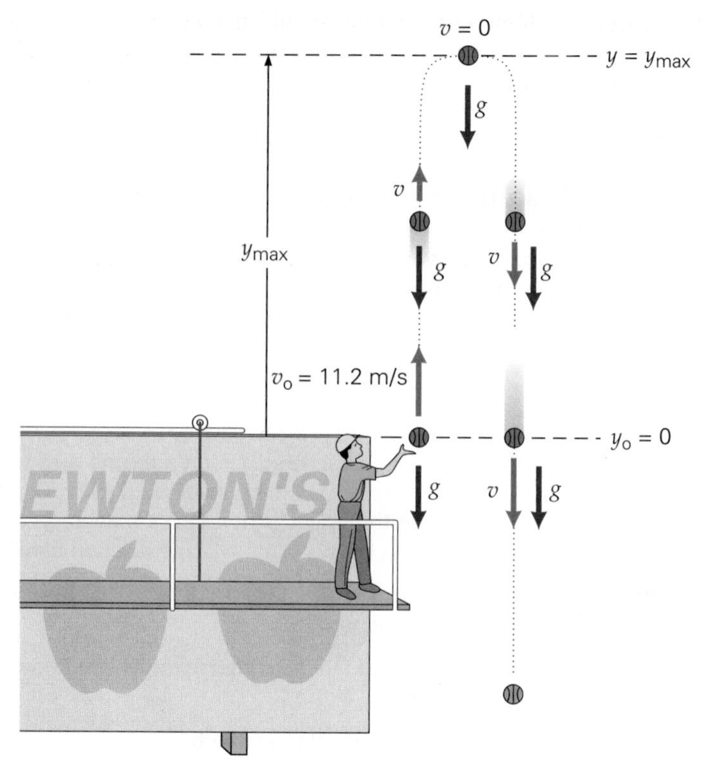

▶ **FIGURE 2.16 Free fall up and down** Note the lengths of the velocity and acceleration vectors at different times. (The upward and downward paths of the ball are horizontally displaced for illustration purposes.) See Example 2.11.

Solution. It might appear that all that is given in the general problem is the initial velocity v_o. However, a couple of other pieces of information are implied, because they should be understood. One is the acceleration g, and the other is the velocity at the maximum height where the ball stops. Here, in changing direction, the velocity of the ball is momentarily zero, so we have (again taking $y_o = 0$):

Given: $v_o = 11.2$ m/s
$g\ (= 9.80\ \text{m/s}^2)$
$v = 0$ (at y_{max})
$t = 2.00$ s [for part(c)]

Find: (a) y_{max} (maximum height)
(b) t_u (time upward)
(c) y (at $t = 2.00$ s)

(a) Notice that we reference the height ($y = 0$) to the top of the billboard. For this part of the problem, we need be concerned with only the upward motion—a ball is thrown upward and stops at its maximum height y_{max}. With $v = 0$ at this height, y_{max} may be found directly from Eq. 2.12′ as

$$v^2 = 0 = v_o^2 - 2gy_{max}$$

So,

$$y_{max} = \frac{v_o^2}{2g} = \frac{(11.2\ \text{m/s})^2}{2(9.80\ \text{m/s}^2)} = 6.40\ \text{m}$$

relative to the top of billboard ($y_o = 0$; see Fig. 2.16).

(b) The time the ball travels upward is designated t_u. This is the time it takes for the ball to reach y_{max}, where $v = 0$. Since we know v_o and v, and can find the time t_u directly from Eq. 2.8′ as

$$v = 0 = v_o - gt_u$$

So,

$$t_u = \frac{v_o}{g} = \frac{11.2\ \text{m/s}}{9.80\ \text{m/s}^2} = 1.14\ \text{s}$$

(c) The height of the ball at $t = 2.00$ s is given directly by Eq. 2.11′:

$$\begin{aligned} y &= v_o t - \tfrac{1}{2}gt^2 \\ &= (11.2\ \text{m/s})(2.00\ \text{s}) - \tfrac{1}{2}(9.80\ \text{m/s}^2)(2.00\ \text{s})^2 = 22.4\ \text{m} - 19.6\ \text{m} = 2.8\ \text{m} \end{aligned}$$

Note that this height is 2.8 m above, or measured upward from, the reference point ($y_o = 0$). The ball has reached its maximum height and is on its way back down.

Considered from another reference point, this situation is like dropping a ball from a height of y_{max} above the top of the billboard with $v_o = 0$ and asking how far it falls in a time $t = 2.00 \text{ s} - t_u = 2.00 \text{ s} - 1.14 \text{ s} = 0.86 \text{ s}$. The answer is (with $y_o = 0$ at the maximum height)

$$y = v_o t - \tfrac{1}{2}gt^2 = 0 - \tfrac{1}{2}(9.80 \text{ m/s}^2)(0.86 \text{ s})^2 = -3.6 \text{ m}$$

This height is the same as the position found previously, but is measured with respect to the maximum height as the reference point; that is,

$$y_{max} - 3.6 \text{ m} = 6.4 \text{ m} - 3.6 \text{ m} = 2.8 \text{ m}$$

Follow-up Exercise. At what height does the ball in this Example have a speed of 5.00 m/s? (*Hint*: The ball attains this height twice—once on the way up, and once on the way down.) *(Answers to all Follow-up Exercises are at the back of the text.)*

Here are a couple of interesting facts about the vertical projectile motion of an object thrown upward in the absence of significant air resistance. First, the times of flight upward and downward are the same. That is, the time it takes the object to reach its maximum height is the same as the time it takes the object to fall from the maximum height back to the initial starting point. Note that at the very top of the trajectory, the object's velocity is zero for an instant, but the acceleration (even at the top) remains a constant 9.8 m/s^2 downward. If the acceleration went to zero, the object would remain there, and gravity would be turned off!

Second, the object returns to the starting point with the same speed as that at which it was launched. (The velocities have the same magnitude, but are opposite in direction.)

These facts can be shown mathematically. See Exercise 89.

Problem-Solving Hint

When working vertical projection problems involving motions up and down, it is often convenient to divide the problem into two parts and consider each part separately. As seen in Example 2.11, for the upward part of the motion, the velocity is zero at the maximum height. A quantity of zero simplifies the calculations. Similarly, the downward part of the motion is analogous to that of an object dropped from a height where the initial velocity is zero.

However, as Example 2.11 shows, the appropriate equations may be used directly for any position or time of the motion. For instance, note in part (c) that the height was found directly for a time *after* the ball had reached the maximum height. The velocity of the ball at that time could also have been found directly from Eq. 2.8′, $v = v_o - gt$.

Also, note that the initial position was consistently taken as $y_o = 0$. This assumption is generally the case and is accepted for convenience when the situation involves only one object (then $y_o = 0$ at $t_o = 0$). Using this convention can save a lot of time in writing and solving equations.

The same is true with only one object in horizontal motion: You can usually take $x_o = 0$ at $t_o = 0$. There are a couple of exceptions to this case, however: first, if the problem specifies the object to be initially located at a position other than $x_o = 0$; and second, if the problem involves two objects, as in Integrated Example 2.7. In the latter case, if one object is taken to be initially at the origin, the other's initial position is not zero.

In our study, these situations do not arise very often, but should be kept in mind. At times, we write the kinematic equations without x_o and y_o, assuming they are taken to be at the origin and equal to zero at $t_o = 0$.

As a final example in this chapter, consider the following Example.

Example 2.12 ■ Free Fall on Mars

The Mars Polar Lander was launched in January 1999 and was lost near the Martian surface in December, 1999. What became of the spacecraft is unknown. Let's assume the retrorockets were fired and shut off, and then the Lander came to a stop, and fell to the surface from a height of 40 m. (Highly unlikely, but let's assume this is correct.) Considering the spacecraft to be in free fall, with what speed did it hit the surface?

Thinking It Through. This appears to be analogous to a simple problem of dropping an object from a height. And it is, but this situation takes place on Mars. It was noted in this section that the acceleration due to gravity on the surface of the Moon is one sixth of that on the Earth. Acceleration due to gravity also varies for other planets. So, we need to know g_{Mars}. Try looking in Appendix III. (The Appendices contain a lot of useful information, so don't forget to check them out.)

Solution.

Given:
$$y = -40 \text{ m } (y_o = 0 \text{ again})$$
$$v_o = 0$$
$$g_{\text{Mars}} = (0.379)\text{g} = (0.379)(9.8 \text{ m/s}^2) = 3.7 \text{ m/s}^2 \text{ (from Appendix III)}$$

Find: v (magnitude, speed)

Then Eq. 2.12′ can be used:

$$v^2 = v_o^2 - 2g_{\text{Mars}}y = 0 - 2(3.7 \text{ m/s}^2)(-40 \text{ m}).$$

So,

$$v^2 = 296 \text{ m}^2/\text{s}^2 \quad \text{and} \quad v = \sqrt{296 \text{ m}^2/\text{s}^2} = \pm 17 \text{ m/s}$$

This is the velocity, which we know is downward, so the negative root is selected, and $v = -17$ m/s. Since the speed is the magnitude of the velocity, the speed is 17 m/s.

Follow-up Exercise. From the 40-m height, how long did the Lander's descent take? Compute this using two different kinematic equations, and compare the answers. *(Answers to all Follow-up Exercises are at the back of the text.)*

Chapter Review

Important Concepts and Equations

- **Motion** involves a change of position; it can be described in terms of the distance moved (a scalar) or the displacement (a vector).
- A **scalar** quantity has magnitude (value and units) only; a **vector** quantity has magnitude *and* direction.
- **Speed** (a scalar) is the time rate of change of position:

$$\text{average speed} = \frac{\text{distance traveled}}{\text{total time to travel that distance}}$$

or

$$\bar{s} = \frac{d}{\Delta t} = \frac{d}{t_2 - t_1} \qquad (2.1)$$

- **Average velocity** (a vector) is the displacement divided by the total travel time:

$$\text{average velocity} = \frac{\text{displacement}}{\text{total travel time}}$$

$$\bar{v} = \frac{\Delta x}{\Delta t} = \frac{x_2 - x_1}{t_2 - t_1} \quad \text{or} \quad x = x_o + \bar{v}t \qquad (2.3)$$

- **Instantaneous velocity** (a vector) describes how fast something is moving and in what direction at a particular instant of time.
- **Acceleration** is the time rate of change of velocity and hence is a vector quantity:

$$\text{average acceleration} = \frac{\text{change in velocity}}{\text{time to make the change}}$$

$$\bar{a} = \frac{\Delta v}{\Delta t} = \frac{v_2 - v_1}{t_2 - t_1} \qquad (2.5)$$

- **The kinematic equations for constant acceleration:**

$$\bar{v} = \frac{v + v_o}{2} \qquad (2.9)$$

$$v = v_o + at \qquad (2.8)$$

$$x = x_o + \tfrac{1}{2}(v + v_o)t \qquad (2.10)$$

$$x = x_o + v_o t + \tfrac{1}{2}at^2 \qquad (2.11)$$

$$v^2 = v_o^2 + 2a(x - x_o) \qquad (2.12)$$

- An object in **free fall** has a constant acceleration of magnitude $g = 9.80\,\text{m/s}^2$ (acceleration due to gravity) near the surface of the Earth.
- Expressing $a = -g$ in the kinematic equations for constant acceleration in the y-direction yields the following:

$$v = v_o - gt \quad (2.8')$$

$$y = y_o + \tfrac{1}{2}(v + v_o)t \quad (2.10')$$

$$y = y_o + v_o t - \tfrac{1}{2}gt^2 \quad (2.11')$$

$$v^2 = v_o^2 - 2g(y - y_o) \quad (2.12')$$

Exercises

2.1 Distance and Speed: Scalar Quantities *and* 2.2 One-Dimensional Displacement and Velocity: Vector Quantities

1. Identify each of the following as a scalar or vector quantity: (a) distance, (b) velocity, (c) speed, and (d) displacement.

2. CQ Two people choose different reference points to specify an object's position. Does this difference affect their descriptions of the object's coordinates? How about their assessment of the object's displacement? Explain.

3. A scalar quantity has (a) only magnitude, (b) only direction, or (c) both direction and magnitude.

4. A vector quantity has (a) only magnitude, (b) only direction, or (c) both direction and magnitude.

5. CQ Can the displacement of a person's trip be zero, yet the distance involved in the trip be nonzero? How about the reverse situation? Explain.

6. CQ You are told that a person has walked 500 m. What can you safely say about the person's final position relative to the starting point?

7. CQ An object travels at a constant velocity. What is the relationship of the object's speed to its velocity?

8. CQ Speed is the magnitude of velocity. Is average speed the magnitude of average velocity? Explain.

9. CQ If the displacement of an object is 300 m north, what can you say about the distance traveled by the object?

10. ■ What is the magnitude of the displacement of a car that travels half a lap along a circle that has a radius of 150 m? How about when the car travels a full lap?

11. ■ A student throws a rock straight upward at shoulder level, which is 1.65 m above the ground. What is the displacement of the rock when it hits the ground?

12. ■ In 1999, the Moroccan runner Hicham El Guerrouj ran the 1-mile race in 3 min, 43.13 s. What was his average speed during the race?

13. ■ A bus travels at an average speed of 90 km/h. On average, how far does the bus travel in 20 min? Is this distance the magnitude of the actual displacement of the bus? Explain.

14. ■ A motorist drives 150 km from one city to another in 2.5 h, but makes the return trip in only 2.0 h. What are the average speeds for (a) each half of the round-trip and (b) the total trip?

15. ■ A senior citizen walks 0.30 km in 10 min, going around a shopping mall. (a) What is her average speed in meters per second? (b) If she wants to increase her average speed by 20% in walking a second lap, what would her travel time in minutes have to be?

16. IE ■ A race car travels a complete lap on a circular track of radius 500 m in 50 s. (a) The average velocity of the race car is (1) zero, (2) 100 m/s, (3) 200 m/s, or (4) none of the preceding. Why? (b) What is the average speed of the race car?

17. IE ■■ A student runs 30 m east, 40 m north, and 50 m west. (a) The magnitude of the student's net displacement is (1) between 0 and 20 m, (2) between 20 m and 40 m, or (3) between 40 m and 60 m. (b) What is his net displacement?

18. ■■ A student throws a ball vertically upward such that it travels 7.1 m to its maximum height. If the ball is caught at the initial height 2.4 s after being thrown, (a) what is the ball's average speed, and (b) what is its average velocity?

19. ■■ An insect crawls along the edge of a rectangular swimming pool of length 27 m and width 21 m (▼ Fig. 2.17). If it crawls from corner A to corner B in 30 min, (a) what is its average speed, and (b) what is the magnitude of its average velocity?

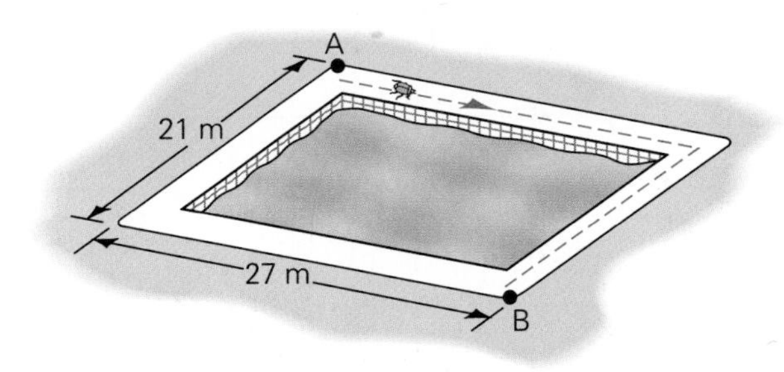

▲ **FIGURE 2.17 Speed versus velocity** See Exercise 19. (Not drawn to scale, insect is displaced for clarity.)

20. ■■ The distance of one lap around an oval dirt-bike track is 1.50 km. If a rider going at a constant speed makes one lap in 1.10 min, what is the speed of the bike and rider in meters per second? Is the velocity of the bike also constant? Explain.

21. ■■ (a) Given that the speed of sound is 340 m/s and the speed of light is 3.00×10^8 m/s (186 000 mi/s), how much time will elapse between a lightning flash and the resulting thunder if the lightning strikes 2.50 km away from the observer? (b) Does your answer change if you assume that light travels with an infinite speed (i.e., the lightning flash is seen instantaneously)?

22. ■■ A plot of position versus time is shown in ▼Fig. 2.18 for an object in linear motion. (a) What are the average velocities for the segments AB, BC, CD, DE, EF, FG, and BG? (b) State whether the motion is uniform or nonuniform in each case. (c) What is the instantaneous velocity at point D?

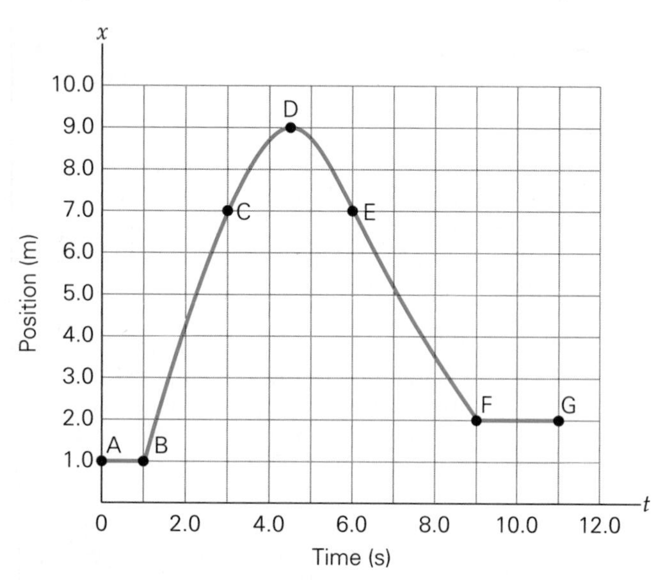

▲ **FIGURE 2.18 Position versus time** See Exercise 22.

23. ■■ In demonstrating a dance step, a person moves in one dimension, as shown in ▼Fig. 2.19. What are (a) the average speed and (b) the average velocity for each phase of the motion? (c) What are the instantaneous velocities at $t = 1.0$ s, 2.5 s, 4.5 s, and 6.0 s? (d) What is the average velocity for the interval between $t = 4.5$ s and $t = 9.0$ s? [*Hint*: Recall that the overall displacement is the displacement between the starting point and the ending point.]

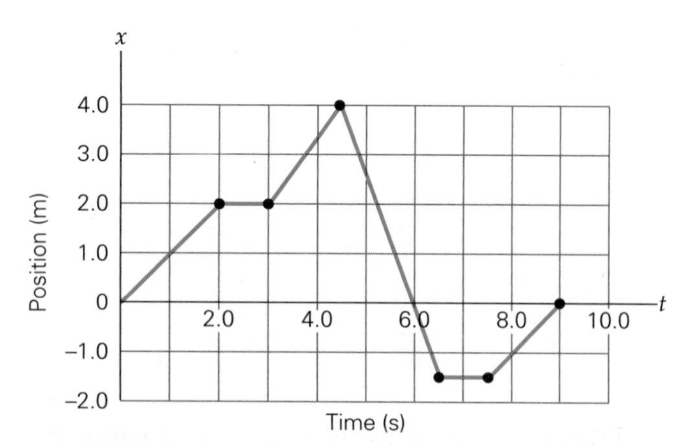

▲ **FIGURE 2.19 Position versus time** See Exercise 23.

24. ■■ You can determine the speed of a car by measuring the time it takes to travel between mile markers on a highway. (a) How many seconds should elapse between two consecutive mile markers if the car's average speed is 65 mi/h? (b) What is the car's average speed if it takes 65 s to travel between the mile markers?

25. ■■ An earthquake releases two types of traveling waves, called "transverse" and "longitudinal." The average speeds of transverse and longitudinal seismic waves in rock are 8.9 km/s and 5.1 km/s, respectively. A seismograph records the arrival of the transverse waves 73 s before that of the longitudinal waves. Assuming that the waves travel in straight lines, how far away is the center of the earthquake from the seismograph?

26. ■■ An airline company operates two types of aircraft. The faster type can cruise at 565 mi/h; the slower type can travel only at 505 mi/h. If it takes the faster aircraft 4.50 hours to cover an established route, how many more minutes will it take the slower one to complete the same trip?

27. ■■■ A student driving home for the holidays starts at 8:00 AM to make the 675-km trip, practically all of which is on nonurban interstate highway. If she wants to arrive home no later than 3:00 PM, what must be her minimum average speed? Will she have to exceed the 65-mi/h speed limit?

28. ■■■ Two runners approaching each other on a straight track have constant speeds of 4.50 m/s and 3.50 m/s, respectively, when they are 100 m apart (▼Fig. 2.20). How long will it take for the runners to meet, and at what position will they meet if they maintain these speeds?

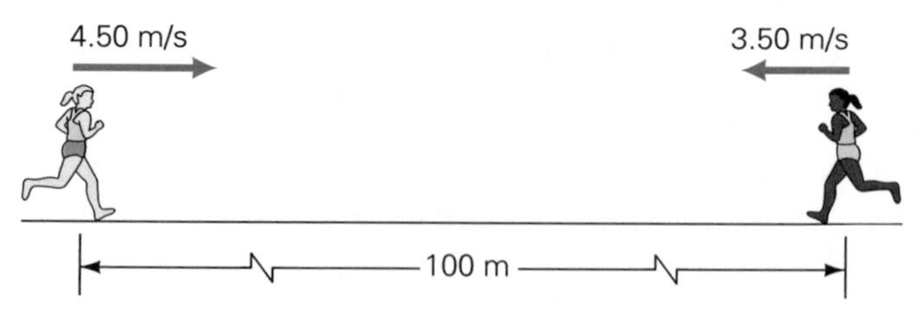

▲ **FIGURE 2.20 When and where do they meet?** See Exercise 28.

29. ■■■ In driving the usual route to school, a student computes his average speed to be 30 km/h. In a hurry to get home that afternoon, he wants to average 60 km/h for the round trip. What would his average speed for the return trip over the same route have to be in order to do this?

2.3 Acceleration

30. **CQ** The gas pedal of an automobile is commonly referred to as the *accelerator*. Which of the following might also be called an acceleration? (a) the brakes; (b) the steering wheel; (c) the gear shift; (d) all of the preceding. Explain.

31. **CQ** A car is traveling at a constant speed of 55 mi/h on a circular track. Is the car accelerating? Explain.

32. On a position-versus-time plot for an object that has a constant acceleration, the graph is (a) a horizontal line, (b) a nonhorizontal and nonvertical straight line, (c) a vertical line, or (d) a curve.

33. **CQ** An object traveling at a constant velocity v_o experiences a constant acceleration in the same direction for a period of time t. Then, an acceleration of equal magnitude is experienced in the opposite direction of v_o for the same period of time t. What is the object's final velocity?

34. **CQ** Does a fast-moving object always have higher acceleration than a slower object? Give a few examples, and explain.

35. **CQ** Can an object have a positive velocity, yet a negative acceleration? Support your answer with an example.

36. **CQ** Describe the motions of the two objects that have the velocity-versus-time plots shown in ▾ Fig. 2.21.

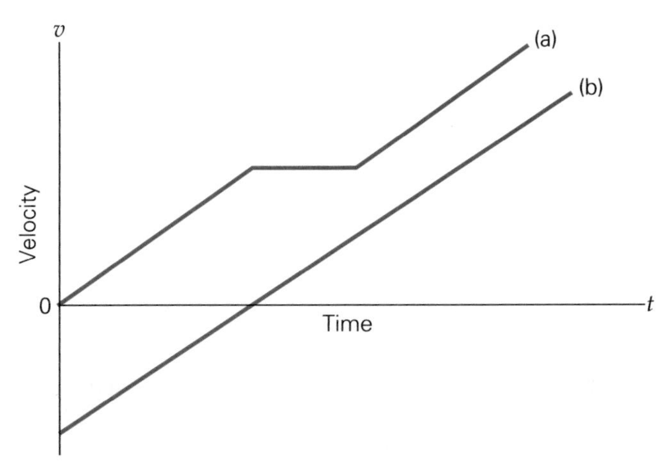

▲ **FIGURE 2.21 Description of motion** See Exercise 36.

37. ■ An automobile traveling at 25.0 km/h along a straight, level road accelerates to 65.0 km/h in 6.00 s. What is the magnitude of the auto's average acceleration?

38. ■ A sports car can accelerate from 0 to 60 mi/h in 3.9 s. What is the magnitude of the average acceleration of the car in meters per second squared?

39. ■ If the sports car in Exercise 38 can accelerate at a rate of $7.2 m/s^2$, how long does it take for the car to accelerate from 0 to 60 mi/h?

40. **IE** ■ A couple is traveling by car 40 km/h down a straight highway. They see an accident in the distance, so the driver applies the brakes, and in 5.0 s the car slows down uniformly to rest. (a) The direction of the acceleration vector is (1) in the same direction as, (2) opposite to, or (3) at 90° relative to the velocity vector. Why? (b) By how much must the velocity change each second from the start of braking to the car's complete stop?

41. ■■ A boat starting from rest on a lake accelerates in a straight line at a constant rate of $2.0 m/s^2$ for 6.0 s. How far does the boat travel during this time?

42. ■■ A car with an initial velocity of 3.5 m/s coasts with the engine off and the transmission in neutral. If the combined effect of air resistance and rolling friction causes a deceleration of $0.50 m/s^2$, after how long a time will the car come to a stop?

43. ■■ What is the acceleration for each graph segment in ▾ Fig. 2.22? Describe the motion of the object over the total time interval.

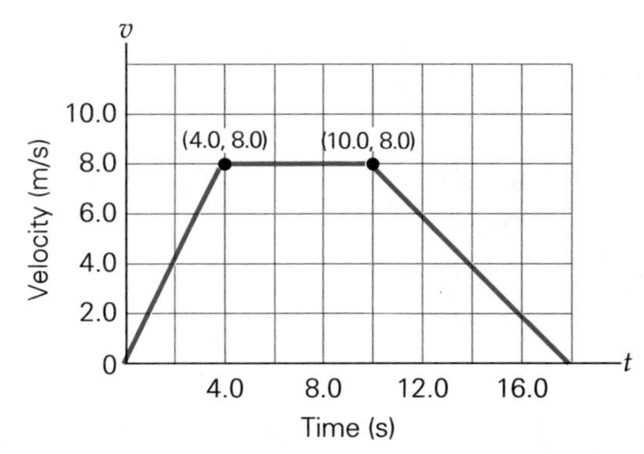

▲ **FIGURE 2.22 Velocity versus time** See Exercises 43 and 66.

44. ■■ ▾ Figure 2.23 shows a plot of velocity versus time for an object in linear motion. (a) Compute the acceleration

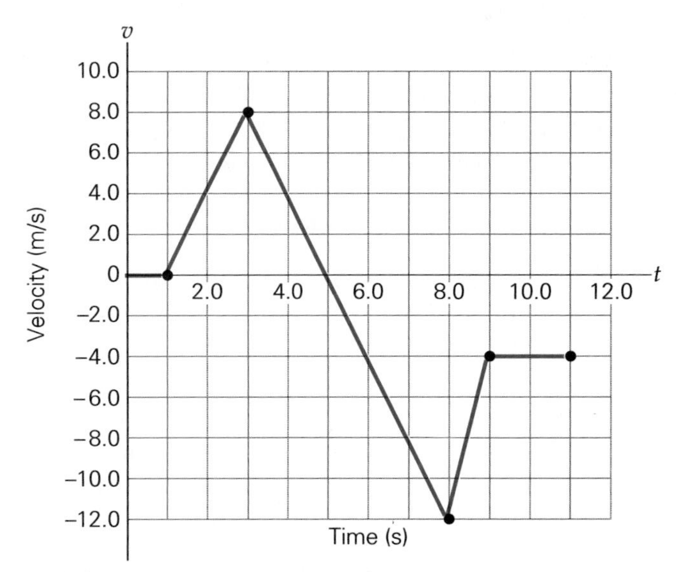

▲ **FIGURE 2.23 Velocity versus time** See Exercises 44 and 67.

for each phase of motion. (b) Describe how the object moves during the last time segment.

45. ■■■ A train normally travels at a uniform speed of 72 km/h on a long stretch of straight, level track. On a particular day, the train must make a 2.0-min stop at a station along this track. If the train decelerates at a uniform rate of $1.0\,\text{m/s}^2$ and, after the stop, accelerates at a rate of $0.50\,\text{m/s}^2$, how much time is lost because of stopping at the station?

2.4 Kinematic Equations (Constant Acceleration)

46. For a constant linear acceleration, the velocity-versus-time graph is (a) a horizontal line, (b) a vertical line, (c) a nonhorizontal and nonvertical straight line, or (d) a curved line.

47. For a constant linear acceleration, the position-versus-time graph would be (a) a horizontal line, (b) a vertical line, (c) a nonhorizontal and nonvertical straight line, or (d) a curve.

48. CQ If an object's velocity-versus-time graph is a horizontal line, what can you say about the object's acceleration?

49. An object accelerates uniformly from rest for t seconds. The object's average speed for this time interval is (a) $\frac{1}{2}at$, (b) $\frac{1}{2}at^2$, (c) $2at$, or (d) $2at^2$.

50. CQ A classmate states that a negative acceleration always means that a moving object is decelerating. Is this statement true? Explain.

51. ■ At a sports-car rally, a car starting from rest accelerates uniformly at a rate of $9.0\,\text{m/s}^2$ over a straight-line distance of 100 m. The time to beat in this event is 4.5 s. Does the driver do it? What must the minimum acceleration be to do so?

52. ■ A car accelerates from rest at a constant rate of $2.0\,\text{m/s}^2$ for 5.0 s. (a) What is the speed of the car at the end of that time? (b) How far does the car travel in this time?

53. ■ A car traveling at 35 mi/h is to stop on a 35-m long shoulder of the road. (a) What is the required magnitude of the minimum acceleration? (b) How much time will elapse during this minimum deceleration until the car stops?

54. ■ A motorboat traveling on a straight course slows down uniformly from 75 km/h to 40 km/h in a distance of 50 m. What is the boat's acceleration?

55. ■■ The driver of a pickup truck going 100 km/h applies the brakes, giving the truck a uniform deceleration of $6.50\,\text{m/s}^2$ while it travels 20.0 m. (a) What is the speed of the truck in kilometers per hour at the end of this distance? (b) How much time has elapsed?

56. ■■ An experimental rocket car starting from rest reaches a speed of 560 km/h after a straight 400-m run on a level salt flat. Assuming that acceleration is constant, (a) what was the time of the run, and (b) what is the magnitude of the acceleration?

57. ■■ A rocket car is traveling at a constant speed of 250 km/h on a salt flat. The driver gives the car a reverse thrust, and the car experiences a continuous and constant deceleration of $8.25\,\text{m/s}^2$. How much time elapses until the car is 175 m from the point where the reverse thrust is applied? Describe the situation(s) for your answer(s).

58. ■■ Two identical cars capable of accelerating at $3.00\,\text{m/s}^2$ are racing on a straight track with running starts. Car A has an initial speed of 2.50 m/s; car B starts with an initial speed of 5.00 m/s. (a) What is the separation of the two cars after 10 s? (b) Which car is moving faster after 10 s?

59. IE ■■ An object moves in the $+x$-direction at a speed of 40 m/s. As it passes through the origin, it starts to experience a constant acceleration of $3.5\,\text{m/s}^2$ in the $-x$-direction. (a) What will happen next? (1) The object will reverse its direction of travel at the origin. (2) The object will keep traveling in the $+x$-direction. (3) The object will travel in the $+x$-direction and then reverse its direction. Why? (b) How much time elapses before the object returns to the origin? (c) What is the velocity of the object when it returns to the origin?

60. ■■ A rifle bullet with a muzzle speed of 330 m/s is fired directly into a special, dense material that stops the bullet in 30 cm. Assuming the bullet's deceleration to be constant, what is its magnitude?

61. ■■ A bullet traveling horizontally at a speed of 350 m/s hits a board perpendicular to the surface, passes through it, and emerges on the other side at a speed of 210 m/s. If the board is 4.00 cm thick, how long does the bullet take to pass through it?

62. ■■ A rock hits the ground at a speed of 10 m/s and leaves a hole 25 cm deep. What is the magnitude of the deceleration of the rock?

63. ■■ A jet aircraft being launched from an aircraft carrier is accelerated from rest along a 94-m track for 2.5 s. (a) What is the acceleration of the aircraft, assuming it is constant? (b) What is the launch speed of the jet?

64. ■■ The speed limit in a school zone is 40 km/h (about 25 mi/h). A driver traveling at this speed sees a child run onto the road 13 m ahead of his car. He applies the brakes, and the car decelerates at a uniform rate of $8.0\,\text{m/s}^2$. If the driver's reaction time is 0.25 s, will the car stop before hitting the child?

65. ■■ Assuming a reaction time of 0.50 s for the driver in Exercise 64, will the car stop before hitting the child?

66. ■■ (a) Show that the area under the curve of a velocity-versus-time plot for a constant acceleration is equal to the displacement. [*Hint*: The area of a triangle is $ab/2$, or one

half the altitude times the base.] (b) Compute the distance traveled for the motion represented by Fig. 2.22.

67. ■■■ Figure 2.23 shows a plot of velocity versus time for an object in linear motion. (a) What are the instantaneous velocities at $t = 8.0$ s and $t = 11.0$ s? (b) Compute the final displacement of the object. (c) Compute the total distance the object travels. (See Exercise 66(a).)

68. IE ■■■ (a) A car traveling at a speed of v can brake to an emergency stop in a distance x. Assuming all other driving conditions are all similar, if the traveling speed of the car doubles, the stopping distance will be (1) $\sqrt{2}x$, (2) $2x$, or (3) $4x$: (b) A driver traveling at 40.0 km/h in a school zone can brake to an emergency stop in 3.00 m. What would be the braking distance if the car were traveling at 60.0 km/h?

69. ■■■ List the four kinematics equations in the text. For each equation, discuss the following questions: (a) What does each symbol represent? (b) Under what conditions does the equation hold?

70. ■■■ An object moves in the positive x-direction with a constant acceleration. At $x = 5.0$ m, its speed is 10 m/s. At 2.5 s later, the object is at $x = 65$ m. What is its acceleration?

2.5 Free Fall (Neglect air resistance)

71. An object is thrown vertically upward. Which one of the following statements is true? (a) Its velocity changes nonuniformly; (b) its maximum height is independent of the initial velocity; (c) its travel time upward is slightly greater than its travel time downward; (d) the speed on returning to its starting point is the same as its initial speed.

72. The "free fall" motion described in this section applies to (a) an object dropped from rest, (b) an object thrown vertically downward, (c) an object thrown vertically upward, or (d) all of the preceding.

73. CQ When a ball is thrown upward, what are its velocity and acceleration at its highest point?

74. CQ A dropped object in free fall (a) falls 9.8 m each second, (b) falls 9.8 m during the first second, (c) has an increase in speed of 9.8 m/s each second, or (d) has an increase in acceleration of 9.8 m/s each second.

75. CQ Imagine you are in space far away from any planet, and you throw a ball as you would on Earth. Describe the ball's motion.

76. CQ From the window of a building, you drop a stone. After a second, you drop another stone. Does the distance separating the two stones (a) increase, (b) decrease, or (c) stay the same, or (d) there is not enough information given to determine the answer. Explain.

77. ■ If a dropped object falls 19.6 m in 2.00 s, how far will it fall in 4.00 s?

78. ■ A student drops a ball from the top of a tall building; it takes 2.8 s for the ball to reach the ground. (a) What was the ball's speed just before hitting the ground? (b) What is the height of the building?

79. IE ■ The time it takes for an object dropped from the top of cliff A to hit the water in the lake below is twice the time it takes for another object dropped from the top of cliff B to reach the lake. (a) The height of cliff A is (1) one half, (2) two, or (3) four times that of cliff B. (b) If it takes 1.80 s for the object to fall from cliff A to the water, what are the heights of cliffs A and B?

80. ■ For the motion of a dropped object in free fall, sketch the general forms of the graphs of (a) v versus t and (b) y versus t.

81. ■ You can perform a popular trick by dropping a dollar bill (lengthwise) through the thumb and forefinger of a fellow student. Tell your fellow student to grab the dollar bill as fast as possible, and he or she can have the dollar if able to catch it. (The length of a dollar is 15.7 cm, and the average human reaction time is about 0.2 s. See Fig. 2.15.). Is this proposal a good deal? Justify your answer.

82. ■ A boy throws a stone straight upward with an initial speed of 15 m/s. What maximum height will the stone reach before falling back down?

83. ■ In Exercise 82, what would be the maximum height of the stone if the boy and the stone were on the surface of the Moon, where the acceleration due to gravity is only 1.67 m/s^2?

84. ■■ A spring-loaded gun shoots a 0.0050-kg bullet vertically upward with an initial velocity of 21 m/s. (a) What is the height of the bullet 3.0 s after the gun fires? (b) At what times is the bullet 12 m above the muzzle of the gun?

85. ■■ The ceiling of a classroom is 3.75 m above the floor. A student tosses an apple vertically upward, releasing it 0.50 m above the floor. What is the maximum initial speed that can be given to the apple if it is not to touch the ceiling?

86. ■■ The Petronas Twin Towers in Malaysia and the Chicago Sears Tower have heights of about 452 m and 443 m, respectively. If objects were dropped from the top of each, what would be the difference in the time it takes the objects to reach the ground?

87. ■■ A stone is thrown vertically downward at an initial speed of 14 m/s from a height of 65 m above the ground. (a) How far does the stone travel in 2.0 s? (b) What is its velocity just before it hits the ground?

88. ■■ An arrow is shot vertically upward. Three seconds later, it is at a height of 35 m. (a) What was the initial speed of the arrow? (b) How long is the arrow in flight from launch to returning to the initial height? (Assume the arrow falls vertically downward.)

89. ■■ Referring to the thrown ball in Example 2.11 and Fig. 2.16, (a) compare the travel time upward (t_u) with the travel time downward (t_d) required for the ball to return to its starting point, and (b) compare the initial velocity of the ball with its velocity upon its return to the starting point.

90. ■■ You throw a stone vertically upward, with an initial speed of 6.0 m/s, from a third-story office window. If the window is 12 m above the ground, find (a) the time the stone is in the air, and (b) the speed of the stone just before it hits the ground.

91. IE ■■ A Superball™ is dropped from a height of 4.00 m. Assuming the ball rebounds with 95% of its impact speed, (a) would the ball bounce to (1) less than 95%, (2) equal to 95.0%, or (3) more than 95% of the initial height? (b) How high will the ball go?

92. ■■ Two balls are thrown vertically, both at the initial speed of 10.0 m/s from a height of 60.0 m above the ground. Ball A is thrown upward, while ball B is projected downward. (a) What is the time lapse between the times two balls hit the ground? (b) Do the masses of the balls affect the result?

93. ■■■ In ▼Fig. 2.24, a student at a window on the second floor of a dorm sees his math professor walking on the sidewalk beside the building. He drops a water balloon from 18.0 m above the ground when the prof is 1.00 m from the point directly beneath the window. If the prof. is 170 cm tall and walks at a rate of 0.450 m/s, does the balloon hit her? If not, how close does it come?

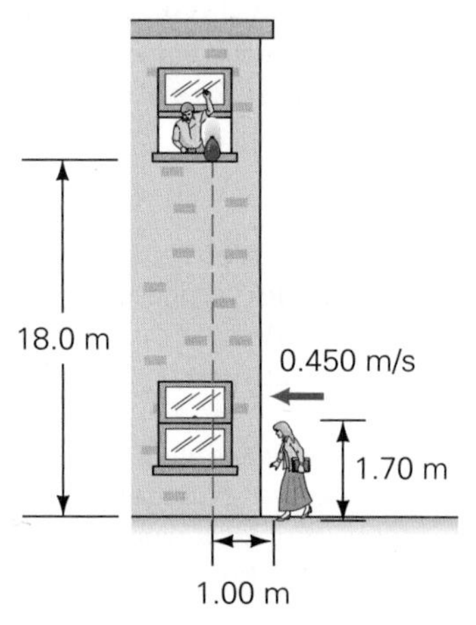

▲ **FIGURE 2.24 Hit the prof** See Exercise 93. (This figure is not drawn to scale.)

94. ■■■ A photographer in a helicopter ascending vertically at a constant rate of 12.5 m/s accidentally drops a camera out the window when the helicopter is 60.0 m above the ground. (a) How long will it take the camera to reach the ground? (b) What will its speed be when it hits?

95. IE ■■■ The acceleration due to gravity on the Moon is about one sixth of that on Earth. (a) If an object were dropped from the same height on the Moon and on the Earth, the time it would take to reach the surface on the Moon is (1) $\sqrt{6}$, (2) 6, or (3) 36 times that it would take on the Earth. (b) For a projectile with an initial velocity of 18.0 m/s upward, what would be the maximum height and the total time of flight on the Moon and on the Earth?

96. ■■■ It takes 0.210 s for a dropped object to pass a window that is 1.35 m tall. From what height above the top of the window was the object released? (See ▼Fig. 2.25.)

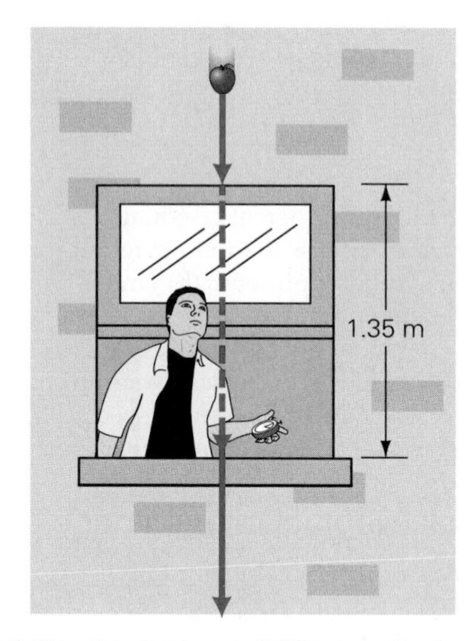

▲ **FIGURE 2.25 From where did it come?** See Exercise 96.

Additional Exercises

97. In throwing an object vertically upward at a speed of 7.25 m/s from the top of a tall building, a student leans over the edge of the building so that the object will not strike the building on the return trip. (a) What is the velocity of the object when it has traveled a total distance of 25.0 m? (b) How long does it take to travel this distance?

98. After landing, a jet liner on a straight runway taxis to a stop at an average velocity of −35.0 km/h. If the plane takes 7.00 s to come to rest, what are the plane's initial velocity and acceleration?

99. A vertically moving projectile reaches a maximum height of 23 m above its starting position. (a) What was the projectile's initial speed? (b) What is its height above the starting point at $t = 1.3$ s?

100. A drag racer traveling at a speed of 200 km/h on a straight track deploys a parachute and slows uniformly to a speed of 20 km/h in 12 s. (a) What is the racer's acceleration? (b) How far does the racer travel in the 12-s interval?

101. On a cross-country trip, a couple drives 500 mi in 10 h on the first day, 380 mi in 8.0 h on the second day, and 600 mi in 15 h on the third day. What was the average speed for the whole trip?

102. A car traveling at 25 mi/h has 1.5 s to come to a stop when approaching a red light. The magnitude of the maximum deceleration of the car is $7.0\,m/s^2$. Will the car stop safely before it reaches the red light?

103. **IE** A car travels three quarters of a lap on a circular track of radius R. (a) The magnitude of the displacement is (1) less than R; (2) greater than R, but less than $2R$; or (3) greater than $2R$. (b) If $R = 50$ m, what is the magnitude of the displacement?

104. From behind a billboard a police officer is watching for speeders at an intersection ($x = 0$). At some instant ($t = 0$), an obvious speeder comes by at 30 m/s (67 mph). The police officer starts a chase at the same instant, maintaining a constant acceleration of $3.5\,m/s^2$ as he tries to catch the speeder, in the $+x$-direction. The speeder maintains his speed throughout the pursuit. (a) On an x-versus-t graph, plot the position for each car. (b) How long does it take for the officer to catch the speeder?

105. At what speed must an object be projected vertically upward for it to reach a maximum height of 14.0 m above its starting point?

106. A train on a straight, level track has an initial speed of 45.0 km/h. A uniform acceleration of $1.50\,m/s^2$ is applied while the train travels 200 m. (a) What is the speed of the train at the end of this distance? (b) How long did it take for the train to travel the 200 m?

107. A car going 85 km/h on a straight road is brought uniformly to a stop in 10 s. How far does the car travel during that time?

108. A car and a motorcycle start from rest at the same time on a straight track, but the motorcycle is 25.0 m behind the car (▾Fig. 2.26). The car accelerates at a uniform rate of $3.70\,m/s^2$ and the motorcycle at a uniform rate of $4.40\,m/s^2$. (a) How much time elapses before the motorcycle overtakes the car? (b) How far will each have traveled during that time? (c) How far ahead of the car will the motorcycle be 2.00 s later? (Both vehicles are still accelerating.)

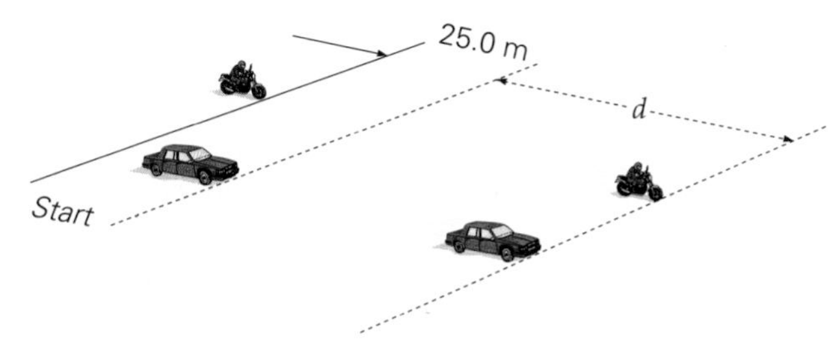

▲ **FIGURE 2.26 A tie race** See Exercise 108. (This figure is not drawn to scale.)

109. A person throws a stone straight upward at an initial speed of 15 m/s on a bridge that is 25 m above the surface of the water. If the stone just misses the bridge on the way down, (a) what is the speed of the stone just before it hits the water? (b) What is the total time the stone is in the air?

110. An object initially at rest experiences an acceleration of $1.5\,m/s^2$ for 6.0 s and then travels at that constant velocity for another 8.0 s. What is the object's average velocity over the 14-s interval?

111. **IE** To find the depth of the surface of water in a well, a person drops a stone from the top of the well and simultaneously starts a stopwatch. The watch is stopped when a splash is heard, giving a reading of 3.65 s. The speed of sound is 340 m/s. (a) Why is the speed of sound considered here? (b) Find the depth of the water surface below the top of the well. Take the person's reaction time for stopping the watch to be 0.250 s.

112. A test rocket containing a probe to determine the composition of the upper atmosphere is fired vertically upward from an initial position at ground level. During the time t while its fuel lasts, the rocket ascends with a constant upward acceleration of magnitude $2g$. Assume that the rocket travels a small enough height that the Earth's gravitational force can be considered constant. (a) What are the speed and height of the rocket when its fuel runs out? (b) What is the maximum height the rocket reaches? (c) If $t = 30.0$ s, calculate the rocket's maximum height.

113. A car starting from rest and traveling in only one direction has velocities of 5.0 m/s, 10 m/s, 15 m/s, 20 m/s, and 25 m/s at 1.0 s, 2.0 s, 3.0 s, 4.0 s, and 5.0 s, respectively. (a) What is the magnitude of the car's acceleration? (b) What is the car's average velocity for the 5-s interval? (c) Sketch a graph of v versus t. (d) Sketch a graph of x versus t.

114. On a walk in the country, a couple goes 1.80 km east along a straight road in 20.0 min and then 2.40 km directly north in 35.0 min. (a) What is the average velocity for each segment of the couple's walk and for the total walk? (b) What is the average speed for the total walk? (c) If the couple takes a straight-line path that gets it back to its original starting place in 25.0 min, what are the couple's average speed and average velocity for the total trip?

115. A student calculates that if he skis at 10 km/h, he will arrive at his cabin in the woods at 1:00 PM. If he skis at 15 km/h, he will arrive at the cabin at 11:00 AM. How fast must he ski to arrive at the cabin at noon?

CHAPTER 3 Motion in Two Dimensions

You *can* get there from here! It's just a matter of knowing which way to head at the crossroads. But did you ever wonder why so many roads meet at right angles? There's a good reason. Living on the Earth's surface, we are used to describing locations in two dimensions, and one of the easiest ways to do this is by referring to a pair of mutually perpendicular axes. When you want to tell someone how to get to a particular place in the city, you might say, "Go uptown for four blocks and then crosstown for three more blocks." In the country, it's "Go south for five miles and then another half mile east." Either way, though, you need to know how far to go in each of *two* directions that are 90° apart.

You can use the same approach to describe motion—and the motion doesn't have to be in a straight line. As you will shortly see, we can use vectors, introduced in Chapter 2, to describe motion in curved paths as well. Such analysis of *curvilinear* motion will eventually allow you to analyze the behavior of batted balls, planets circling the Sun, and even electrons in atoms.

Curvilinear motion can be analyzed by using rectangular components of motion. Essentially, you break down, or *resolve*, the curved motion into rectangular (x and y) components and look at the motion in both dimensions simultaneously. You can apply to those components the kinematic equations introduced in Chapter 2. For an object moving in a curved path, for example, the x- and y-coordinates of the motion at any time give the object's position as the point (x, y).

3.1 Components of Motion

OBJECTIVES: To (a) analyze motion in terms of its components and (b) apply the kinematic equations to components of motion.

An object moving in a straight line was considered in Chapter 2 to be moving along one of the Cartesian axes (x or y). But what if the motion is not along an axis? For example, consider the situation illustrated in ▾ Fig. 3.1. Here, three balls are moving uniformly across a tabletop. The ball rolling in a straight line along the side of the table, designated as the x-direction, is moving in one dimension. That is, its motion can be described with a single coordinate, x, as was done for motions in Chapter 2. Similarly, the motion of the ball rolling in the y-direction can be described by a single y-coordinate. However, both x- and y-coordinates are needed to describe the motion of the ball rolling diagonally across the table. We say that this motion is *in two dimensions.*

You might observe that if the diagonally moving ball were the only object you had to consider, the x-axis could be chosen to be in the direction of that ball's motion, and the motion would thereby be reduced to one dimension. This observation is true, but once the coordinate axes are fixed, motions not along the axes must be described with two coordinates (x, y), or in two dimensions. Also, keep in mind that not all motions in a plane (two dimensions) are in straight lines. Think about the path of a ball you toss to another person. The path is curved for such projectile motion; and this concept will be considered in Section 3.4.

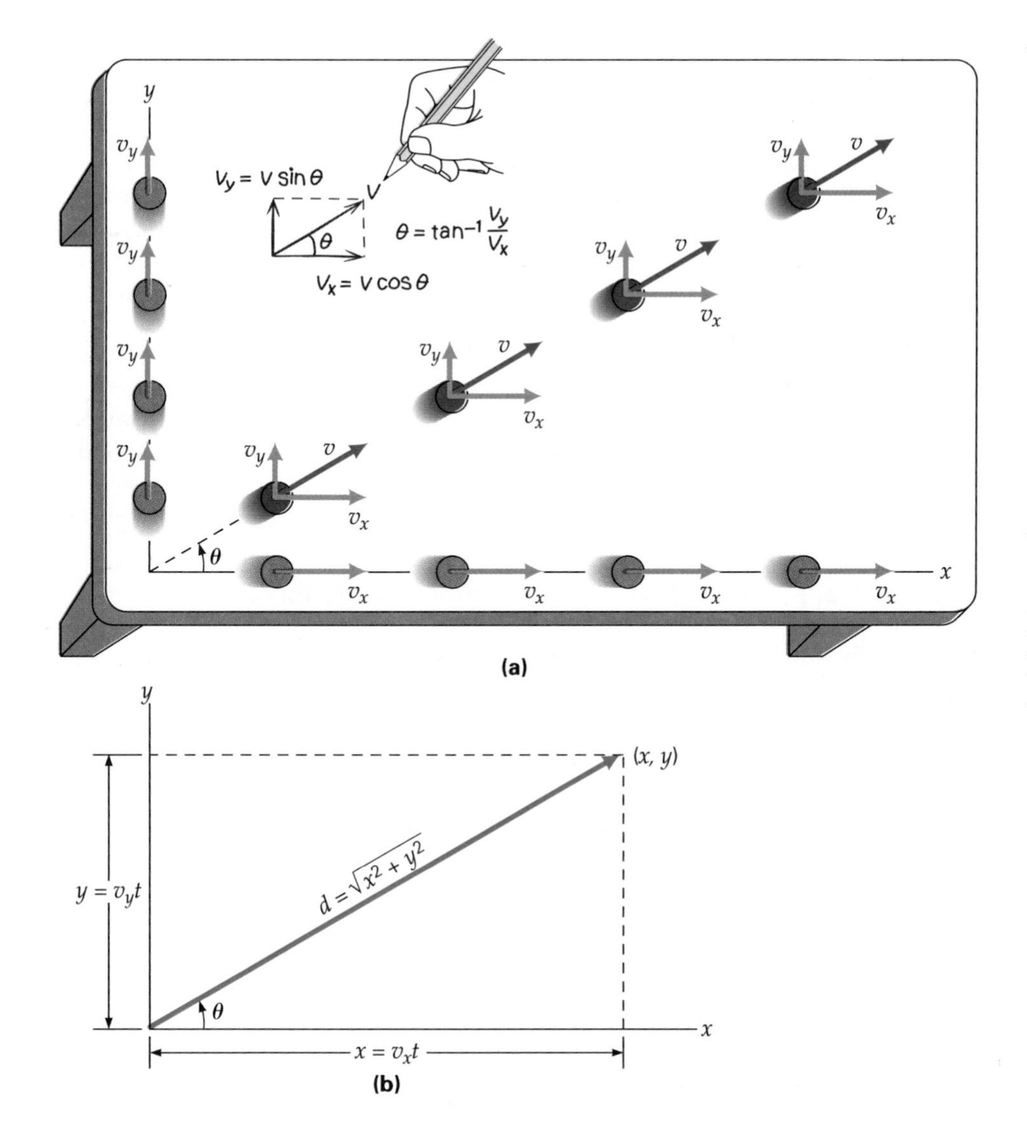

◀ **FIGURE 3.1 Components of motion** **(a)** The velocity (and displacement) for uniform, straight-line motion—that of the dark purple ball—may have x- and y-components (v_x and v_y as shown in the pencil drawing), because of the chosen orientation of the coordinate axes. Note that the velocity and displacement of the ball in the x-direction are exactly the same as those that a ball rolling along the x-axis with a uniform velocity of v_x would have. A comparable relationship holds true for the ball's motion in the y-direction. Since the motion is uniform, the ratio v_y/v_x (and therefore θ) is constant. **(b)** The coordinates (x, y) of the ball's position and the distance d the ball has traveled from the origin can be found at any time t.

In considering the motion of the ball moving diagonally across the table in Fig. 3.1a, we can think of the ball as moving in the x- and y-directions simultaneously. That is, it has a velocity in the x-direction (v_x) *and* a velocity in the y-direction (v_y) at the same time. The combined velocity components describe the actual motion of the ball. If the ball has a constant velocity v in a direction at an angle θ relative to the x-axis, then the velocities in the x- and y-directions are obtained by resolving, or breaking down, the velocity vector into **components of motion** in these directions, as shown in the pencil drawing in Fig. 3.1a. As this drawing shows, the v_x and v_y components have magnitudes of

$$v_x = v \cos \theta \qquad (3.1a)$$

and

$$v_y = v \sin \theta \qquad (3.1b)$$

respectively. (Notice that $v = \sqrt{v_x^2 + v_y^2}$, so v is a combination of the velocities in the x- and y-directions.)

You are familiar with the use of two-dimensional length components in finding the x- and y-coordinates in a Cartesian system. For the ball rolling on the table, its position (x, y), or the distance traveled from the origin in each of the component directions at time t, is given by

$$x = x_o + v_x t \qquad (3.2a)$$

$$y = y_o + v_y t \qquad (3.2b)$$

Magnitudes of displacement components (under conditions of constant velocity and zero acceleration)

respectively, just as it is for motion in the x- and y-directions separately. (Here, the x_o and y_o are the ball's coordinates at $t = 0$, which may be other than zero.) The ball's straight-line distance from the origin is then $d = \sqrt{x^2 + y^2}$ (Fig. 3.1b).

Note that $\tan \theta = v_y/v_x$, so the direction of the motion relative to the x-axis is given by $\theta = \tan^{-1}(v_y/v_x)$. (See the hand-drawn sketch in Fig. 3.1a.) Also, $\theta = \tan^{-1}(y/x)$. Why?

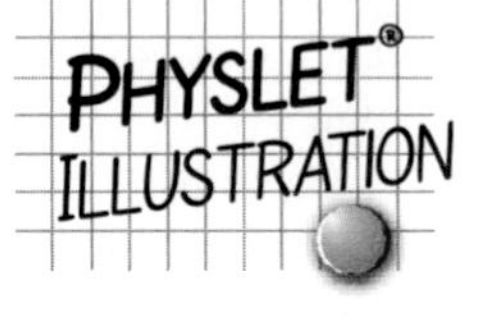

Motion in Two Dimensions

In this introduction to components of motion, the velocity vector has been taken to be in the first quadrant ($0 < \theta < 90°$), where both the x- and y-components are positive. But, as will be shown in more detail in the next section, vectors may be in any quadrant, and their components can be negative. Can you tell in which quadrants the v_x or v_y components would be negative?

Example 3.1 ■ On a Roll: Using Components of Motion

If the diagonally moving ball in Fig. 3.1a has a constant velocity of 0.50 m/s at an angle of 37° relative to the x-axis, find how far it travels in 3.0 s by using x- and y-components of its motion.

Thinking It Through. Given the magnitude and direction (angle) of the velocity of the ball, we can find the x- and y-components of the velocity. Then we can compute the distance in each direction. Since the x- and y-axes are at right angles to each other, the Pythagorean theorem gives the distance of the straight-line path of the ball as shown in Fig. 3.1b. (Note the procedure: Separate the motion into components, calculate what is needed in each direction, and recombine if necessary.)

Solution. Organizing the data, we have

Given: $v = 0.50$ m/s *Find:* d (distance traveled)
$\theta = 37°$
$t = 3.0$ s

The distance traveled by the ball in terms of its x- and y-components is given by $d = \sqrt{x^2 + y^2}$. To find x and y as given by Eq. 3.2, we must first compute the velocity components v_x and v_y (Eq. 3.1):

$$v_x = v \cos 37° = (0.50 \text{ m/s})(0.80) = 0.40 \text{ m/s}$$
$$v_y = v \sin 37° = (0.50 \text{ m/s})(0.60) = 0.30 \text{ m/s}$$

Then, the component distances are

$$x = v_x t = (0.40 \text{ m/s})(3.0 \text{ s}) = 1.2 \text{ m}$$

and

$$y = v_y t = (0.30 \text{ m/s})(3.0 \text{ s}) = 0.90 \text{ m}$$

and the actual distance of the path is

$$d = \sqrt{x^2 + y^2} = \sqrt{(1.2 \text{ m})^2 + (0.90 \text{ m})^2} = 1.5 \text{ m}$$

Follow-up Exercise. Suppose that a ball were rolling diagonally across a table with the same speed as in Example 3.1, but from the lower right corner, which is taken as the origin of the coordinate system, toward the upper left corner at an angle of 37° relative to the $-x$-axis. What would be the velocity components in this case? (Would the distance change?) *(Answers to all Follow-up Exercises are at the back of the text.)*

Problem-Solving Hint

Note that for this simple case, the distance can also be obtained directly from $d = vt = (0.50 \text{ m/s})(3.0 \text{ s}) = 1.5$ m. However, we have solved this Example in a more general way to illustrate the use of components of motion. The direct solution would have been evident if the equations had been combined algebraically before calculation, that is, as

$$x = v_x t = (v \cos \theta)t$$

and

$$y = v_y t = (v \sin \theta)t$$

from which it follows that

$$d = \sqrt{x^2 + y^2} = \sqrt{(v \cos \theta)^2 t^2 + (v \sin \theta)^2 t^2} = \sqrt{v^2 t^2 (\cos^2 \theta + \sin^2 \theta)} = vt$$

Before embarking on the first solution strategy that occurs to you, pause for a moment to see whether there might be an easier or more direct way of approaching the problem.

Kinematic Equations for Components of Motion

Example 3.1 involved two-dimensional motion in a plane. With a constant velocity (constant components v_x and v_y), the motion is in a straight line. The motion may also be accelerated. For motion in a plane *with a constant acceleration* that has components a_x and a_y, the displacement and velocity components are given by the kinematic equations of Chapter 2 for the x- and y-directions:

$$x = x_o + v_{x_o} t + \tfrac{1}{2} a_x t^2 \quad (3.3a)$$

$$y = y_o + v_{y_o} t + \tfrac{1}{2} a_y t^2 \quad (3.3b)$$

$$v_x = v_{x_o} + a_x t \quad (3.3c)$$

$$v_y = v_{y_o} + a_y t \quad (3.3d)$$

(constant acceleration only)

Kinematic equations for displacement and velocity components

If an object is initially moving with a constant velocity and suddenly experiences an acceleration in the direction of the velocity (0°) or opposite to it (180°), it will continue in a straight-line path, either speeding up or slowing down, respectively.

If, however, the acceleration vector is at some angle other than 0° or 180° to the velocity vector, the motion is along a curved path. For the motion of an object to be *curvilinear*—that is, to vary from a straight-line path—an acceleration is required. For a curved path, the ratio of the velocity components varies with time. That is, the direction of the motion, $\theta = \tan^{-1}(v_y/v_x)$, varies with time, because one or both of the velocity components do, so the motion is not in a straight line.

Consider a ball initially moving along the x-axis, as illustrated in ▾Fig. 3.2. Assume that, starting at a time $t_o = 0$, the ball receives a constant acceleration a_y in the y-direction. The magnitude of the x-component of the ball's displacement is given by $x = v_x t$; the $\frac{1}{2}a_x t^2$ term of Eq. 3.3a drops out, since there is no acceleration in the x-direction. Prior to t_o, the motion is in a straight line along the x-axis. But at

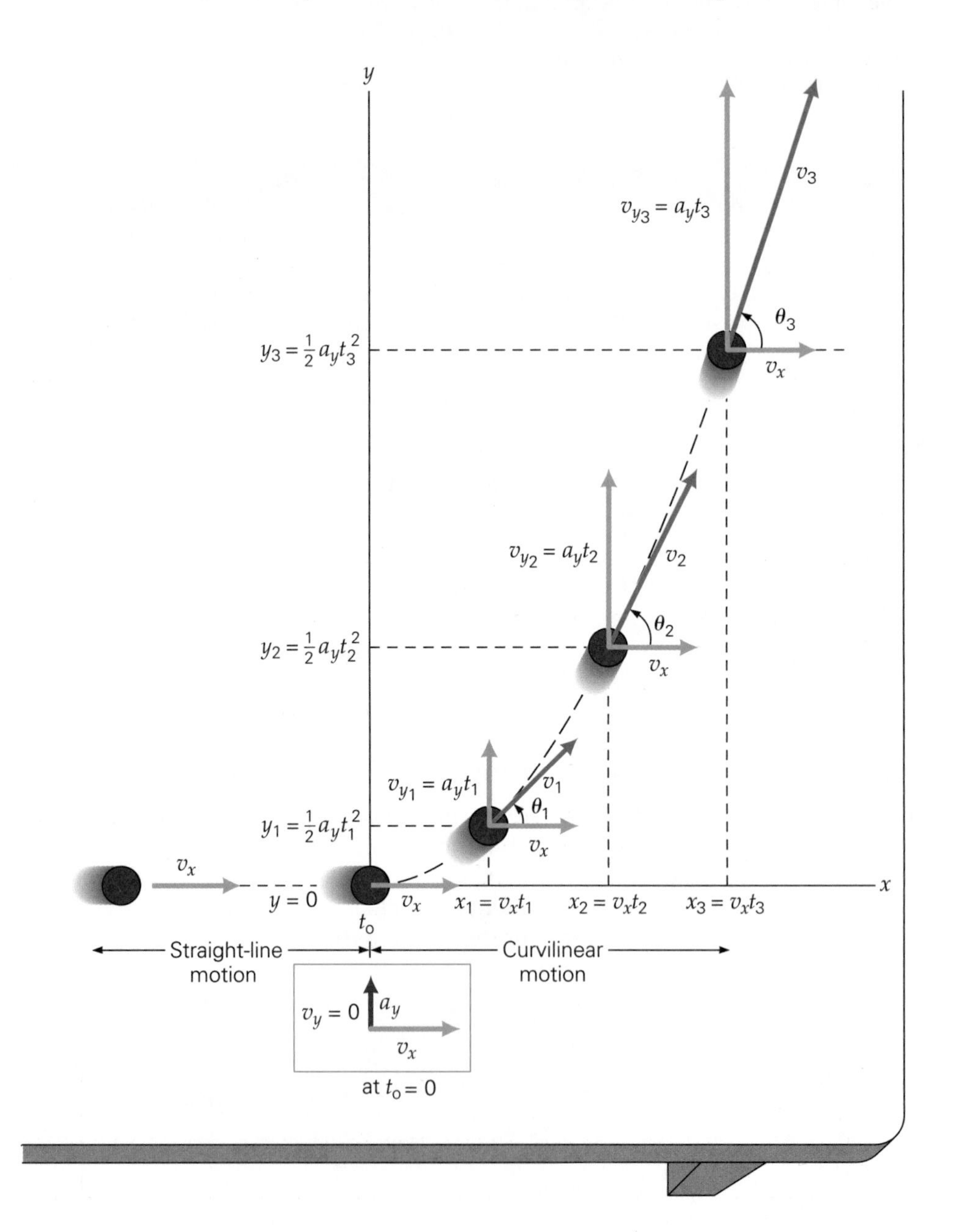

▶ FIGURE 3.2 Curvilinear motion An acceleration not parallel to the instantaneous velocity produces a curved path. Here, an acceleration a_y is applied at $t_o = 0$ to a ball initially moving with a constant velocity v_x. The result is a curved path with the velocity components as shown. Notice how v_y increases with time, while v_x remains constant.

any time after t_o, there is a y-displacement with a magnitude of $y = \frac{1}{2}a_y t^2$ (as given by Eq. 3.3b with $y_o = 0$ and $v_{y_o} = 0$). The result is a curved path for the ball.

Note that the length (magnitude) of the velocity component v_y changes with time, while that of the v_x component remains constant. The total velocity vector *at any time* is tangent to the curved path of the ball. It is at an angle θ relative to the positive x-axis, given by $\theta = \tan^{-1}(v_y/v_x)$, which now changes with time, as we see in Fig. 3.2 and in Example 3.2.

Example 3.2 ■ A Curving Path: Vector Components

Suppose that the ball in Fig. 3.2 has an initial velocity of 1.50 m/s along the x-axis and, starting at $t_o = 0$, receives an acceleration of 2.80 m/s² in the y-direction. (a) What is the position of the ball 3.00 s after t_o? (b) What is the velocity of the ball at that time?

Thinking It Through. Keep in mind that the motions in the x- and y-directions can be analyzed independently. That is, both component motions occur at the same time. For (a), simply compute the x- and y-positions at the given time, taking into account the acceleration in the y-direction. For (b), find the component velocities, and vectorially combine them to get the total velocity.

Solution. Referring to Fig. 3.2, we have the following:

Given: $v_{x_o} = v_x = 1.50$ m/s
$v_{y_o} = 0$
$a_x = 0$
$a_y = 2.80$ m/s²
$t = 3.00$ s

Find: (a) (x, y) (position coordinates)
(b) v (velocity)

(a) At 3.00 s after $t_o = 0$, Eqs. 3.3a and 3.3b tell us that the ball has traveled the following distances from the origin ($x_o = y_o = 0$) in the x- and y-directions, respectively:

$$x = v_{x_o}t + \tfrac{1}{2}a_x t^2 = (1.50\ \text{m/s})(3.00\ \text{s}) + 0 = 4.50\ \text{m}$$
$$y = v_{y_o}t + \tfrac{1}{2}a_y t^2 = 0 + \tfrac{1}{2}(2.80\ \text{m/s}^2)(3.00\ \text{s})^2 = 12.6\ \text{m}$$

Thus, the position of the ball is $(x, y) = (4.50\ \text{m}, 12.6\ \text{m})$. If you had computed the distance $d = \sqrt{x^2 + y^2}$, what would you have gotten? (Note that this quantity is not the actual distance the ball has traveled in 3.00 s, but rather the magnitude of the *displacement*, or straight-line distance, from the origin at $t = 3.00$ s.)

Note: Don't confuse the direction of the velocity with the direction of the displacement from the origin. The direction of the velocity is always tangent to the path.

(b) The x-component of the velocity is given by Eq. 3.3c:

$$v_x = v_{x_o} + a_x t = 1.50\ \text{m/s} + 0 = +1.50\ \text{m/s}$$

(This component is constant, since there is no acceleration in the $+x$-direction.) Similarly, the y-component of the velocity is given by Eq. 3.3d:

$$v_y = v_{y_o} + a_y t = 0 + (2.80\ \text{m/s}^2)(3.00\ \text{s}) = 8.40\ \text{m/s}$$

The velocity therefore has a magnitude of

$$v = \sqrt{v_x^2 + v_y^2} = \sqrt{(1.50\ \text{m/s})^2 + (8.40\ \text{m/s})^2} = 8.53\ \text{m/s}$$

and its direction relative to the $+x$-axis is

$$\theta = \tan^{-1}\left(\frac{v_y}{v_x}\right) = \tan^{-1}\left(\frac{8.40\ \text{m/s}}{1.50\ \text{m/s}}\right) = 79.9^\circ$$

Follow-up Exercise. Suppose that the ball in this Example also received an acceleration of 1.00 m/s² in the $+x$-direction starting at t_o. What would be the position of the ball 3.00 s after t_o in this case? *(Answers to all Follow-up Exercises are at the back of the text.)*

Problem-Solving Hint

When using the kinematic equations, it is important to note that motion in the x- and y-directions can be analyzed independently—the factor connecting them is time t. That is, both components of motion occur at the same time, so that you find (x, y) and/or (v_x, v_y) at a given time t. Also, keep in mind that we often set $x_o = 0$ and $y_o = 0$, which means that we locate the object at the origin at $t_o = 0$. If the object is actually elsewhere at $t_o = 0$, then an x_o and/or a y_o would have to be used in the appropriate equations. (See Eqs. 3.3a and b.)

3.2 Vector Addition and Subtraction

OBJECTIVES: To (a) learn vector notation, (b) be able to add and subtract vectors graphically and analytically, and (c) use vectors to describe motion in two dimensions.

Many physical quantities, including those describing motion, have a direction associated with them—that is, they are vectors. You have already worked with a few such quantities related to motion (displacement, velocity, and acceleration) and will encounter more during this course of study. A very important technique in the analysis of many physical situations is the addition (and subtraction) of vectors. By adding or combining such quantities (**vector addition**), you can obtain the overall, or net, effect that occurs—the *resultant*, as we call the vector sum.

You have already been adding vectors. In Chapter 2, we added displacements to get the net displacement. In this chapter, we will add vector components of motion to get net effects. Notice that, in Example 3.2, we combined the velocity components v_x and v_y to get the resultant velocity.

In this section, we will look at vector addition and subtraction in general, along with common vector notation. As you will learn, these operations are not the same as scalar, or numerical, addition and subtraction, with which you are already familiar. Vectors have magnitudes *and* directions, so different rules apply.

In general, there are geometric (graphical) methods and analytical (computational) methods of vector addition. The geometric methods are useful in helping you visualize the concepts of vector addition, particularly with a quick sketch. Analytical methods are more commonly used, however, because they are faster and more precise.

Vector Addition: Geometric Methods

Note: In vector notation, vectors are represented by boldface symbols, e.g., **A** and **B**, and their magnitudes by italic symbols, *A* and *B*. When handwritten, an arrow over the symbol is commonly used to denote a vector, e.g., $\vec{A}$ and $\vec{B}$, and the magnitudes by the symbols without arrows, A and B.

Triangle Method To add two vectors—say, to add **B** to **A** (that is, to find **A** + **B**) by the **triangle method**—you first draw **A** on a sheet of graph paper to some scale (▸Fig. 3.3a). For example, if **A** is a displacement in meters, a convenient scale is 1 cm : 1 m, or 1 cm of vector length on the graph corresponding to 1 m of displacement. As shown in Fig. 3.3b, the direction of the **A** vector is specified as being at an angle θ_A relative to a coordinate axis, usually the x-axis.

Next, draw **B** with its tail starting at the tip of **A**. (Thus, this method is also called the *tip-to-tail method*.) The vector from the tail of **A** to the tip of **B** is then the vector sum **R**, or the resultant of the two vectors: **R** = **A** + **B**.

If the vectors had been drawn to scale, the magnitude of **R** can be found by measuring its length and using the scale conversion. In such a graphical approach, the direction angle θ_R is measured with a protractor. If we know the magnitudes and directions (angles θ) of **A** and **B**, we can also find the magnitude and direction of **R** analytically by using trigonometric methods. For the nonright triangle in Fig. 3.3b, the laws of sines and cosines could be used. (See Appendix I.)

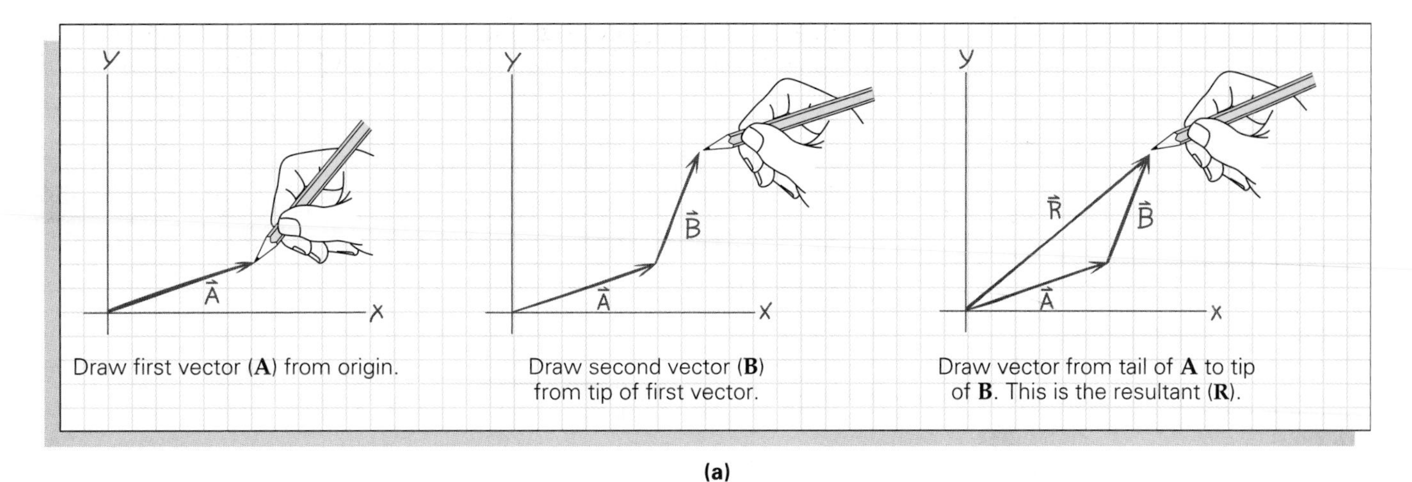

(a)

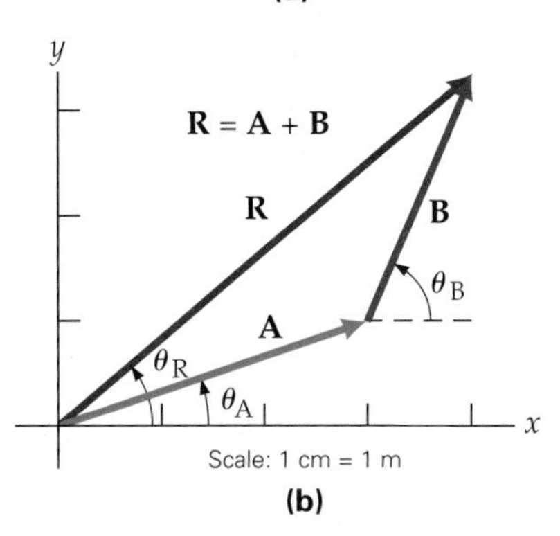

(b)

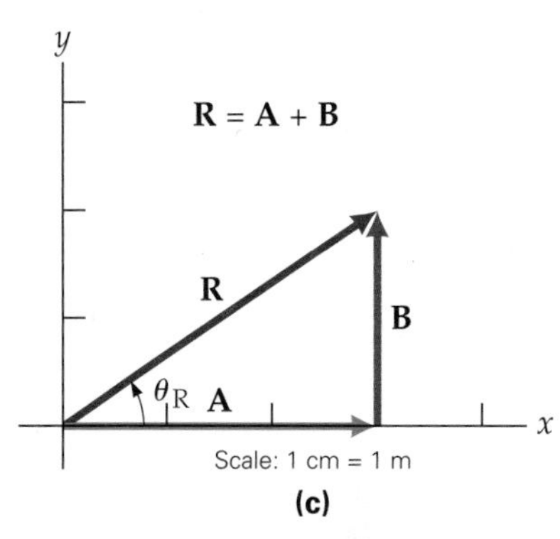

(c)

▲ **FIGURE 3.3 Triangle method of vector addition** **(a)** The vectors **A** and **B** are placed tip to tail. The vector that extends from the tail of **A** to the tip of **B**, forming the third side of the triangle, is the resultant or sum **R** = **A** + **B**. **(b)** When the vectors are drawn to scale, the magnitude of **R** can be found by measuring the length of **R** and using the scale conversion, and the direction angle θ_R can be measured with a protractor. Analytical methods can also be used. For a nonright triangle, as in (b), the laws of sines and cosines can be used to determine the magnitude of **R** and θ (Appendix I). **(c)** If the vector triangle is a right triangle, **R** is easily obtained via the Pythagorean theorem, and the direction angle is given by an inverse trigonometric function.

The resultant of the vector right triangle in Fig. 3.3c would be much easier to find, by using the Pythagorean theorem for the magnitude and an inverse trigonometric function to find the direction angle. (Notice that **R** is made up of x- and y-components **A** and **B**.)

Parallelogram Method Another graphical method of vector addition, similar to the triangle method, is the **parallelogram method**. In ▸Fig. 3.4, **A** and **B** are drawn tail to tail, and a parallelogram is formed as shown. The resultant vector **R** lies along the diagonal of the parallelogram. By drawing the diagram to scale with proper orientations, the magnitude and direction of **R** can be measured directly from the diagram as in the triangle method.

Notice that **B** could be moved to the other side of the parallelogram, forming the **A** + **B** triangle (and demonstrating why the triangle and parallelogram methods are equivalent). In general, a vector (arrow) can be moved around in vector addition methods. As long as you don't change its length (magnitude) or direction, you don't change the vector. In Fig. 3.4, this shifting of vector arrows shows that **A** + **B** = **B** + **A**, that is, the vectors can be added in either order.

Note: In general, a vector (arrow) can be moved around in vector addition methods. As long as you don't change its length (magnitude) or direction, you don't change the vector.

Polygon Method The triangle method can be extended to include the addition of any number of vectors. The method is then called the **polygon method**, because the resulting graphical figure is a polygon. This method is illustrated for four vectors in ▸Fig. 3.5, where **R** = **A** + **B** + **C** + **D**. Note that

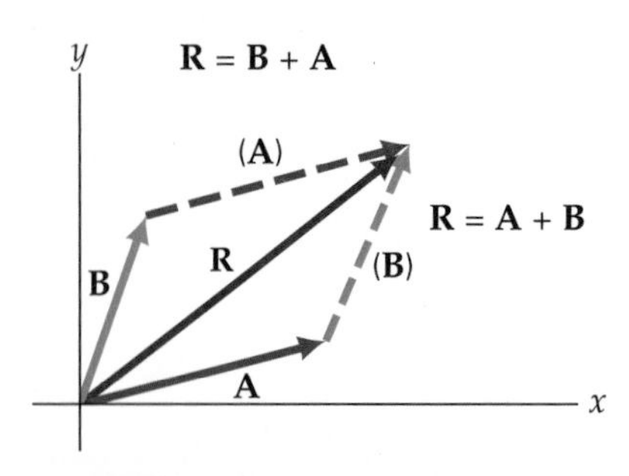

▲ **FIGURE 3.4 Parallelogram method of vector addition** The diagonal of the parallelogram formed after **A** and **B** are drawn with their tails at the origin is the resultant **R** = **A** + **B**. If the vectors are drawn to scale, the magnitude and direction of **R** can be measured directly from the diagram as in a triangle method. The parallelogram method is equivalent to the triangle method. Shifting **B** to the right forms the same **A** + **B** vector triangle as shown in Fig. 3.3b. Shifting **A** up has the same effect, with **R** = **B** + **A**.

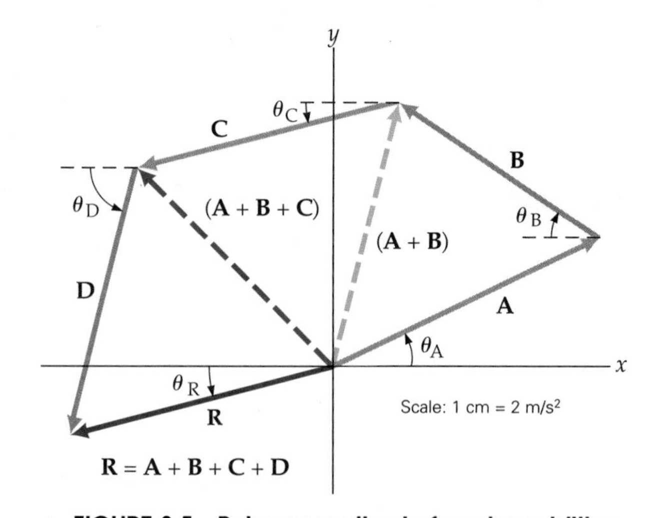

▲ **FIGURE 3.5 Polygon method of vector addition** The vectors to be added are placed tip to tail. The resultant **R** is the vector from the tail of the first vector **A** to the tip of the last vector **D** and **R** completes the polygon. This method is essentially composed of multiple applications of the triangle method: (**A** + **B**), (**A** + **B**) + **C**, and so on.

this addition is essentially three applications of the triangle method. The length and direction of the resultant could be found analytically by successive applications of the laws of sines and cosines (see Appendix I), but an easier analytical method, the component method, will be described shortly. As in the parallelogram method, the four vectors (or any number of vectors) can be added in any order.

Vector Subtraction Vector subtraction is a special case of vector addition:

$$\mathbf{A} - \mathbf{B} = \mathbf{A} + (-\mathbf{B})$$

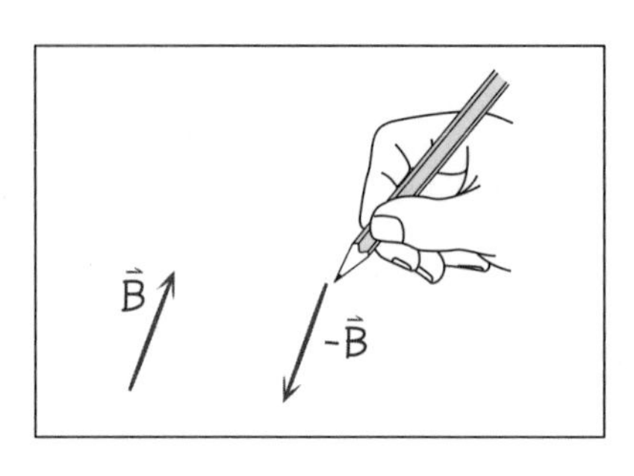

That is, to subtract **B** from **A**, a *negative* **B** is added to **A**. In Chapter 2, you learned that a minus sign simply means that the direction of a vector is opposite that of one with a plus sign (for example, $+x$ and $-x$). The same is true with vectors represented by bold face notation. The vector $-\mathbf{B}$ has the same magnitude as the vector **B**, but is in the opposite direction (◀Fig. 3.6). The vector diagram in Fig 3.6 provides a graphical representation of **A** − **B**.

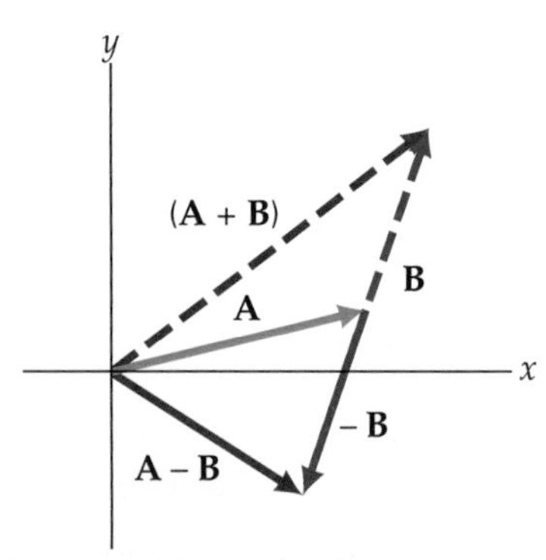

▲ **FIGURE 3.6 Vector subtraction** Vector subtraction is a special case of vector addition; that is, $\mathbf{A} - \mathbf{B} = \mathbf{A} + (-\mathbf{B})$, where $-\mathbf{B}$ has the same magnitude as **B**, but is in the opposite direction. (See the sketch.) Thus, **A** + **B** is not the same as **B** − **A**, either in length or direction. Can you show that $\mathbf{B} - \mathbf{A} = -(\mathbf{A} - \mathbf{B})$ geometrically?

Vector Components and the Analytical Component Method

Probably the most widely used analytical method for adding multiple vectors is the **component method**. It will be used again and again throughout the course of our study, so a basic understanding of the method is *essential*. Learn this section well.

Adding Rectangular Vector Components By *rectangular components*, we mean vector components at right (90°) angles to each other, usually taken in the rectangular-coordinate x- and y-directions. You have already had an introduction to the addition of such components in the discussion of the velocity components of motion in Section 3.1. For the general case, suppose that **A** and **B**, two vectors at right angles, are added, as illustrated in ▶Fig. 3.7a. The right angle makes the math easy. The magnitude of **C** is given by the Pythagorean theorem:

$$C = \sqrt{A^2 + B^2} \tag{3.4a}$$

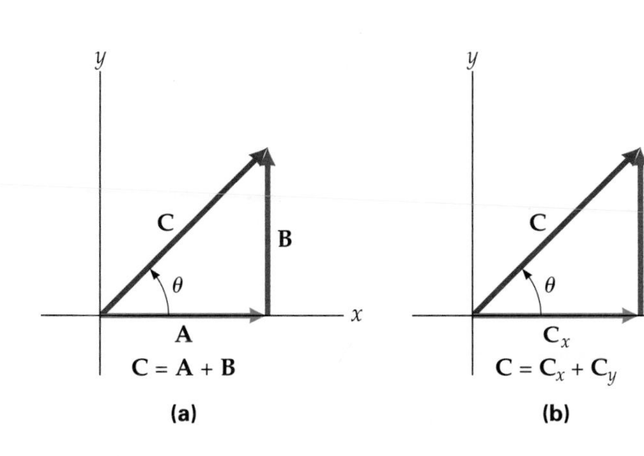

◀ **FIGURE 3.7 Vector components** **(a)** The vectors **A** and **B** along the x- and y-axes, respectively, add to give **C**. **(b)** A vector **C** may be resolved into rectangular components $\mathbf{C}_x$ and $\mathbf{C}_y$.

The orientation of **C** relative to the x-axis is given by the angle

$$\theta = \tan^{-1}\left(\frac{B}{A}\right) \qquad (3.4b)$$

Note: The notation $\tan^{-1} x$ stands for arctangent x, or the angle whose tangent is x.

This notation is how a resultant is expressed in **magnitude–angle form.**

Magnitude–angle form of a vector

Resolving a Vector into Rectangular Components; Unit Vectors Resolving a vector into rectangular components is essentially the reverse of adding the rectangular components of the vector. Given a vector **C**, Fig. 3.7b illustrates how it may be resolved into x and y vector components $\mathbf{C}_x$ and $\mathbf{C}_y$. Simply complete the vector triangle with x- and y-components. As the diagram shows, the magnitudes, or vector lengths, of these components are given by

$$C_x = C\cos\theta \qquad (3.5a)$$

$$C_y = C\sin\theta \qquad (3.5b)$$

magnitudes of components

respectively (similar to $v_x = v\cos\theta$ and $v_y = v\sin\theta$ in Example 3.1).* The angle of direction of **C** can also be expressed in terms of the components, since $\tan\theta = C_y/C_x$, or

$$\theta = \tan^{-1}\left(\frac{C_y}{C_x}\right) \qquad (3.6)$$

direction of vector from magnitudes of components

A general notation for expressing the magnitude and direction of a vector involves the use of unit vectors. For example, as illustrated in ▶Fig. 3.8, a vector **A** can be written as $\mathbf{A} = A\hat{\mathbf{a}}$. The numerical magnitude is represented by A, and $\hat{\mathbf{a}}$ is called a **unit vector**. That is, it has a magnitude of unity, or one, but no units and thus simply indicates the vector's direction. For example, a velocity along the x-axis might be written $\mathbf{v} = (4.0\text{ m/s})\,\hat{\mathbf{x}}$ (that is, 4.0 m/s magnitude in the $+x$-direction).

Note in Fig. 3.8 how $-\mathbf{A}$ would be represented in this notation. Although the minus sign is sometimes put in front of the numerical magnitude, this quantity is an absolute number; the minus actually goes with the unit vector: $-\mathbf{A} = -A\hat{\mathbf{a}} = A(-\hat{\mathbf{a}})$.† That is, the unit vector is in the $-\hat{\mathbf{a}}$ direction (opposite $\hat{\mathbf{a}}$). A velocity of $\mathbf{v} = (-4.0\text{ m/s})\,\hat{\mathbf{x}}$ has a magnitude of 4.0 m/s in the $-x$ direction; that is, $\mathbf{v} = (4.0\text{ m/s})\,(-\hat{\mathbf{x}})$.

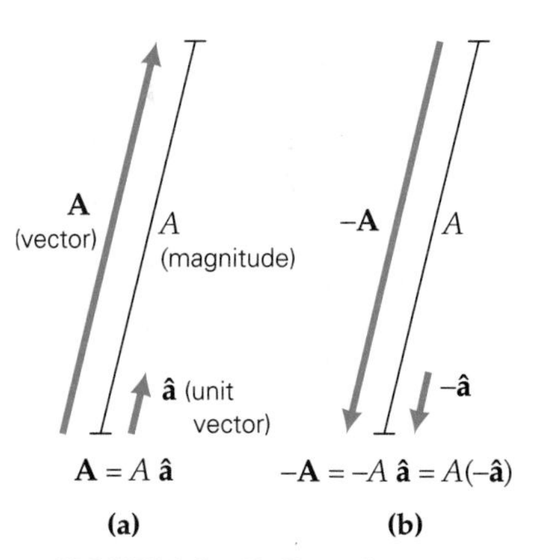

▲ **FIGURE 3.8 Unit vectors** **(a)** A unit vector $\hat{\mathbf{a}}$ has a magnitude of unity, or one, and thereby simply indicates a vector's direction. Written with the magnitude A, it represents the vector **A**, and $\mathbf{A} = A\hat{\mathbf{a}}$. **(b)** For the vector $-\mathbf{A}$, the unit vector is $-\hat{\mathbf{a}}$, and $-\mathbf{A} = -A\hat{\mathbf{a}} = A(-\hat{\mathbf{a}})$. The magnitude A is a positive number—that is, it is $|A|$.

*Figure 3.7b illustrates only a vector in the first quadrant, but the equations hold for all quadrants when vectors are referenced to either the positive or negative x-axis. The directions of the components are indicated by + and − signs, as will be shown shortly.

†The notation is sometimes written with an absolute value, $\mathbf{A} = |A|\hat{\mathbf{a}}$, or $-\mathbf{A} = -|A|\hat{\mathbf{a}}$, so as to clearly show that the magnitude of **A** is a positive quantity.

This notation can be used to express explicitly the rectangular components of a vector. For example, the ball's displacement from the origin in Example 3.2 could be written $\mathbf{d} = (4.50 \text{ m})\,\hat{\mathbf{x}} + (12.6 \text{ m})\,\hat{\mathbf{y}}$, where $\hat{\mathbf{x}}$ and $\hat{\mathbf{y}}$ are unit vectors in the x- and y-directions, respectively. In some instances, it may be more convenient to express a general vector in this unit-vector **component form**:

Component form of a vector

$$\mathbf{C} = C_x\,\hat{\mathbf{x}} + C_y\,\hat{\mathbf{y}} \tag{3.7}$$

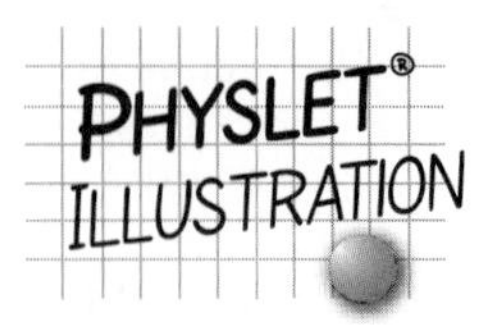

Components of Vectors

Vector Addition Using Components The **analytical component method** of vector addition involves resolving the vectors into rectangular components and adding the components for each axis independently. This method is illustrated graphically in ▾Fig. 3.9 for two vectors $\mathbf{F}_1$ and $\mathbf{F}_2$.* The sums of the x- and y-components of the vectors being added are then equal to the corresponding components of the resultant vector.

The same principle applies if you are given three (or more) vectors to add. You could find the resultant by applying the graphical tip-to-tail method, as illustrated in ▸Fig. 3.10a. However, this technique involves drawing the vectors to scale and using a protractor to measure angles, which is time consuming. Note that the magnitude of the directional angle θ is not obvious in the figure and would have to be measured (or computed trigonometrically).

However, if you use the component method, you do not have to draw the vectors tip to tail. In fact, it is usually more convenient to put all of the tails together at the origin, as shown in Fig. 3.10b. Also, the vectors do not have to be drawn to scale, since the approximate sketch is just a visual aid in applying the analytical method.

In the component method, you resolve the vectors to be added into their x- and y-components, add the respective components, and recombine to find the resultant. The resultant is shown in Fig. 3.10c. By looking at the x-components, it can be seen that the vector sum of these components is in the $-x$-direction. Similarly, the sum of the y-components is in the $+y$-direction. (Note that $\mathbf{v}_2$ is in the y-direction and has a zero x-component, just as a vector in the x-direction would have a zero y-component.)

▾ **FIGURE 3.9 Component addition** **(a)** In adding vectors by the component method, each vector is first resolved into its x- and y-components. **(b)** The sums of the x- and y-components of vectors $\mathbf{F}_1$ and $\mathbf{F}_2$ are $\mathbf{F}_x = \mathbf{F}_{x_1} + \mathbf{F}_{x_2}$ and $\mathbf{F}_y = \mathbf{F}_{y_1} + \mathbf{F}_{y_2}$, respectively.

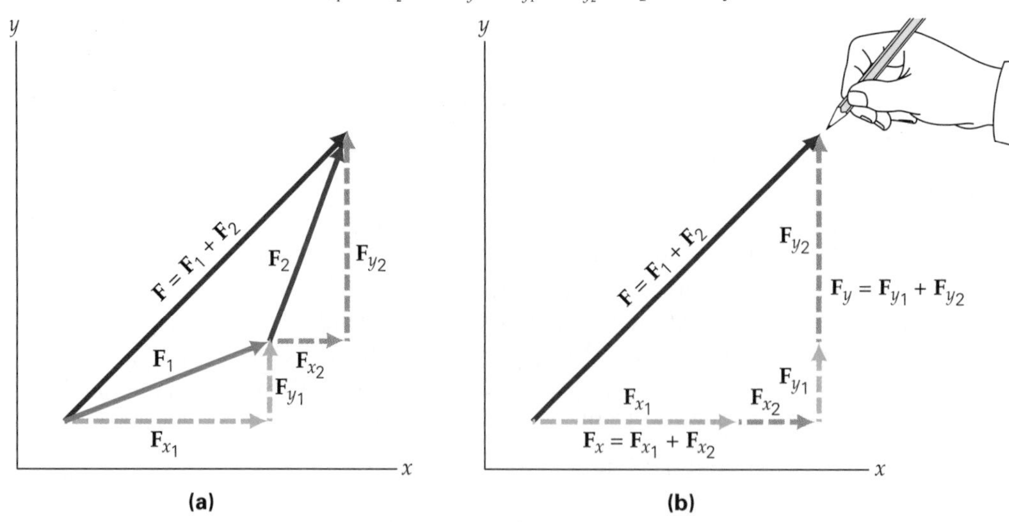

*The symbol **F** is commonly used to denote force, a very important vector quantity that you will study in Chapter 4. Here, **F** is employed as a general vector, but its use provides familiarity with the notation used in the next chapter, where a knowledge of the addition of forces is essential.

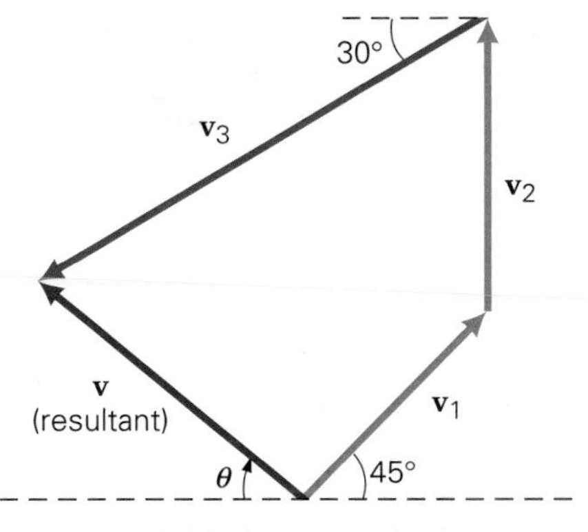

(a) Polygon method

◀ **FIGURE 3.10 Component method of vector addition** **(a)** Several vectors may be added graphically to find the resultant **v**, but this technique is time consuming and less accurate than the component method. **(b)** In the analytical component method, all the vectors to be added ($\mathbf{v}_1$, $\mathbf{v}_2$, and $\mathbf{v}_3$) are first placed with their tails at the origin so that they may be easily resolved into rectangular components. **(c)** The respective summations of all the x-components and all the y-components are then added to give the components of the resultant **v**.

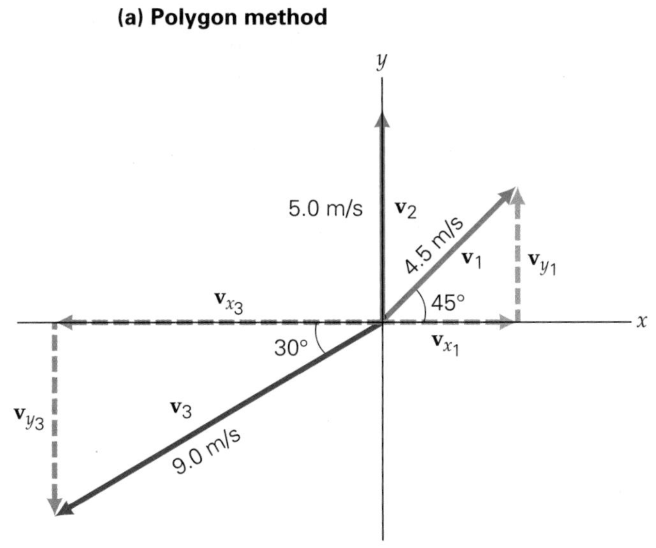

(b) Component method
(resolving into components)

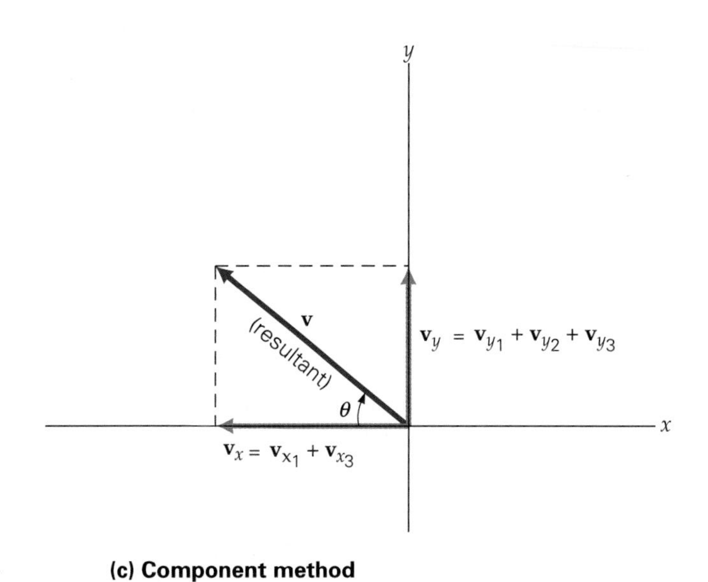

(c) Component method
(adding x- and y-components, shown as offset dashed arrows, and finding resultant)

In using the plus and minus notation to indicate directions, we write the x- and y-components of the resultant: $v_x = v_{x_1} - v_{x_3}$ and $v_y = v_{y_1} + v_{y_2} - v_{y_3}$, as shown in Fig. 3.10c. When the numerical values of the vector components are computed and put into these equations, you will have values for $-v_x$ and $+v_y$.

Notice also in Fig. 3.10c that the directional angle θ of the resultant is referenced to the x-axis, as are the individual vectors in Fig. 3.10b. *In adding vectors by the component method, we will reference all vectors to the nearest x-axis—that is, the +x-axis* or *−x-axis*. This policy eliminates angles greater than 90° (as occurs when we customarily measure angles counterclockwise from the $+x$-axis) and the use of double-angle formulas, such as $\cos(\theta + 90°)$. This restriction greatly simplifies calculations. The recommended procedures for adding vectors analytically by the component method can be summarized as follows:

Procedures for Adding Vectors by the Component Method

1. Resolve the vectors to be added into their x- and y-components. Use the acute angles (angles less than 90°) between the vectors and the x-axis, and indicate the directions of the components by plus and minus signs (▶ Fig. 3.11).
2. Add all of the x-components together, and all of the y-components together vectorially to obtain the x- and y-components of the resultant, or vector sum.
3. Express the resultant vector, using:
   (a) the component form—for example, $\mathbf{C} = C_x\,\hat{\mathbf{x}} + C_y\,\hat{\mathbf{y}}$—or
   (b) the magnitude–angle form.

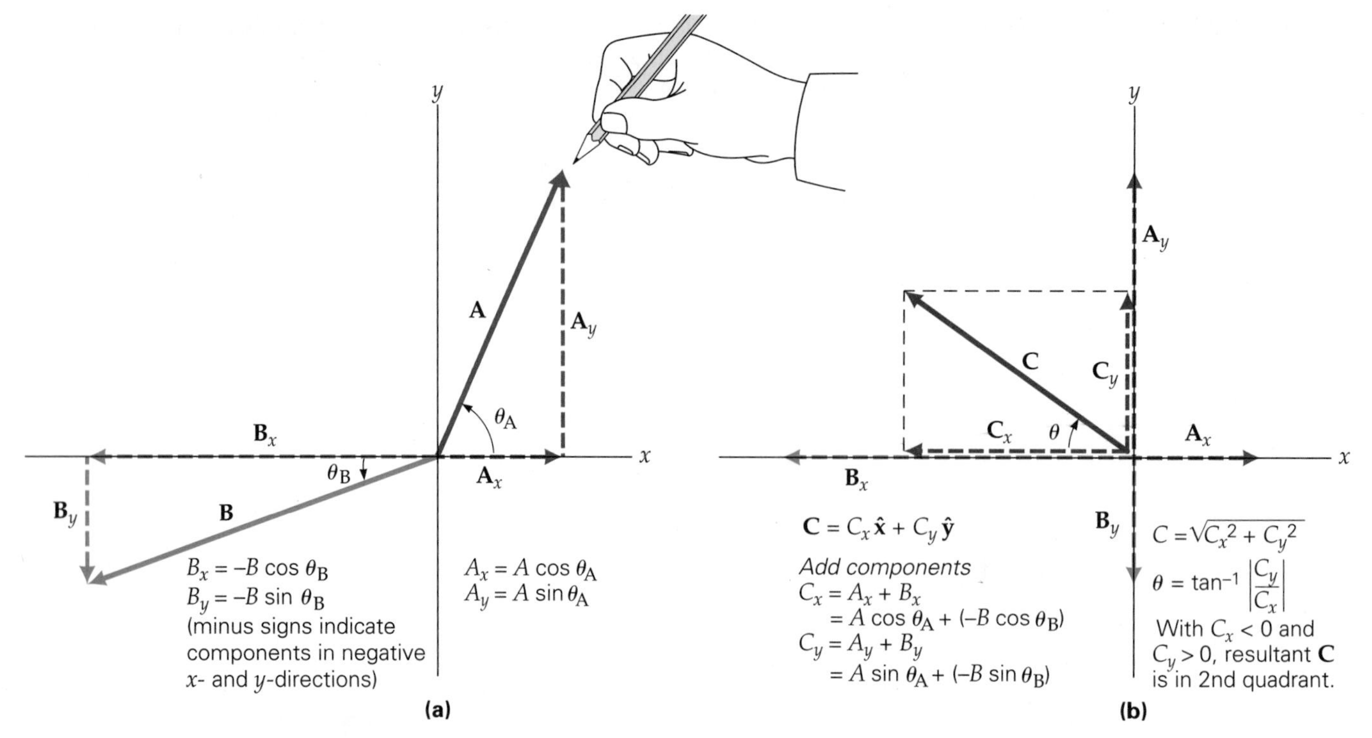

▲ **FIGURE 3.11 Vector addition by the analytical component method** **(a)** Resolve the vectors into their x- and y-components. **(b)** Add all of the x-components and all of the y-components together vectorially to obtain the x- and y-components $\mathbf{C}_x$ and $\mathbf{C}_y$, respectively, of the resultant. Express the resultant in either component form or magnitude–angle form. All angles are referenced to the $+x$- or $-x$-axis to keep them less than 90°.

For the latter notation, find the magnitude of the resultant by using the summed x- and y-components and the Pythagorean theorem:

$$C = \sqrt{C_x^2 + C_y^2}$$

Find the angle of direction (relative to the x-axis) by taking the inverse tangent ($\tan^{-1}$) of the *absolute value* (that is, the positive value, ignoring any minus signs) of the ratio of the y- and x-components :

$$\theta = \tan^{-1} \left| \frac{C_y}{C_x} \right|$$

Note: The absolute value indicates that minus signs are ignored (for example, $|-3| = 3$). This operation is done to avoid negative values and angles greater than 90°.

Designate the quadrant in which the resultant lies. This information is obtained from the signs of the summed components or from a sketch of their addition via the triangle (or parallelogram) method. (See Fig. 3.11.) The angle θ is the angle between the resultant and the x-axis in that quadrant.

Example 3.3 ■ Applying the Analytical Component Method: Separating and Combining x- and y-components

Let's apply the procedural steps of the component method to the addition of the vectors in Fig. 3.10b. The vectors with units of meters per second represent velocities.

Thinking It Through. Follow and learn the steps of the procedure. Basically, you resolve the vectors into components and add the respective components to get the components of the resultant, which then may be expressed in component form or magnitude–angle form.

Solution

1. The rectangular components of the vectors are shown in Fig. 3.10b.

2. Summing these components gives

$$\mathbf{v} = v_x\,\hat{\mathbf{x}} + v_y\,\hat{\mathbf{y}} = (v_{x_1} + v_{x_2} + v_{x_3})\,\hat{\mathbf{x}} + (v_{y_1} + v_{y_2} + v_{y_3})\,\hat{\mathbf{y}}$$

where

$$\begin{aligned} v_x &= v_{x_1} + v_{x_2} + v_{x_3} = v_1 \cos 45° + 0 - v_3 \cos 30° \\ &= (4.5\ \text{m/s})(0.707) - (9.0\ \text{m/s})(0.866) = -4.6\ \text{m/s} \end{aligned}$$

and

$$\begin{aligned} v_y &= v_{y_1} + v_{y_2} + v_{y_3} = v_1 \sin 45° + v_2 - v_3 \sin 30° \\ &= (4.5\ \text{m/s})(0.707) + (5.0\ \text{m/s}) - (9.0\ \text{m/s})(0.50) = 3.7\ \text{m/s} \end{aligned}$$

In tabular form, the components are provided as follows:

	x-components		y-components
v_{x_1}	$+v_1 \cos 45° = +3.2$ m/s	v_{y_1}	$+v_1 \sin 45° = +3.2$ m/s
v_{x_2}	$= 0$ m/s	v_{y_2}	$= +5.0$ m/s
v_{x_3}	$-v_3 \cos 30° = -7.8$ m/s	v_{y_3}	$-v_3 \sin 30° = -4.5$ m/s
Sums:	$v_x = -4.6$ m/s		$v_y = +3.7$ m/s

The directions of the components are indicated by signs. (The + sign is sometimes omitted as being understood.) In this case, v_2 has no x-component. Note that in general, for the analytical component method, the x-components are cosine functions and the y-components are sine functions, as long as we reference to the nearest x-axis.

3. In component form, the resultant vector is

$$\mathbf{v} = (-4.6\ \text{m/s})\,\hat{\mathbf{x}} + (3.7\ \text{m/s})\,\hat{\mathbf{y}}$$

In magnitude–angle form, the resultant velocity has a magnitude of

$$v = \sqrt{v_x^2 + v_y^2} = \sqrt{(-4.6\ \text{m/s})^2 + (3.7\ \text{m/s})^2} = 5.9\ \text{m/s}$$

Since the x-component is negative and the y-component is positive, the resultant lies in the second quadrant at an angle of

$$\theta = \tan^{-1}\left|\frac{v_y}{v_x}\right| = \tan^{-1}\left(\frac{3.7\ \text{m/s}}{4.6\ \text{m/s}}\right) = 39°$$

above the negative x-axis (See Fig. 3.10c.)

Follow-up Exercise. Suppose in this Example that there were an additional velocity vector $\mathbf{v}_4 = (+4.6\ \text{m/s})\,\hat{\mathbf{x}}$. What would be the resultant of all four vectors in this case? *(Answers to all Follow-up Exercises are at the back of the text.)*

Although our discussion is limited to motion in two dimensions (in a plane), the component method is easily extended to three dimensions. For a velocity in three dimensions, the vector has x-, y-, and z-components: $\mathbf{v} = v_x\,\hat{\mathbf{x}} + v_y\,\hat{\mathbf{y}} + v_z\,\hat{\mathbf{z}}$ and magnitude $v = \sqrt{v_x^2 + v_y^2 + v_z^2}$

Conceptual Example 3.4 ■ Vector Components in Action: Sailing "into" the Wind

A sailboat (or wind surfer) on a lake travels in the direction the wind is blowing and then returns. Traveling "into" the wind, how does the boat get back home? *Clearly establish the reasoning and physical principle(s) used in determining your answer before checking it here. That is,* **why** *did you select your answer?*

Reasoning and Answer. Sailing into the wind is called *tacking*. This method is not a direct mode of sailing, but is a wise use of vector components. Here, we will consider components of force, which is a vector quantity. As you know from experience, a single force (or force component), such as a push, gives rise to motion in the direction in which

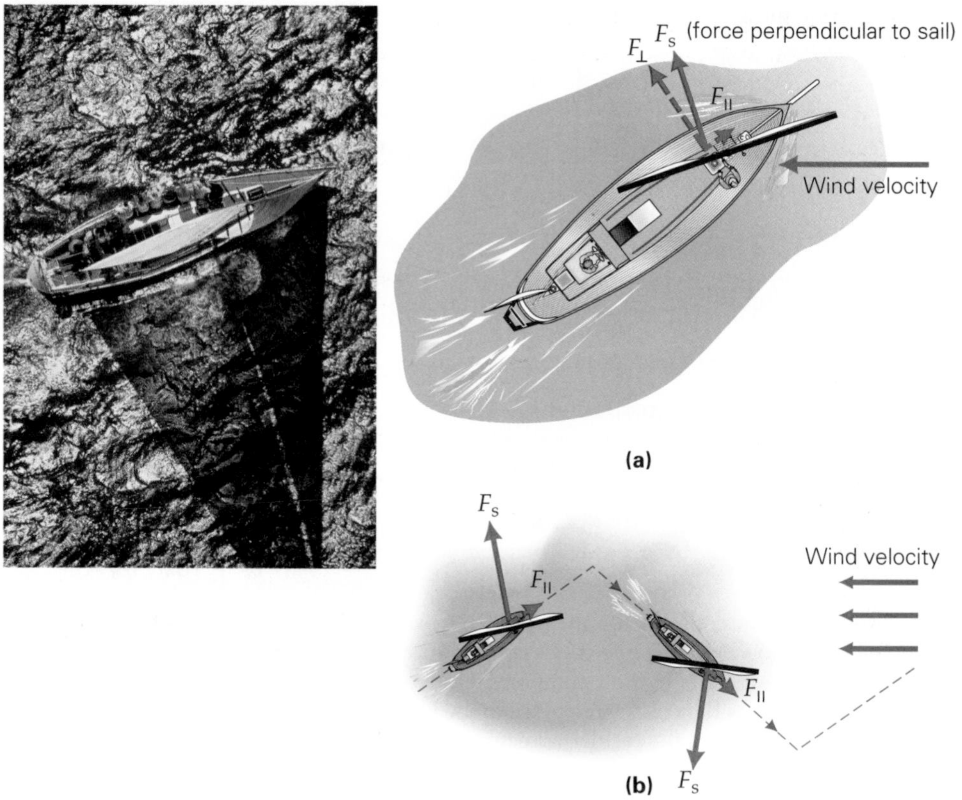

▶ **FIGURE 3.12 Let's go tacking** **(a)** The wind filling the sail exerts a force perpendicular to the sail ($\mathbf{F}_s$). We can resolve this force vector into components. The one parallel to the motion of the boat ($\mathbf{F}_{\parallel}$) has an upwind component. **(b)** By changing the direction of the sail, the sailor can "tack" upwind. See Conceptual Example 3.4.

the force is applied. (We shall learn much more about forces in Chapter 4.) For simplicity, let's assume that the wind fills the sail and exerts a force perpendicular to the sail, $\mathbf{F}_s$, as illustrated in ▲Fig. 3.12a. (Ignore friction and water current effects.)

Note that this force is resolved into components. The force ($\mathbf{F}_{\parallel}$) in the direction of the boat's velocity is at an acute angle ($<90°$) to the direction of the wind and is an "upwind" force on the boat. But, before the boat heads too far to the northeast (as in Fig. 3.12a), the sail is turned so that the direction of $\mathbf{F}_{\parallel}$ is changed by about 90° (Fig. 3.12b). The boat then comes back more in line with the desired upwind course. Using this zigzag process, the boat sails "into" the wind and eventually gets home.

Follow-up Exercise. The zigzag, straight-line path in Fig. 3.12b was drawn for simplicity. Would this path be the actual path of the boat? Explain. [*Hint*: Consider $\mathbf{F}_{\perp}$.] *(Answers to all Follow-up Exercises are at the back of the text.)*

Integrated Example 3.5 ■ Find the Vector: Add Them Up

You are given two displacement vectors: **A**, with a magnitude of 8.0 m in a direction 45° below the $+x$-axis, and **B**, which has an x-component of $+2.0$ m and a y-component of $+4.0$ m. (a) Sketch the vectors as accurately as you can, using x–y coordinates. (b) Find a vector **C** so that **A** + **B** + **C** equals a vector **D** that has a magnitude of 6.0 m in the $+y$-direction.

(a) Conceptual Reasoning. In drawing a vector, the length of the vector arrow is proportional to the magnitude of the vector. This length is usually set to some scale—for example, 1 cm per meter (as will be used here). The scale lengths could be measured with a ruler, but in practice, one usually makes a sketch, estimating the vector lengths as best one can. [*See the Learn by Drawing (LBD) figure on the next page.*]

(b) Thinking It Through. Here again, a sketch helps to understand the situation and gives a general idea of the attributes of **C**. Note in the second LBD figure that both **A** and **B** have $+x$-components, so **C** would have to have a $-x$ component to cancel these components out. (Resultant **D** points only in the $+y$-direction.) $\mathbf{B}_y$ and **D** are in the $+y$-direction, but the $\mathbf{A}_y$-component is larger in the $-y$-direction, so **C** would have to have a $+y$-component. With this information, we see that **C** would lie in the second quadrant if its tail were placed at the origin. A polygon sketch (shown in the LBD figure) confirms this observation.

So, we know that **C** has second quadrant components and that it has a relatively large magnitude (from the lengths of the vectors in the polygon drawing). This information gives us an idea of what we are looking for, making it easier to see if the results from the analytic solution are reasonable.

Given: **A**: 8.0 m, 45° below the $-x$-axis (fourth quadrant)
$\mathbf{B}_x = (+2.0\text{ m})\,\hat{\mathbf{x}}$
$\mathbf{B}_y = (+4.0\text{ m})\,\hat{\mathbf{y}}$

Find: (b) **C** such that $\mathbf{A} + \mathbf{B} + \mathbf{C} = \mathbf{D} = (+6.0\text{ m})\,\hat{\mathbf{y}}$

Let's set up the components in tabular form again so they can be easily seen:

x-components	y-components
$A_x = A\cos 45° = (8.0\text{ m})(0.707) = +5.7\text{ m}$	$A_y = A\sin 45° = (8.0\text{ m})(0.707)$ $= -5.7\text{ m}$
$B_x = +2.0\text{ m}$	$B_y = +4.0\text{ m}$
$C_x = ?$	$C_y = ?$
$D_x = 0$	$D_y = +6.0\text{ m}$

To find the components of **C**, where $\mathbf{A} + \mathbf{B} + \mathbf{C} = \mathbf{D}$, we sum the x- and y-components of the vectors:

$$x:\quad \mathbf{A}_x + \mathbf{B}_x + \mathbf{C}_x = \mathbf{D}_x$$

or

$$+5.7\text{ m} + 2.0\text{ m} + C_x = 0 \quad\text{and}\quad C_x = -7.7\text{ m}$$

$$y:\quad \mathbf{A}_y + \mathbf{B}_y + \mathbf{C}_y = \mathbf{D}_y$$

or

$$-5.7\text{ m} + 4.0\text{ m} + C_y = 6.0\text{ m} \quad\text{and}\quad C_y = +7.7\text{ m}$$

So,

$$\mathbf{C} = (-7.7\text{ m})\,\hat{\mathbf{x}} + (7.7\text{ m})\,\hat{\mathbf{y}}$$

We can also express the result in magnitude–angle form:

$$C = \sqrt{C_x^2 + C_y^2} = \sqrt{(-7.7\text{ m})^2 + (7.7\text{ m})^2} = 11\text{ m}$$

and

$$\theta = \tan^{-1}\left|\frac{C_y}{C_x}\right| = \tan^{-1}\left|\frac{7.7\text{ m}}{-7.7\text{ m}}\right| = 45°\ (\text{above the } -x \text{ axis})$$

Follow-Up Example. Suppose **D** pointed in the opposite direction $[\mathbf{D} = (-6.0\text{ m})\,\mathbf{y}]$. What would **C** be in this case?

Learn by Drawing

Make a Sketch and Add Them Up

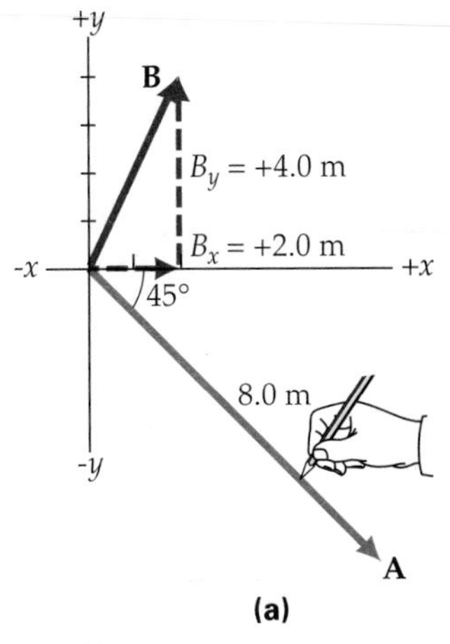

(a)

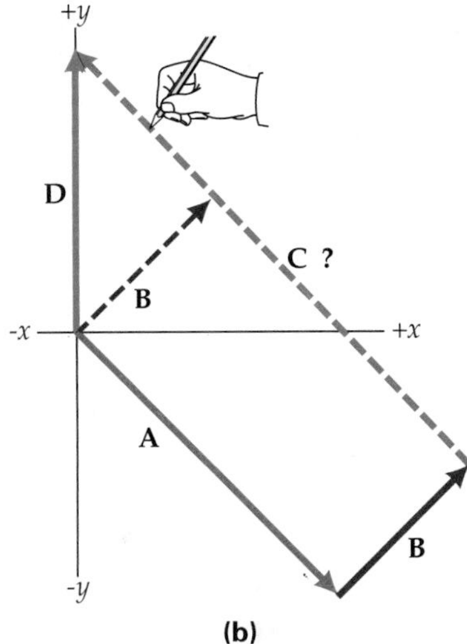

(b)

(a) A sketch is made for the vectors **A** and **B**. In a vector drawing, the vector lengths are usually set to some scale—for example, 1 cm per meter—but in a quick sketch, the vector lengths are estimated. **(b)** By shifting **B** to the tip of **A** and putting in **D**, the vector **C** can be found from $\mathbf{A} + \mathbf{B} + \mathbf{C} = \mathbf{D}$.

3.3 Relative Velocity: Applying Vector Addition

OBJECTIVE: To determine relative velocities through vector addition and subtraction.

Measurements must be made with respect to some reference. This reference is usually taken to be the origin of a coordinate system. The point you designate as the origin of a set of coordinate axes is arbitrary and entirely a matter of choice. For example, you may "attach" the coordinate system to the road or the ground and then measure the displacement or velocity of a car relative to these axes. You may then change the origin of coordinate axes to reflect a different perspective of the car's position.

We can analyze a situation from any frame of reference. For example, the origin of the coordinate axes may be attached to a car moving along a highway. In analyzing motion from another reference frame, you do not change the physical situation or what is taking place, only the point of view from which you describe it. Hence, we say that motion is *relative* (to some reference frame), and we refer to **relative velocity**. Since velocity is a vector, vector addition and subtraction are helpful in determining relative velocities.

Relative Velocities in One Dimension

When the velocities are linear (along a straight line) in the same or opposite directions and all have the same reference (such as the ground), we can find relative velocities by using vector subtraction. As an illustration, consider cars moving with constant velocities along a straight, level highway, as in ▼Fig. 3.13. The velocities shown in the figure are *relative to the Earth, or the ground*, as indicated by the reference set of coordinate axes in Fig. 3.13a, with motions along the x-axis. They are also relative to the stationary observers standing by the highway and sitting in the parked car A. That is, these observers see the cars as moving with velocities $\mathbf{v}_B = +90$ km/h and $\mathbf{v}_C = -60$ km/h. The relative velocity of two objects is given by the velocity (vector) difference between them. For example, the velocity of car B *relative to car A* is given by

Note: Use subscripts carefully! $\mathbf{v}_{AB}$ = velocity of *A* relative to B.

$$\mathbf{v}_{BA} = \mathbf{v}_B - \mathbf{v}_A = (+90\text{ km/h})\,\hat{\mathbf{x}} - 0 = (+90\text{ km/h})\,\hat{\mathbf{x}}$$

Thus, a person sitting in car A would see car B move away (in the positive x-direction) with a speed of 90 km/h. For this linear case, the directions of the velocities are indicated by plus and minus signs (in addition to the minus sign in the equation).

Similarly, the velocity of car C relative to an observer in car A is

$$\mathbf{v}_{CA} = \mathbf{v}_C - \mathbf{v}_A = (-60\text{ km/h})\,\hat{\mathbf{x}} - 0 = (-60\text{ km/h})\,\hat{\mathbf{x}}$$

◀ **FIGURE 3.13 Relative velocity** The observed velocity of a car depends on, or is relative to, the frame of reference. The velocities shown in **(a)** are relative to the ground or to the parked car. In **(b)**, the frame of reference is with respect to car *B*, and the velocities are those that a driver of car *B* would observe. **(c)** These aircraft, performing air-to-air refueling, are normally described as traveling at hundreds of kilometers per hour. To what frame of reference do these velocities refer? What is their velocity relative to each other?

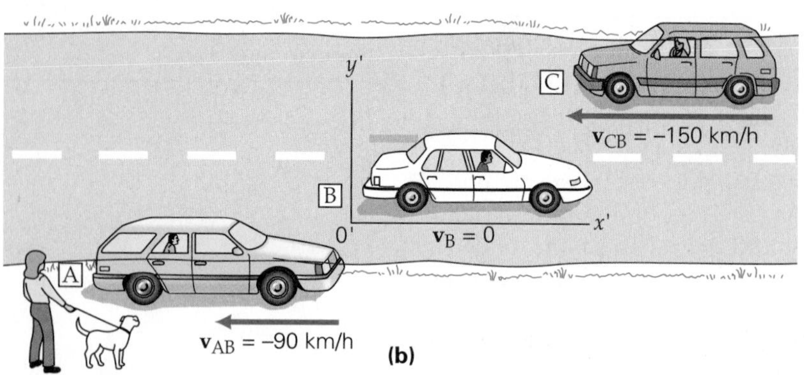

(c)

The person in car A would see car C approaching (in the negative x-direction) with a speed of 60 km/h.

But suppose that you want to know the velocities of the other cars *relative to car B* (that is, from the point of view of an observer in car B) or relative to a set of coordinate axes with the origin fixed to car B (Fig. 3.13b). Relative to those axes, car B is not moving; it acts as the fixed reference point. The other cars are moving relative to car B. The velocity of car C relative to car B is

$$\mathbf{v}_{CB} = \mathbf{v}_C - \mathbf{v}_B = (-60 \text{ km/h})\,\hat{\mathbf{x}} - (+90 \text{ km/h})\,\hat{\mathbf{x}} = (-150 \text{ km/h})\,\hat{\mathbf{x}}$$

Similarly, car A has a velocity relative to car B of

$$\mathbf{v}_{AB} = \mathbf{v}_A - \mathbf{v}_B = 0 - (+90 \text{ km/h})\,\hat{\mathbf{x}} = (-90 \text{ km/h})\,\hat{\mathbf{x}}$$

Notice that relative to B, the other cars are both moving in the negative x-direction. That is, C is approaching B with a velocity of 150 km/h in the $-x$-direction, and A appears to be receding from B with a velocity of 90 km/h in the $-x$-direction. (Imagine yourself in car B, and take that position as stationary. Car C would appear to be coming toward you at a high rate of speed, and car A would be getting farther and farther away, as though it were moving backward relative to you.) Note that, in general,

$$\mathbf{v}_{AB} = -\mathbf{v}_{BA}$$

What about the velocities of cars A and B relative to car C? From the point of view (or reference point) of car C, cars A and B would both appear to be approaching or moving in the positive x-direction. For the velocity of B relative to C, we have

$$\mathbf{v}_{BC} = \mathbf{v}_B - \mathbf{v}_C = (90 \text{ km/h})\,\hat{\mathbf{x}} - (-60 \text{ km/h})\,\hat{\mathbf{x}} = (+150 \text{ km/h})\,\hat{\mathbf{x}}$$

Can you show that $\mathbf{v}_{AC} = +60$ km/h? Also note the situation in Fig. 3.13c.

In some instances, we may need to work with velocities that do not all have the same reference point. In such cases, relative velocities can be found by means of vector addition. To solve problems of this kind, *it is essential to identify the velocity references with care.*

Let's look first at a one-dimensional (linear) example. Suppose that a straight moving walkway in a major airport moves with a velocity of $\mathbf{v}_{wg} = (+1.0 \text{ m/s})\,\hat{\mathbf{x}}$, where the subscripts indicate the velocity of the walkway (w) relative to the ground (g). A passenger (p) on the walkway (w) trying to make a flight connection walks with a velocity of $\mathbf{v}_{pw} = (+2.0 \text{ m/s})\,\hat{\mathbf{x}}$ relative to the walkway. What is the passenger's velocity relative to an observer standing next to the walkway (that is, relative to the ground)?

The velocity we are seeking, $\mathbf{v}_{pg}$, is given by

$$\mathbf{v}_{pg} = \mathbf{v}_{pw} + \mathbf{v}_{wg} = (2.0 \text{ m/s})\,\hat{\mathbf{x}} + (1.0 \text{ m/s})\,\hat{\mathbf{x}} = (3.0 \text{ m/s})\,\hat{\mathbf{x}}$$

Thus, the stationary observer sees the passenger as traveling with speed of 3.0 m/s down the walkway. (Make a sketch, and show how the vectors add.)

Problem-Solving Hint

Notice the pattern of the subscripts in this example. On the right side of the equation, the two inner subscripts out of the four total subscripts are the same (w). The outer subscripts (p and g) are sequentially the same as those for the relative velocity on the left side of the equation. When adding relative velocities, always check to make sure that the subscripts have this relationship—it indicates that you have set up the equation correctly.

What if a passenger got on the walkway going in the opposite direction and walked with the same speed as that of the walkway? Now it is essential to indicate the direction in which the passenger is walking by means of a minus sign: $\mathbf{v}_{pw} = (-1.0 \text{ m/s})\,\hat{\mathbf{x}}$. In this case, relative to the stationary observer,

$$\mathbf{v}_{pg} = \mathbf{v}_{pw} + \mathbf{v}_{wg} = (-1.0 \text{ m/s})\,\hat{\mathbf{x}} + (1.0 \text{ m/s})\,\hat{\mathbf{x}} = 0$$

so the passenger is stationary with respect to the ground, and the walkway acts as a treadmill. (Excellent physical exercise!)

Relative Velocities in Two Dimensions

Of course, velocities are not always in the same or opposite directions. However, if we know how to use rectangular components to add or subtract vectors, we can solve problems involving relative velocities in two dimensions, as Examples 3.6 and 3.7 show.

Example 3.6 ■ Across and Down the River: Relative Velocity and Components of Motion

The current of a 500-m-wide straight river has a flow rate of 2.55 km/h. A motorboat that travels with a constant speed of 8.00 km/h in still water crosses the river (▾Fig. 3.14). (a) If the boat's bow points directly across the river toward the opposite shore, what is the velocity of the boat relative to the stationary observer sitting at the corner of the bridge? (b) How far downstream will the boat's landing point be from the point directly opposite its starting point? (c) What is the distance traveled by the boat in crossing the river? (Assume that the boat comes instantaneously to rest on a grassy shore.)

Thinking It Through. Careful designation of the given quantities is very important—the velocity of what, relative to what? Once this is done, part (a) should be straightforward. (See the previous Problem-Solving Hint.) For parts (b) and (c), we use kinematics, where the time it takes the boat to cross the river is the key.

Solution. As indicated in Fig. 3.14, we take the river's flow velocity ($\mathbf{v}_{rs}$, river to shore) to be in the x-direction and the boat's velocity ($\mathbf{v}_{br}$, boat to river) to be in the y-direction. Note that the river's flow velocity is *relative to the shore* and that the boat's velocity is *relative to the river*, as indicated by the subscripts. Listing the data, we have:

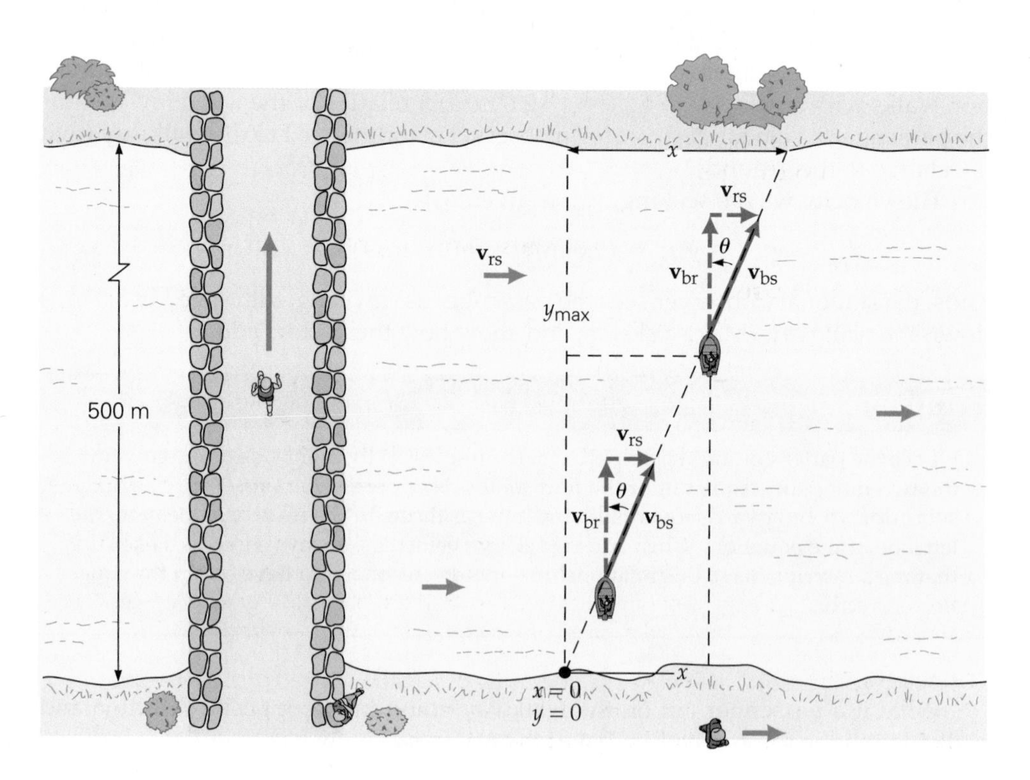

▶ **FIGURE 3.14 Relative velocity and components of motion** As the boat moves across the river, it is carried downstream by the current. See Example 3.6.

Given: $y_{max} = 500$ m (river width)
$\mathbf{v}_{rs} = (2.55 \text{ km/h})\,\hat{\mathbf{x}}$
$= (0.709 \text{ m/s})\,\hat{\mathbf{x}}$
(velocity of river *relative to shore*)
$\mathbf{v}_{br} = (8.00 \text{ km/h})\,\hat{\mathbf{y}}$
$= (2.22 \text{ m/s})\,\hat{\mathbf{y}}$
(velocity of boat *relative to river*)

Find: (a) $\mathbf{v}_{bs}$ (velocity of boat *relative to shore*)
(b) x (distance downstream)
(c) d (distance traveled by boat)

Notice that as the boat moves toward the opposite shore, it is also carried downstream by the current. These velocity components would be clearly apparent relative to the jogger crossing the bridge and to the person sauntering downstream in Fig. 3.14. If both observers stay even with the boat, the velocity of each will match one of the components of the boat's velocity. Since the velocity components are constant, the boat travels in a straight line diagonally across the river (much like the ball rolling across the table in Example 3.1).

(a) The velocity of the boat relative to the shore ($\mathbf{v}_{bs}$) is given by vector addition. In this case, we have

$$\mathbf{v}_{bs} = \mathbf{v}_{br} + \mathbf{v}_{rs}$$

Since the velocities are not along one axis, their magnitudes cannot be added directly. Notice in Fig. 3.14 that the vectors form a right triangle, so we can apply the Pythagorean theorem to find the magnitude of $\mathbf{v}_{bs}$:

$$v_{bs} = \sqrt{v_{br}^2 + v_{rs}^2} = \sqrt{(2.22 \text{ m/s})^2 + (0.709 \text{ m/s})^2}$$
$$= 2.33 \text{ m/s}$$

The direction of this velocity is defined by

$$\theta = \tan^{-1}\left(\frac{v_{rs}}{v_{br}}\right) = \tan^{-1}\left(\frac{0.709 \text{ m/s}}{2.22 \text{ m/s}}\right) = 17.7°$$

(b) To find the distance x that the current carries the boat downstream, we use components. Note that in the y-direction, $y_{max} = v_{br}t$, and

$$t = \frac{y_{max}}{v_{br}} = \frac{500 \text{ m}}{2.22 \text{ m/s}} = 225 \text{ s}$$

which is the time it takes the boat to cross the river.

During this time, the boat is carried downstream by the current a distance of

$$x = v_{rs}t = (0.709 \text{ m/s})(225 \text{ s}) = 160 \text{ m}$$

(c) We could find the distance d the boat travels by using x and y_{max} with the Pythagorean theorem again, but let's use the magnitude of the relative velocity and time instead:

$$d = v_{bs}t = (2.33 \text{ m/s})(225 \text{ s}) = 524 \text{ m}$$

Follow-up Exercise. In part (c), find the distance d by using the Pythagorean theorem. (The answer may be slightly different. Why?) *(Answers to all Follow-up Exercises are at the back of the text.)*

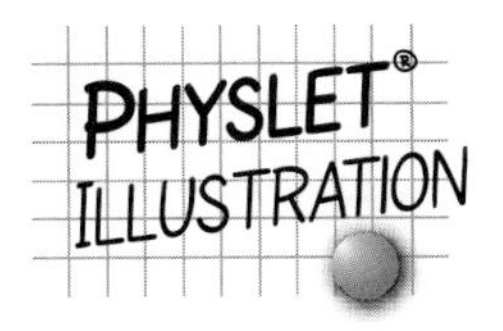

Relative Motion

Example 3.7 ■ Flying Into the Wind: Relative Velocity

An airplane with an air speed of 200 km/h (its speed in still air) flies in a direction such that with a west wind of 50.0 km/h blowing, it travels in a straight line northward. (Wind direction is specified by the direction *from* which the wind blows, so a west wind blows from west to east.) To maintain its course due north, the plane must fly at an angle, as illustrated in ▶Fig. 3.15. What is the speed of the plane along its northward path?

Thinking It Through. Here again, the velocity designations are important, but Fig. 3.15 shows that the velocity vectors form a right triangle, and the magnitude of the unknown velocity can be found by using the Pythagorean theorem.

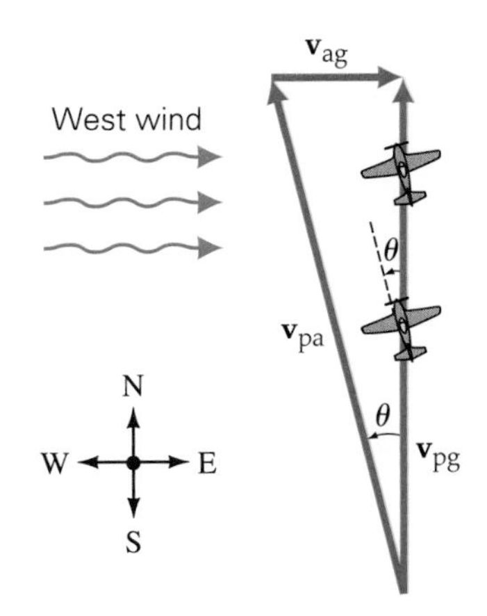

▲ **FIGURE 3.15 Flying into the wind** To fly directly north, the plane's heading (θ-direction) must be west of north. See Example 3.7.

Solution. As always, it is important to identify the reference frame to which the given velocities are relative.

Given: $\mathbf{v}_{pa} = 200$ km/h at angle θ (velocity of plane with respect to still air = air speed)
$\mathbf{v}_{ag} = 50.0$ km/h east (velocity of air with respect to the Earth, or ground, = wind speed)
Plane flies due north with velocity $\mathbf{v}_{pg}$

Find: v_{pg} (ground speed of plane)

The speed of the plane with respect to the Earth, or the ground, v_{pg}, is called the plane's *ground speed*; v_{pa} is its air speed. Vectorially, the respective velocities are related by

$$\mathbf{v}_{pg} = \mathbf{v}_{pa} + \mathbf{v}_{ag}$$

If there were no wind blowing ($v_{ag} = 0$), the ground speed and air speed would be equal. However, a head wind (a wind blowing directly toward the plane) would cause a slower ground speed, and a tail wind would cause a faster ground speed. The situation is analogous to that of a boat going upstream versus downstream.

Here, $\mathbf{v}_{pg}$ is the resultant of the other two vectors, which can be added by the triangle method. We use the Pythagorean theorem to find v_{pg}, noting that v_{pa} is the hypotenuse of the triangle:

$$v_{pg} = \sqrt{v_{pa}^2 - v_{ag}^2} = \sqrt{(200\text{ km/h})^2 - (50.0\text{ km/h})^2} = 194\text{ km/h}$$

(Note that it was convenient to use the units of kilometers per hour, since the calculation did not involve any other units.)

Follow-up Exercise. What must be the plane's heading (θ-direction) in this Example for the plane to fly directly north? *(Answers to all Follow-up Exercises are at the back of the text.)*

3.4 Projectile Motion

OBJECTIVES: To analyze projectile motion to find (a) position, (b) time of flight, and (c) range.

A familiar example of two-dimensional, curvilinear motion is the motion of objects that are thrown or projected by some means. The motion of a stone thrown across a stream or a golf ball driven off a tee is **projectile motion**. A special case of projectile motion in one dimension occurs when an object is projected vertically upward. This case was treated in Chapter 2 in terms of free fall (air resistance neglected). We will treat projectile motion as free fall, too, so that the only acceleration of a projectile is due to gravity.

Note: Review Section 2.5 (free fall).

We can use vector components to analyze projectile motion. We simply break up the motion into its x- and y-components and treat them separately.

Horizontal Projections

It is worthwhile to analyze first the special case of the motion of an object projected horizontally, or parallel to a level surface. Suppose that you throw an object horizontally with an initial velocity v_{x_o} (▸Fig. 3.16a). Projectile motion is analyzed beginning at the instant of release ($t = 0$). Once the object is released, there is no longer a horizontal acceleration ($a_x = 0$), so throughout the object's path, the horizontal velocity remains constant: $v_x = v_{x_o}$.

According to the equation $x = x_o + v_x t$ (Eq. 3.2a), the projected object would continue to travel in the horizontal direction indefinitely. However, you know that this is not what happens. As soon as the object is projected, it is in free fall in the vertical direction, with $v_{y_o} = 0$ (as though it were dropped) and $a_y = -g$. In other words, the projected object travels at a uniform velocity in the horizontal direction while *at the same time* undergoing acceleration in the downward direction under the

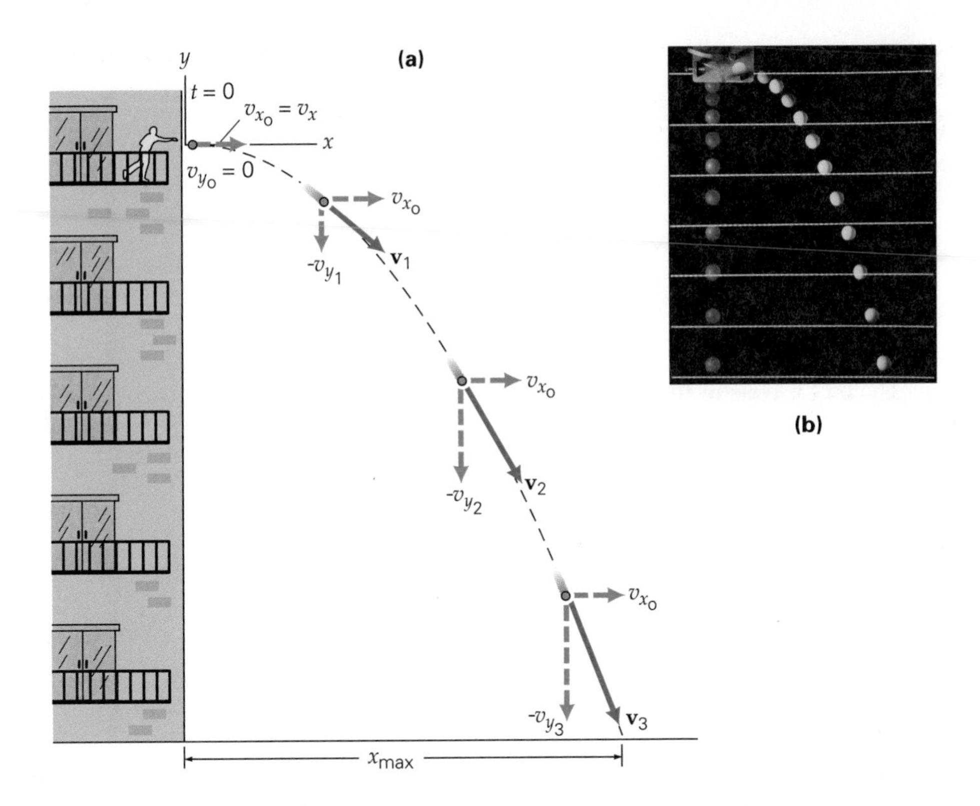

◀ **FIGURE 3.16 Horizontal projection** **(a)** The velocity components of a projectile launched horizontally show that the projectile travels to the right as it falls downward. **(b)** A multiflash photograph shows the paths of two golf balls. One was projected horizontally at the same time that the other was dropped straight down. The horizontal lines are 15 cm apart, and the interval between flashes was $\frac{1}{30}$ s. The vertical motions of the balls are the same. Why? Can you describe the horizontal motion of the yellow ball?

influence of gravity. The result is a curved path, as illustrated in Fig. 3.16. (Compare the motions in Fig. 3.16 and Fig. 3.2. Do you see any similarities?) If there were no horizontal motion, the object would simply drop to the ground in a straight line. In fact, the time of flight of the projected object is *exactly the same as if it were falling vertically.*

Note the components of the velocity vector in Fig. 3.16a. The length of the horizontal component of the velocity vector remains the same, but the length of the vertical component increases with time. What is the instantaneous velocity at any point along the path? (Think in terms of vector addition, covered in Section 3.3.) The photo in Fig. 3.16b shows the actual motions of a horizontally projected golf ball and one that is simultaneously dropped from rest. The horizontal reference lines show that the balls fall vertically at the same rate. The only difference is that the horizontally projected ball also travels to the right as it falls.

Example 3.8 ■ Starting at the Top: Horizontal Projection

Suppose that the ball in Fig. 3.16a is projected from a height of 25.0 m above the ground and is thrown with an initial horizontal velocity of 8.25 m/s. (a) How long is the ball in flight before striking the ground? (b) How far from the building does the ball strike the ground?

Thinking It Through. In looking at the components of motion, we find that part (a) involves the time it takes the ball to fall vertically, analogous to a ball dropped from that height. This time is also the time the ball travels in the horizontal direction. The horizontal speed is constant, so we can find the horizontal distance, requested in part (b).

Solution. Writing the data with the origin chosen as the point from which the ball is thrown and downward taken as the negative direction, we have

Given: $y = -25.0$ m
$v_{x_o} = 8.25$ m/s
$a_x = 0$
$v_{y_o} = 0$
$a_y = -g$
($x_o = 0$ and $y_o = 0$ because of our choice of axes location.)

Find: (a) t (time of flight)
(b) x (horizontal distance)

(a) As noted previously, the time of flight is the same as the time it takes for the ball to fall vertically to the ground. To find this time, we can use the equation $y = y_o + v_{y_o}t - \frac{1}{2}gt^2$, in which the negative direction of g is expressed explicitly, as was done in Chapter 2. With $v_{y_o} = 0$, we have

$$y = -\tfrac{1}{2}gt^2$$

So,

$$t = \sqrt{\frac{2y}{-g}} = \sqrt{\frac{2(-25.0\text{ m})}{-9.80\text{ m/s}^2}} = 2.26\text{ s}$$

(b) The ball travels in the x-direction for the same amount of time it travels in the y-direction (that is, 2.26 s). Since there is no acceleration in the horizontal direction, the ball travels in this direction with a uniform velocity. Thus, with $a_x = 0$, we have

$$x = v_{x_o}t = (8.25\text{ m/s})(2.26\text{ s}) = 18.6\text{ m}$$

Follow-up Exercise. (a) Choose the axes to be at the base of the building, and show that the resulting equation is the same as in the Example. (b) What is the velocity (in component form) of the ball just before it strikes the ground? *(Answers to all Follow-up Exercises are at the back of the text.)*

Projections at Arbitrary Angles

The general case of projectile motion involves an object projected at an arbitrary angle θ relative to the horizontal—for example, a golf ball struck by a club (▼Fig. 3.17). During projectile motion, the object travels up and down while traveling horizontally with a constant velocity. (Does the ball have acceleration? Yes. At each point of the motion, gravity acts, and $\mathbf{a} = -g\,\hat{\mathbf{y}}$.)

This motion is also analyzed by using its components. As before, upward is taken as the positive direction and downward as the negative direction. The initial velocity v_o is first resolved into rectangular components:

$$v_{x_o} = v_o \cos\theta \quad \text{(3.8a)}$$

$$v_{y_o} = v_o \sin\theta \quad \text{(3.8b)}$$

initial velocity components ($t_o = 0$)

▼ **FIGURE 3.17 Projection at an angle** The velocity components of the ball are shown for various times. Note that $v_y = 0$ at the top of the arc, or at y_{max}. The range R is the maximum horizontal distance, or x_{max}.

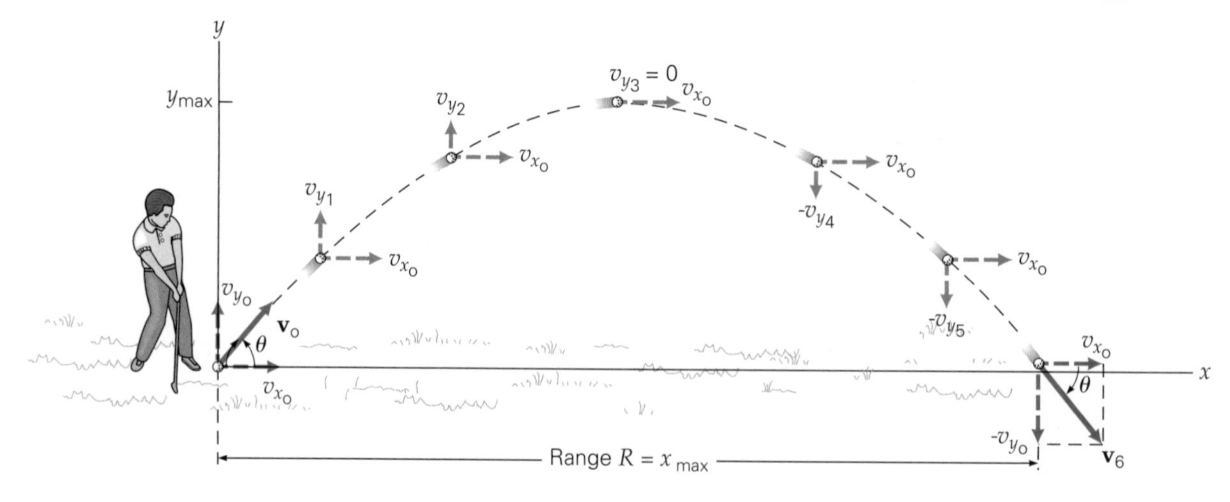

Since there is no horizontal acceleration and gravity acts in the negative y-direction, the x-component of the velocity is constant, and the y-component varies with time (see Eq. 3.3):

$$v_x = v_{x_o} = v_o \cos\theta \qquad (3.9a)$$

$$v_y = v_{y_o} - gt = v_o \sin\theta - gt \qquad (3.9b)$$

projectile motion velocity components

The components of the instantaneous velocity at various times are illustrated in Fig. 3.17. The instantaneous velocity is the sum of these components and is tangent to the curved path of the ball at any point. Notice that the ball strikes the ground at the same speed as it was launched (but with $-v_{y_o}$) and at the same angle below the horizontal.

Similarly, the displacement components are given by

$$x = v_{x_o}t = (v_o \cos\theta)t \qquad (3.10a)$$

$$y = v_{y_o}t - \tfrac{1}{2}gt^2 = (v_o \sin\theta)t - \tfrac{1}{2}gt^2 \qquad (3.10b)$$

projectile motion displacement components

The curve produced by these equations, or the path of motion of the projectile, is called a **parabola**. The path of projectile motion is often referred to as a *parabolic arc*. Such arcs are commonly observed (▶ Fig. 3.18).

Note that, as in the case of horizontal projection, *time is the common feature shared by the components of motion*. Aspects of projectile motion that may be of interest in various situations include the time of flight, the maximum height reached, and the **range** (R), which is the maximum horizontal distance traveled.

▲ **FIGURE 3.18 Parabolic arcs** Sparks of hot metal from welding describe parabolic arcs.

Example 3.9 ■ Teeing Off: Projection at an Angle

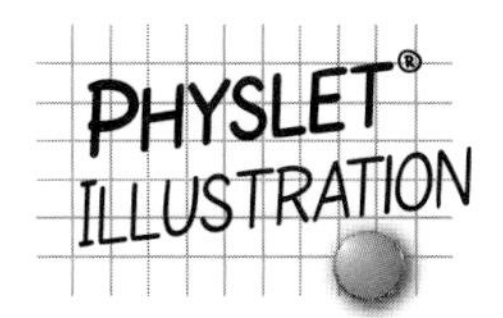

Projectile Motion

Suppose a golf ball is hit off the tee with an initial velocity of 30.0 m/s at an angle of 35° to the horizontal, as in Fig. 3.17. (a) What is the maximum height reached by the ball? (b) What is its range?

Thinking It Through. The maximum height involves the y-component; the procedure for finding it is like that for finding the maximum height of a ball projected vertically upward. The ball travels in the x-direction for the same amount of time it would take for the ball to go up and down.

Solution.

Given: $v_o = 30.0$ m/s
$\theta = 35°$
$a_y = -g$
(x_o and $y_o = 0$
and final $y_f = 0$)

Find: (a) y_{max}
(b) $R = x_{max}$

Let us compute v_{x_o} and v_{y_o} explicitly so that we can use simplified kinematic equations:

$$v_{x_o} = v_o \cos 35° = (30.0\text{ m/s})(0.819) = 24.6\text{ m/s}$$

$$v_{y_o} = v_o \sin 35° = (30.0\text{ m/s})(0.574) = 17.2\text{ m/s}$$

(a) Just as for an object thrown vertically upward, $v_y = 0$ at the maximum height (y_{max}). Thus, we can find the time to reach the maximum height (t_u) by using Eq. 3.9b with v_y set equal to zero:

$$v_y = 0 = v_{y_o} - gt_u$$

Solving for t_u, we have

$$t_u = \frac{v_{y_o}}{g} = \frac{17.2\text{ m/s}}{9.80\text{ m/s}^2} = 1.76\text{ s}$$

Note: A projectile launched at an angle to the horizontal follows a parabolic path.

(Note that t_u represents the amount of time the ball moves upward.)

The maximum height y_{max} is then obtained by substituting t_u into Eq. 3.10b:

$$y_{max} = v_{y_o}t_u - \tfrac{1}{2}gt_u^2 = (17.2\text{ m/s})(1.76\text{ s}) - \tfrac{1}{2}(9.80\text{ m/s}^2)(1.76\text{ s})^2 = 15.1\text{ m}$$

The maximum height could also be obtained directly from Eq. 2.11′, $v_y^2 = v_{y_o}^2 - 2gy$, with $y = y_{max}$ and $v_y = 0$. However, the method of solution used here illustrates how the time of flight is obtained.

(b) As in the case of vertical projection, the time in going up is equal to the time in coming down, so the total time of flight is $t = 2t_u$ (to return to the elevation from which the object was projected, $y - y_o = v_{y_o}t - \frac{1}{2}gt^2 = 0$, and $t = 2v_{y_o}/g = 2t_u$.)

The range R is equal to the horizontal distance traveled (x_{max}), which is easily found by substituting the total time of flight $t = 2t_u = 2(1.76\text{ s}) = 3.52\text{ s}$ into Eq. 3.10a:

$$R = x_{max} = v_x t = v_{x_o}(2t_u) = (24.6\text{ m/s})(3.52\text{ s}) = 86.6\text{ m}$$

Follow-up Exercise. How would the values of maximum height (y_{max}) and the range (x_{max}) compare with those found in this Example if the golf ball had been similarly teed off on the surface of the Moon? (*Hint:* $g_M = g/6$; that is, acceleration due to gravity on the Moon is one sixth of that on Earth.) Do not do any numerical calculations. Find the answers by "sight reading" the equations. *(Answers to all Follow-up Exercises are at the back of the text.)*

The range of a projectile is an important consideration in various applications. This factor is particularly important in sports in which a maximum range is desired, such as golf and javelin throwing.

In general, what is the range of a projectile launched with velocity v_o at an angle θ? In order to answer this question, we must consider the equation used in Example 3.9 to calculate the range, $R = v_x t$. First let's look at the expressions for v_x and t. Since there is no acceleration in the horizontal direction, we know that

$$v_x = v_{x_o} = v_o \cos\theta$$

and the total time t (as shown in Example 3.9) is

$$t = \frac{2v_{y_o}}{g} = \frac{2v_o \sin\theta}{g}$$

Then,

$$R = v_x t = (v_o \cos\theta)\left(\frac{2v_o \sin\theta}{g}\right) = \frac{2v_o^2 \sin\theta\cos\theta}{g}$$

Using the trigonometric identity $\sin 2\theta = 2\cos\theta\sin\theta$ (see Appendix I), we have

$$R = \frac{v_o^2 \sin 2\theta}{g} \qquad \textit{projectile range } x_{max} \; (\textit{only for } y_{initial} = y_{final}) \qquad (3.11)$$

Note that the range depends on the magnitude of the initial velocity (or speed), v_o, and the angle of projection, θ, and g is assumed to be constant. Keep in mind that this equation applies only to the *special*, but common, case of $y_{initial} = y_{final}$— that is, when the landing point is at the same height as the launch point.

Example 3.10 ■ A Throw from the Bridge

A young girl standing on a bridge throws a stone with an initial velocity of 12 m/s at a downward angle of 45° to the horizontal, in an attempt to hit a block of wood floating in the river below (▶Fig. 3.19). If the stone is thrown from a height of 20 m and it

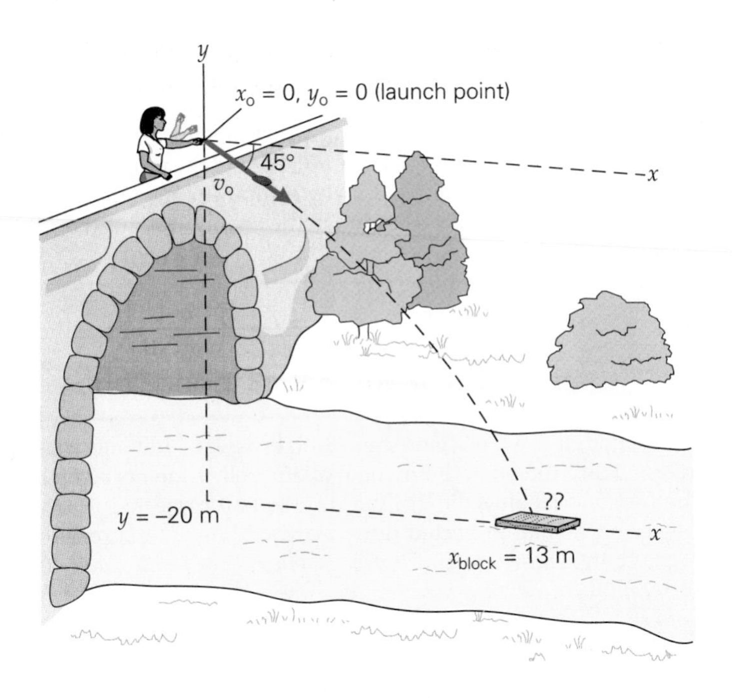

FIGURE 3.19 A throw from the bridge—hit or miss? See Example 3.10.

reaches the river when the block is 13 m from the bridge, does the stone hit the block? (Assume that the block does not move appreciably and that it is in the plane of the throw.)

Thinking It Through. The question is, what is the range of the stone? If this range is the same as the distance between the block and the bridge, then the stone hits the block. To find the range of the stone, we need to find the time of descent (from the y-component of motion) and then use this time to find the distance x_{max}. (Time is the connecting factor.)

Solution.

Given: $v_o = 12\text{ m/s}$
$\theta = 45°$ $\quad v_{x_o} = v_o \cos 45° = 8.5\text{ m/s}$
$y = -20\text{ m}$ $\quad v_{y_o} = -v_o \sin 45° = -8.5\text{ m/s}$
$x_{block} = 13\text{ m}$
$(x_o = y_o = 0)$

Find: Range or x_{max} of stone from bridge. (Is it the same as the block's distance from the bridge?)

To find the time for upward projections, we have previously used $v_y = v_{y_o} - gt$, where $v_y = 0$ at the top of the arc. However, in this case, v_y is not zero when the stone reaches the river, so to use this equation, we need to find v_y. This value may be found from the kinematic equation Eq. 2.11′,

$$v_y^2 = v_{y_o}^2 - 2gy$$

as

$$v_y = \sqrt{(-8.5\text{ m/s})^2 - 2(9.8\text{ m/s}^2)(-20\text{ m})} = -22\text{ m/s}$$

(minus root because v_y is downward).

Then solving $v_y = v_{y_o} - gt$ for t,

$$t = \frac{v_{y_o} - v_y}{g} = \frac{-8.5\text{ m/s} - (-22\text{ m/s})}{9.8\text{ m/s}^2} = 1.4\text{ s}$$

The stone's horizontal distance from the bridge at this time is

$$x_{max} = v_{x_o}t = (8.5\text{ m/s})(1.4\text{ s}) = 12\text{ m}$$

So the girl's throw falls short by a meter (block at 13 m).

Note that Eq. 3.10b, $y = y_o + v_{y_o}t - \frac{1}{2}gt^2$, could have been used to find the time, but this calculation would have involved solving a quadratic equation.

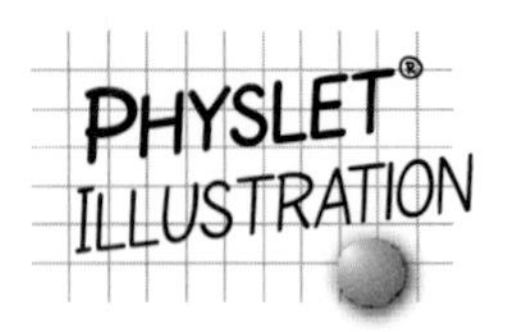

The Monkey and Hunter

Follow-up Exercise. (a) Why was it assumed that the block was in the plane of the throw? (b) Why wasn't Eq. 3.11 used in this Example to find the range? Show that Eq. 3.11 works in Example 3.9, but not in Example 3.10, by computing the range in each case and comparing your results with the answers found in the Examples. *(Answers to all Follow-up Exercises are at the back of the text.)*

Conceptual Example 3.11 ■ Which Has the Greater Velocity?

Consider two balls, both thrown with the same initial speed v_o, but one at an angle of 45° above the horizontal and the other at an angle of 45° below the horizontal (▼Fig. 3.20). Determine whether, on reaching the ground, (a) the ball projected upward will have the greater speed, (b) the ball projected downward will have the greater speed, or (c) both balls will have the same speed. *Clearly establish the reasoning and physical principle(s) used in determining your answer before checking it below. That is,* ***why*** *did you select your answer?*

Reasoning and Answer. At first, you might think the answer is (b), because this ball is projected downward. But the ball projected upward falls from a greater maximum height, perhaps the answer is (a). To solve this dilemma, look at the horizontal line in Fig. 3.20 between the two velocity vectors that extends beyond the upper trajectory. From this diagram, you should be able to see that the trajectories for both balls are the same below this line. Moreover, the downward velocity of the upper ball on reaching this line is v_o at an angle of 45° below the horizontal. (See Fig. 3.17.) Therefore, relative to the horizontal line and below, the conditions are identical, with the same y-component and same, constant x-component. So, the answer is (c).

Follow-Up Exercise. Suppose the ball thrown downward was thrown at an angle of −40°. Which ball would hit the ground with the greater speed in this case? *(Answers to all Follow-up Exercises are at the back of the text.)*

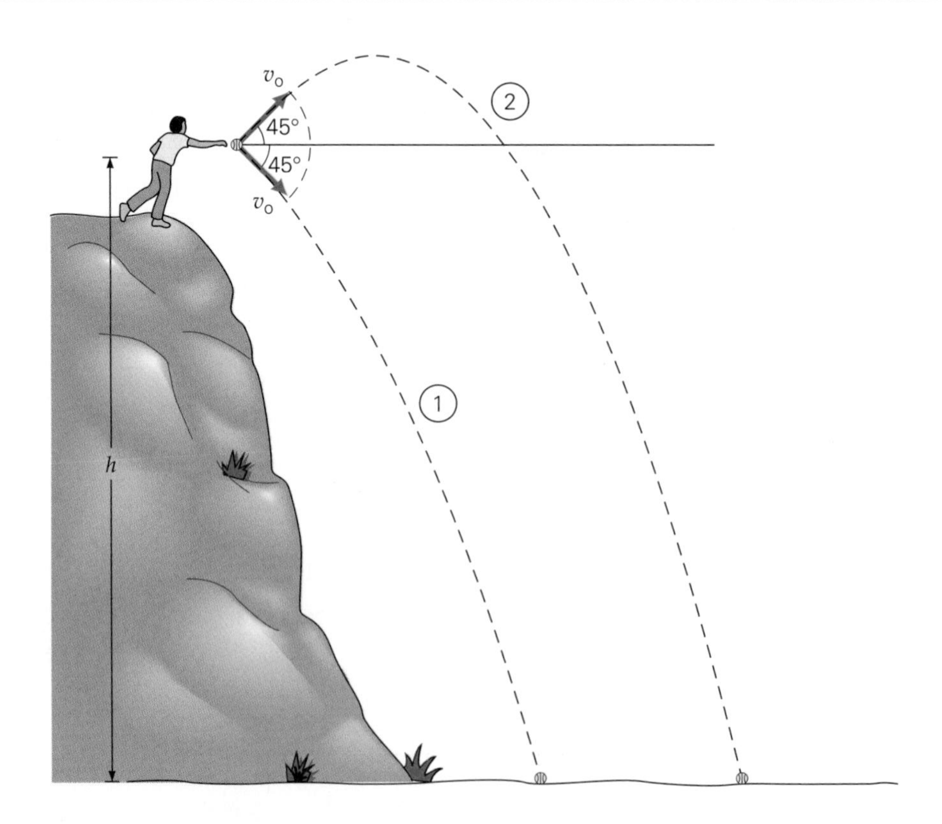

▶ **FIGURE 3.20 Which has the greater velocity?** See Example 3.11.

Problem-Solving Hint

The range of a downward projectile, as in Fig. 3.20, is found as illustrated in Example 3.10. But what about the range of the upward projectile? This task might be thought of as an "extended-range" problem. One way to solve it is to divide the trajectory into two parts—(1) the arc above the horizontal line and (2) the downward part below the horizontal line—such that $x_{max} = x_1 + x_2$. You know how to find x_1 (Example 3.9) and x_2 (Example 3.10). Another way to solve the problem is to use $y = y_o + v_{y_o}t - \frac{1}{2}gt^2$, where y is the final position of the projectile, and solve for t, the total time of flight. You would then use that value in the equation $x = v_{x_o}t$.

Equation 3.11 allows us to compute the range for a particular projection angle and initial velocity. However, we are sometimes interested in the maximum range for a given initial velocity—for example, the maximum range of an artillery piece that fires a projectile with a particular muzzle velocity. Is there an optimum angle that gives the maximum range? Under ideal conditions, the answer is yes.

For a particular v_o, the range is a maximum (R_{max}) when $\sin 2\theta = 1$, since this value of θ yields the maximum value of the sine function (which varies from 0 to 1). Thus,

$$R_{max} = \frac{v_o^2}{g} \quad (y_{initial} = y_{final}) \tag{3.12}$$

Because this maximum range is obtained when $\sin 2\theta = 1$ and because $\sin 90° = 1$, we have

$$2\theta = 90° \quad \text{or} \quad \theta = 45°$$

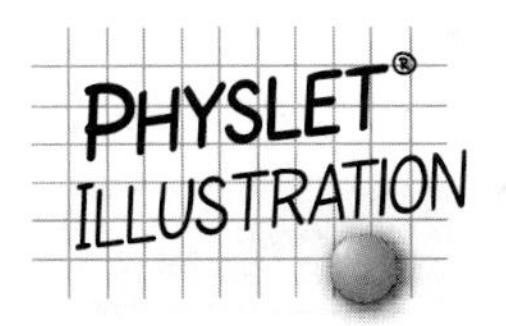

Range of a Projectile

for the maximum range for a given initial speed when the projectile returns to the elevation from which it was projected. At a greater or smaller angle, for a projectile with the same initial speed, the range will be less as illustrated in ▼Fig. 3.21. Also, the range is the same for angles equally above and below 45°, such as 30° and 60°.

Thus, to get the maximum range, a projectile *ideally* should be projected at an angle of 45°. However, up to now, we have neglected air resistance. In actual situations, such as when a ball or object is thrown or hit hard, this factor may have a significant effect. Air resistance reduces the speed of the projectile, thereby

▼ **FIGURE 3.21 Range** For a projectile with a given initial speed, the maximum range is ideally attained with a projection of 45° (no air resistance). For projection angles above and below 45°, the range is shorter, and it is equal for angles equally different from 45° (for example, 30° and 60°).

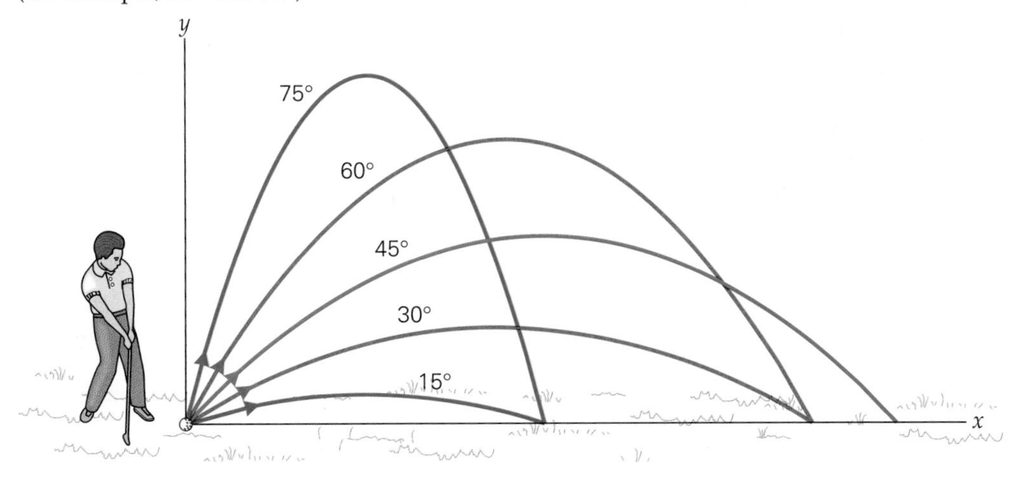

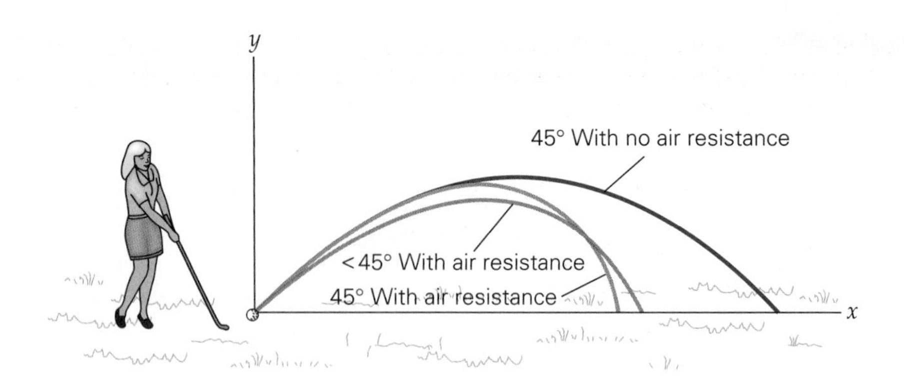

▶ **FIGURE 3.22 Air resistance and range** When air resistance is a factor, the angle of projection for maximum range is less than 45°.

reducing the range. As a result, when air resistance is a factor, the angle of projection for maximum range is less than 45°, which gives a greater initial horizontal velocity (▲Fig. 3.22). Other factors, such as spin and wind, may also affect the range of a projectile. For example, backspin on a driven golf ball provides lift, and the projection angle for the maximum range may be considerably less than 45°.

Keep in mind that for the maximum range to occur at a projection angle of 45°, the components of initial velocity must be equal—i.e., $\tan^{-1}(v_{y_o}/v_{x_o}) = 45°$ and $\tan 45° = 1$, so that $v_{y_o} = v_{x_o}$. However, this condition may not always be physically possible, as Conceptual Example 3.12 shows.

Conceptual Example 3.12 ■ The Longest Jump: Theory and Practice

In a long-jump event, the jumper normally has a launch angle of (a) less than 45°, (b) exactly 45°, or (c) greater than 45°? *Clearly establish the reasoning and physical principle(s) used in determining your answer before checking it below. That is, **why** did you select your answer?*

Reasoning and Answer. Air resistance is not a major factor here (although wind speed is taken into account for record setting in track-and-field events). Therefore, it would seem that, to achieve maximum range, the jumper would take off at an angle of 45°. But there is another physical consideration. Let's look more closely at the jumper's initial velocity components.

To maximize a long jump, the jumper runs as fast as possible and then pushes upward as strongly as possible to maximize the velocity components. The initial vertical velocity component v_{y_o} depends on the upward push of the jumper's legs, whereas the initial horizontal velocity component v_{x_o} depends mostly on the running speed toward the jump point. In general, a greater velocity can be achieved by running than by jumping, so $v_{x_o} > v_{y_o}$. Then, since $\theta = \tan^{-1}(v_{y_o}/v_{x_o})$, we have $\theta < 45°$, where $v_{y_o}/v_{x_o} < 1$ in this case. Hence, the answer is (a)—it certainly could not be (c). A typical launch angle for a long jump is 20° to 25°. (If a jumper increased her launch angle to be closer to the ideal 45°, then her running speed would have to decrease, resulting in a decrease in range.)

Follow-up Exercise. When jumping to score, basketball players seem to be suspended momentarily, or to "hang" in the air (◀Fig. 3.23). Explain the physics of this effect. *(Answers to all Follow-up Exercises are at the back of the text.)*

▲ **FIGURE 3.23 Hanging in there** Basketball players seem to "hang" in the air at the peak of their jump. Why is this? See the Follow-up Exercise for Conceptual Example 3.12.

Integrated Example 3.13 ■ A "Slap Shot": Is It Good?

A hockey player hits a "slap shot" in practice (with no goalie present) when he is 15.0 m directly in front of the net. The net is 1.20 m high, and the puck is initially hit at an angle of 5.00° above the ice with a speed of 35.0 m/s. (a) Make a sketch of the situation using

x–y coordinates, assuming that the puck is at the origin at the time it is hit. Be sure to locate the net in the sketch and show its height. (b) Determine if the puck makes it into the net. If it does, determine whether the puck is rising or falling vertically as it crosses the front plane of the net.

(a) Conceptual Reasoning. A sketch of the situation is shown in ▼Fig. 3.24. Note that the launch angle is exaggerated. An angle of 5.00° is quite small, but then again, the top of the net is not overly high (1.2 m).

(b) Thinking It Through. To determine if the shot is of goal quality, we need to know if the puck's trajectory takes it above the net or into the net. That is, what is the puck's height (y) when its horizontal distance is $x = 15$ m? Whether or not the puck is rising or falling at this horizontal distance depends on when the puck reaches its maximum height. The appropriate equation(s) should tell us this information; we must keep in mind that time is the connecting factor between the x- and y-components. Listing the data as usual, we have

Given:

$x = 15.0\text{ m}, x_o = 0$

$y_{net} = 1.20\text{ m}, y_o = 0$

$\theta = 5.00°$

$v_o = 35.0\text{ m/s}$

$v_{x_o} = v_o \cos 5.00° = 34.9\text{ m/s}$

$v_{y_o} = v_o \sin 5.00° = 3.05\text{ m/s}$

Find: (b) If the puck goes into the net and if so, if it is rising or falling

The vertical location of the puck at any time t is given by $y = v_{y_o}t - \frac{1}{2}gt^2$, so we need to know how long it takes for the puck to travel the 15.0 m to the net. The connecting factor of the components is time, so this time can be found from the x motion:

$$x = v_{x_o}t \quad \text{or} \quad t = \frac{x}{v_{x_o}} = \frac{15.0\text{ m}}{34.9\text{ m/s}} = 0.430\text{ s}$$

So, on reaching the front of the net, the puck is at a height of

$$y = v_{y_o}t - \tfrac{1}{2}gt^2 = (3.05\text{ m/s})(0.430\text{ s}) - \tfrac{1}{2}(9.80\text{ m/s}^2)(0.430\text{ s})^2$$
$$= 1.31\text{ m} - 0.906\text{ m} = 0.40\text{ m}$$

Goal!

The time (t_u) for the puck to reach its maximum height is given by $v_y = v_{y_o} - gt_u$, where $v_y = 0$ and

$$t_u = \frac{v_{y_o}}{g} = \frac{3.05\text{ m/s}}{9.80\text{ m/s}^2} = 0.311\text{ s}$$

and with the puck reaching the net in 0.430 s, it is descending.

Follow-up Exercise. At what distance from the net did the puck start to descend? *(Answers to all Follow-up Exercises are at the back of the text.)*

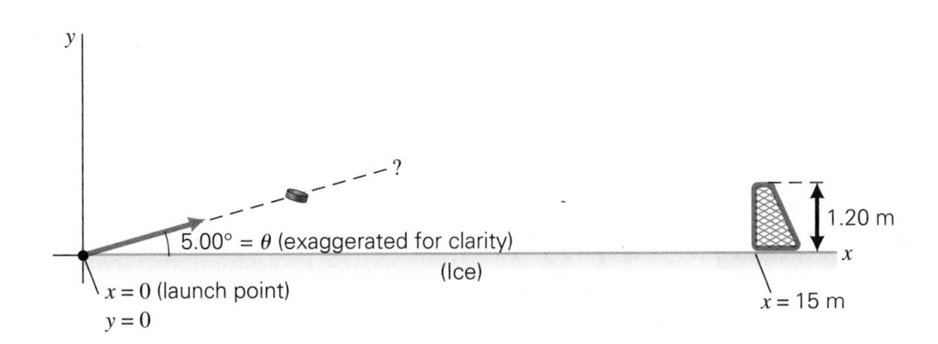

◀ **FIGURE 3.24 Slap shot** Is it a goal? See Integrated Example 3.13.

Chapter Review

Important Concepts and Equations

- Motion in two dimensions is analyzed by considering the motion of linear components. The connecting factor between components is time.

  Components of Initial Velocity:

  $$v_{x_o} = v_o \cos\theta \quad (3.1a)$$

  $$v_{y_o} = v_o \sin\theta \quad (3.1b)$$

  Components of Displacement *(constant acceleration only):*

  $$x = x_o + v_{x_o}t + \tfrac{1}{2}a_x t^2 \quad (3.3a)$$

  $$y = y_o + v_{y_o}t + \tfrac{1}{2}a_y t^2 \quad (3.3b)$$

  Components of Velocity *(constant acceleration only):*

  $$v_x = v_{x_o} + a_x t \quad (3.3c)$$

  $$v_y = v_{y_o} + a_y t \quad (3.3d)$$

- Of the various methods of vector addition, the component method is most useful. A resultant vector can be expressed in **magnitude–angle form** or in **unit-vector component form**.

  Vector Representation:

  $$\left.\begin{aligned} C &= \sqrt{C_x^2 + C_y^2} \\ \theta &= \tan^{-1}\left|\frac{C_y}{C_x}\right| \end{aligned}\right\} \text{ magnitude–angle form} \quad (3.4a)$$

  $$\mathbf{C} = C_x\,\hat{\mathbf{x}} + C_y\,\hat{\mathbf{y}} \quad \text{component form} \quad (3.7)$$

- **Relative velocity** is expressed *relative* to a particular reference frame.
- **Projectile motion** is analyzed by considering horizontal and vertical components separately—constant velocity in the horizontal direction and an acceleration due to gravity, g, in the downward vertical direction. (The foregoing equations for constant acceleration then have an acceleration of $a = -g$ instead of a.)

Exercises

3.1 Components of Motion

1. On Cartesian axes, the x-component of a vector is generally associated with a (a) cosine, (b) sine, (c) tangent, or (d) none of the foregoing.

2. CQ Can the x-component of a vector be greater than the magnitude of the vector? How about the y-component? Explain.

3. CQ Is it possible for an object's velocity to be perpendicular to the object's acceleration? If so, describe the motion.

4. For an object in curvilinear motion, (a) the object's velocity components are constant, (b) the y-velocity component is necessarily greater than the x-velocity component, (c) there is an acceleration nonparallel to the object's path, or (d) the velocity and acceleration vectors must be at right angles (90°).

5. CQ Describe the motion of an object that is initially traveling with a constant velocity and then receives an acceleration of constant magnitude (a) in a direction parallel to the initial velocity, (b) in a direction perpendicular to the initial velocity, and (c) that is always perpendicular to the instantaneous velocity or direction of motion.

6. IE ■ A golf ball is hit with an initial speed of 35 m/s at an angle less than 45° above the horizontal. (a) The horizontal velocity component is (1) greater than, (2) equal to, or (3) less than the vertical velocity component. Why? (b) If the ball is hit at an angle of 37°, what are the initial horizontal- and vertical-velocity components?

7. IE ■ The x- and y-components of an acceleration vector are 3.0 m/s^2 and 4.0 m/s^2, respectively. (a) The magnitude of the acceleration vector is (1) less than 3.0 m/s^2, (2) between 3.0 m/s^2 and 4.0 m/s^2, (3) between 4.0 m/s^2 and 7.0 m/s^2, or (4) equal to 7.0 m/s^2. (b) What are the magnitude and direction of the acceleration vector?

8. ■ If the magnitude of a velocity vector is 7.0 m/s and the x-component is 3.0 m/s, what is the y-component?

9. ■■ The x-component of a velocity vector that has an angle of 37° to the $+x$-axis has a magnitude of 4.8 m/s. (a) What is the magnitude of the velocity? (b) What is the magnitude of the y-component of the velocity?

10. IE ■■ A student walks 100 m west and 50 m south. (a) To get back to the starting point, the student must walk in a general direction of (1) south of west, (2) north of east,

(3) south of east, or (4) north of west. (b) What displacement will bring the student back to the starting point?

11. ■■ A student strolls diagonally across a level rectangular campus plaza, covering the 50-m distance in 1.0 min (▼Fig. 3.25). (a) If the diagonal route makes a 37° angle with the long side of the plaza, what would be the distance if the student had walked halfway around the outside of the plaza instead of along the diagonal route? (b) If the student had walked the outside route in 1.0 min at a constant speed, how much time would she have spent on each side?

▲ **FIGURE 3.25 Which way?** See Exercise 11.

12. ■■ The displacement vector of a moving object initially at the origin has a magnitude of 12.5 cm and is at an angle of 30° below the $-x$-axis at a particular instant. What are the coordinates of the object at that instant?

13. ■■ A ball rolls at a constant velocity of 1.50 m/s at an angle of 45° below the $+x$-axis in the fourth quadrant. If we take the ball to be at the origin at $t = 0$, what are its coordinates (x, y) 1.65 s later?

14. ■■ A ball rolling on a table has a velocity with rectangular components $v_x = 0.60$ m/s and $v_y = 0.80$ m/s. What is the displacement of the ball in an interval of 2.5 s?

15. ■■ A ball has an initial velocity of 1.30 m/s along the $+y$-axis and, starting at t_o, receives an acceleration of 2.10 m/s^2 in the $+x$-direction. (a) What is the position of the ball 2.50 s after t_o? (b) What is the velocity of the ball at that time?

16. ■■ A small plane takes off at a constant velocity of 150 km/h at an angle of 37°. At 3.00 s, (a) how high is the plane above the ground, and (b) what horizontal distance has the plane traveled from the liftoff point?

17. ■■ A ball rolls diagonally across tabletop from corner to corner with a constant speed of 0.75 m/s. The tabletop is 3.0 m wide and 4.0 m long. Another ball, starting at the same time as the first one and from the same corner, rolls along the longer edge of the table. What constant speed must the second ball have in order to reach the same corner at the same time as the ball traveling diagonally?

18. ■■ A particle moves at a speed of 2.5 m/s in the $+x$-direction. Upon reaching the origin, the particle receives a continuous constant acceleration of 0.75 m/s^2 in the $-y$-direction. What is the position of the particle 4.0 s later?

19. ■■■ An automobile travels, at a constant speed of 60 km/h, 800 m along a straight highway that is inclined 5.0° to the horizontal. An observer notes only the vertical motion of the car. What is the car's (a) vertical velocity magnitude and (b) vertical travel distance?

3.2 Vector Addition and Subtraction*

20. CQ Two vectors of magnitudes 3 and 4, respectively, are added. The magnitude of the resultant vector is (a) 1, (b) 7, or (c) between 1 and 7.

21. CQ In Exercise 20, under what condition would the magnitude of the resultant equal 1? How about 7? How about 5?

22. CQ The resultant of $\mathbf{A} - \mathbf{B}$ is the same as (a) $\mathbf{B} - \mathbf{A}$, (b) $-\mathbf{A} + \mathbf{B}$, (c) $-(\mathbf{A} + \mathbf{B})$, or (d) $-(\mathbf{B} - \mathbf{A})$.

23. CQ Can a nonzero vector have a zero x-component? Explain.

24. CQ Is it possible to add a vector quantity to a scalar quantity?

25. ■ Find the rectangular components of a velocity vector that has a magnitude of 10.0 m/s and is oriented at an angle of 30° above the $+x$-axis.

26. ■ Using the triangle method, show graphically that (a) $\mathbf{A} + \mathbf{B} = \mathbf{B} + \mathbf{A}$ and (b) if $\mathbf{A} - \mathbf{B} = \mathbf{C}$, then $\mathbf{A} = \mathbf{B} + \mathbf{C}$.

27. IE ■ (a) Is vector addition associative? That is, does $(\mathbf{A} + \mathbf{B}) + \mathbf{C} = \mathbf{A} + (\mathbf{B} + \mathbf{C})$? (b) Justify your answer graphically.

28. ■ A vector has an x-component of -2.5 m and a y-component of 4.2 m. Express the vector in magnitude–angle form.

29. ■ Consider yourself to be in boat A traveling along a straight path on a lake with a speed of $v_A = 30$ km/h. Another boat, boat B, travels at a speed of $v_B = 45$ km/h. Find the difference in the velocities, $\mathbf{v}_{BA} = \mathbf{v}_B - \mathbf{v}_A$, when (a) the other boat travels in the same direction in front of you and (b) the other boat is approaching you from the opposite direction.

30. ■ For the two vectors $\mathbf{x}_1 = (20\text{ m})\,\hat{\mathbf{x}}$ and $\mathbf{x}_2 = (15\text{ m})\,\hat{\mathbf{x}}$, compute and show graphically (a) $\mathbf{x}_1 + \mathbf{x}_2$, (b) $\mathbf{x}_1 - \mathbf{x}_2$, and (c) $\mathbf{x}_2 - \mathbf{x}_1$.

*There are a few exercises in this section that use force vectors (**F**). These vectors should be treated as vectors to be added, just as you would treat velocity vectors. The SI unit of force is the newton (N). A force vector might be written as $\mathbf{F} = 50$ N at an angle of 20°, similar to how we would specify a velocity vector $\mathbf{v} = 30$ m/s at an angle of 40°. Some familiarity with **F** vectors will be helpful in Chapter 4.

31. ■ During a takeoff (in still air), an airplane moves at a speed of 120 mi/h at an angle of 25° above the ground. What is the ground speed of the plane?

32. ■■ A dog walks northeast for 15 m and then east for 25 m. Find the resultant (or sum) displacement vector by (a) the graphical method and (b) the component method.

33. ■■ An airplane flies northwest for 250 mi and then west for 150 mi. Find the resultant (or sum) displacement vector by (a) the graphical method and (b) the component method.

34. ■■ Two boys are pulling a box across a horizontal floor as shown in ▸Fig 3.26. If $F_1 = 50.0$ N and $F_2 = 100$ N, find the resultant (or sum) force by (a) the graphical method and (b) the component method.

35. ■■ For each of the given vectors, give a vector that, when added to it, yields a *null vector* (a vector with a magnitude of zero). Express the vector in the form other than that in which it is given (component or magnitude–angle). (a) $\mathbf{A}$ = 4.5 cm, 40° above the $+x$-axis; (b) $\mathbf{B} = (2.0 \text{ cm})\,\hat{\mathbf{x}} - (4.0 \text{ cm})\,\hat{\mathbf{y}}$; (c) $\mathbf{C}$ = 8.0 cm at an angle of 60° above the $-x$-axis.

36. IE ■■ (a) If each of the two components (x and y) of a vector are doubled, (1) the vector's magnitude doubles, but the direction remains unchanged; (2) the vector's magnitude remains unchanged, but the direction angle doubles; or (3) both the vector's magnitude and direction angle double. (b) If the x- and y-components of a vector of 10 m at 45° are tripled, what is the new vector?

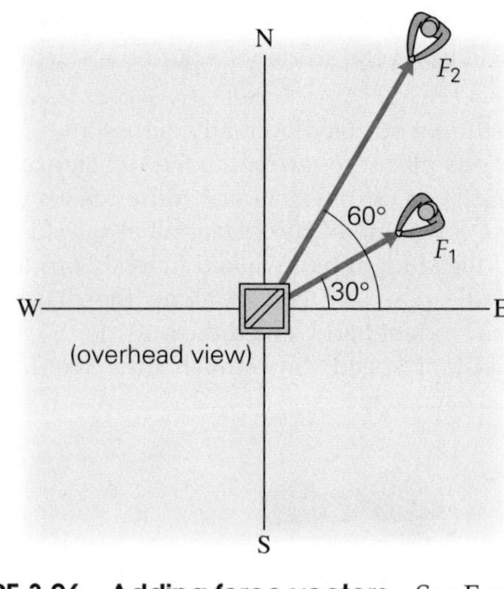

▲ **FIGURE 3.26 Adding force vectors** See Exercises 34 and 51.

37. ■■ (a) Find the resultant (or sum) of the vectors $\mathbf{F}_1$ and $\mathbf{F}_2$ in ▾Fig. 3.27. (b) If $\mathbf{F}_1$ in the figure were at an angle of 27° instead of 37° with the $+x$-axis, what would be the resultant (or sum) of $\mathbf{F}_1$ and $\mathbf{F}_2$?

38. ■■ Given two vectors $\mathbf{A}$, which has a length of 10.0 and makes an angle of 45° below the $-x$-axis, and $\mathbf{B}$, which has an x-component of +2.0 and a y-component of +4.0, (a) sketch the vectors on x–y axes, with all their "tails" starting at the origin, and (b) calculate $\mathbf{A} + \mathbf{B}$.

▶ **FIGURE 3.27 Vector addition** See Exercise 37.

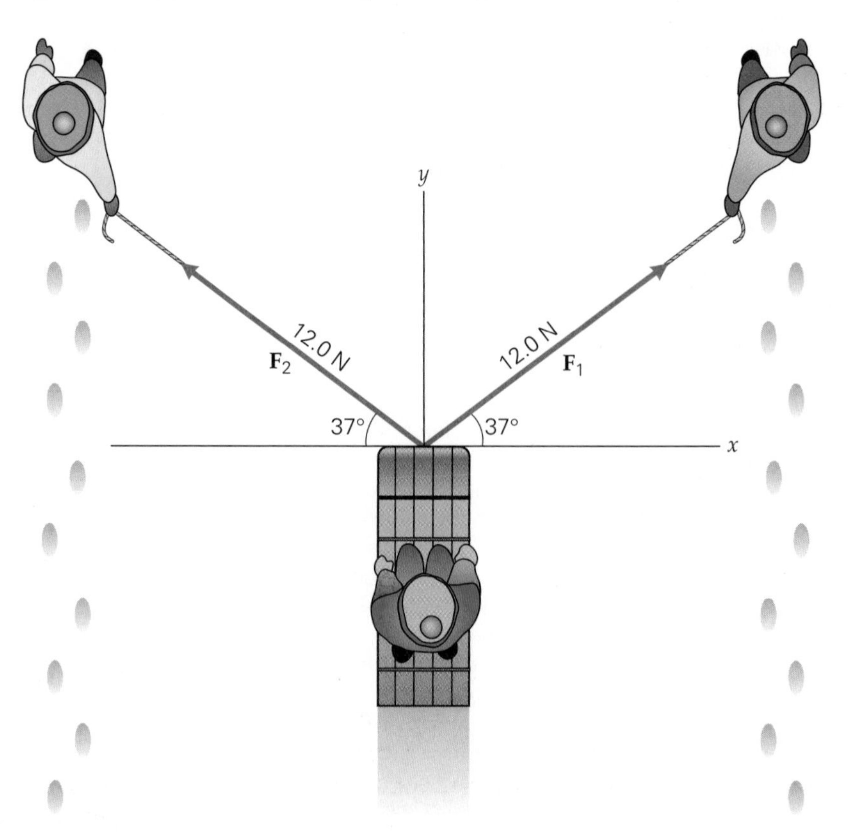

39. ■■ For the velocity vectors shown in ▼Fig. 3.28, determine **A** + **B** + **C**.

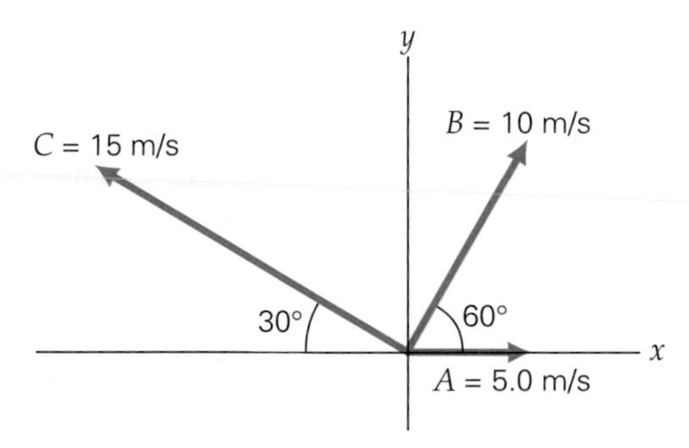

▲ **FIGURE 3.28 Adding velocity vectors** See Exercises 39 and 40.

40. ■■ For the velocity vectors shown in Fig. 3.28, determine **A** − **B** − **C**.

41. ■■ Given two vectors **A** and **B** with magnitude A and B, respectively, you can subtract **B** from **A** to get a third vector **C** = **A** − **B**. If the magnitude of **C** is equal to $C = A + B$, what is the relative orientation of vectors **A** and **B**?

42. ■■ Two force vectors $\mathbf{F}_1 = (3.0\text{ N})\,\hat{\mathbf{x}} - (3.0\text{ N})\,\hat{\mathbf{y}}$ and $\mathbf{F}_2 = (-6.0\text{ N})\,\hat{\mathbf{x}} + (4.5\text{ N})\,\hat{\mathbf{y}}$ are applied to a particle. What third force $\mathbf{F}_3$ would make the net, or resultant, force on the particle zero?

43. ■■ Two force vectors $\mathbf{F}_1$ = 8.0 N at an angle of 60° above the $+x$-axis and $\mathbf{F}_2$ = 5.5 N at an angle of 45° below the $+x$-axis are applied to a particle at the origin. What third force $\mathbf{F}_3$ would make the net, or resultant, force on the particle zero?

44. ■■ A student works three problems involving the addition of two different vectors $\mathbf{F}_1$ and $\mathbf{F}_2$. He states that the magnitudes of the three resultants are given by (a) $F_1 + F_2$, (b) $F_1 - F_2$, and (c) $\sqrt{F_1^2 + F_2^2}$. Are these results possible? If so, describe the vectors in each case.

45. ■■ A block weighing 50 N rests on an inclined plane. Its weight is a force directed vertically downward, as illustrated in ▼Fig. 3.29. Find the components of the force parallel to the surface of the plane and perpendicular to it.

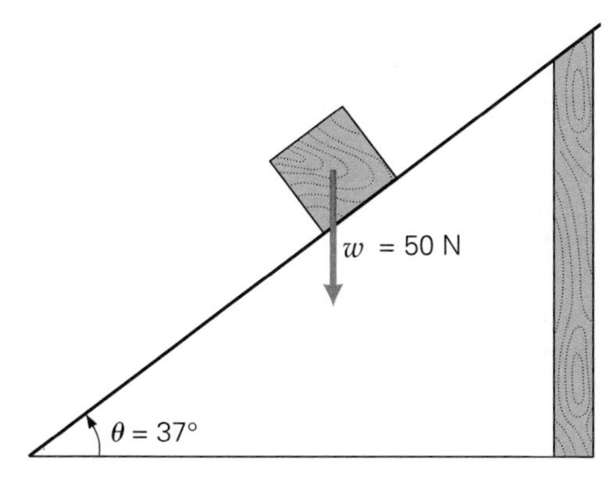

▲ **FIGURE 3.29 Block on an inclined plane** See Exercise 45.

46. ■■■ A roller coaster at an amusement park starts out on a level track 50.0 m long and then goes up a 25.0-m incline at an angle of 30° to the horizontal. It then goes down a 15.0-m ramp with an incline of 40° to the horizontal. When the roller coaster has reached the bottom of the ramp, what is its displacement from its starting point?

47. ■■■ A person walks from point A to point B as shown in ▼Fig. 3.30. What is the person's displacement relative to A?

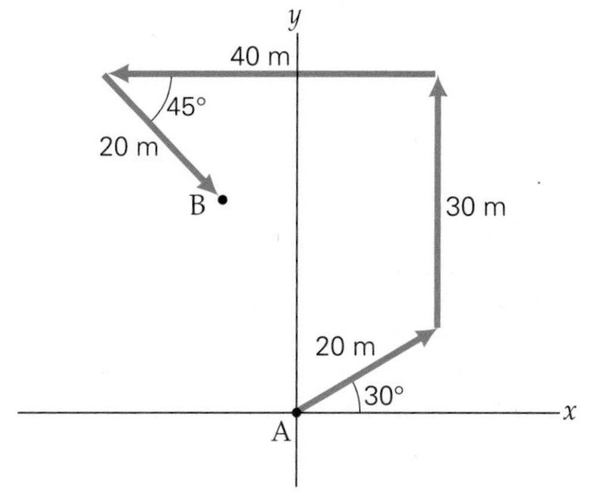

▲ **FIGURE 3.30 Adding displacement vectors** See Exercise 47.

48. IE ■■■ A meteorologist tracks the movement of a thunderstorm with Doppler radar. At 8:00 PM, the storm was 60 mi northeast of her station. At 10:00 PM, the storm is at 75 mi north. (a) The general direction of the thunderstorm's velocity is (1) south of east, (2) north of west, (3) north of east, or (4) south of west. (b) What is the average velocity of the storm?

49. IE ■■■ A flight controller determines that an airplane is 20.0 mi south of him. Half an hour later, the same plane is 35.0 mi northwest of him. (a) The general direction of the airplane's velocity is (1) east of south, (2) north of west, (3) north of east, or (4) west of south. (b) If the plane is flying with constant velocity, what is its velocity during this time?

50. ■■■ A ship is seen on a radar screen to be 10 km east of the radar site. Some time later, the ship is at 15 km northwest. What is the displacement of the ship?

51. ■■■ Two students are pulling a box as shown in Fig. 3.26. If F_1 = 100 N and F_2 = 150 N and a third student wants to stop the box, what force should he apply?

3.3 Relative Velocity

52. A student walks on a treadmill moving at 4.0 m/s and remains at the same place in the gym. (a) What is the student's velocity relative to the gym floor? (b) What is the student's speed relative to the treadmill?

53. CQ You are running in the rain along a straight sidewalk to your dorm. If the rain is falling vertically downward relative to the ground, how should you hold your umbrella so as to minimize the rain landing on you? Explain.

54. CQ When driving to the basket for a layup, a basketball player usually tosses the ball gently upward relative to herself. Explain why?

55. CQ When you are riding in a fast-moving car, in what direction would you throw an object up so it will return to your hand? Explain.

56. ■ While you are traveling in a car on a straight, level interstate highway at 90 km/h, another car passes you in the same direction; its speedometer reads 120 km/h. (a) What is your velocity relative to the other driver? (b) What is the other car's velocity relative to you?

57. ■ A shopper is in a hurry to catch a bargain in a department store. She walks up the escalator, rather than letting it carry her, at a speed of 1.0 m/s relative to the escalator. If the escalator is 20 m long and moves at a speed of 0.50 m/s, how long does it take for the shopper to get to the next floor?

58. ■ A person riding in the back of a pickup truck traveling at 70 km/h on a straight, level road throws a ball with a speed of 15 km/h relative to the truck in the direction opposite to the truck's motion. What is the velocity of the ball (a) relative to a stationary observer by the side of the road, and (b) relative to the driver of a car moving in the same direction as the truck at a speed of 90 km/h?

59. ■ In Exercise 58, what are the relative velocities if the ball is thrown in the direction of the truck?

60. ■ A boat heads upstream for 30 s at 5.0 m/s relative to still water. If the speed of the current is 3.0 m/s, what distance does the boat travel? How about if the boat were heading downstream?

61. ■■ In a 500-m stretch of a river, the speed of the current is a steady 5.0 m/s. How long does it take for a boat to finish a round-trip (upstream and downstream) if the speed of the boat is 7.5 m/s relative to still water?

62. ■■ Suppose you are climbing up the mast of a sailboat at a speed of 0.20 m/s. If the sailboat is moving with a speed of 0.60 m/s in a lake, what is your relative velocity to the lake?

63. ■■ A moving walkway in an airport is 75 m long and moves at a speed of 0.30 m/s. A passenger, after traveling 25 m while standing on the walkway, starts to walk at a speed of 0.50 m/s relative to the surface of the walkway. How long does it take her to travel the total distance of the walkway?

64. IE ■■ A swimmer swims north at 0.15 m/s relative to still water across a river that flows at a rate of 0.20 m/s from west to east. (a) The general direction of the swimmer's velocity, relative to the river bank, is (1) north of east, (2) south of west, (3) north of west, or (4) south of east. (b) Calculate the swimmer's velocity relative to the riverbank.

65. ■■ A swimmer maintains a speed of 0.15 m/s relative to the water when he swims directly toward the opposite shore of a river. The river has a current that flows at 0.75 m/s. (a) How far downstream is he carried in 1.5 min? (b) What is his velocity relative to an observer on shore?

66. ■■ A boat that travels at a speed of 6.75 m/s in still water is to go directly across a river and back (▼Fig. 3.31). The current flows at 0.50 m/s. (a) At what angle(s) must the boat be steered? (b) How long does it take to make the round-trip? (Assume that the boat's speed is constant at all times, and neglect turnaround time.)

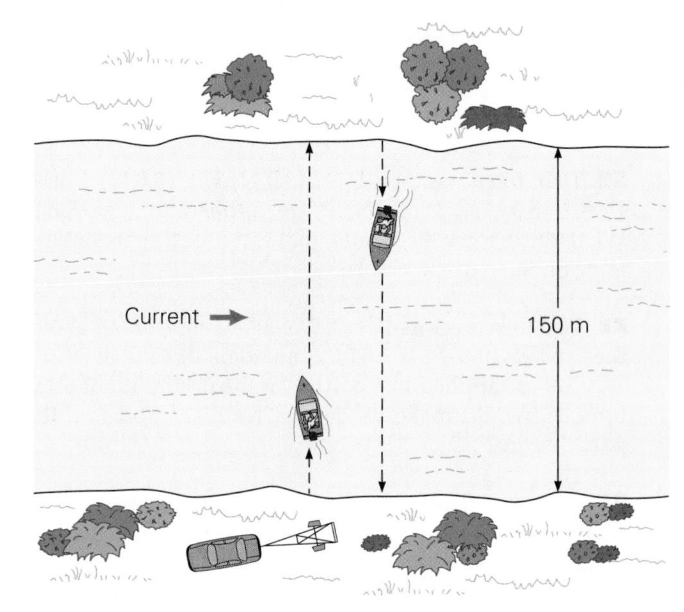

▲ **FIGURE 3.31 Over and back** See Exercise 66. (Not drawn to scale.)

67. IE ■■ It is raining, and there is no wind. When you are sitting in a stationary car, the rain falls straight down relative to the car and the ground. But when you're driving, the rain appears to hit the windshield at an angle. (a) As the velocity of the car increases, this angle (1) also increases, (2) remains the same, or (3) decreases. Why? (b) If the raindrops fall straight down at a speed of 10 m/s, but appear to make an angle of 25° to the vertical, what is the speed of the car?

68. ■■ Swimming at 0.15 m/s relative to still water, a swimmer heads directly across a 100-m-wide river. He arrives 50 m downstream from a point directly across the river from his starting point. (a) What is the speed of the current in the river? (b) In what direction should the swimmer head so as to arrive at a point directly opposite his starting point?

69. ■■■ An airplane is flying at 150 mi/h (its speed in still air) in a direction such that with a wind of 60.0 mi/h blowing from east to west, the airplane travels in a straight line southward. (a) What must be the plane's heading direction for it to fly directly south? (b) If the plane has to go 200 mi in the southward direction, how long does it take?

3.4 Projectile Motion*

70. If air resistance is neglected, the motion of an object projected at an angle consists of a uniform downward acceleration combined with (a) an equal horizontal acceleration, (b) a uniform horizontal velocity, (c) a constant upward velocity, or (d) an acceleration that is always perpendicular to the path of motion.

71. CQ A golf ball is hit on a level fairway. When it lands, its velocity vector has rotated through an angle of 90°. What was the launch angle of the golf ball? [*Hint*: See Fig. 3.17.]

72. CQ Figure 3.16b shows a multiflash photograph of one ball dropping from rest and, at the same time, another ball projected horizontally at the same height. The two balls hit the ground at the same time. Why? Explain.

73. CQ In ▼Fig. 3.32, a spring-loaded "cannon" on a wheeled car fires a metal ball vertically. The car is given a push and set in motion horizontally with constant velocity. A pin is pulled with a string to launch the ball, which travels upward and then falls back into the moving cannon every time. Why does the ball always fall back into the cannon? Explain.

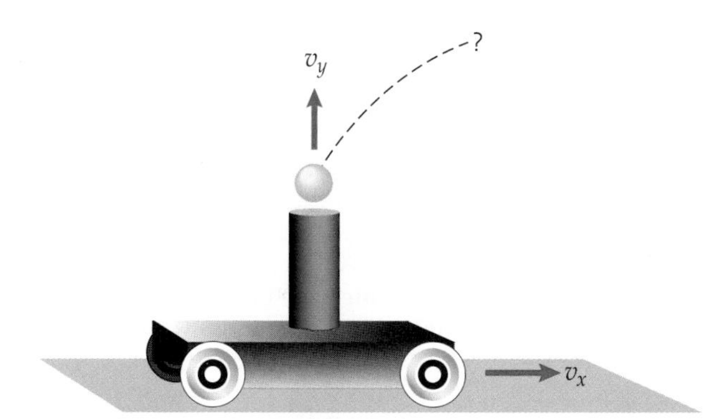

▲ **FIGURE 3.32 A ballistics car** See Exercises 73 and 83.

74. ■ A ball with a horizontal speed of 1.5 m/s rolls off a bench 2.0 m high. (a) How long will it take the ball to reach the floor? (b) How far from a point on the floor directly below the edge of the bench will the ball land?

75. ■ An electron is ejected horizontally at a speed of 1.5×10^6 m/s from the electron gun of a computer monitor. If the viewing screen is 35 cm away from the end of the gun, how far will the electron travel in the vertical direction before hitting the screen? Based on your answer, do you think designers need to worry about this gravitational effect?

76. ■ A ball is thrown horizontally, with a speed of 15 m/s, from the top of a 6.0-m tall hill. How far from the point on the ground directly below the launch point does the ball strike the ground?

77. ■ If Exercise 76 were to take place on the surface of the Moon, where the acceleration due to gravity is only 1.67 m/s^2, what would be the answer?

78. ■ A ball rolls horizontally with a speed of 7.6 m/s off the edge of a tall platform. If the ball lands 8.7 m from the point on the ground directly below the edge of the platform, what is the height of the platform?

79. ■ A golf ball is hit at a speed of 30 m/s at an angle of 30° above the horizontal. What are the horizontal and vertical components of the ball's velocity?

80. ■■ A pitcher throws a fastball horizontally at a speed of 140 km/h toward home plate, 18.4 m away. (a) If the batter's combined reaction and swing times total 0.350 s, how long can the batter watch the ball after it has left the pitcher's hand before swinging? (b) In traveling to the plate, how far does the ball drop from its original horizontal line?

81. IE ■■ Ball A rolls at a constant speed of 0.25 m/s on a table 0.95 m above the floor, and ball B rolls on the floor directly under the first ball and with the same speed and direction. (a) When ball A rolls off the table and hits the floor, (1) ball B is ahead of ball A, (2) ball B collides with ball A, or (3) ball A is ahead of ball B. Why? (b) When ball A hits the floor, how far from the point directly below the edge of the table will both balls be?

82. ■■ A package of supplies is to be dropped from an airplane so that it hits the ground at a designated spot near some campers. The airplane, moving horizontally at a constant velocity of 140 km/h, approaches the spot at an altitude of 0.500 km above level ground. Having the designated point in sight, the pilot prepares to drop the package. (a) What should the angle be between the horizontal and the pilot's line of sight when the package is released? (b) What is the location of the plane when the package hits the ground?

83. ■■ A wheeled car with a spring-loaded cannon fires a metal ball vertically (◄Fig. 3.32). If the vertical initial speed of the ball is 5.0 m/s as the cannon moves horizontally at a speed of 0.75 m/s, (a) how far from the launch point does the ball fall back into the cannon, and (b) what would happen if the cannon were accelerating?

84. ■■ A soccer player kicks a stationary ball, giving it a speed of 20.0 m/s at an angle of 15.0° to the horizontal. (a) What is the maximum height reached by the ball?

*Assume angles to be exact for significant figure purposes.

(b) What is the ball's range? (c) How could the range be increased?

85. ■■ A rifle fires a bullet at a speed of 250 m/s at an angle of 37° above the horizontal. (a) What height does the bullet reach? (b) How long is the ball in the air? (c) What is the ball's horizontal range?

86. ■■ A golf ball, hit off a tee on level ground, lands 62 m away 3.0 s later. What was the initial velocity of the golf ball?

87. ■■ An arrow has an initial launch speed of 18 m/s. If it must strike a target 31 m away at the same elevation, what should be the projection angle?

88. ■■ An astronaut on the Moon fires a projectile from a launcher on a level surface so as to get the maximum range. If the launcher gives the projectile a muzzle velocity of 25 m/s, what is the range of the projectile? [*Hint*: The acceleration due to gravity on the Moon is only one sixth of that on the Earth.]

89. ■■ A stone thrown off a bridge 20 m above a river has an initial velocity of 12 m/s at an angle of 45° above the horizontal (▼Fig. 3.33). (a) What is the range of the stone? (b) At what velocity does the stone strike the water?

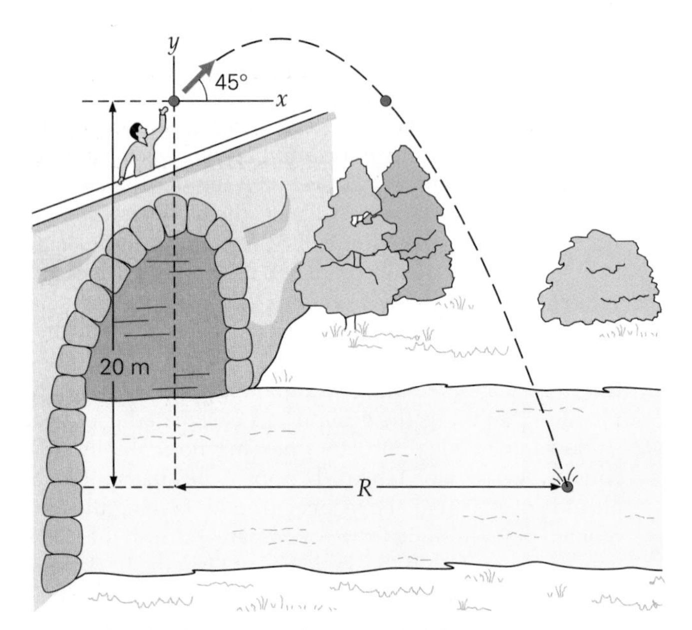

▲ **FIGURE 3.33 A view from the bridge** See Exercise 89.

90. ■■ William Tell is said to have shot an apple off his son's head with an arrow. If the arrow was shot with an initial speed of 55 m/s and the boy was 15 m away, at what launch angle did Bill aim the arrow? (Assume that the arrow and apple are initially at the same height above the ground.)

91. ■■■ This time, William Tell is shooting at an apple that hangs on a tree (▶Fig. 3.34). The apple is a horizontal distance of 20.0 m away and at a height of 4.00 m above the ground. If the arrow is released from a height of 1.00 m above the ground and hits the apple 0.500 s later, what is the arrow's initial velocity?

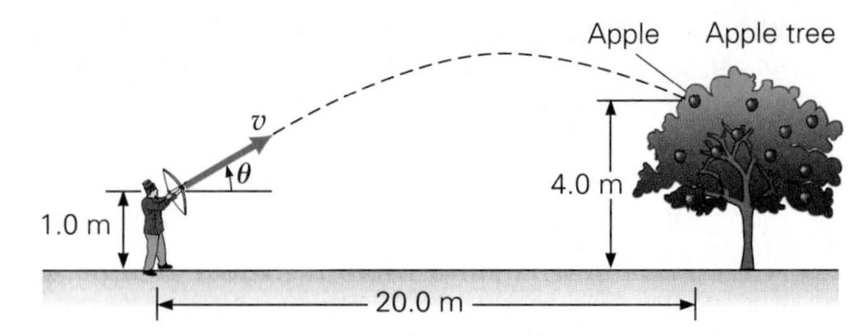

▲ **FIGURE 3.34 Hit the apple** See Exercise 91. (Not drawn to scale.)

92. ■■■ A ditch 2.5 m wide crosses a trail bike path (▼Fig 3.35). An upward incline of 15° has been built up on the approach so that the top of the incline is level with the top of the ditch. What is the minimum speed a trail bike must be moving to clear the ditch? (Add 1.4 m to the range for the back of the bike to clear the ditch safely.)

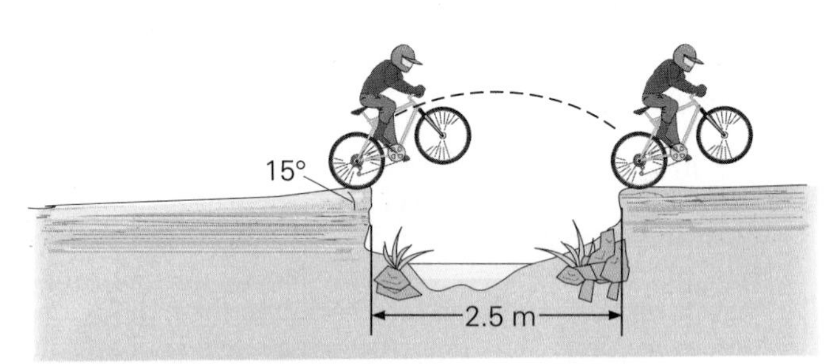

▲ **FIGURE 3.35 Clear the ditch** See Exercise 92. (Not drawn to scale.)

93. ■■■ A quarterback passes a football—at a velocity of 50 ft/s at an angle of 40° to the horizontal—toward an intended receiver 30 yd downfield. The pass is released 5.0 ft above the ground. Assume that the receiver is stationary and that he will catch the ball if it comes to him. Will the pass be completed? If not, will the throw be long or short?

94. ■■■ A 2.05-m-tall basketball player takes a shot when he is 6.02 m from the basket (at the three-point line). If the launch angle is 25° and the ball was launched at the level of the player's head, what must be the release speed of the ball for the player to make the shot? The basket is 3.05 m above the floor.

95. ■■■ The hole on a level, elevated golf green is a horizontal distance of 150 m from the tee and at an elevation of 12.0 m above the tee. A golfer hits a ball at an angle 10.0° greater than that of the hole above the tee and makes a hole in one! (a) Sketch the situation. (b) What

was the initial speed of the ball? (c) Suppose the next golfer hits her ball toward the hole at the same speed, but at an angle of 10.5° greater than that of the hole above the tee. Does the ball go in the hole, or is the shot too long or too short?

Additional Exercises

96. The apparatus for a popular lecture demonstration is shown in ▾Fig. 3.36. A gun is aimed directly at a can, which is simultaneously released when the gun is fired. This gun won't miss as long as the initial speed of the bullet is sufficient to reach the falling target before the target hits the floor. Verify this statement, using the figure. [*Hint*: Note that $y_o = x \tan\theta$.]

97. What is the resultant velocity vector of the following three velocity vectors? $\mathbf{v}_1 = (3.0\ \text{m/s})\ \hat{\mathbf{x}} + (4.0\ \text{m/s})\ \hat{\mathbf{y}}$; $\mathbf{v}_2 = (-4.0\ \text{m/s})\ \hat{\mathbf{x}} + (5.0\ \text{m/s})\ \hat{\mathbf{y}}$; $\mathbf{v}_3 = (5.0\ \text{m/s})\ \hat{\mathbf{x}} - (7.0\ \text{m/s})\ \hat{\mathbf{y}}$. Express your result in both component and magnitude–angle forms.

98. A motorboat travels at a speed of 40.0 km/h in a straight path on a still lake. Suddenly, a strong, steady wind pushes the boat at a speed of 15.0 km/h perpendicularly to its straight-line path for 5.00 s. Relative to its position just when the wind started to blow, where is the boat located at the end of this time?

99. You are traveling and start out 200 mi directly south of your destination. If you first go 150 mi at 25° west of north to visit your friends, what must be your second displacement in order for you to get to your destination?

100. If the flow rate of the current in a straight river is greater than the speed of a boat in the water, the boat cannot make a trip *directly across* the river. Prove this statement.

101. A student throws a softball horizontally from a dorm window 15.0 m above the ground. Another student standing 10.0 m away from the dorm catches the ball at a height of 1.50 m above the ground. What is the initial velocity of the ball?

102. In two attempts, a javelin is thrown at angles of 35° and 60°, respectively, to the horizontal from the same height and at the same speed in each case. For which throw does the javelin go farther, and how many times farther? (Assume that the landing place is at the same height as the launching place.)

103. If the maximum height reached by a projectile launched on level ground is equal to half the projectile's range, what is the launch angle?

104. In a movie, a monster climbs to the top of a building 30 m above the ground and hurls a boulder downward with a speed of 25 m/s at an angle of 45° below the horizontal. How far from the building does the boulder land?

105. The shells fired from an artillery piece have a muzzle speed of 150 m/s, and the target is at a horizontal distance of 2.00 km. (a) At what angle relative to the horizontal should the gun be aimed? (b) Could the gun hit a target 3.00 km away?

106. A hockey player hits a "slap shot" in practice at a horizontal distance of 15 m from the net (with no goalie present). The net is 1.2 m high, and the puck is initially hit at an angle of 5.0° above the horizontal with a speed of 50 m/s. Does the puck make it into the net?

107. A ball is thrown horizontally from the top of a building at a height of 32.5 m above the ground and hits the level ground 56.0 m from the base of the building. (a) What is the initial speed of the ball? (b) What is the velocity of the ball just before it hits the ground?

108. A field goal is attempted when the football is at the center of the field, 40 yd from the goalposts. If the kicker gives the ball a velocity of 70 ft/s toward the goalposts at an angle of 45° to the horizontal, will the kick be good? (The crossbar of the goalposts is 10 ft above the ground, and the ball must be higher than the crossbar when it reaches the goalposts for the field goal to be good.)

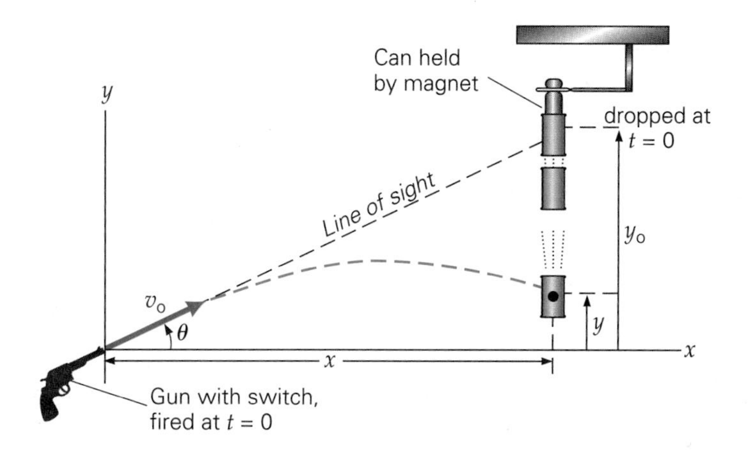

▶ **FIGURE 3.36 A sure shot** See Exercise 96. (Not drawn to scale.)

109. (a) An object moving at a speed of 10 m/s in a straight line has a velocity with an x-component of +6.0 m/s. In what directions could the the object be moving? (b) What is the value(s) of the y-component of the velocity?

110. At a track-and-field meet, the best long jump is measured as 8.20 m. The jumper took off at an angle of 37° to the horizontal. (a) What was the jumper's initial speed? (b) If there were another meet on the Moon and the same jumper could attain only half of the initial speed he had on the Earth, what would be the maximum jump there? (Air resistance does not have to be neglected in part (b). Why?)

111. An airplane with a speed of 150 km/h heads directly north while a west wind blows at a constant speed of 30 km/h. How far does the plane travel during the 4-hour flight?

Force and Motion

CHAPTER 4

You don't have to understand any physics to know what's needed to get the car in the picture (or anything else) moving: a push or a pull. If the frustrated motorist (or the tow truck that he will soon call) can apply enough *force*, the car will move.

But what's keeping the car stuck in the snow? A car's engine can generate plenty of force—so why doesn't the motorist just put the car into reverse and back out? For a car to move, another force is needed besides that exerted by the engine: *friction*. Here, the problem is most likely that there is not enough friction between the tires and the snow.

In Chapters 2 and 3, we learned how to analyze motion in terms of kinematics. Now we need to know more about the *dynamics* of motion—that is, what *causes* motion and changes in motion? This inquiry leads us to the concept of force and inertia.

The study of force and motion occupied many early scientists. It was the English scientist Isaac Newton (1642–1727) (▸Fig. 4.1) who summarized the various relationships and principles of those early scientists into three statements, or laws, which, not surprisingly, are known as *Newton's laws of motion*. These laws sum up the concepts of dynamics. In this chapter, you'll learn what Newton had to say about force and motion.

4.1 The Concepts of Force and Net Force

OBJECTIVES: **To (a) relate force and motion and (b) explain what is meant by a net or unbalanced force.**

Let's first take a closer look at the meaning of force. It is easy to give examples of forces, but how would you generally define this concept? An operational definition of force is based on observed effects. That is, a force is described in terms of what it does. From your own experience, you

▲ **FIGURE 4.1 Isaac Newton** Newton (1642–1727), one of the greatest scientific minds of all time, made fundamental contributions to mathematics, astronomy, and several branches of physics, including optics and mechanics. He formulated the laws of motion and universal gravitation and was one of the inventors of calculus. He did some of his most profound work when he was in his midtwenties.

know that *forces can produce changes in motion*. A force can set a stationary object into motion. It can also speed up or slow down a moving object or change the direction of its motion. In other words, a force can produce a change in velocity (speed and/or direction)—that is, an acceleration. Therefore, an observed change in motion, including motion starting from rest, is evidence of a force. This concept leads to a common definition of **force**:

> A force is something that is capable of changing an object's state of motion (its velocity).

The word "capable" is very significant here. It takes into account the fact that a force may be acting on an object, but its capability to produce a change in motion may be balanced, or canceled, by one or more other forces. The net effect is then zero. Thus, a force may *not necessarily* produce a change in motion. However, it follows that if a force acts *alone*, the object on which it acts *will* accelerate.

Since a force can produce an acceleration—a vector quantity—force must itself be a vector quantity, with both magnitude and direction. When several forces act on an object, you will often be interested in their combined effect—the net force. The **net force**, $\mathbf{F}_{net}$, is the vector sum $\Sigma\mathbf{F}_i$, or resultant, of all the forces acting on an object or system. (See the note in the margin.) Consider the opposite forces illustrated in ▾Fig. 4.2a. The net force is zero when forces of equal magnitude act in opposite directions (Fig. 4.2b). Such forces are said to be *balanced forces*. A nonzero net force is referred to as an unbalanced force (Fig. 4.2c). In this case, *the situation can be analyzed as though only one force equal to the net force were acting*. An unbalanced, or nonzero, net force produces an acceleration. In some instances, an applied unbalanced force may also deform an object, that is, change its size and/or shape (as we shall see in Chapter 7). A deformation involves a change in motion for some part of an object; hence, there is an acceleration.

Forces are sometimes divided into two types or classes. The more familiar of these classes is *contact forces*. Such forces arise because of physical contact between objects. For example, when you push on a door to open it or throw or kick a ball, you exert a contact force on the door or ball.

Note: In the notation ΣF_i, the Greek letter sigma means the "sum of" the individual forces, as indicated by the i subscript: $\Sigma F_i = F_1 + F_2 + F_3 + F_4$, that is, a vector sum. The i subscripts are sometimes omitted as being understood, and we write ΣF.

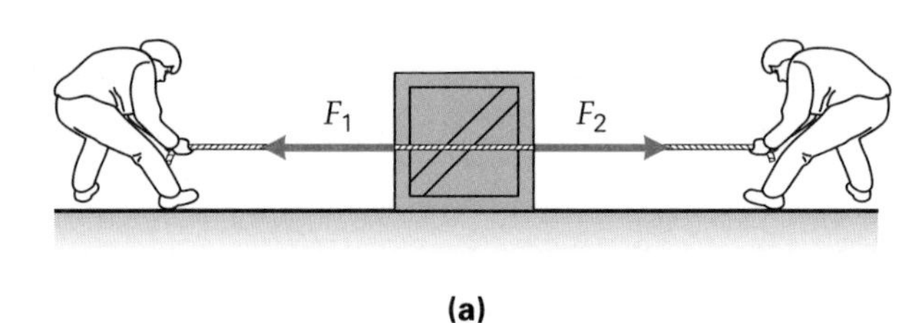

(a)

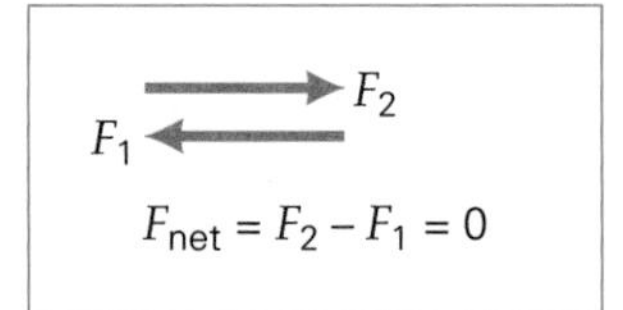

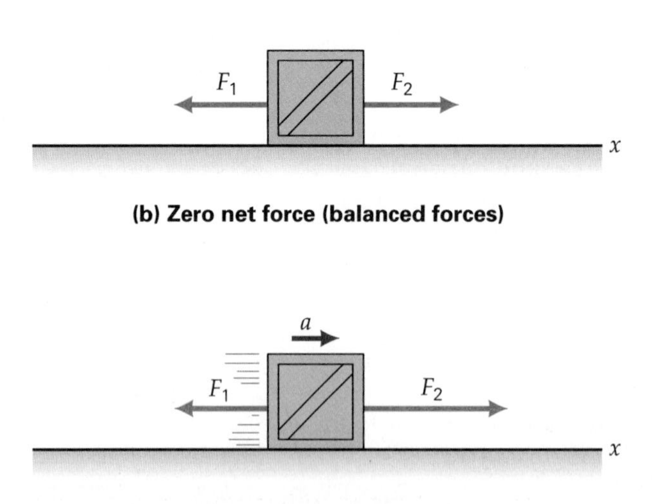

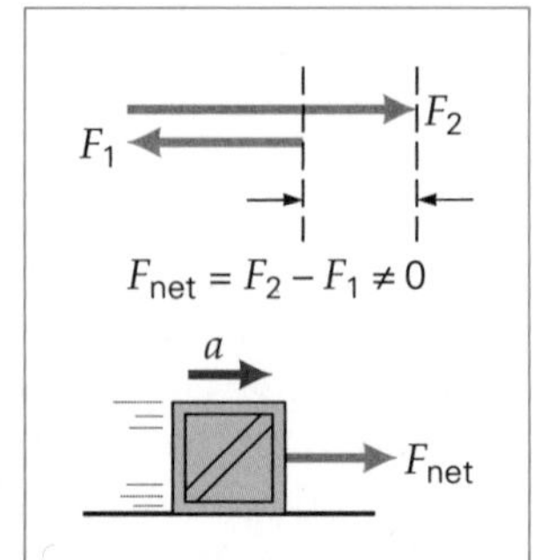

▶ **FIGURE 4.2 Net force** **(a)** Opposite forces are applied to a crate. **(b)** If the forces are of equal magnitude, the vector resultant, or the net force acting on the crate in the x-direction, is zero. The forces acting on the crate are said to be balanced. **(c)** If the forces are unequal in magnitude, the resultant is not zero. A nonzero net force, or an unbalanced force, then acts on the crate, producing an acceleration (for example, setting the crate in motion if it was initially at rest).

The other class of forces is called *action-at-a-distance forces.* Examples of these forces include gravity, the electrical force between two charges, and the magnetic force between two magnets. The Moon is attracted to the Earth and maintained in orbit by a gravitational force, but there seems to be nothing physically transmitting that force.

Now, with a better understanding of the concept of force, let's see how force and motion are related through Newton's laws.

4.2 Inertia and Newton's First Law of Motion

OBJECTIVES: **To (a) state and explain Newton's first law of motion, and (b) describe inertia and its relationship to mass.**

The groundwork for Newton's first law of motion was laid by Galileo. In his experimental investigations, Galileo dropped objects to observe motion under the influence of gravity. (See the related Insight in Chapter 2.) However, the relatively large acceleration due to gravity causes dropped objects to move quite fast and quite far in a short time. From the kinematic equations in Chapter 2, you can see that 3.0 s after being dropped (if we neglect air resistance), an object in free fall has a speed of about 29 m/s (64 mi/h) and has fallen a distance of 44 m (about 48 yd, or almost half the length of a football field). Thus, experimental measurements of free-fall distance versus time were particularly difficult to make with the instrumentation available in Galileo's time.

To slow things down so that he could study motion, Galileo used balls rolling on inclined planes. He allowed a ball to roll down one inclined plane and then up another with a different degree of incline (▼Fig. 4.3). Galileo noted that the ball rolled to approximately the same height in every case, but it rolled farther in the horizontal direction when the angle of incline was smaller. When allowed to roll onto a horizontal surface, the ball traveled a considerable distance and went even farther when the surface was made smoother. Galileo wondered how far the ball would travel if the horizontal surface could be made perfectly smooth (frictionless). Although this situation was impossible to attain experimentally, Galileo reasoned that in this ideal case with an infinitely long surface, the ball would continue to travel (actually slide) indefinitely with straight-line, uniform motion, since there would be nothing (no net force) to cause its motion to change.

According to Aristotle's theory of motion, which had been accepted for about 1500 years prior to Galileo's time, the normal state of a body was to be at rest (with the exception of celestial bodies, which were thought to be naturally in motion). Aristotle probably observed that objects moving on a surface tend to slow down and come to rest, so this conclusion would have seemed logical to him. However, from his experiments, Galileo concluded that bodies in motion exhibit the behavior of maintaining that motion and that if an object is initially at rest, it will remain so, unless something causes it to move.

Galileo called this tendency of an object to maintain its initial state of motion **inertia.** That is,

Definition of: Inertia

> Inertia is the natural tendency of an object to maintain a state of rest or to remain in uniform motion in a straight line (constant velocity).

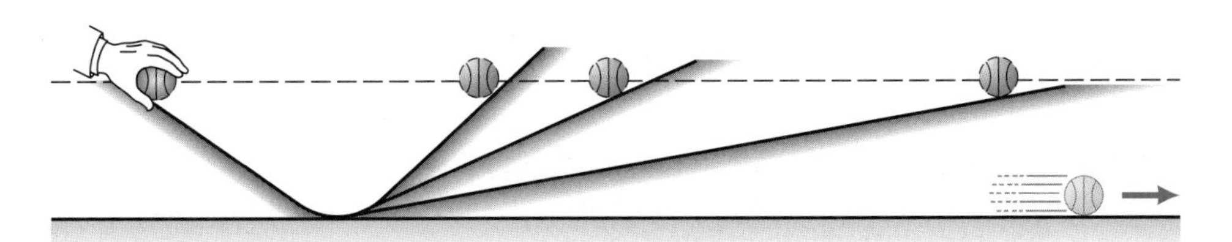

◀ **FIGURE 4.3 Galileo's experiment** A ball rolls farther along the upward incline as the angle of incline is decreased. On a smooth, horizontal surface, the ball rolls a greater distance before coming to rest. How far would the ball travel on an ideal, perfectly smooth surface?

For example, if you've ever tried to stop a slowly rolling automobile by pushing on it, you felt its resistance to a change in motion, to slowing down. Physicists describe the property of inertia in terms of observed behavior, as they do for all physical phenomena. A comparative example of inertia is illustrated in ◂Fig. 4.4. If the two punching bags have the same density (mass per unit volume; see Chapter 1), the larger one has more mass and therefore more inertia, as you would quickly notice when you try to punch both bags.

Newton related the concept of inertia to mass. Originally, he called mass a quantity of matter, but he later redefined it as follows:

Relationship of mass and inertia

> Mass is a quantitative measure of inertia.

That is, a massive object has more inertia, or more resistance to a change in motion, than does a less massive object. For example, a car has more inertia than a bicycle.

Newton's first law—the law of inertia

Newton's first law of motion, sometimes called the *law of inertia*, summarizes these observations:

Note: Inertia is *not* a force.

> In the absence of an unbalanced applied force ($\mathbf{F}_{net} = 0$), a body at rest remains at rest, and a body already in motion remains in motion with a constant velocity (constant speed and direction).

That is, if the net force acting on an object is zero, then its acceleration is zero.

▲ **FIGURE 4.4 A difference in inertia** The larger punching bag has more mass and hence more inertia, or resistance to a change in motion.

4.3 Newton's Second Law of Motion

OBJECTIVES: To (a) state and explain Newton's second law of motion, (b) apply it to physical situations, and (c) distinguish between weight and mass.

A change in motion, or an acceleration (i.e., a change in speed and/or direction), is evidence of a net force. All experiments indicate that an acceleration is directly proportional to, and in the direction of, the applied net force; that is,

$$\mathbf{a} \propto \mathbf{F}_{net}$$

where the boldface symbols indicate vector quantities. For example, if you hit an identical second ball twice as hard as the first one (i.e., you applied twice as much force), you would expect the acceleration of the second ball to be twice as great as that of the first ball (but still in the direction of the force).

However, as Newton recognized, the inertia or mass of the object also plays a role. For a given net force, the more massive the object, the *less* its acceleration will be. That is, the magnitude of the acceleration and mass (m) of an object are inversely proportional:

$$a \propto \frac{1}{m}$$

For example, if you hit two balls of different masses with the same force, the less massive ball would experience a greater acceleration.

Then combining these relationships, we have

$$\mathbf{a} \propto \frac{\mathbf{F}_{net}}{m}$$

or, in words,

> The acceleration of an object is directly proportional to the net force acting on it and inversely proportional to its mass. The direction of the acceleration is in the direction of the applied net force.

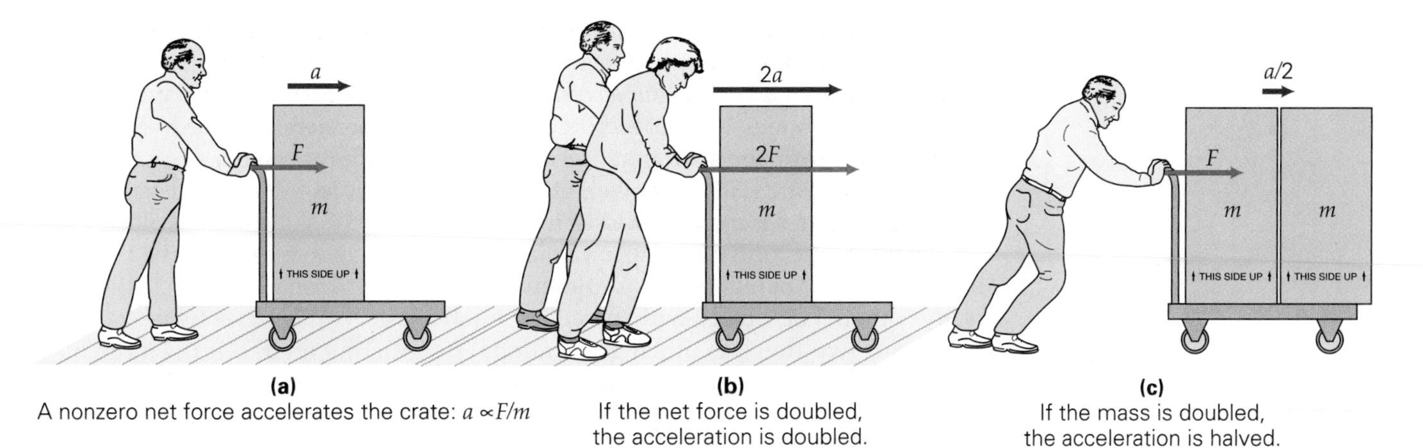

(a) A nonzero net force accelerates the crate: $a \propto F/m$ **(b)** If the net force is doubled, the acceleration is doubled. **(c)** If the mass is doubled, the acceleration is halved.

▲ **FIGURE 4.5 Newton's second law** The relationships among force, acceleration, and mass shown here are expressed by Newton's second law of motion (assuming no friction).

▲Figure 4.5 presents some illustrations of this principle.

Newton's second law—force and acceleration

With $\mathbf{F}_{\text{net}} \propto m\mathbf{a}$, **Newton's second law of motion** is commonly expressed in equation form as

$$\mathbf{F}_{\text{net}} = m\mathbf{a} \quad \textit{Newton's second law} \tag{4.1}$$

SI unit of force: newton (N) or kilogram-meter per second squared ($\text{kg}\cdot\text{m/s}^2$)

where $\mathbf{F}_{\text{net}} = \Sigma\mathbf{F}_i$. Equation 4.1 defines the SI unit of force, which is appropriately called the newton (N).

Equation 4.1 also shows that (by unit analysis) a newton in base units is defined as $1\text{ N} = 1\text{ kg}\cdot\text{m/s}^2$. That is, a net force of 1 N gives a mass of 1 kg an acceleration of 1 m/s^2 (▸Fig. 4.6). The British-system unit of force is the pound (lb). One pound is equivalent to about 4.5 N (actually, 4.448 N). An average apple weighs about 1 N.

Thus, if the net force acting on an object is zero, the object's acceleration is zero, and it remains at rest or in uniform motion, which is consistent with the first law. For a nonzero net force (an unbalanced force), the resulting acceleration is in the same direction as the force.*

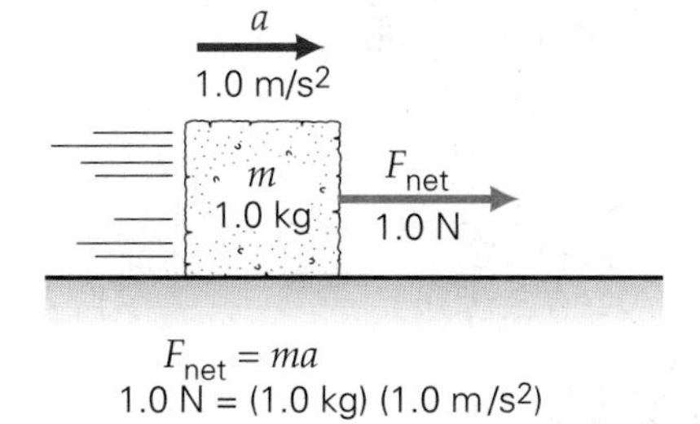

▲ **FIGURE 4.6 The newton (N)** A net force of 1.0 N acting on a mass of 1.0 kg produces an acceleration of 1.0 m/s^2 (on a frictionless surface).

Weight

Equation 4.1 can be used to relate mass and weight. Recall from Chapter 1 that weight is the gravitational force of attraction that a celestial body exerts on an object. For us, this force is the gravitational attraction of the Earth. Its effects are easily demonstrated: When you drop an object, it falls (accelerates) toward the Earth. Since there is only one force acting on the object, its **weight** (**w**) is the net force $\mathbf{F}_{\text{net}}$, and the acceleration due to gravity (**g**) can be substituted for **a** in Eq. 4.1. We can therefore write, in terms of magnitude,

$$w = mg \tag{4.2}$$

$$(F_{\text{net}} = ma)$$

The magnitude of the weight of 1.0 kg of mass is $w = mg = (1.0\text{ kg})(9.8\text{ m/s}^2) = 9.8\text{ N}$.

*It may appear that Newton's first law is a special case of Newton's second law, but this is not so. The first law *defines* what is called an *inertial reference system*: a system in which there is no net force, that is not accelerating, or in which an isolated object is stationary or moves with a constant velocity. If Newton's first law holds, then the second law in the form $\mathbf{F}_{\text{net}} = m\mathbf{a}$ applies to the system.

Thus, 1.0 kg of mass has a weight of approximately 9.8 N, or 2.2 lb near the Earth's surface. But, although weight and mass are simply related through Eq. 4.2, keep in mind that *mass is the fundamental property*. Mass doesn't depend on the value of g, but weight does. As pointed out previously, the acceleration due to gravity on the Moon is about one sixth that on the Earth. The weight of an object on the Moon would thus be one sixth of its weight on the Earth, but its mass, which reflects the quantity of matter it contains and its inertia, would be the same in both places.

Newton's second law also explains why all objects in free fall have the same acceleration. Consider, for example, two falling objects, one with twice the mass of the other. The object with twice as much mass would have twice as much weight, or two times as much gravitational force acting on it. But the more massive object also has twice the inertia, so twice as much force is needed to give it the same acceleration. Expressing this relationship mathematically, for the smaller mass (m), we can write $F_{net}/m = mg/m = g$, and for the larger mass ($2m$), we have the same acceleration: $F_{net}/m = 2mg/2m = g$ (▸Fig. 4.7). Some other effects of g, which you may have experienced, are discussed in the following Insight.

INSIGHT

g's of Force and Effects on the Human Body

The value of g at the Earth's surface is referred to as the standard acceleration and is sometimes used as a nonstandard unit. For example, when a spacecraft lifts off, astronauts are said to experience an acceleration of "several g's." This expression means that the astronauts' acceleration is several times the standard acceleration g. Since $g = w/m$, we can also think of g as the (weight) *force per unit mass*. Thus, the term **g's of force** is sometimes used for the force corresponding to multiples of the standard acceleration.

To help you better understand this nonstandard unit of force, let's look at some examples. During the takeoff of a jet airliner, you experience an average horizontal force of about 0.20 g. This means that as the plane accelerates down the runway, the seat back exerts on you a horizontal force of about one fifth of your weight (to accelerate you along with the plane), but you experience a feeling of being pushed back into the seat. On takeoff at an angle of 30°, the force increases to about 0.70 g, with a component of gravity helping to "push" you back into the seat.

In situations where a person is subjected to several g's vertically, blood can begin to pool in the lower extremities, which may cause blood vessels to distend or capillaries to rupture. Under such conditions, the heart has a difficult time pumping blood throughout the body. At a force of about four g's, the pooling of blood in the lower body deprives the head of sufficient oxygen. Lack of blood circulation to the eyes can cause temporary blindness, and if the brain is deprived of oxygen, a person becomes disoriented and eventually "blacks out" or loses consciousness. The average person can withstand several g's of force only for a short period of time. You may have experienced the feeling of these effects on a roller coaster when it is climbing out of a big dip.

The maximum force on astronauts in a space shuttle upon blastoff is about three g's. But jet-fighter pilots are subjected to as much as nine g's when pulling out of a downward dive. However, these folks wear "g-suits," which are specially designed to prevent blood pooling. The common g-suit is inflated by compressed air and applies pressure to the pilot's lower body to prevent the blood from accumulating there. (Work is being done on the development of a hydrostatic g-suit that contains liquid, which is less restrictive than air. When the number of g's increases, the liquid, like the blood in the body, flows into the lower part of the suit and applies pressure to the legs.) Also, although astronauts are in a reclined position on blastoff, the seating in a jet fighter is slightly horizontal. When a pilot is positioned horizontally, his or her blood flows from front to back and does not pool in the lower extremities. This configuration helps the heart keep pumping oxygenated blood throughout the body. (See the Insight on blood pressure in Chapter 7.)

Meanwhile, back on Earth, where there is only 1 g, a partial "g-suit" of sorts is being used to prevent blood clots in patients—most of whom are over the age of 65—who have undergone hip replacement surgery. It is estimated that each year 400 to 800 people die in the first three months after such surgery. The patients die primarily because of blood clots forming in a leg, breaking off into the blood stream, and finally lodging in the lungs—giving rise to a condition called *pulmonary embolism*. In other cases, a blood clot in the leg may slow the flow of blood to the heart. These complications arise more often after hip replacement surgery than after almost any other surgery and occur after the patient has left the hospital.

Studies have shown that pneumatic (operated by air) compression of the legs during the hospital stay reduces these risks. A plastic, thigh-high leg cuff inflates every few minutes, forcing the blood from the ankle to the thigh. This mechanical massaging is thought to prevent blood from pooling in the veins and clotting. By using both this technique and anticlotting drug therapy, it is hoped that many of the postoperative deaths can be prevented.

Newton's second law allows us to analyze dynamic situations. In using this equation, you should keep in mind that F_{net} is the *magnitude of the net force* and m is the *total mass of the system*. The boundaries defining a system may be real or imaginary. For example, a system might consist of all the gas molecules in a particular sealed vessel. But you might also define a system to be all the gas molecules in an arbitrary cubic meter of air. In studying dynamics, we often have occasion to work with systems made up of one or more discrete masses—the Earth and Moon, for instance, or a series of blocks on a tabletop, or a tractor and wagon, as in Example 4.1.

Note: In $F_{net} = ma$, m is the total mass of the system.

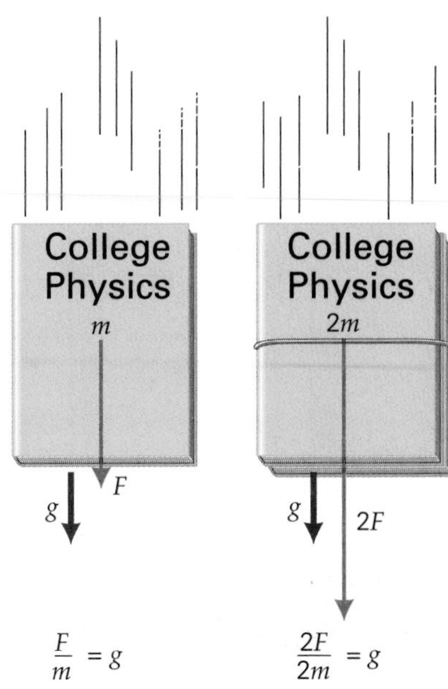

▲ **FIGURE 4.7 Newton's second law and free fall** In free fall, all objects fall with the same constant acceleration g. An object with twice the mass of another has twice as much gravitational force acting on it. But with twice the mass, the object also has twice as much inertia, so twice as much force is needed to give it the same acceleration.

Example 4.1 ■ Newton's Second Law: Finding Acceleration

A tractor pulls a loaded wagon on a level road with a constant force of 440 N (▼Fig. 4.8). If the total mass of the wagon and its contents is 275 kg, what is the wagon's acceleration? (Ignore any frictional forces.)

Thinking It Through. This problem is a direct application of Newton's second law. Note that the total mass is given; we treat the two separate masses (wagon and contents) as one and look at the whole system.

Solution. Listing the data, we have

Given: $F = 440\text{ N}$, $m = 275\text{ kg}$ *Find:* a (acceleration)

In this case, F is the net force, and the acceleration is given by Eq. 4.1, $F_{net} = ma$. Solving for the magnitude of a,

$$a = \frac{F_{net}}{m} = \frac{440\text{ N}}{275\text{ kg}} = 1.60\text{ m/s}^2$$

and the direction of a is that in which the tractor is pulling.

Note that m is the *total* mass of the wagon and its contents. If the masses of the wagon and its contents had been given separately—say, $m_1 = 75$ kg and $m_2 = 200$ kg, respectively—they would have been added together in Newton's law: $F = (m_1 + m_2)a$. Also, in reality, there would be an opposing force of friction. Suppose there were an effective frictional force of $f = 140$ N. In this case, the net force would be the vector sum of the force exerted by the tractor and the frictional force, and the acceleration would be (using directional signs)

$$a = \frac{F_{net}}{m} = \frac{F - f}{m_1 + m_2} = \frac{440\text{ N} - 140\text{ N}}{275\text{ kg}} = 1.09\text{ m/s}^2$$

Again, the direction of a would be the direction in which the tractor is pulling.

With a constant net force, the acceleration is also constant, so the kinematic equations of Chapter 2 can be applied. Suppose the wagon started from rest ($v_o = 0$). Could you find how far it traveled in 4.00 s? Using the appropriate kinematic equation (Eq. 2.11, with $x_o = 0$) for the case with friction, we have

$$x = v_o t + \tfrac{1}{2}at^2 = 0 + \tfrac{1}{2}(1.09\text{ m/s}^2)(4.00\text{ s})^2 = 8.72\text{ m}$$

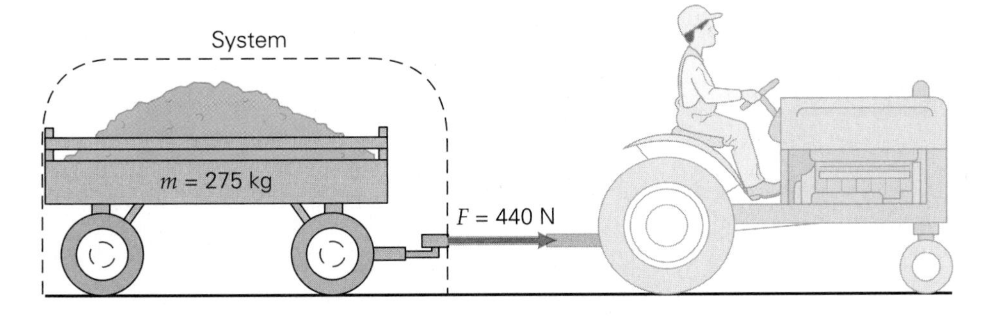

◀ **FIGURE 4.8 Force and acceleration** See Example 4.1.

Follow-up Exercise. Suppose the applied force on the wagon is 550 N. With the same frictional force, what would be the wagon's velocity 4.0 s after starting from rest? *(Answers to all Follow-up Exercises are at the back of the text.)*

Example 4.2 ■ Newton's Second Law: Finding Mass

A student weighs 588 N. What is her mass?

Thinking It Through. Newton's second law allows us to determine an object's mass if we know the object's weight (force), since g is known.

Solution.

Given: $w = 588$ N *Find:* m (mass)

Recall that weight is a (gravitational) force and that Newton's second law, $F_{net} = ma$, can be written in the form $w = mg$ (Eq. 4.2), where g is the acceleration due to gravity ($9.80\ \text{m/s}^2$). Rearranging the equation, we have

$$m = \frac{w}{g} = \frac{588\ \text{N}}{9.80\ \text{m/s}^2} = 60.0\ \text{kg}$$

On the surface of the Earth, this is equivalent to 60.0 kg (2.2 lb/kg) = 132 lb. In countries that use the metric system, the kilogram unit of mass, rather than a force unit, is used to express "weight." It would be said that this student weighs 60.0 "kilos."

Follow-up Exercise. (a) A person in Europe is a bit overweight and would like to lose 5.0 "kilos." What would be the equivalent loss in pounds? (b) What is your "weight" in kilos? *(Answers to all Follow-up Exercises are at the back of the text.)*

A dynamic system may consist of more than one object. In applications of Newton's second law, it is often advantageous, and sometimes necessary, to isolate a given object within a system. This isolation is possible because the motion of any part of a system is also described by Newton's second law, as Example 4.3 shows.

Example 4.3 ■ Newton's Second Law: All or Part of the System?

Two blocks with masses $m_1 = 2.5$ kg and $m_2 = 3.5$ kg rest on a frictionless surface and are connected by a light string (▶Fig. 4.9).* A horizontal force (F) of 12.0 N is applied to m_1, as shown in the figure. (a) What is the magnitude of the acceleration of the masses (that is, of the total system)? (b) What is the magnitude of the force (T) in the string? [When a rope or string is stretched taut, it is said to be under tension, which is represented by the magnitude of the force acting at any point. For a very light string, the force at the right end of the string has the same magnitude (T) as the force at the left end.]

Thinking It Through. It is important to remember that Newton's second law may be applied to a total system or any part of it (a subsystem, so to speak). This capability allows for the analysis of a particular component of a system, if desired. Identification of the acting forces is critical, as this Example shows. We then apply $F_{net} = ma$ to each subsystem or component.

Solution. Carefully listing the data and what we want to find, we have the following information:

Given: $m_1 = 2.5$ kg *Find:* (a) a (acceleration)
$m_2 = 3.5$ kg (b) T (tension, a force)
$F = 12.0$ N

Given an applied force, such as a light string, the acceleration of the masses can be found from Newton's second law. In using Newton's second law, it is important to keep in mind that it applies to the total system *or to any part of it*—that is, to the total mass

*When an object is described as being "light," its mass can be ignored in analyzing the situation given in the problem. That is, its mass is negligible relative to the other masses.

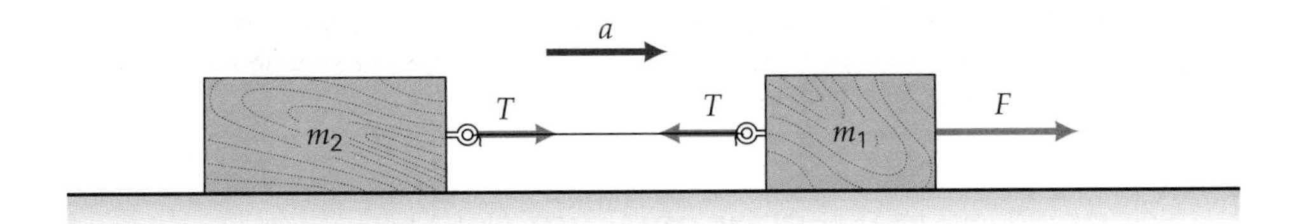

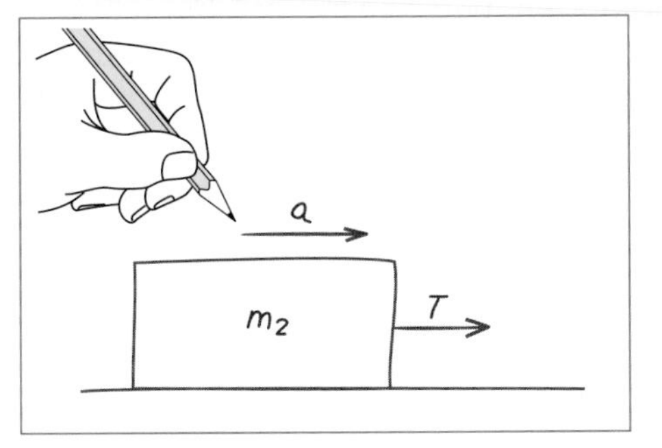

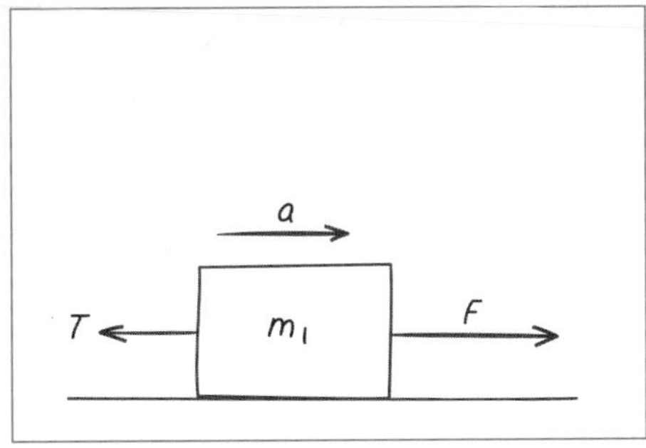

Isolating the masses

◀ **FIGURE 4.9 An accelerated system** See Example 4.3.

$(m_1 + m_2)$, to m_1 individually, or to m_2 individually. However, *we must be sure to identify correctly the appropriate force or forces in each case.* The net force acting on the combined masses, for example, is not the same as the net force acting on m_2 considered separately, as will be seen.

(a) First, taking the system as a whole (i.e., considering both m_1 and m_2), we see that the net force acting on this system is F. Note that in considering the total system, we are concerned only about the net external force acting on it. The *internal* equal and opposite T forces are not a consideration in this case. Representing the total mass as M, we can thus write

$$a = \frac{F_{\text{net}}}{M} = \frac{F}{m_1 + m_2} = \frac{12.0 \text{ N}}{2.5 \text{ kg} + 3.5 \text{ kg}} = 2.0 \text{ m/s}^2$$

The acceleration is in the direction of the applied force, as the figure indicates. Note that M is the *total* mass of the system, or all the mass that is accelerated. (The mass of the light string is small enough to be ignored.)

(b) Under tension, a force is exerted on an object by flexible strings (or ropes or wires) and is directed along the string. Note in the figure that we are assuming the tension to be transmitted *undiminished* through the string. That is, the tension is the same everywhere in the string. Thus, the magnitude of **T** acting on m_2 is the same as that acting on m_1. This is actually true only if the string has zero mass. Only such idealized *light* (i.e., of negligible mass) strings or ropes will be considered in this book.

So, there is a force of magnitude T on each of the masses, because of tension in the connecting string. To find the value of T, we must consider a *part* of the system that is affected by this force.

Each block may be considered as a separate system to which Newton's second law applies. In these subsystems, the tension comes into play explicitly. Looking at the sketch of the isolated m_2 in Fig. 4.9, we see that the only force acting to accelerate this mass is T. From the values of m_2 and a, the magnitude of this force is given directly by

$$F_{\text{net}} = T = m_2 a = (3.5 \text{ kg})(2.0 \text{ m/s}^2) = 7.0 \text{ N}$$

An isolated sketch of m_1 is also shown in Fig. 4.9, and Newton's second law can equally well be applied to this block to find T. We must add the forces vectorially to get the net force on m_1 that produces its acceleration. Recalling that vectors in one dimension can be written with directional signs and magnitudes, we have

$$F_{\text{net}} = F - T = m_1 a \quad (\text{direction of } \mathbf{F} \text{ taken to be positive})$$

Then, solving for the magnitude of **T**,

$$\begin{aligned} T &= F - m_1 a \\ &= 12.0 \text{ N} - (2.5 \text{ kg})(2.0 \text{ m/s}^2) = 12.0 \text{ N} - 5.0 \text{ N} = 7.0 \text{ N} \end{aligned}$$

Follow-up Exercise. Suppose there were an additional horizontal force to the left of 3.0 N applied to m_2 in Fig. 4.9. What would be the tension in the connecting string in this case? *(Answers to all Follow-up Exercises are at the back of the text.)*

The Second Law in Component Form

Not only does Newton's second law hold for any part of a system, but it also applies to the components of motion. For example, a force may be expressed in component notation in two dimensions as follows:

$$\Sigma \mathbf{F}_i = m\mathbf{a}$$

and

$$\Sigma(F_x\hat{\mathbf{x}} + F_y\hat{\mathbf{y}}) = m(a_x\hat{\mathbf{x}} + a_y\hat{\mathbf{y}}) = ma_x\hat{\mathbf{x}} + ma_y\hat{\mathbf{y}} \quad (4.3a)$$

Hence, to satisfy both x and y together, we have the components

$$\Sigma F_x = ma_x \quad \text{and} \quad \Sigma F_y = ma_y \quad (4.3b)$$

and Newton's second law applies separately to each component of motion. Note that *both* equations must be true. Example 4.4 demonstrates how the second law is applied using components.

Example 4.4 ■ Newton's Second Law: Components of Force

Force and Acceleration

A block of mass 0.50 kg travels with a speed of 2.0 m/s in the x-direction on a flat, frictionless surface. On passing through the origin, the block experiences a constant force of 3.0 N at an angle of 60° relative to the x-axis for 1.5 s (▼Fig. 4.10). What is the velocity of the block at the end of this time?

Thinking It Through. With the force at an angle to the initial motion, it would appear that the solution is complicated. But note in the insert in Fig. 4.10 that the force can be resolved into components. The motion can then be analyzed in each component direction.

Solution. First, we write the given data and what is to be found:

Given: $m = 0.50$ kg
$v_{x_o} = 2.0$ m/s
$v_{y_o} = 0$
$F = 3.0$ N, $\theta = 60°$
$t = 1.5$ s

Find: $\mathbf{v}$ (velocity at the end of 1.5 s)

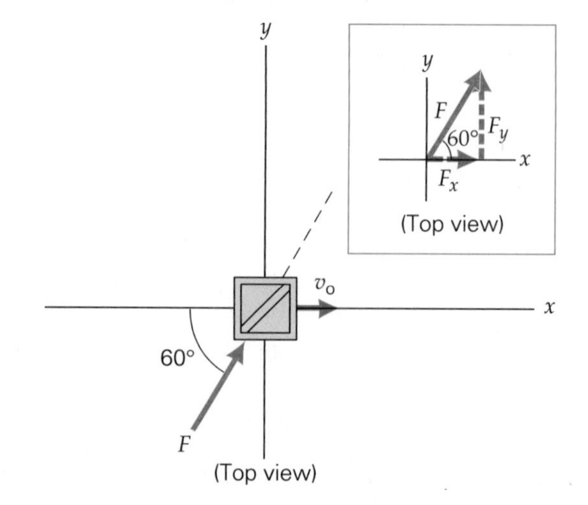

▶ **FIGURE 4.10 Off the straight and narrow** A force is applied to a moving block when it reaches the origin, and the block deviates from its straight-line path. See Example 4.4.

Let's find the magnitudes of the forces in the component (x and y) directions:

$$F_x = F \cos 60° = (3.0\ \text{N})(0.500) = 1.5\ \text{N}$$
$$F_y = F \sin 60° = (3.0\ \text{N})(0.866) = 2.6\ \text{N}$$

Then, applying Newton's second law to each direction to find the components of acceleration, we get

$$a_x = \frac{F_x}{m} = \frac{1.5\ \text{N}}{0.50\ \text{kg}} = 3.0\ \text{m/s}^2$$
$$a_y = \frac{F_y}{m} = \frac{2.6\ \text{N}}{0.50\ \text{kg}} = 5.2\ \text{m/s}^2$$

Next, from the kinematic equation relating velocity and acceleration (Eq. 2.8), the velocity components of the block are given by

$$v_x = v_{x_o} + a_x t = 2.0\ \text{m/s} + (3.0\ \text{m/s}^2)(1.5\ \text{s}) = 6.5\ \text{m/s}$$
$$v_y = v_{y_o} + a_y t = 0 + (5.2\ \text{m/s}^2)(1.5\ \text{s}) = 7.8\ \text{m/s}$$

At the end of the 1.5 s, the velocity of the block is

$$\mathbf{v} = v_x\hat{\mathbf{x}} + v_y\hat{\mathbf{y}} = (6.5\ \text{m/s})\ \hat{\mathbf{x}} + (7.8\ \text{m/s})\ \hat{\mathbf{y}}$$

Follow-up Exercise. (a) What is the direction of motion at the end of the 1.5 s? (b) If the force were applied at an angle of 30° (rather than 60°) relative to the x-axis, how would the results of this Example be different? *(Answers to all Follow-up Exercises are at the back of the text.)*

4.4 Newton's Third Law of Motion

OBJECTIVES: **To (a) state and explain Newton's third law of motion and (b) identify action-reaction force pairs.**

Newton formulated a third law that is as far reaching in its physical significance as the first two laws. For a simple introduction to the third law, consider the forces involved in seatbelt safety. When the brakes are suddenly applied when you are riding in a moving car, you continue to move forward. (The frictional force on the seat of your pants is not enough to stop you.) In doing so, you exert forces on the seatbelt and shoulder strap. The belt and strap exert corresponding reaction forces on you, causing you to slow down with the car. If you haven't buckled up, you may keep on going (Newton's first law) until another force, such as that applied by the dashboard or windshield, slows you down.

We commonly think of forces as occurring singly. However, Newton recognized that it is impossible to have a single force. He observed that in any application of force, there is always a mutual interaction, and forces always occur in pairs. An example given by Newton was the following: If you press on a stone with a finger, then the finger is also pressed by, or receives a force from, the stone.

Newton's third law—action and reaction

Newton termed the paired forces *action* and *reaction*, and **Newton's third law of motion** is as follows:

> For every force (action), there is an equal and opposite force (reaction).

In symbol notation, Newton's third law is

$$\mathbf{F}_{12} = -\mathbf{F}_{21}$$

That is, $\mathbf{F}_{12}$ is the force exerted *on* object 1 *by* object 2, and $-\mathbf{F}_{21}$ is the equal and opposite force exerted *on* object 2 *by* object 1. (The minus sign indicates the opposite direction.) *Which force is considered the action or the reaction is arbitrary;* $\mathbf{F}_{21}$ may be the reaction to $\mathbf{F}_{12}$ or vice versa.

Newton's third law at first glance may seem to contradict Newton's second law: If there are always equal and opposite forces, how can there be a nonzero net force? An important thing to remember about the force pair of the third law is that

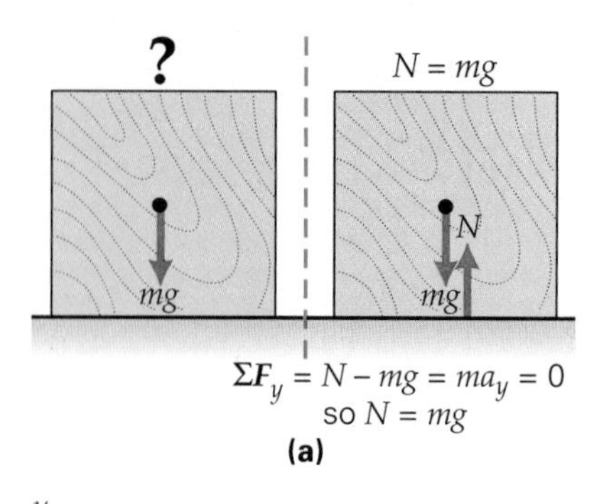

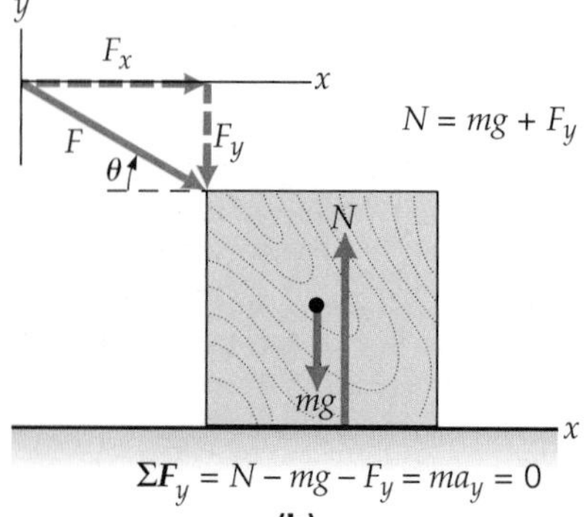

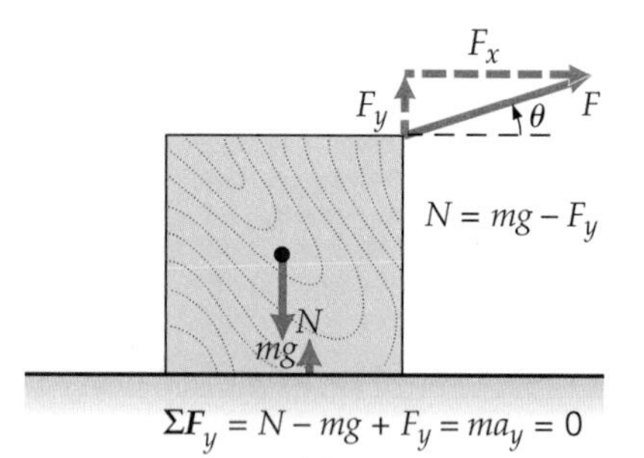

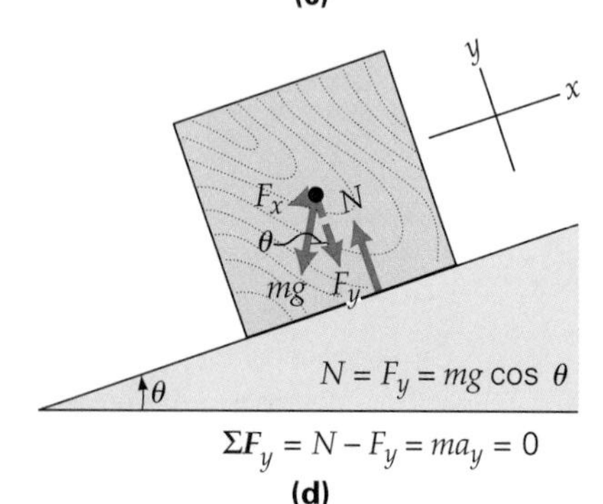

▲ **FIGURE 4.11 Distinctions between Newton's second and third laws** Newton's second law deals with the forces acting on a particular object (or system). Newton's third law deals with the force pair that acts on different objects. This distinction is illustrated for various situations. (See the text for descriptions.)

the action–reaction forces do not act on the same object. The second law is concerned with force(s) acting on a particular object (or system). The opposing forces of the third law act on *different* objects. Hence, the forces cannot cancel each other out or have a vector sum of zero when we apply the second law to the individual objects.

To illustrate this distinction, consider the situations shown in ◂Fig. 4.11. We often tend to forget the reaction force. For example, in the left portion of Fig. 4.11a, the obvious force that acts on a block sitting on a table is the Earth's gravitational attraction, which is expressed by the weight mg. But, there *has to be another force* acting on the block. For the block not to accelerate, the table must exert an upward force **N** whose magnitude is equal to the block's weight. Thus, $\Sigma \mathbf{F}_y = +N - mg = ma_y = 0$, where the direction of the vectors on the right side of the equation are indicated by plus and minus signs.

In reaction to **N**, the block exerts a downward force on the table, $-\mathbf{N}$, whose magnitude is the same as the block's weight, mg. However, $-\mathbf{N}$ is *not* the object's weight. Weight and $-\mathbf{N}$ have two different origins: Weight is the action-at-a-distance gravitational force, and $-\mathbf{N}$ is a contact force between the two surfaces.

You could easily demonstrate that this upward force on the block is there by placing the block on your hand and holding it stationary—you would exert an upward force on the block. (And you would feel a reaction force of $-\mathbf{N}$ on your hand.) If you applied a greater force, that is, $N > mg$, then the block would accelerate upward.

We call the force that a surface exerts on an object a *normal* force and use the symbol N to denote the force. *Normal* means *perpendicular*. The **normal force** that a surface exerts on an object is always perpendicular to the surface. In Fig. 4.11a, the normal force is equal and opposite to the weight of the block.

The normal force is not always equal and opposite to an object's weight, however. The normal force is a "reaction" force; it reacts to the situation. If a force is applied to a block downward at an angle, as shown in Fig. 4.11b, then a downward component (F_y) acts on the block in addition to the block's weight; thus, the normal force must balance both forces $(\Sigma \mathbf{F}_y = +N - mg - F_y = ma_y = 0)$, and the magnitude of $N = mg + F_y > mg$.

In Fig. 4.11b, the block could accelerate to the right. (Why?) However, this horizontal component (F_x) might be balanced by a frictional force, as it often is. We'll bring friction into the picture in a later section; the normal force will be quite important there.

For the situation in Fig. 4.11c, the normal force is reduced to less than w. Can you see why? Note that the F_y component of the applied force is opposite in direction to the weight. In this situation, $\Sigma \mathbf{F}_y = +N - mg + F_y = ma_y = 0$, and in magnitude, $N = mg - F_y < mg$.

Inclined planes are important in both physics and the real world. For a block on an inclined plane (Fig. 4.11d), the normal force on the block is *perpendicular to the surface of the plane*. This force is the reaction to the block's force on the surface of the plane, and since $a_y = 0$ (i.e., there is no acceleration in the y-direction), we have $\Sigma \mathbf{F}_y = N - F_y = ma_y = 0$, and in magnitude, $N = F_y = mg \cos\theta$. The weight component (F_x) accelerates the block down the plane in the absence of an equal opposing friction force between the block and the surface of the plane.

As another example, consider the situation in ▸Fig. 4.12a. Two third-law force pairs are acting when the person is holding the briefcase. First, there is a pair of contact forces: The person's hand exerts an upward force on the handle, and the handle exerts an equal downward force on the hand. That is, $+F_1 = -F_1$. This force pair is an action–reaction pair, with the forces acting on different objects. The other third-law force pair consists of action-at-a-distance forces associated with gravitational attraction: The Earth attracts the briefcase (its weight), and the briefcase attracts the Earth, or $+F_2 = -F_2$.

Concentrating on the briefcase in isolation, we can see that only two of the four forces in Fig. 4.12a act on it—the upward force on the handle $(+F_1)$ and the

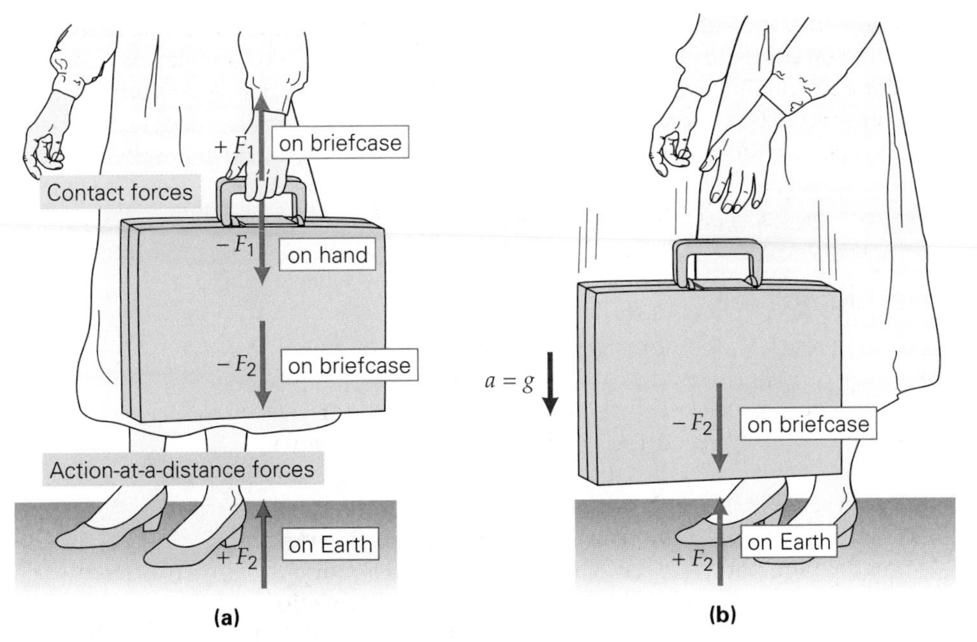

FIGURE 4.12 Force pairs of Newton's third law **(a)** When a person holds a briefcase, there are two force pairs: a contact pair ($+F_1$ and $-F_1$) and an action-at-a-distance (gravity) pair ($+F_2$ and $-F_2$). The net force acting on the briefcase is zero: The upward contact force ($+F_1$) balances the downward weight force. Note, however, that the upward contact force and downward weight force are *not* a third-law pair. **(b)** When the briefcase is released, there is an unbalanced, or nonzero net, force acting on the briefcase (its weight force), and it accelerates downward (at g for free fall).

downward force of the briefcase's weight ($-F_2$). These two forces *cannot* constitute a third-law force pair, however, because they act on the same object. Since the briefcase does not accelerate, these forces must be equal and opposite. Thus, the net force on the isolated stationary briefcase is zero, as required by Newton's first and second laws.

When the person drops the briefcase (Fig. 4.12b), there is then a nonzero net force (the unbalanced force of gravity) on the briefcase, and it accelerates toward the Earth. But there is still a pair of third-law forces *acting on different objects*—the briefcase and the Earth. (The Earth actually accelerates upward toward the briefcase as well, but the amount of the acceleration is infinitesimal. Can you explain why?)

Jet propulsion is yet another example of Newton's third law in action. In the case of a rocket, the rocket and exhaust gases exert equal and opposite forces on each other. As a result, the exhaust gases are accelerated away from the rocket, and the rocket is accelerated in the opposite direction. When a big rocket "blasts off," as in a space-shuttle launch, there is a fiery release of exhaust from the rocket. A common misconception is that the exhaust gases "push" against the launch pad to accelerate the rocket. If this interprets were true, there would be no space travel, since there is nothing to "push" against in space. The correct explanation is one of action (gases exerting a force on the rocket) and reaction (rocket exerting an opposite force on the gases).

Another action–reaction pair is given in the Insight on p. 116.

4.5 More on Newton's Laws: Free-Body Diagrams and Translational Equilibrium

OBJECTIVES: To (a) apply Newton's laws in analyzing various situations, using free-body diagrams, and (b) understand the concept of translational equilibrium.

Now that you have been introduced to Newton's laws and some applications in analyzing motion, the importance of these laws should be evident. They are so simply stated, yet so far reaching. The second law is probably the most often applied, because of its mathematical relationship. However, the first and third laws are often used in qualitative analysis, as our continuing study of the different areas of physics will reveal.

The simple relationship expressed by Newton's second law, $\mathbf{F}_{\text{net}} = m\mathbf{a}$, allows the quantitative analysis of force and motion. We can think of it as a cause-and-effect relationship, with force being the cause and acceleration being the motional effect.

In general, we will be concerned with applications that involve constant forces. Constant forces result in constant accelerations and allow us to use the kinematic equations from Chapter 2 in analyzing the motion. When there is a variable force, Newton's second law holds for the *instantaneous* force and acceleration, but the acceleration will vary with time, requiring calculus to analyze. We will generally limit our-

INSIGHT

Action and Reaction: The Harrier "Jump" Jet

The action–reaction principle of Newton's third law is used to power jet aircraft (and propeller-driven planes), usually for propulsion rather than directly for lift. However, there is one type of aircraft that uses jet propulsion to take off vertically—no runway needed, like a helicopter: the Harrier "Jump" jet, originally developed by the British (Fig. 1). This plane has four engine nozzles that can be swiveled to point at any angle from vertical to horizontal. These engines provide the power for both vertical and horizontal flight.

A Harrier takeoff is illustrated in Fig. 2. (Other small jets on the plane that help control and stabilize the aircraft are not shown.) As shown in Fig. 2a, the nozzles are directed downward for takeoff, and the reaction forces raise the plane. After the plane has achieved a proper altitude, the nozzles are swiveled, and a forward component of the force gives the plane a forward acceleration (Fig. 2b). Finally, with the jets horizontal, the planes flies conventionally (Fig. 2c).

But wait! Did you notice something missing in Fig. 2c? The plane has weight, or a downward gravitational force acting on it, that is not shown. What is the counterbalancing force to this weight that keeps the plane from falling? As you will learn in Chapter 7, this *lift* force results from the curved wing surface and fluid (air) dynamics.

FIGURE 1 "Jump" jet A Harrier "Jump" jet lifting off vertically.

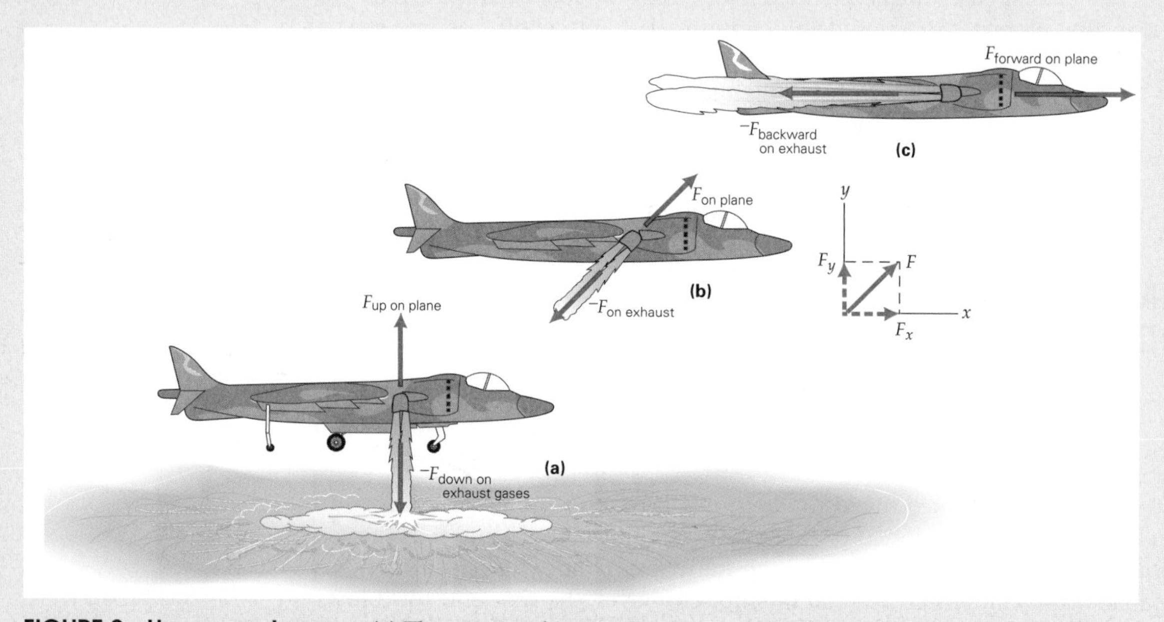

FIGURE 2 Up, up, and away **(a)** The reaction force to the downward exhaust force from the engines raises the plane. Only one nozzle is shown, for simplicity. **(b)** At the appropriate altitude, the engine nozzles are swiveled, and a forward force component gives the plane a forward acceleration (while the plane still gains altitude—why?). **(c)** With the nozzles swiveled 90° from their position in (a), the plane flies conventionally.

selves to constant accelerations and forces. This section presents several examples of applications of Newton's second law so that you can become familiar with its use. This small, but powerful, equation will be used again and again throughout this text.

Newton's second law gives the acceleration resulting from an applied force, but it can also be used to find the force from motional effects, as Example 4.5 shows.

Example 4.5 ■ A Braking Car: Finding a Force from Motional Effects

A car traveling at 72.0 km/h along a straight, level road is brought uniformly to a stop in a distance of 40.0 m. If the car weighs 8.80×10^3 N, what is the braking force?

Thinking It Through. We know that the car's velocity changes, so there is an acceleration. Given a distance, we might surmise that first the acceleration is found by using a kinematic equation, and then the acceleration is used to compute the force.

Solution. In bringing the car to a stop, the braking force caused an acceleration (actually a deceleration), as illustrated in ▼Fig. 4.13. Listing what is given and what must be found, we have

Given: $v_o = 72.0 \text{ km/h} = 20.0 \text{ m/s}$ *Find:* F_b (braking force)
$v = 0$
$x = 40.0 \text{ m}, x_o = 0$
$w = 8.80 \times 10^3 \text{ N}$

We know that $F_{net} = ma$, so we can easily calculate F_b if we can find m and a. The car's mass m can be obtained from the car's weight, which is given. The other given quantities should remind you of a kinematic equation from Chapter 2 from which the acceleration a can be found. Since the car is brought uniformly to a stop, the acceleration is constant, and we may use Eq. 2.11, $v^2 = v_o^2 + 2ax$, to find a:

$$a = \frac{v^2 - v_o^2}{2x} = \frac{0 - (20.0 \text{ m/s})^2}{2(40.0 \text{ m})} = -5.00 \text{ m/s}^2$$

The minus sign indicates that the acceleration is opposite to $+v_o$, as expected for a braking force, which slows the car.

The mass of the car is obtained from the car's weight: $w = mg$, or $m = w/g$. Using this expression along with the acceleration obtained previously gives a braking force of

$$F_{net_x} = F_b = ma = \left(\frac{w}{g}\right)a = \left[\frac{8.80 \times 10^3 \text{ N}}{9.80 \text{ m/s}^2}\right](-5.00 \text{ m/s}^2) = -4.49 \times 10^3 \text{ N}$$

Follow-up Exercise. A 1000-kg car starting from rest travels in a straight line and uniformly reaches a speed of 10 m/s in 5.0 s. What is the magnitude of the net force that accelerates the car? *(Answers to all Follow-up Exercises are at the back of the text.)*

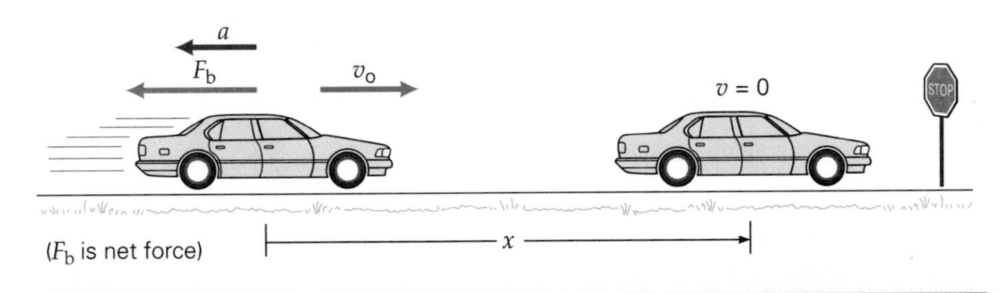

◀ **FIGURE 4.13 Finding force from motional effects** See Example 4.5.

Problem-Solving Strategy: Free-Body Diagrams

In illustrations of physical situations, sometimes called *space diagrams,* force vectors may be drawn at different locations to indicate their points of application. However, because we are presently concerned only with linear motions, vectors in free-body

Learn by Drawing

Drawing a Free-Body Diagram

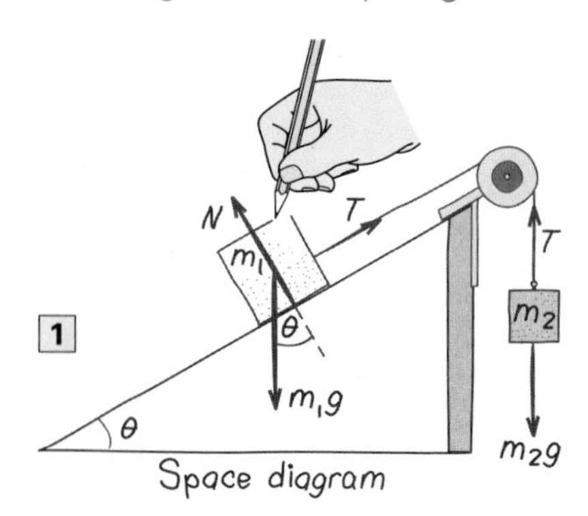

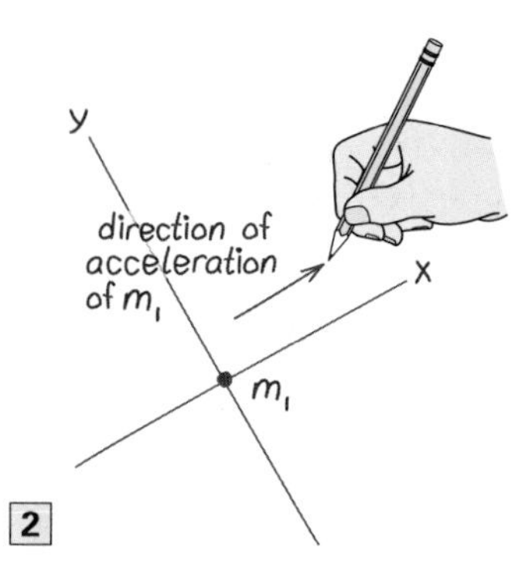

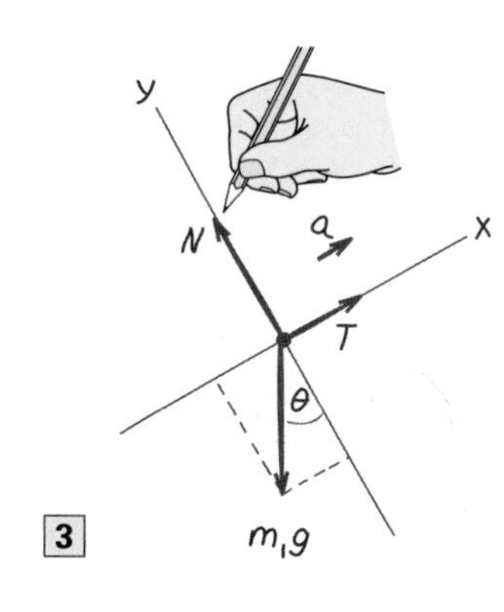

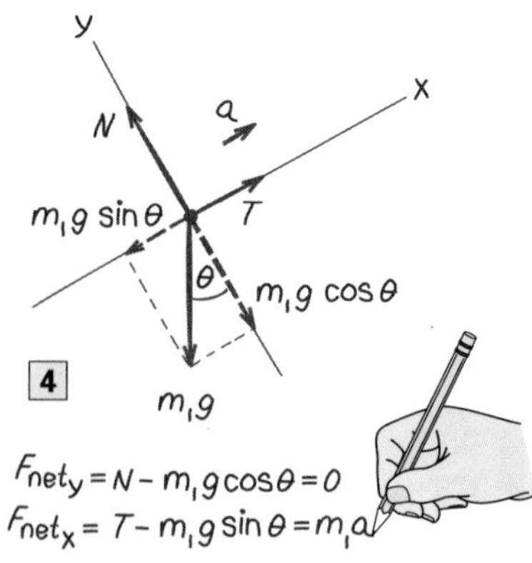

$F_{net_y} = N - m_1g\cos\theta = 0$
$F_{net_x} = T - m_1g\sin\theta = m_1a$

diagrams may be shown as emanating from a common point, which is chosen as the origin of the x–y axes. One of the axes is generally chosen along the direction of the net force acting on a body, since that is the direction in which the body will accelerate. Also, it is often important to resolve force vectors into components, and properly chosen x–y axes simplify this task.

In a free-body diagram, the vector arrows do not have to be drawn exactly to scale. However, it should be made apparent if there is a net force, and whether forces balance each other in a particular direction. When the forces aren't balanced, we know from Newton's second law that there must be an acceleration.

In summary, the general steps in constructing and using free-body diagrams are as follows (refer to the accompanying Learn by Drawing as you read):

1. Make a sketch, or space diagram, of the situation (if one is not already available), and identify the forces acting on each body of the system. (A space diagram is an illustration of the physical situation that identifies the force vectors.)
2. Isolate the body for which the free-body diagram is to be constructed. Draw a set of Cartesian axes, with the origin at a point through which the forces act and with one of the axes along the direction of the body's acceleration. (The acceleration will be in the direction of the net force, if there is one.)
3. Draw properly oriented force vectors (including angles) on the diagram, emanating from the origin of the axes. If there is an unbalanced force, assume a direction of acceleration, and indicate it with an acceleration vector. Be sure to include only those forces that act on the isolated body.
4. Resolve any forces that are not directed along the x- or y-axes into x- or y-components (use plus and minus signs to indicate direction). Use the free-body diagram to analyze the forces in terms of Newton's second law of motion. (*Note*: If you assume that the acceleration is in one direction, and in the solution it comes out with the opposite sign, then the acceleration is actually in the opposite direction from that assumed. For example, if you assume that **a** is in the $+x$-direction, but you get a negative answer, then **a** is in the $-x$-direction.)

Free-body diagrams are a particularly useful way of following one of the Suggested Problem-Solving Procedures in Chapter 1: Draw a diagram as an aid in visualizing and analyzing the physical situation of the problem. *Make it a practice to draw free-body diagrams for force problems, as is done in the following Examples.*

Example 4.6 ■ Up or Down?: Motion on a Frictionless Inclined Plane

Two masses are connected by a light string running over a light pulley of negligible friction as illustrated in the Learn By Drawing diagrams. One mass ($m_1 = 5.0$ kg) is on a frictionless 20° inclined plane, and the other ($m_2 = 1.5$ kg) is freely suspended. What is the acceleration of the masses? (Only the free-body diagram for m_1 is shown in the Learn By Drawing diagram. You need to draw the free-body diagram for m_2.)

Thinking It Through. Apply the preceding Problem-Solving Strategy.

Solution. Following our usual procedure, we write

Given: $m_1 = 5.0$ kg *Find:* **a** (acceleration)
$m_2 = 1.5$ kg
$\theta = 20°$

To help us visualize the forces involved, we isolate m_1 and m_2 and draw free-body diagrams for each mass. For mass m_1, there are three concurrent forces (forces acting through a common point). These forces are T, its weight m_1g, and N, where T is the tension force of the string on m_1 and N is the normal force of the plane on the block (LBD-3). The forces are shown as emanating from their common point of action. (Recall that a vector can be moved as long as its direction and magnitude are not changed.)

We will start by assuming that m_1 accelerates up the plane, which is taken to be in the $+x$-direction. (It makes no difference whether it is assumed that m_1 accelerates up or down the plane, as we shall see shortly.) Notice that $m_1 g$ (the weight) is broken down into components. The x-component is opposite to the assumed direction of acceleration, and the y-component acts perpendicularly to the plane and is balanced by the normal force N. (There is no acceleration in the y-direction, so there is no net force in this direction.)

Then, applying Newton's second law in component form (Eq. 4.3b) to m_1, we have

$$\Sigma \mathbf{F}_{x_1} = T - m_1 g \sin\theta = m_1 a$$

$$\Sigma \mathbf{F}_{y_1} = N - m_1 g \cos\theta = m_1 a_y = 0 \quad (a_y = 0, \textit{no net force, so the forces cancel})$$

And for m_2,

$$\Sigma \mathbf{F}_{y_2} = m_2 g - T = m_2 a_y = m_2 a$$

where the masses of the string and pulley have been neglected. Since the accelerations of m_1 and m_2 have the same magnitudes, we can use $a_x = a_y = a$.

Adding the first and last equations to eliminate T, we have

$$m_2 g - m_1 g \sin\theta = (m_1 + m_2)g$$
$$(\text{net force} = \textit{total} \text{ mass} \times \text{acceleration})$$

(Note that this is the equation that would be obtained by applying Newton's second law to the system as a whole, because in the system of both blocks, the $\pm T$ forces are internal forces and cancel.)

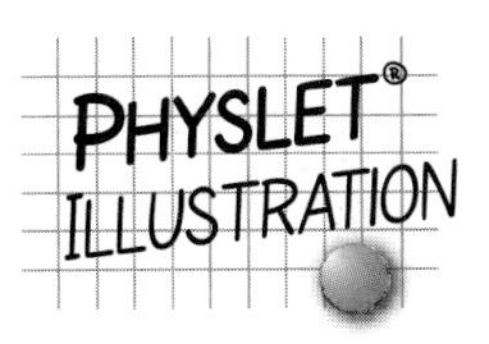

Block Sliding on a Incline

Then, solving for a:

$$\begin{aligned} a &= \frac{m_2 g - m_1 g \sin 20^\circ}{m_1 + m_2} \\ &= \frac{(1.5\text{ kg})(9.8\text{ m/s}^2) - (5.0\text{ kg})(9.8\text{ m/s}^2)(0.342)}{5.0\text{ kg} + 1.5\text{ kg}} \\ &= -0.32\text{ m/s}^2 \end{aligned}$$

The minus sign indicates that the acceleration is opposite to the assumed direction. That is, m_1 actually accelerates down the plane, and m_2 accelerates upward. As this example shows, if you assume the acceleration to be in the wrong direction, the sign on the result will give you the correct direction anyway.

Could you find the tension force T in the string if you were asked to do so? How this task could be done should be quite evident from the free-body diagram.

Follow-up Exercise. (a) In this Example, what is the minimum amount of mass for m_2 that would cause m_1 barely to accelerate up the plane? (b) Keeping the masses the same as in the Example, how should the angle of incline be adjusted so that m_1 would barely accelerate up the plane? *(Answers to all Follow-up Exercises are at the back of the text.)*

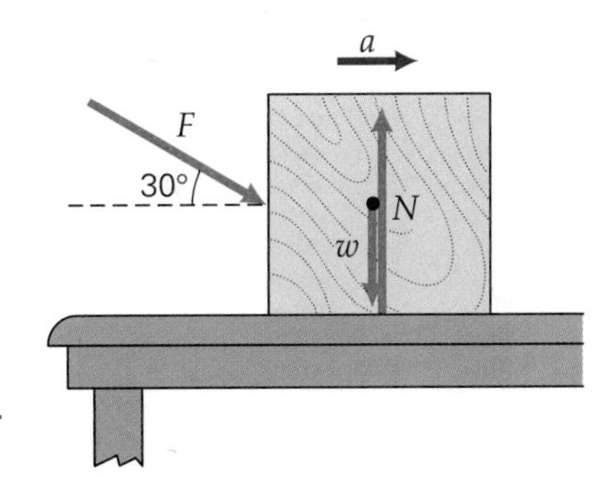

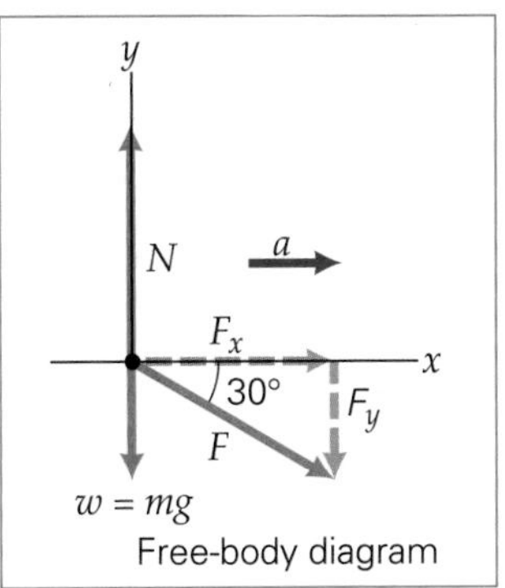

▲ **FIGURE 4.14 Newton's second law and components of force** See Example 4.7

Example 4.7 ■ Components of Force and Free-Body Diagrams

A force of 10.0 N is applied at an angle of 30° to the horizontal on a 1.25-kg block at rest on a frictionless surface, as illustrated in ▸Fig. 4.14. (a) What is the magnitude of the resulting acceleration of the block? (b) What is the magnitude of the normal force?

Thinking It Through. The applied force may be resolved into components. The horizontal component accelerates the block. The vertical component affects the normal force. (Review Fig. 4.11.)

Solution. First we write down the given data and what is to be found:

Given: $F = 10.0\text{ N}$, $m = 1.25\text{ kg}$, $\theta = 30^\circ$, $v_o = 0$

Find: (a) a (acceleration)
(b) N (normal force)

Then we draw a free-body diagram for the block, as in Fig. 4.14.

(a) The acceleration of the block can be calculated using Newton's second law. We choose our axes so that a is in the $+x$-direction. As the free-body diagram shows, only a component (F_x) of the applied force F acts in this direction. The component of F in the direction of motion is $F_x = F\cos\theta$. We apply Newton's second law in the $+x$-direction to calculate the acceleration:

$$F_x = F\cos 30° = ma_x$$

$$a_x = \frac{F\cos 30°}{m} = \frac{(10.0\text{ N})(0.866)}{1.25\text{ kg}} = 6.93\text{ m/s}^2$$

(b) The acceleration found in part (a) is the total acceleration of the block, since the block moves only in the x-direction (i.e., it does not accelerate in the y-direction). With $a_y = 0$, the sum of the forces in the y-direction must then be zero. That is, the downward component of F acting on the block, F_y, and its downward weight force w must be balanced by the upward normal force N that the surface exerts on the block. If this were not the case, then there would be a net force and an acceleration in the y-direction.

We sum the forces in the y-direction with upward taken as positive and

$$N - F_y - w = 0$$

or

$$N - F\sin 30° - mg = 0$$

and

$$N = F\sin 30° + mg = (10.0\text{ N})(0.500) + (1.25\text{ kg})(9.80\text{ m/s}^2) = 17.3\text{ N}$$

The surface then exerts a force of 14.9 N upward on the block, which balances the sum of the downward forces acting on it, $w = mg$ and F_y.

Follow-up Exercise. (a) Suppose the applied force on the block is applied for only a short time. What is the magnitude of the normal force after the applied force is removed? (b) If the block slides off the edge of the table, what would be the net force on the block just after it leaves the table (with the applied force removed)? *(Answers to all Follow-up Exercises are at the back of the text.)*

Problem-Solving Hint

There is no single fixed way to go about solving a problem. However, there are general strategies or procedures that are helpful in solving problems involving Newton's second law. When using our Suggested Problem-Solving Procedures introduced in Chapter 1, you might include the following steps when solving problems involving force applications:

- Draw a free-body diagram for each individual body, showing all of the forces acting on that body.
- Depending on what is to be found, apply Newton's second law either to the system as a whole (in which case internal forces cancel) or to a part of the system. Basically, *you want to obtain an equation (or set of equations) containing the quantity for which you want to solve.* Review Example 4.3. (If there are two unknown quantities, application of Newton's second law to two parts of the system may give you two equations and two unknowns. See Example 4.6.)
- Keep in mind that Newton's second law may be applied to components of motion and that forces may be resolved into components to do this. Review Example 4.7.

Translational Equilibrium

Forces may act on an object without producing an acceleration. In such a case, with $\mathbf{a} = 0$, we know from Newton's second law that

$$\Sigma \mathbf{F}_i = 0 \qquad (4.4)$$

That is, the vector sum of the forces, or the net force, is zero, so the object either remains at rest (as in ▸Fig. 4.15) or moves with a constant velocity. In such cases, objects are said to be in **translational equilibrium**. When remaining at rest, an object is said to be in *static translational equilibrium*.

It follows that the sums of the rectangular components of the forces for an object in translational equilibrium are also zero (why?):

$$\Sigma \mathbf{F}_x = 0 \qquad \Sigma \mathbf{F}_y = 0 \qquad \textit{(translational equilibrium only)} \tag{4.5}$$

For three-dimensional problems, we note that $\Sigma \mathbf{F}_z = 0$. However, we will restrict our discussion of forces to two dimensions.

Equations 4.5 give what is often referred to as the **condition for translational equilibrium**. Let's apply this translational-equilibrium condition to a case involving static equilibrium.

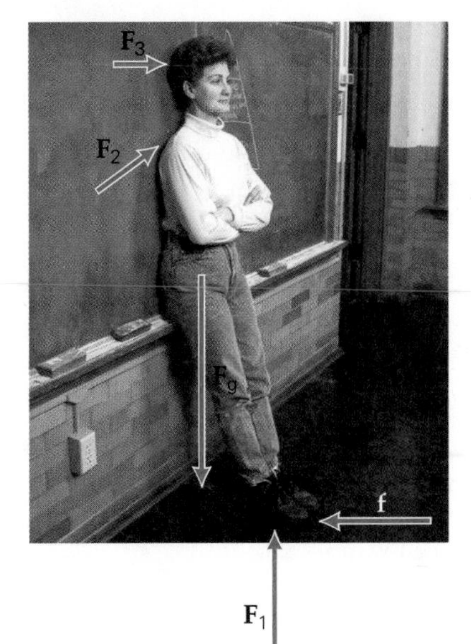

(a)

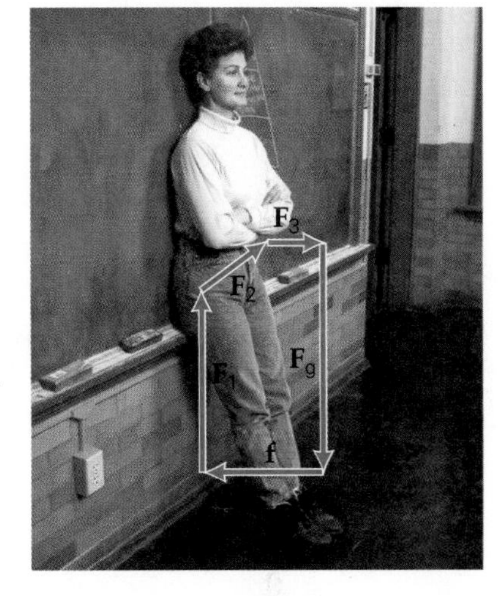

(b)

▲ **FIGURE 4.15 Many forces, no acceleration** **(a)** At least five different external forces act on this physics professor. (Here, **f** is the force of friction.) Nevertheless, she experiences no acceleration. Why? **(b)** Adding the force vectors by the polygon method reveals that the vector sum of the forces is zero. The professor is in static translational equilibrium.

Example 4.8 ■ A Hanging Sign: Static Translational Equilibrium

A 3.0-kg sign hangs in a hall in the physics department as shown in ▸Fig. 4.16a. (a) What is the minimum tensile strength necessary for the cord used to hang the sign? (The minimum tensile strength of the cord is the amount of tension the cord must be able to support without breaking.) (b) Suppose the sign were hung off-center and one segment of the support cords was longer than the other. Would this have any effect?

Thinking It Through. The sign hangs motionless on the wall, so it is in static translational equilibrium. Hence, the sum of the forces is zero, and here we see that there will be components in two dimensions.

Solution.

Given: $m = 3.0$ kg, $\theta_1 = \theta_2 = 45°$ *Find:* T_1 and T_2 (tensions in cord segments)

(a) With a cord of sufficient strength, the sign will hang in static equilibrium. We want to find the values of T_1 and T_2 that will just support the weight (mg) of the sign.

The rectangular components of the tensions are shown in the free-body diagram (Fig. 4.16b). Applying the component conditions for static translational equilibrium (Eq. 4.5), we have

$$\Sigma \mathbf{F}_x = T_{1_x} - T_{2_x} = 0$$

or

$$T_{1_x} = T_{2_x}$$

Hence, the magnitudes of the x-components of the tensions are equal, as you might have expected from symmetry. (They are the *only* forces in the x-direction, and they must balance each other, since $a_x = 0$.) However, this relationship gives no direct information about the magnitude of the tensions.

Since angles θ_1 and θ_2 are equal, we also know that $T_{1_y} = T_{2_y}$. (Why?) We now apply the other component condition:

$$\Sigma \mathbf{F}_y = T_{1_y} + T_{2_y} - mg = 2T_{1_y} - mg = ma_y = 0$$

Therefore,

$$2(T_1 \sin 45°) - mg = 0$$

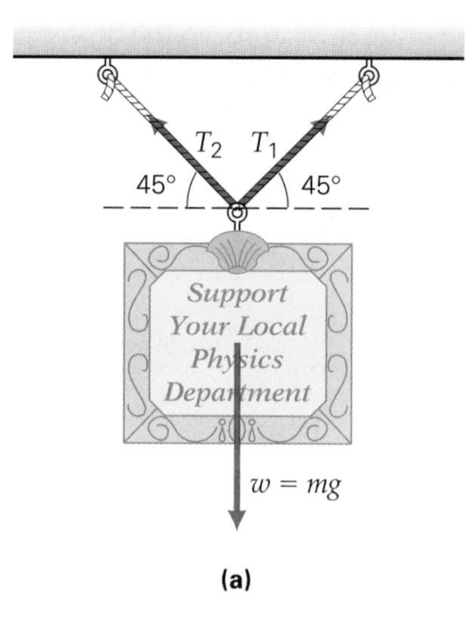

(a)

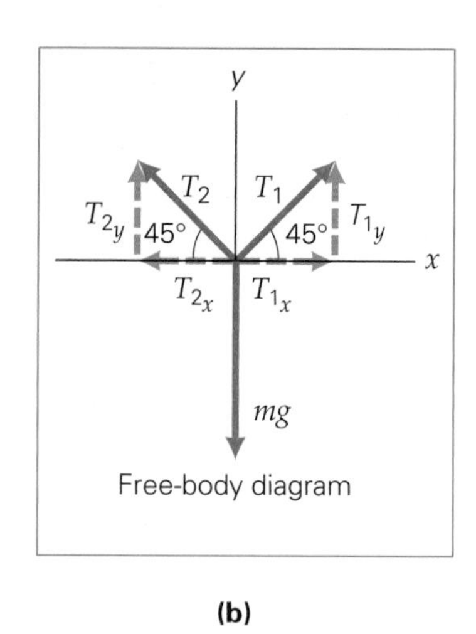

(b)

▶ **FIGURE 4.16 Static translational equilibrium**
See Example 4.8.

Solving for T_1, we obtain

$$T_1 = \frac{mg}{2 \sin 45°} = \frac{(3.0 \text{ kg})(9.8 \text{ m/s}^2)}{2(0.707)} = 21 \text{ N}$$

Thus, $T_1 = T_2 = 21$ N, so the sign should be hung from a cord with a tensile strength of at least 21 N.

(b) If the sign were hung off-center, as illustrated in the Learn By Drawing diagram, there would be a greater tension in the shorter cord segment, and if a 21-N test cord were used, this segment would break.

Follow-up Exercise. Suppose the angles in the LBD figure were 60° and 30°. Show that the tension in the shorter segment (T_1) is greater than 21 N.

Learn by Drawing

Vector Diagram

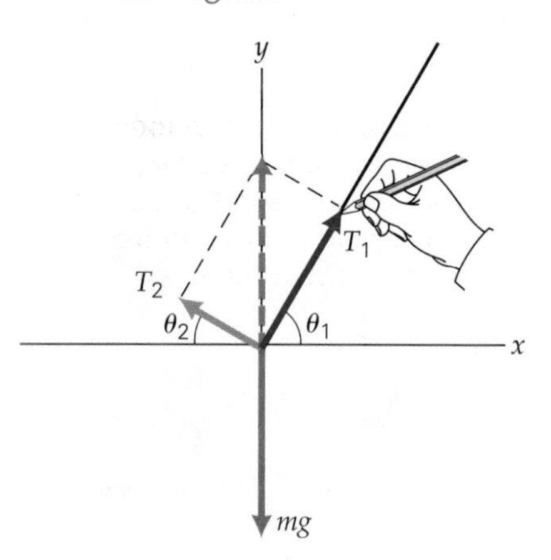

Vector diagram for Example 4.8

Example 4.9 ■ On Your Toes: In Static Equilibrium

An 80-kg person stands on one foot with the heel elevated (▶Fig. 4.17a). This gives rise to a tibia force F_1 and an Achilles-tendon force F_2, as illustrated in Fig. 4.17b. Typical angles are $\theta_1 = 15°$ and $\theta_2 = 21°$, respectively. (a) Find general equations for F_1 and F_2, and show that θ_2 must be greater than θ_1 to prevent damage to the Achilles tendon. (b) Compare the force of the Achilles tendon with the weight of the person.

Thinking It Through. This is a case of static translational equilibrium, so we can sum the x- and y-components to get equations for F_1 and F_2.

Solution. Listing what is given and what is to be found, we have

Given: $m = 80$ kg
F_1 = tibia force
F_2 = tendon "pull"
$\theta_1 = 15°, \theta_2 = 21°$
N = normal force of floor on foot

Find: (a) general equations for F_1 and F_2
(b) comparison of F_2 and the person's weight

(a) It is assumed that the person is at rest, standing on one foot. Then, summing the force components, we have

$$\Sigma F_x = +F_1 \sin \theta_1 - F_2 \sin \theta_2 = 0$$
$$\Sigma F_y = +N - F_1 \cos \theta_1 + F_2 \cos \theta_2 - m_f g = 0$$

Where m_f is the mass of the foot. From the F_x equation, we have,

$$F_1 = F_2\left(\frac{\sin \theta_2}{\sin \theta_1}\right) \quad (1)$$

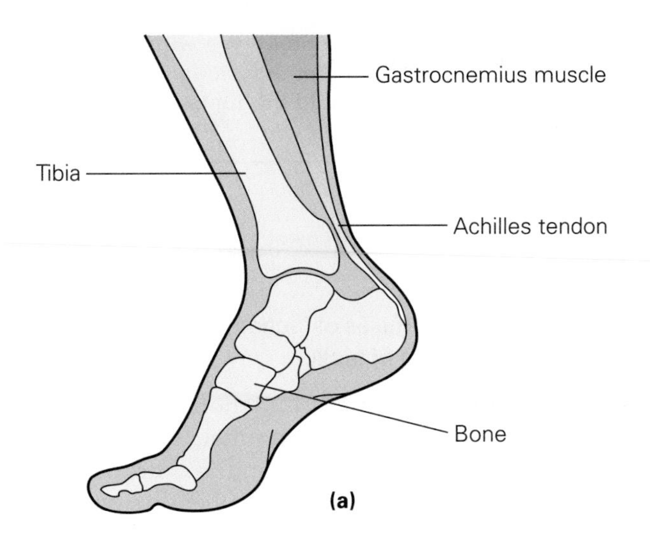

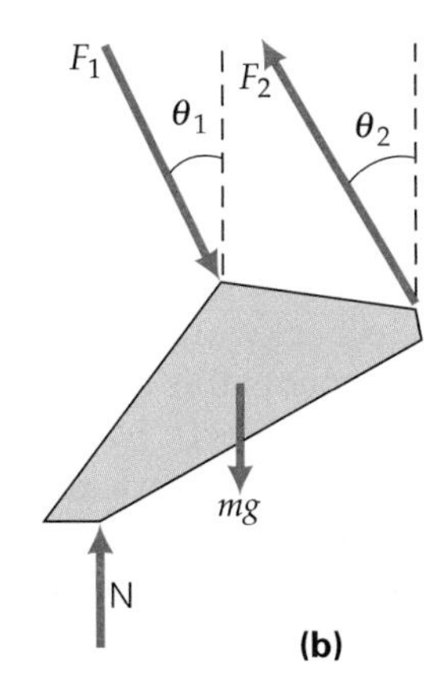

◀ **FIGURE 4.17 On your toes**
(a) A person stands on one foot with the heel elevated. **(b)** The forces involved for this position (not to scale). See Example 4.9.

And substituting into the F_y equation, we obtain

$$N - F_2\left(\frac{\sin\theta_2}{\sin\theta_1}\right)\cos\theta_1 + F_2\cos\theta_2 - m_f g = 0$$

solving for F_2 yields

$$F_2 = \frac{N - m_f g}{\left(\dfrac{\sin\theta_2}{\tan\theta_2}\right) - \cos\theta_2} = \frac{N}{\cos\theta_2\left(\dfrac{\tan\theta_2}{\tan\theta_1} - 1\right)} \qquad (2)$$

Then, examining the F_2 in equation (Eq. 2), we see that if $\theta_2 = \theta_1$, or $\tan\theta_2 = \tan\theta_1$, then F_2 is very large—infinite! (Why?) So, to have a finite force, we must have $\tan\theta_2 > \tan\theta_1$ or $\theta_2 > \theta_1$, and $21° > 15°$, so Nature obviously knows her physics.
(b) The weight of the person is $w = mg = (80\text{ kg})(9.8\text{ m/s}^2) = 7.8 \times 10^2\text{ N}$. To compare F_2 (Eq. 2) with this quantity, we need to know the normal force N. Thinking big, we find that the y-component equilibrium condition for the *total* body would be

$$\Sigma F_y = 0 = N - w \qquad \text{or} \qquad N = w = mg$$

where m is the mass of the person's body and $m >> m_f$. Then

$$F_2 = \frac{w - m_f g}{\cos\theta_2\left(\dfrac{\tan\theta_2}{\tan\theta_1} - 1\right)} \approx \frac{w}{\cos 21°\left(\dfrac{\tan 21°}{\tan 15°} - 1\right)} = 2.5\,w$$

The Achilles tendon force is thus approximately 2.5 times the person's weight. No wonder folks stretch or tear this tendon, even without jumping!

Follow-up Exercise. (a) Compare the tibia force with the weight of the person. (b) Suppose the person jumped upward from the one-foot toe position (as in taking a running jump shot in basketball). How would this jump affect F_1 and F_2? (*Answer to all Follow-up Exercises are at the back of the text.*)

4.6 Friction

OBJECTIVES: To explain (a) the causes of friction and (b) how friction is described by using coefficients of friction.

Friction refers to the ever-present resistance to motion that occurs whenever two materials, or media, are in contact with each other. This resistance occurs for all types of media—solids, liquids, and gases—and is characterized as the **force of friction** (f). For simplicity, we have up to now generally ignored all kinds of friction (including air resistance) in examples and problems. Now that you know how to describe motion, we are ready to consider situations that are more realistic, in that the effects of friction are included.

In some real situations, we want to increase friction—for example, by putting sand on an icy road or sidewalk to improve traction. This might seem contradictory, since an increase in friction presumably would increase the resistance to motion. However, consider the forces involved in walking, as illustrated in ◀Fig. 4.18. Without friction, the foot would slip backward. (Think about walking on a slippery surface.) The force of friction prevents this slipping and sometimes needs to be increased on slippery surfaces (▶Fig. 4.19a). In other situations, we try to reduce friction (Fig. 4.19b). For instance, we lubricate moving machine parts to allow them to move more freely, thereby lessening wear and reducing the expenditure of energy. Automobiles would not run without friction-reducing oils and greases.

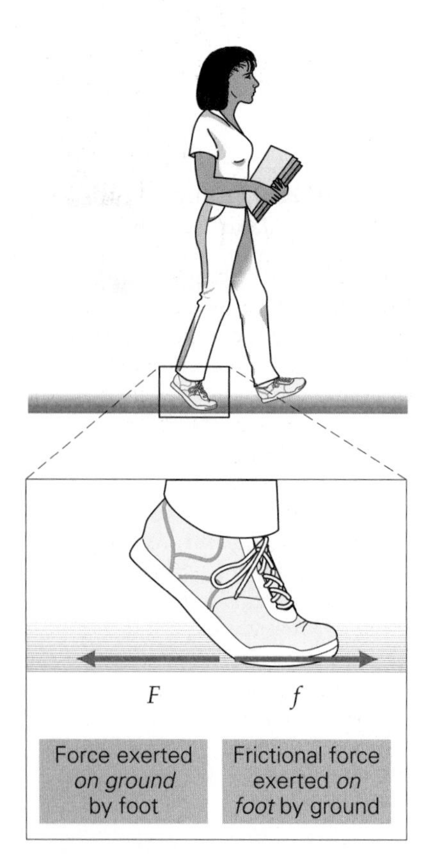

▲ **FIGURE 4.18 Friction and walking** The force of friction, f, is shown in the direction of the walking motion. This direction may seem wrong at first glance, but it's not. The force of friction prevents the foot from slipping backward while the other foot is brought forward. If you walk on a deep-pile rug, F is evident in that the pile will be bent backward.

This section is concerned chiefly with friction between solid surfaces. All surfaces are microscopically rough, no matter how smooth they appear or feel. It was originally thought that friction was due primarily to the mechanical interlocking of surface irregularities, or *asperities* (high spots). However, research has shown that friction between the contacting surfaces of ordinary solids (metals in particular) is due mostly to local adhesion. When surfaces are pressed together, local welding or bonding occurs in a few small patches where the largest asperities make contact. To overcome this local adhesion, a force great enough to pull apart the bonded regions must be applied. Once contacting surfaces are in relative motion, another form of friction may result when the asperities of a harder material dig into a softer material, with a "plowing" effect.

Friction between solids is generally classified into three types: static, sliding (kinetic), and rolling. **Static friction** includes all cases in which the frictional force is sufficient to prevent relative motion between surfaces. Suppose you want to move a large desk. You push it, but the desk doesn't move. The force of static friction between the desk's legs and the floor opposes and equals the horizontal force you are applying, so there is no motion—a static condition.

Sliding friction, or **kinetic friction**, occurs when there is relative (sliding) motion at the interface of the surfaces in contact. In pushing on the desk, you eventually get it sliding, but there is still a great deal of resistance between the desk's legs and the floor—kinetic friction.

Rolling friction occurs when one surface rotates as it moves over another surface, but does not slip or slide at the point or area of contact. Rolling friction, such as occurs between a train wheel and a rail, is attributed to small local deformations in the contact region. This type of friction is somewhat difficult to analyze.

Frictional Forces and Coefficients of Friction

In this subsection, we will consider the forces of friction on stationary and sliding objects. These forces are called the *force of static friction* and the *force of kinetic* (or *sliding*) *friction*, respectively. Experimentally, it has been found that the force of friction depends on both the nature of the two surfaces and the *load*, or the contact force that presses the surfaces together. For an object on a horizontal surface, this force is equal in magnitude to the object's weight. (Why?) However, as was shown in Example 4.6, on an inclined plane, only a component of the weight force contributes to the load.

Thus, to avoid confusion, remember that the force of friction is proportional to the normal force N in magnitude; that is, $f \propto N$. As we learned earlier, the normal force always acts perpendicular to, and away from, the surface. (It is the force exerted *by* the surface *on* the object.) In the absence of other perpendicular forces, the normal force is equal in magnitude to the component of the weight force acting perpendicular to the surface.

The force of static friction (f_s) between parallel surfaces in contact acts in the direction that opposes the initiation of relative motion between the surfaces. The magnitude has different values such that

$$f_s \leq \mu_s N \quad \textit{(static conditions)} \tag{4.6}$$

where μ_s is the **coefficient of static friction**. ("μ" is the Greek letter mu. Note that it is a dimensionless constant. How do you know this from the equation?)

The less-than-or-equal-to sign $(\leq)$ indicates that the force of static friction may have different values or magnitudes up to some maximum. To understand this concept, look at ▸Fig. 4.20. In Fig. 4.20a, one person pushes on a file cabinet, but it doesn't move. With no acceleration, the net force on the cabinet is zero, and $F - f_s = 0$, or $F = f_s$. Suppose that a second person also pushes, and the file cabinet still doesn't budge (Fig. 4.20b). Then f_s must now be larger, since the applied force has been increased. Finally, if the applied force is made large enough to overcome the static friction, motion occurs (Fig. 4.20c). The greatest, or maximum, force of static friction is exerted just before the cabinet starts to slide (Fig. 4.20b), and for this case, Eq. 4.6 can be written with an equal sign:

$$f_{s_{max}} = \mu_s N \tag{4.7}$$

Once an object is sliding, the force of friction changes to kinetic friction (f_k). This force acts in the direction opposite to the direction of motion and has a magnitude of

$$f_k = \mu_k N \quad \textit{(sliding conditions)} \tag{4.8}$$

where μ_k is the **coefficient of kinetic friction** (sometimes called the *coefficient of sliding friction*). Note that Eqs. 4.6 and 4.8 are *not* vector equations, since f and N are in different directions. Generally, the coefficient of kinetic friction is less than the coefficient of static friction $(\mu_k < \mu_s)$, which means that the force of kinetic friction is less than $f_{s_{max}}$, as illustrated in Fig. 4.20. The coefficients of friction between some common materials are listed in Table 4.1.

Note that the force of static friction (f_s) exists in response to an applied force. The magnitude of f_s and its direction depend on the magnitude and direction of the applied force. Up to its maximum value, the force of static friction is equal in magnitude and opposite in direction to the applied force (F), since there is no acceleration ($F - f_s = ma = 0$). Thus, if the person in Fig. 4.20a were to push on the cabinet in the opposite direction, f_s would change to oppose the new push. If there were no applied force F, then f_s would be zero. When F exceeds $f_{s_{max}}$, the

(a)

(b)

▲ **FIGURE 4.19 Increasing and decreasing friction** **(a)** To get a fast start, drag racers need to make sure that their wheels don't slip when the starting light goes on and they floor the accelerator. They therefore try to maximize the friction between their tires and the track by "burning in" the tires just before the start of the race. This "burn in" is done by spinning the wheels with the brakes on until the tires are extremely hot. The rubber becomes so sticky that it almost welds itself to the surface of the road. **(b)** Water serves as a good lubricant to reduce friction in rides such as this one.

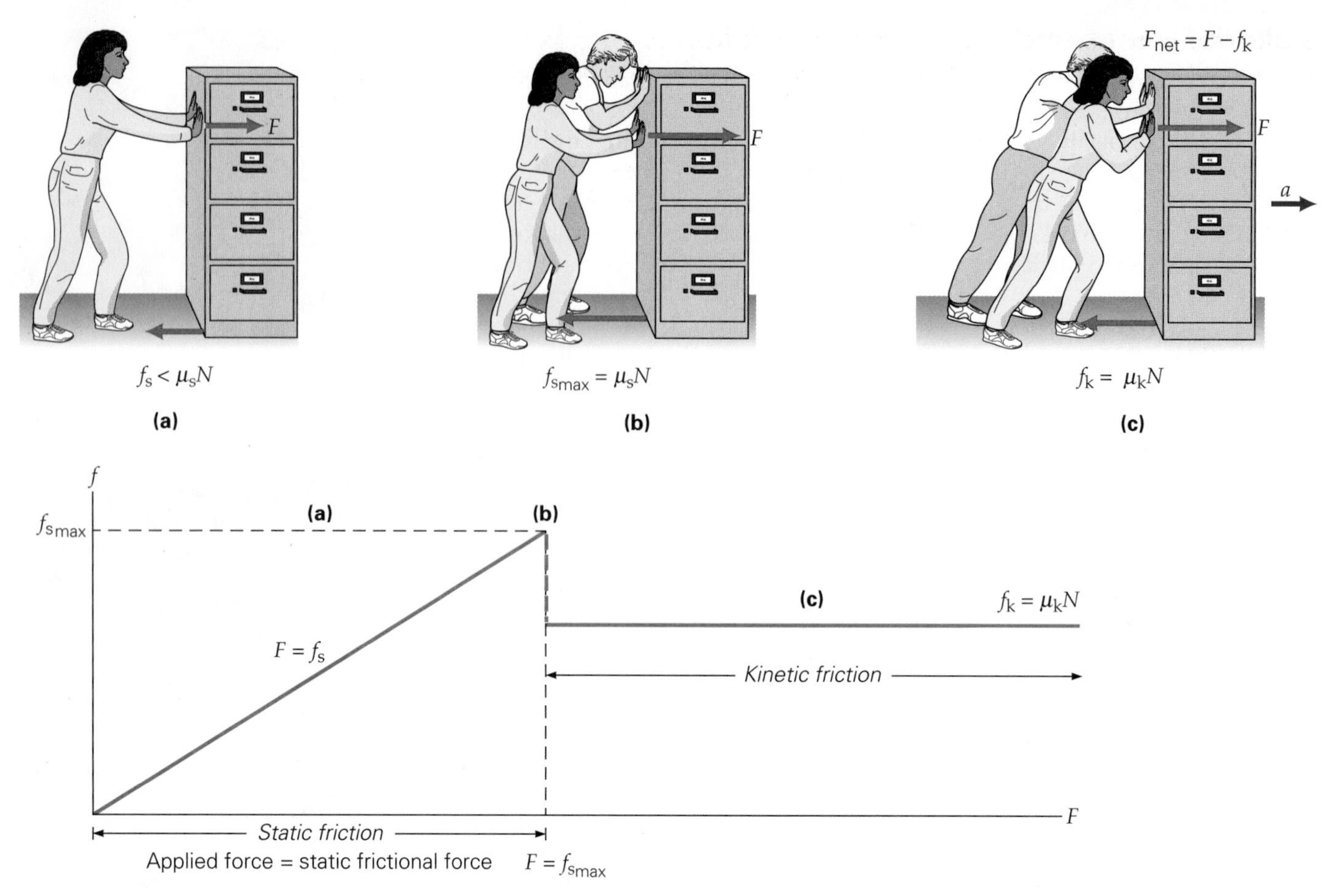

▲ **FIGURE 4.20 Force of friction versus applied force** **(a)** In the static region of the graph, as the applied force F increases, so does f_s; that is, $f_s = F$ and $f_s < \mu_s N$. **(b)** When the applied force F exceeds $f_{s_{max}} = \mu_s N$, the heavy file cabinet is set into motion. **(c)** Once the cabinet is moving, the frictional force is decreased, since kinetic friction is less than static friction ($f_k < f_{s_{max}}$). Thus, if the applied force is maintained, there is a net force, and the cabinet is accelerated. For the cabinet to move with constant velocity, the applied force must be reduced to equal the kinetic friction force: $f_k = \mu_k N$.

TABLE 4.1 Approximate Values for Coefficients of Static and Kinetic Friction between Certain Surfaces

Friction between Materials	μ_s	μ_k
aluminum on aluminum	1.90	1.40
glass on glass	0.94	0.35
rubber on concrete		
dry	1.20	0.85
wet	0.80	0.60
steel on aluminum	0.61	0.47
steel on steel		
dry	0.75	0.48
lubricated	0.12	0.07
Teflon on steel	0.04	0.04
Teflon on Teflon	0.04	0.04
waxed wood on snow	0.05	0.03
wood on wood	0.58	0.40
lubricated ball bearings	<0.01	<0.01
synovial joints (at the ends of most long bones—for example, elbows and hips)	0.01	0.01

cabinet begins moving (accelerates), and kinetic friction comes into effect, with $f_k = \mu_k N$. If F is reduced to f_k, the cabinet will slide with a constant velocity; if F is maintained as greater than f_k, the cabinet will continue to accelerate.

It has been experimentally determined that the coefficients of friction (and therefore the forces of friction) are nearly independent of the size of the contact area between metal surfaces. This means that the force of friction between a brick-shaped metal block and a metal surface is the same regardless of whether the block is lying on a larger side or a smaller side. The observation is generally not valid for other surfaces, such as wood, and does not apply to plastic or polymer surfaces.

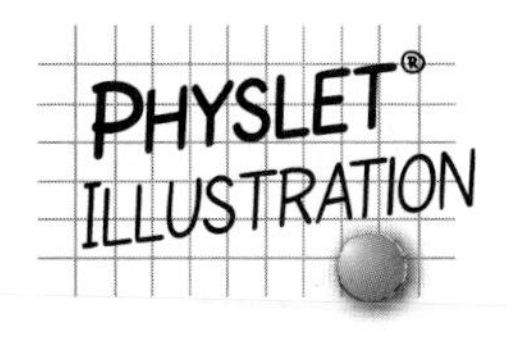

Static and Kinetic Friction

Finally, keep in mind that although the equation $f = \mu N$ holds in general for frictional forces, friction may not be linear over a wide range. That is, μ is not always constant. For example, the coefficient of kinetic friction varies somewhat with the relative speed of the surfaces. However, for speeds up to several meters per second, the coefficients are relatively constant. Thus, this discussion will neglect any variations due to speed (or area), and the forces of static and kinetic friction will be assumed to depend only on the load (N) and the nature of the materials as expressed by the given coefficients of friction.

Example 4.10 ■ Pulling a Crate: Static and Kinetic Forces of Friction

(a) In ▼Fig. 4.21, if the coefficient of static friction between the 40.0-kg crate and the floor is 0.650, with what minimum horizontal force must the worker pull to get the crate moving? (b) If the worker maintains that force once the crate starts to move and the coefficient of kinetic friction between the surfaces is 0.500, what is the magnitude of the acceleration of the crate?

Thinking It Through. This scenario involves applications of the forces of friction. In (a), the maximum force of static friction must be calculated. In (b), if the worker maintains an applied force of this magnitude after the crate is in motion, there will be an acceleration, since $f_k < f_{s_{max}}$.

Solution. Listing the given data and what we want to find, we have

Given: $m = 40.0$ kg, $\mu_s = 0.650$, $\mu_k = 0.500$

Find: (a) F (minimum force necessary to move crate)
(b) a (acceleration)

(a) The crate will not move until the applied force F slightly exceeds the maximum static frictional force $f_{s_{max}}$. So we must find $f_{s_{max}}$ to see what force the worker must apply.

▼ FIGURE 4.21 Forces of static and kinetic friction See Example 4.10.

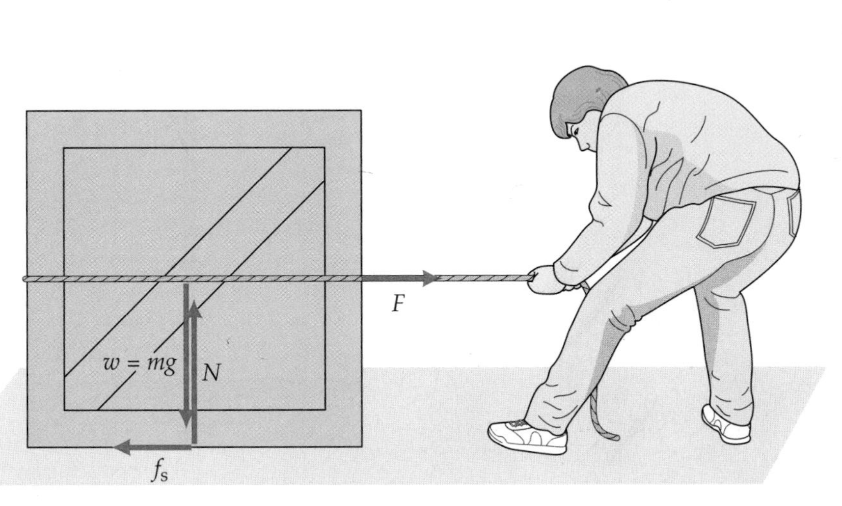

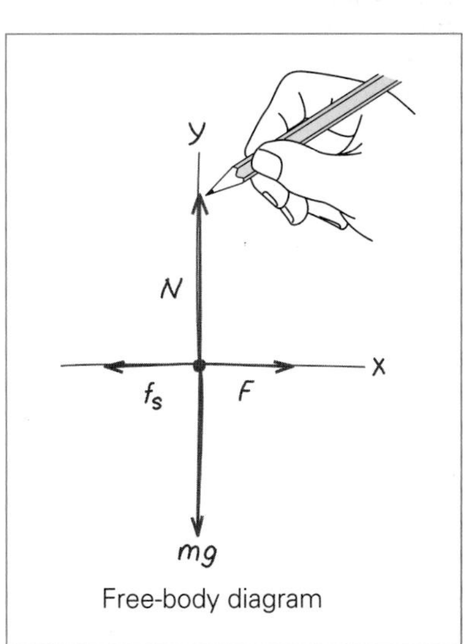

The weight of the crate and the normal force are equal in magnitude in this case (see the free-body diagram in Fig. 4.21), so the maximum force of static friction is

$$\begin{aligned} f_{s_{max}} &= \mu_s N = \mu_s (mg) \\ &= (0.650)(40.0 \text{ kg})(9.80 \text{ m/s}^2) = 255 \text{ N} \end{aligned}$$

The crate moves if the applied force F exceeds 255 N.

(b) Now the crate is in motion, and the worker maintains a constant applied force $F = f_{s_{max}} = 255$ N. The force of kinetic friction f_k acts on the crate, but this force is smaller than F, because $\mu_k < \mu_s$. Hence, there is a net force, and the acceleration of the crate may be found by using Newton's second law in the x-direction:

$$\Sigma \mathbf{F}_x = +F - f_k = F - \mu_k N = ma_x$$

Solving for a_x, we obtain

$$\begin{aligned} a_x &= \frac{F - \mu_k N}{m} = \frac{F - \mu_k (mg)}{m} \\ &= \frac{255 \text{ N} - (0.500)(40.0 \text{ kg})(9.80 \text{ m/s}^2)}{40.0 \text{ kg}} = 1.5 \text{ m/s}^2 \end{aligned}$$

Follow-up Exercise. On the average, by what factor does μ_s exceed μ_k for nonlubricated, metal-on-metal surfaces? (See Table 4.1.) *(Answers to all Follow-up Exercises are at the back of the text.)*

Let's look at another worker with the same crate, but this time assume that the worker applies the force at an angle (▼Fig. 4.22).

Example 4.11 ■ Pulling at an Angle: A Closer Look at the Normal Force

A worker pulling a crate applies a force at an angle of 30° to the horizontal, as shown in Fig. 4.22. How large a force must he apply to move the crate? (Before looking at the solution, would you expect that the force needed in this case would be greater or lesser than that in Example 4.10?)

Thinking It Through. We see from the figure that the applied force is at an angle to the horizontal surface, so the vertical component will affect the normal force. (See Fig. 4.11). This change in the normal force will, in turn, affect the maximum force of static friction.

▼ **FIGURE 4.22 Normal force** See Example 4.11.

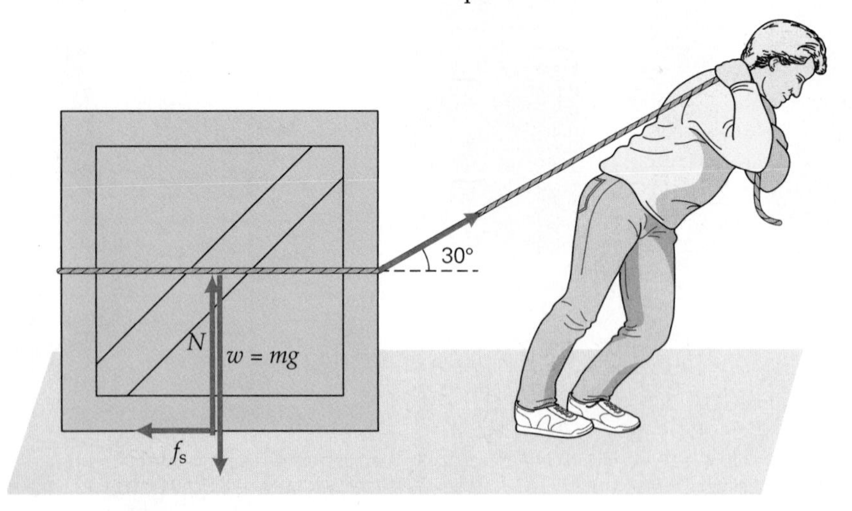

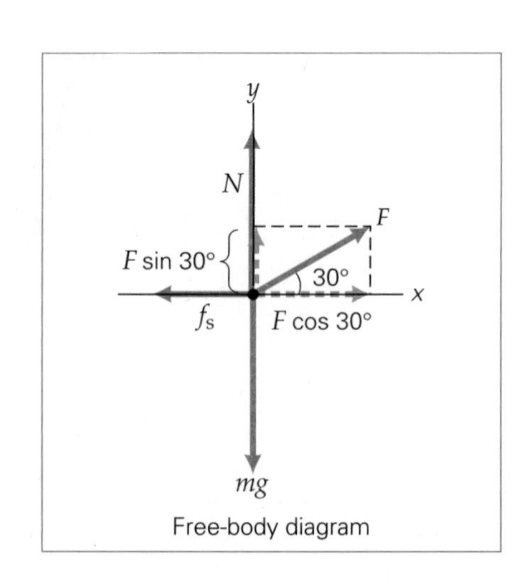

Solution. The data are the same as in Example 4.10, except that the force is applied at an angle.

Given: $\theta = 30°$ *Find:* F (minimum force necessary to move crate)

In this case, the crate will move when the *horizontal component* of the applied force, $F \cos 30°$, slightly exceeds the maximum static friction force. So, we may write the following for the maximum friction:

$$F \cos 30° = f_{s_{max}} = \mu_s N$$

However, the magnitude of the normal force is not equal to the weight of the crate here, because of the upward component of the applied force. (See the free-body diagram in Fig. 4.22.) By Newton's second law, since $a_y = 0$, we have

$$\Sigma \mathbf{F}_y = +N + F \sin 30° - mg = 0$$

or

$$N = mg - F \sin 30°$$

In effect, the applied force partially supports the weight of the crate. Substituting this expression for N into the first equation gives

$$F \cos 30° = \mu_s(mg - F \sin 30°)$$

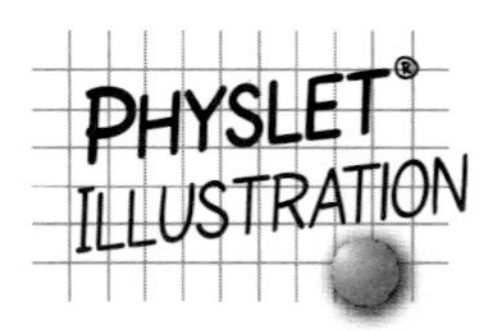

Pulling a Block

Solving for F gives

$$F = \frac{mg}{(\cos 30°/\mu_s) + \sin 30°}$$
$$= \frac{(40.0 \text{ kg})(9.80 \text{ m/s}^2)}{(0.866/0.650) + 0.500} = 214 \text{ N}$$

Thus, less applied force is needed in this case, reflecting the fact that the frictional force is less, because of the reduced normal force.

Follow-up Exercise. Note that in this Example, applying the force at an angle produces two effects. As the angle between the applied force and the horizontal increases, the horizontal component of the applied force is reduced. However, the normal force also gets smaller, resulting in a lower $f_{s_{max}}$. Does one effect always outweigh the other? That is, does the applied force F necessary to move the crate always decrease with increasing angle? (*Hint*: Investigate F for different angles. For example, compute F for 20° and 50°. You already have a value for 30°. What do the results tell you?) *(Answers to all Follow-up Exercises are at the back of the text.)*

Integrated Example 4.12 ■ No Slip, No Slide: Static Friction

A crate sits in the middle of the bed on a flatbed truck that is traveling at a speed of 80 km/h on a straight, level road. The coefficient of static friction between the crate and the truck bed is 0.40. When the truck comes uniformly to a stop, the crate does not slide, but remains stationary on the truck. (a) Draw a free-body diagram for the crate while the truck is stopping. (b) What is the minimum stopping distance for the truck so the crate does not slide on the truck bed?

Solution.

(a) Conceptual Reasoning. There are three forces on the crate, as shown in the free-body diagram in ▸Fig. 4.23 (assuming that the truck is initially traveling in the $+x$-direction). But wait. There is a net force in the $-x$-direction, and hence there should be an acceleration in that direction $(-a_x)$. What does this mean? It means that relative to the ground, the crate is decelerating at the same rate as the truck, which is necessary for the crate not to slide—the crate and the truck slow down uniformly together.

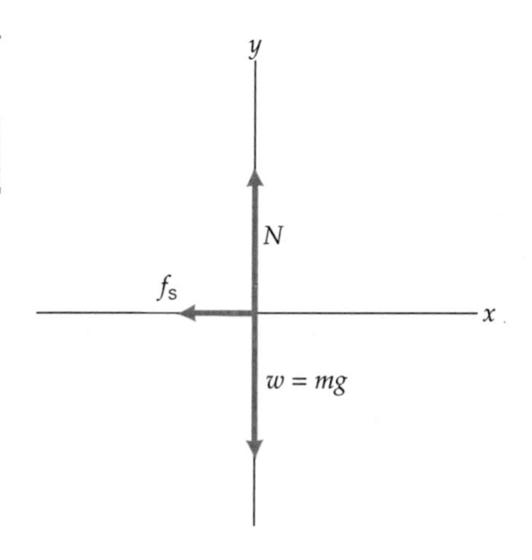

▲ **FIGURE 4.23 Free-body diagram** See Example 4.12.

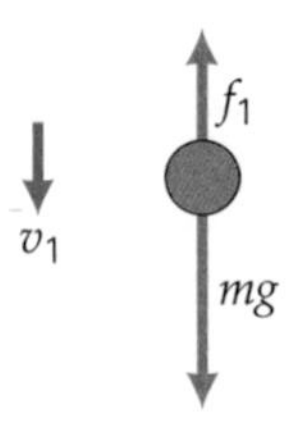

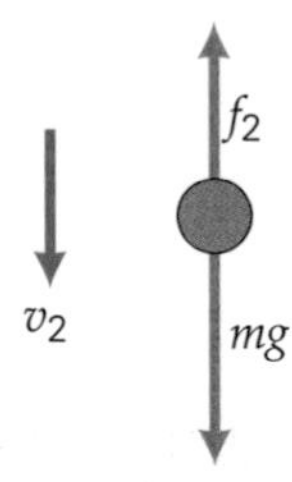

(a) As v increases, so does f.

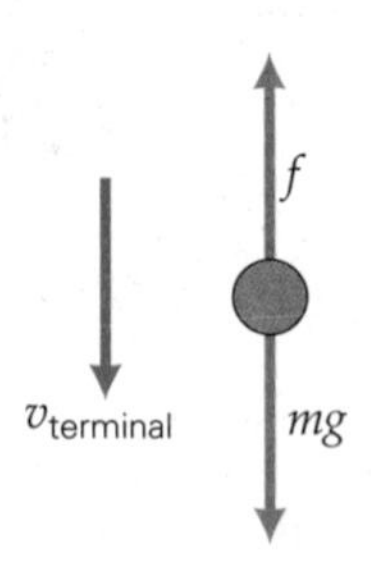

(b) When $f = mg$, the object falls with a constant (terminal) velocity.

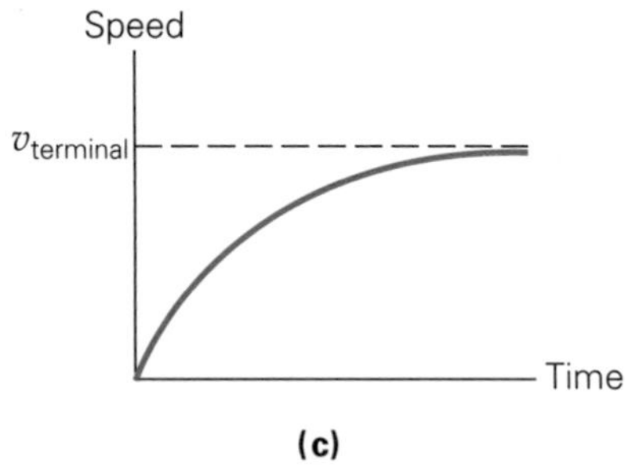

(c)

▲ **FIGURE 4.25 Air resistance and terminal velocity** **(a)** As the speed of a falling object increases, so does the frictional force of air resistance. **(b)** When this force of friction equals the weight of the object, the net force is zero, and the object falls with a constant (terminal) velocity. **(c)** A plot of speed versus time, showing these relationships.

▶ **FIGURE 4.24 Air foil** The air foil at the top of the truck's cab makes the truck streamlined and therefore reduces air resistance.

(b) Thinking It Through. The force creating this acceleration for the crate is the static force of friction. The acceleration is found using Newton's second law, and then used in one of the kinematic equations to find the distance.

Given: $v_{x_o} = 80\text{ km/h} = 22\text{ m/s}$ ***Find:*** (b) minimum stopping distance
$\mu_s = 0.40$

Applying Newton's second law:

$$\Sigma \mathbf{F}_x = -f_s = -\mu_s N = -\mu_s mg = ma_x$$

Solving for a_x, we obtain

$$a_x = -\mu_s g = -(0.40)(9.8\text{ m/s}^2) = -3.9\text{ m/s}^2$$

which is the maximum deceleration of the truck so the crate does not slide. Otherwise, $ma_x > f_{s_{max}}$, and kinetic friction would take over (sliding). Hence, the minimum stopping distance (x) for the truck is given by Eq. 2.11, where $v_x = 0$ and x_o is taken to be zero. So,

$$v_x^2 = 0 = v_{x_o}^2 + 2(a_x)x$$

Solving for x, we obtain

$$x = \frac{v_{x_o}^2}{-2a} = \frac{(22\text{ m/s})^2}{-2(-3.9\text{ m/s}^2)} = +62\text{ m}$$

Is the answer reasonable? This length is about two thirds of a football field.

Follow-up Exercise. Draw a free-body diagram, and describe what happens in terms of accelerations and coefficients of friction if the crate starts to slide forward when the truck is braking to a stop (in other words, if a_x exceeds -3.9 m/s^2). *(Answers to all Follow-up Exercises are at the back of the text.)*

Air Resistance

Air resistance refers to the resistance force acting on an object as it moves through air. In other words, air resistance is a type of frictional force. In analyses of falling objects, you can generally ignore the effect of air resistance and still get valid approximations for falling relatively short distances. However, for longer distances, air resistance cannot be ignored.

Air resistance occurs when a moving object collides with air molecules. Therefore, air resistance depends on the object's shape and size (which determine the area of the object that is exposed to collisions) as well as its speed. The larger the object and the faster it moves, the more collisions there will be with air molecules. (Air density is also a factor, but this quantity can be assumed to be constant near the Earth's surface.) To reduce air resistance (and fuel consumption), automobiles are made more "streamlined," and air foils are used on trucks and campers (▲Fig. 4.24).

Consider now a falling object. Since air resistance depends on speed, as a falling object accelerates under the influence of gravity, the retarding force of air resistance increases (◀Fig. 4.25a). Eventually, the magnitude of the retarding force equals that of the object's weight force (Fig. 4.25b), so the net force on the object is zero. The object then falls with a maximum constant velocity, which is called the **terminal velocity**.

This can be easily seen from Newton's second law. For the falling object, we have

$$F_{net} = ma$$

or

$$mg - f = ma$$

where downward has been taken as positive for convenience. Solving for a, we obtain

$$a = g - \frac{f}{m}$$

where a is the magnitude of the instantaneous acceleration.

Notice that the acceleration for a falling object when air resistance is included is less than g; that is, $a < g$, or $a < 9.8\ \text{m/s}^2$. As the object continues to fall, its speed increases, and thus the force of air resistance, f, increases (since it is speed dependent) until $a = 0$, when $f = mg$ and $f - mg = 0$. The object then falls at its constant terminal velocity.

For a sky diver with an unopened parachute, the terminal velocity is about 200 km/h (about 125 mi/h). To reduce the terminal velocity so that it can be reached sooner and the time of fall extended, a sky diver will try to increase exposed body area to a maximum by assuming a spread-eagle position (▸Fig. 4.26). This position takes advantage of the dependence of air resistance on the size and shape of the falling object. Once the parachute is open (giving a larger exposed area and a shape that catches the air), the additional air resistance slows the diver down to about 40 km/h (or 25 mi/h), which is preferable for landing.

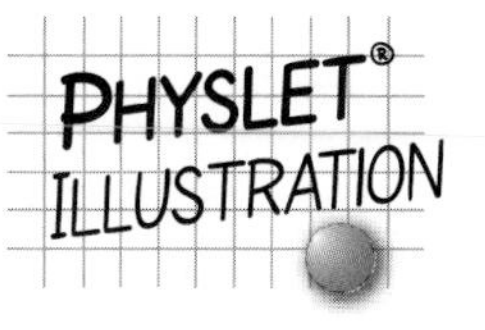

Air Resistance

▲ **FIGURE 4.26 Terminal velocity** Sky divers assume a spread-eagle position to maximize air resistance. This causes them to reach terminal velocity more quickly and prolongs the time of fall.

Conceptual Example 4.13 ■ Race You Down: Air Resistance and Terminal Velocity

From a high altitude, a balloonist simultaneously drops two balls of identical size, but appreciably different in weight. Assuming that both balls reach terminal velocity during the fall, which of the following is true? (a) The heavier ball reaches terminal velocity first; (b) the balls reach terminal velocity at the same time; (c) the heavier ball hits the ground first; (d) the balls hit the ground at the same time? *Clearly establish the reasoning and physical principle(s) used in determining your answer before checking it below. That is,* ***why*** *did you select your answer?*

Reasoning and Answer. Terminal velocity is reached when the weight of a ball is balanced by the frictional air resistance. Both balls initially experience the same acceleration, g, and their speeds and the retarding forces of air resistance increase at the same rate. The weight of the lighter ball will be balanced first, so (a) and (b) are incorrect. The lighter ball reaches terminal velocity ($a = 0$) first, but the heavier ball continues to accelerate, speeding up, and pulls ahead of the lighter ball. Hence, the heavier ball hits the ground first, and the answer is (c), and (d) does not apply.

Follow-up Exercise. Suppose the heavier ball were much larger in size than the lighter ball. How might this difference affect the outcome? *(Answers to all Follow-up Exercises are at the back of the text.)*

You see an example of terminal velocity quite often. Why do clouds stay seemingly suspended in the sky? Certainly the water droplets or ice crystals (high clouds) should fall—and they do. However, they are so small that their terminal velocity is reached quickly, and the very slow rate of their descent goes unnoticed. Also, there may be some helpful updrafts that keep the water and ice from reaching the ground.

Chapter Review

Important Concepts and Equations

- A **force** is something that is capable of changing an object's state of motion. To produce a change in motion, there must be a nonzero net, or unbalanced, force:

$$\mathbf{F}_{\text{net}} = \Sigma \mathbf{F}_i$$

- **Newton's first law of motion** is also called the *law of inertia*, where inertia is the natural tendency of an object to maintain its state of motion. It states that in the absence of a net applied force, a body at rest remains at rest, and a body in motion remains in motion with constant velocity.
- **Newton's second law** relates the net force acting on an object or system to the (total) mass and the resulting acceleration. It defines the cause-and-effect relationship between force and acceleration:

$$\Sigma \mathbf{F}_i = \mathbf{F}_{\text{net}} = m\mathbf{a} \quad (4.1)$$

The equation for **weight** in terms of mass is a form of Newton's second law:

$$w = mg \quad (4.2)$$

The component form of Newton's second law:

$$\Sigma(F_x\hat{\mathbf{x}} + F_y\hat{\mathbf{y}}) = m(a_x\hat{\mathbf{x}} + a_y\hat{\mathbf{y}}) = ma_x\hat{\mathbf{x}} + ma_x\hat{\mathbf{y}} \quad (4.3a)$$

and

$$\Sigma F_x = ma_x \quad \text{and} \quad \Sigma F_y = ma_y \quad (4.3b)$$

- **Newton's third law** states that for every force, there is an equal and opposite reaction force. The opposing forces of a third-law pair always act on different objects.
- An object is said to be in **translational equilibrium** when it either is at rest or moves with a constant velocity. When remaining at rest, an object is said to be in *static translational equilibrium*. The condition for translational equilibrium is represented as

$$\Sigma \mathbf{F}_i = 0 \quad (4.4)$$

or

$$\Sigma \mathbf{F}_x = 0 \quad \text{and} \quad \Sigma \mathbf{F}_y = 0 \quad (4.5)$$

- **Friction** is the resistance to motion that occurs between contacting surfaces. (In general, friction occurs for all types of media—solids, liquids, and gases.)
- The frictional force between surfaces is characterized by coefficients of friction (μ), one for the static case and one for the kinetic (moving) case. In many cases, $f = \mu N$, where N is the normal force—the force perpendicular to the surface (i.e., the force exerted *by* the surface *on* the object). As a ratio of forces (f/N), μ is unitless.

Force of Static Friction:

$$f_s \leq \mu_s N \quad (4.6)$$

$$f_{s_{\max}} = \mu_s N \quad (4.7)$$

Force of Kinetic (Sliding) Friction:

$$f_k = \mu_k N \quad (4.8)$$

- The force of air resistance on a falling object increases with increasing speed. It eventually attains a constant velocity, called the *terminal velocity*.

Exercises

Note: Unless otherwise stated, all objects are located near the Earth's surface, where $g = 9.80\ \text{m/s}^2$.

4.1 The Concept of Force and Net Force *and* 4.2 Inertia and Newton's First Law of Motion

1. CQ If an object is at rest, there must be no force acting on it. Is this statement correct? Explain.

2. The tendency of an object to maintain its state of motion is called (a) Newton's second law, (b) Galileo's principle, or (c) inertia.

3. CQ When on a jet airliner that is taking off, you feel that you are being "pushed" back into the seat. Use Newton's first law to explain why.

4. CQ The net force on an object is zero. Can you conclude that the object is at rest? Explain.

5. If an object is moving at constant velocity, (a) there must be a force in the direction of the velocity, (b) there must be no force in the direction of the velocity, (c) there must be no net force, or (d) there must be a net force in the direction of the velocity.

6. If the net force on an object is zero, the object could (a) be at rest, (b) be in motion at a constant velocity, (c) have zero acceleration, or (d) all of the preceding.

7. CQ An object weighs 300 N on Earth and 50 N on the Moon. Does the object also have less inertia on the Moon?

8. CQ Consider an air-bubble level that is sitting on a horizontal surface (▶Fig. 4.27). Initially, the air bubble is in the middle of the horizontal glass tube. (a) If the level is pushed and a force is applied to accelerate it, which way would the

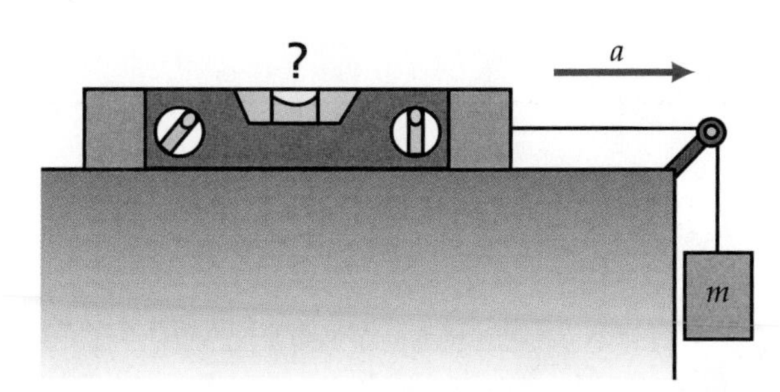

▲ **FIGURE 4.27 An air-bubble level/accelerometer** See Exercise 8.

bubble move? Which way would the bubble move if the force is then removed and the level slows down, due to friction? (b) Such a level is sometimes used as an "accelerometer" to indicate the direction of the acceleration. Explain the principle involved. [*Hint*: Think about pushing a pan of water.]

9. CQ As a follow-up to Exercise 8, consider the situation of a child holding a helium balloon in a closed car at rest. What would the child observe when the car (a) accelerates from rest and (b) brakes to a stop? (The balloon does not touch the roof of the car.)

10. CQ Objects have no appreciable weight in deep space. How can you then distinguish their masses?

11. CQ The following is an old trick: If a tablecloth is yanked out very quickly, the dishes on top of it will barely move (▼Fig. 4.28). Why?

▲ **FIGURE 4.28 No more dinner?** See Exercise 11.

12. CQ If your car is moving around a circular track at a constant speed of 55 mi/h, is there a net force acting on your car? Explain.

13. ■ Which has more inertia, 20 cm^3 of water or 10 cm^3 of aluminum, and how many times more? (See Table 7.2.)

14. IE ■■ (a) You are told that an object has zero acceleration. Which of the following is true? (1) The object is at rest; (2) the object is moving with constant velocity; (3) either (1) or (2) is possible; or (4) neither (1) nor (2) is possible. (b) Two forces on the object are $\mathbf{F}_1 = 3.6$ N at 74° below the $+x$-axis and $\mathbf{F}_2 = 3.6$ N at 34° above the $-x$-axis. Is there a third force on the object, and why? If yes, what is it?

15. ■■ A 5.0-kg block at rest on a frictionless surface is acted on by forces $F_1 = 5.5$ N and $F_2 = 3.5$ N, as illustrated in ▼Fig. 4.29. What additional horizontal force will keep the block at rest?

16. ■■■ A 1.5-kg object moves up the y-axis at a constant speed. When it reaches the origin, the forces $\mathbf{F}_1 = 5.0$ N at 37° above the $+x$-axis, $\mathbf{F}_2 = 2.5$ N in the $+x$-direction, $\mathbf{F}_3 = 3.5$ N at 45° below the $-x$-axis, and $\mathbf{F}_4 = 1.5$ N in the $-y$-direction are applied to it. (a) Will the object continue to move along the y-axis? (b) If not, what simultaneously applied force will keep it moving along the y-axis at a constant speed?

4.3 Newton's Second Law of Motion

17. The newton unit of force is equivalent to (a) kg · m/s, (b) kg · m/s^2, (c) kg · m^2/s, or (d) none of the preceding.

18. CQ In general, this chapter has considered forces that are applied to objects of constant mass. What would be the situation if mass were added to or lost from a system while a force was being applied to the system? Give examples of situations in which this set of events might happen.

19. CQ The engines of most rockets produce a constant thrust (forward force). However, when a rocket is fired into space, its acceleration increase with time as the engine continues to operate. Is this situation a violation of Newton's second law? Explain.

20. CQ An astronaut has a mass of 70 kg when measured on Earth. What is his weight in deep space, far from any celestial body? What is his mass there?

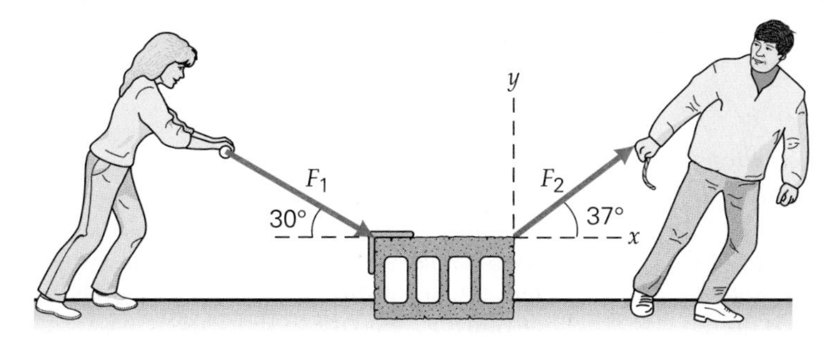

◀ **FIGURE 4.29 Two applied forces** See Exercises 15 and 94.

21. CQ In football, good wide receivers usually have "soft" hands for catching balls (▼Fig. 4.30). How would you interpret this description on the basis of Newton's second law?

▲ **FIGURE 4.30 Soft hands** See Exercise 21.

22. ■ A 3.0-N net force is applied to a 1.5-kg mass. What is the object's acceleration?

23. ■ What is the mass of an object that accelerates at 3.0 m/s^2 under the influence of a 5.0-N net force?

24. ■ A worker pushes on a crate that experiences a net force of 75 N. If the crate also experiences an acceleration of 0.50 m/s^2, what is its weight?

25. ■ A loaded Boeing 747 jumbo jet has a mass of 2.0×10^5 kg. What net force is required to give the plane an acceleration of 3.5 m/s^2 down the runway for takeoffs?

26. IE ■ A 6.0-kg object is brought to the Moon, where the acceleration due to gravity is only one sixth of that on the Earth. (a) The mass of the object on the Moon is (1) zero, (2) 1.0 kg, (3) 6.0 kg, or (4) 36 kg. Why? (b) What is the weight of the object on the Moon?

27. ■ What is the mass of a person weighing 740 N on the Earth?

28. ■ What is the net force acting on a 1.0-kg object in free fall?

29. ■ What is the weight of an 8.0-kg mass in newtons? How about in pounds?

30. ■■ What is the weight of a 150-lb person in newtons? What is his mass in kilograms?

31. IE ■■ ▸Fig. 4.31 shows a product label. (a) This label is correct (1) on the Earth; (2) on the Moon, where the acceleration due to gravity is only one sixth of that on the Earth; (3) in deep space, where there is little gravity; or (4) all of the preceding. (b) What mass of lasagne would a label show for the amount that weighs 2 lb on the Moon?

▲ **FIGURE 4.31 Correct label?** See Exercise 31.

32. ■■ In a college homecoming competition, 16 students lift a sports car. While holding the car off the ground, each student exerts an upward force of 400 N. (a) What is the mass of the car in kilograms? (b) What is its weight in pounds?

33. ■■ A horizontal force of 12 N acts on an object that rests on a level, frictionless surface on the Earth, where the object has a weight of 98 N. (a) What is the magnitude of the acceleration of the object? (b) What would be the acceleration of the same object in a similar situation on the Moon?

34. ■■ The engine of a 1.0-kg toy plane exerts a 15-N forward force. If the air exerts a 8.0-N resistive force on the plane, what is the magnitude of the acceleration of the plane?

35. ■■ When a horizontal force of 300 N is applied to a 75.0-kg box, the box slides on a level floor, opposed by a force of kinetic friction of 120 N. What is the magnitude of the acceleration of the box?

36. IE ■■ (a) A horizontal force acts on an object on a frictionless horizontal surface. If the force is halved and the mass of the object is doubled, the acceleration will be (1) four times, (2) two times, (3) one half, or (4) one fourth as great. (b) If the acceleration of the object is 1.0 m/s^2, and the force on it is doubled and its mass is halved, what is the new acceleration?

37. ■■ A stalled 1500-kg automobile is pushed toward a gas station by a man and a woman on a level road. The applied horizontal forces are 200 N for the woman and 300 N for the man. (a) If there is an effective force of friction of 300 N on the car as it moves, what is its acceleration? (b) Once the car is moving appreciably, what would be an appropriate combined applied force, and why?

38. ■■ In an emergency stop to avoid an accident, a shoulder-strap seat belt holds a 60-kg passenger firmly in place. If the car were initially traveling at 90 km/h and came to a stop in 5.5 s along a straight, level road, what was the average force applied to the passenger by the seatbelt?

39. ■■ A jet catapult on an aircraft carrier accelerates a 2000-kg plane uniformly from rest to a launch speed of 320 km/h in 2.0 s. What is the magnitude of the net force on the plane?

40. ■■ In serving, a tennis player accelerates a 56-g tennis ball horizontally from rest to a speed of 35 m/s. Assuming that the acceleration is uniform when the racquet is applied over a distance of 0.50 m, what is the magnitude of the force exerted on the ball by the racquet?

4.4 Newton's Third Law of Motion

41. A brick hits a glass window. The brick breaks the glass, so (a) the magnitude of the force of the brick on the glass is greater than the magnitude of the force of the glass on the brick, (b) the magnitude of the force of the brick on the glass is smaller than the magnitude of the force of the glass on the brick, (c) the magnitude of the force of the brick on the glass is equal to the magnitude of the force of the glass on the brick, or (d) none of the previous.

42. A freight truck collides head on with a passenger car, causing a lot more damage to the car than to the truck. From this condition, we can say that (a) the magnitude of the force of the truck on the car is greater than the magnitude of the force of the car on the truck, (b) the magnitude of the force of the truck on the car is smaller than the magnitude of the force of the car on the truck, (c) the magnitude of the force of the truck on the car is equal to the magnitude of the force of the car on the truck, or (d) none of the preceding.

43. CQ Here is a story of a horse and a farmer: One day, the farmer attaches a heavy cart to the horse and demands that the horse pull the cart. "Well," says the horse, "I cannot pull the cart, because, according to Newton's third law, if I apply a force to the cart, the cart will apply an equal and opposite force on me. The net result will be that I cannot pull the cart, since all the forces will cancel. Therefore, it is impossible for me to pull this cart." The farmer was very upset! What could he say to convince the horse to move?

44. The force pair of Newton's third law (a) consists of forces that are always opposite, but not always equal; (b) always cancels when the second law is applied to a body; (c) always acts on the same object; or (d) consists of forces that are equal and opposite, but act on different objects.

45. CQ Is there something wrong with the following statements? When a baseball is hit with a bat, there are equal and opposite forces on the bat and baseball. The forces then cancel, and there is no motion.

46. IE A book is sitting on a horizontal surface. (a) There is (are) (1) one, (2) two, or (3) three force(s) acting on the book. (b) Identify the reaction force to each force on the book.

47. CQ By using the right technique, a karate master can exert huge forces on objects. If a brick is hit by a fist with a force of 800 N, what else do we know, according to Newton's third law? Is this something you should try at home?

48. A person pushes on a block of wood that has been placed against a wall. Draw a free-body diagram and identify the reaction forces to all the forces on the block.

49. ■■ In an Olympic figure-skating event, a 60-kg male skater pushes a 45-kg female skater, causing her to accelerate at a rate of 2.0 m/s^2. At what rate will the male skater accelerate? What is the direction of his acceleration?

50. ■■ Jane and John, with masses of 50 kg and 60 kg, respectively, stand on a frictionless surface 10 m apart. John pulls on a rope that connects him to Jane, giving Jane an acceleration of 0.92 m/s^2 toward him. (a) What is John's acceleration? (b) If the pulling force is applied constantly, where will Jane and John meet?

4.5 More on Newton's Laws: Free-Body Diagrams and Translational Equilibrium

Note: In Exercises with strings and pulleys, "ideal conditions" means that the masses of the string(s) and pulley(s), as well as the friction of the pulley(s), should be neglected.

51. Draw a free-body diagram of a car coasting (with its engine off) up a long, straight ramp. Clearly mark the forces, and identify their sources.

52. IE ■ (a) When an object is on a inclined plane, the normal force exerted by the inclined plane on the object is (1) less than, (2) equal to, or (3) more than the weight of the object. Why? (b) For a 10-kg object on a 30° inclined plane, what are the object's weight and the normal force exerted on the object by the inclined place?

53. IE ■■ The weight of a 500-kg object is 4900 N. (a) When the object is on a moving elevator, its measured weight could be (1) zero, (2) between zero and 4900 N, (3) more than 4900 N, or (4) all of the preceding. Why? (b) Describe the motion if the object's measured weight is only 4000 N in a moving elevator.

54. ■■ A 75.0-kg person is standing on a scale in an elevator. What is the reading of the scale in newtons if the elevator is (a) at rest, (b) moving up at a constant velocity of 2.00 m/s, and (c) accelerating up at 2.00 m/s^2?

55. ■■ In Exercise 54, what if the elevator is accelerating down?

56. ■■ Two boats pull a 75.0-kg water skier, as illustrated in ▾Fig. 4.32. (a) If each boat pulls with a force of 600 N and the skier travels at a constant velocity, what is the magnitude of the retarding force between the water and the skis? (b) Assuming that the retarding force remains constant, if each boat pulls with a force of 700 N, what is the magnitude of the acceleration of the skier?

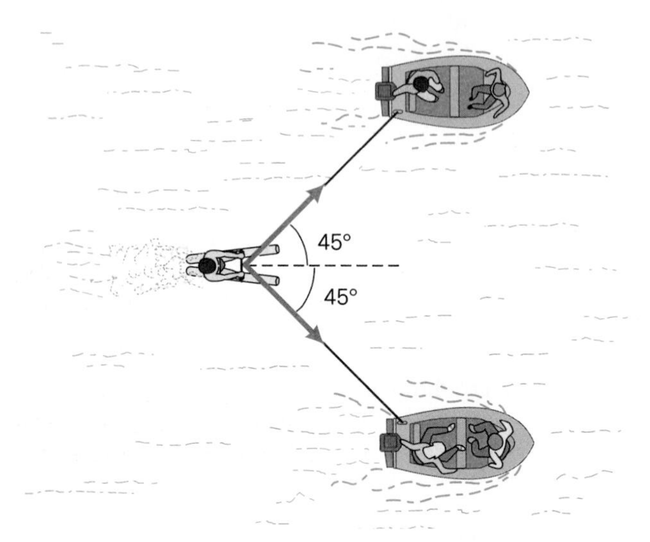

▲ **FIGURE 4.32 Double tow** See Exercise 56.

57. ■■ (a) A 65-kg water skier is pulled by a boat with a horizontal force of 400 N due east with a water drag on the skis of 300 N. A sudden gust of wind supplies another horizontal force of 50 N on the skier at an angle of 60° north of east. At that instant, what is the skier's acceleration? (b) What would be the skier's acceleration if the wind force were in the opposite direction to that in part (a)?

58. ■■ A boy pulls a box of mass 30 kg with a force of 25 N in the direction shown in ▾Fig. 4.33. (a) Ignoring friction, what is the acceleration of the box? (b) What is the normal force exerted on the box by the ground?

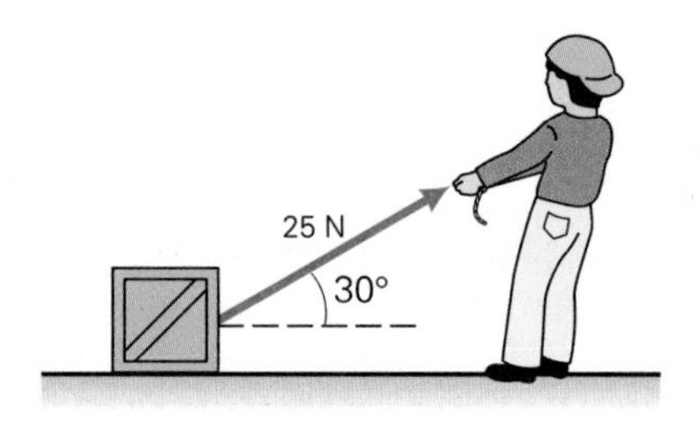

▲ **FIGURE 4.33 Pulling a box** See Exercises 58 and 89.

59. ■■ A girl pushes a 25-kg lawn mower as shown in ▸Fig. 4.34. If $F = 30$ N and $\theta = 37°$, (a) what is the acceleration of the mower, and (b) what is the normal force exerted on the mower by the lawn? Ignore friction.

▲ **FIGURE 4.34 Mowing the lawn** See Exercise 59.

60. IE ■■ (a) An Olympic skier coasts down a slope with an angle of inclination of 37°. Neglecting friction, there is (are) (1), one, (2) two, or (3) three force(s) acting on the skier. (b) What is the acceleration of the skier? (c) If the skier has a speed of 5.0 m/s at the top of the slope, what is his speed when he reaches the bottom of the 35-m-long slope?

61. ■■ A car coasts (engine off) up a 30° grade. If the speed of the car is 25 m/s at the bottom of the grade, what is the distance traveled by the car before it comes to rest?

62. ■■ A horizontal force of 40 N acting on a block on a frictionless level surface produces an acceleration of 2.5 m/s^2. A second block, with a mass of 4.0 kg, is dropped onto the first. What is the magnitude of the acceleration of the combination of blocks if the same force continues to act? (Assume that the second block does not slide on the first block.)

63. IE ■■ A rope is fixed at both ends on two trees, and a bag is hung in the middle of the rope, causing the rope to sag vertically. (a) The tension in the rope depends on (1) only the tree separation, (2) only the sag, (3) both the tree separation and sag, or (4) neither the tree separation nor the sag. (b) If the tree separation is 10 m, the mass of the bag is 5.0 kg, and the sag is 0.20 m, what is the tension in the line?

64. ■■ A 50-kg gymnast hangs vertically from a pair of parallel rings. (a) If the ropes supporting the rings are attached to the ceiling directly above, what is the tension in each rope? (b) If the ropes are supported so that they make an angle of 45° with the ceiling, what is the tension in each rope?

65. ■■ A 3000-kg truck tows a 1500-kg car by a chain. If the net forward force on the truck by the ground is 3200 N, (a) what is the acceleration of the car, and (b) what is the tension in the connecting chain?

66. ■■ Three blocks are pulled along a frictionless surface by a horizontal force as shown in ▸Fig. 4.35. (a) What is the acceleration of the system? (b) What are the tension forces in the light strings? (*Hint*: Can T_1 equal T_2? Investigate by drawing free-body diagrams of each block separately.)

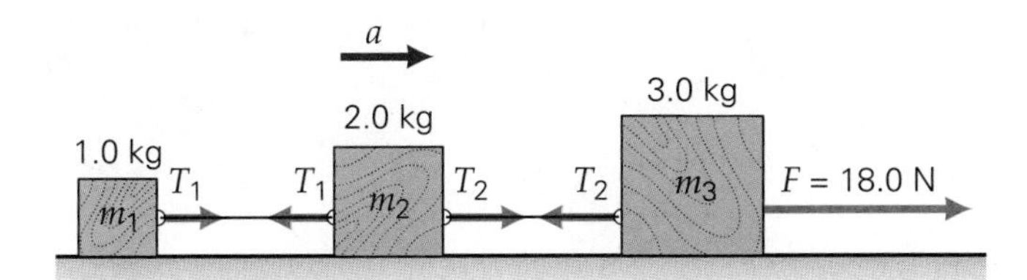

▲ **FIGURE 4.35 Three-block system** See Exercises 66 and 95.

67. ■■ Assume ideal conditions for the apparatus illustrated in ▼Fig. 4.36. What is the acceleration of the system if (a) $m_1 = 0.25$ kg, $m_2 = 0.50$ kg, and $m_3 = 0.25$ kg, and (b) $m_1 = 0.35$ kg, $m_2 = 0.15$ kg, and $m_3 = 0.50$ kg?

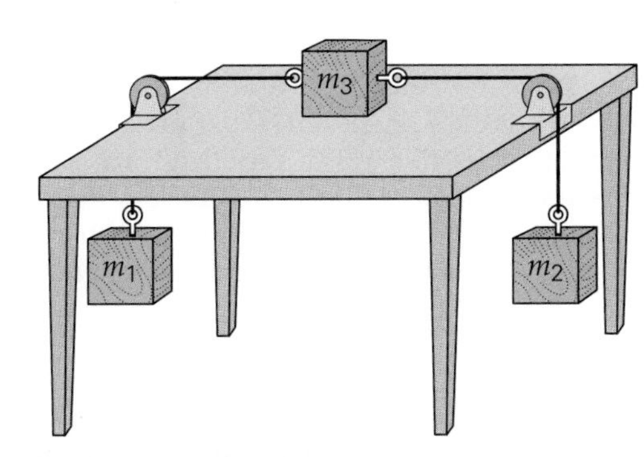

▲ **FIGURE 4.36 Which way will they accelerate?** See Exercises 67, 97, and 98.

68. ■■ The *Atwood machine* consists of two masses suspended from a fixed pulley, as shown in ▼Fig. 4.37. It is named after British scientist George Atwood (1746–1807), who used it to study motion and to measure the value of g. If $m_1 = 0.55$ kg and $m_2 = 0.80$ kg, (a) what is the acceleration of the system, and (b) what is the magnitude of the tension in the string?

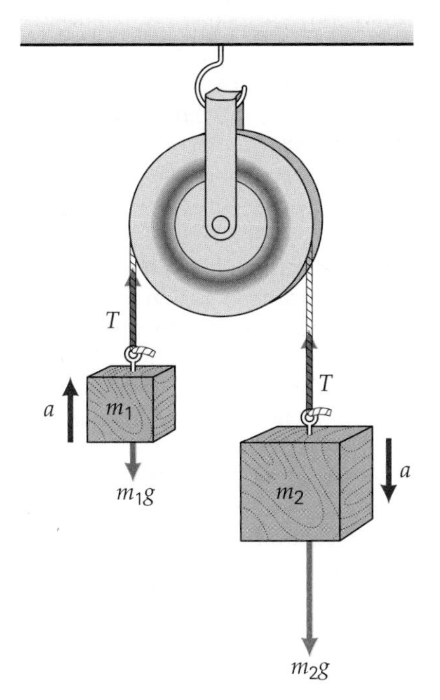

▲ **FIGURE 4.37 Atwood machine** See Exercises 68, 69, 70, and 107.

69. ■■ An Atwood machine (see Fig. 4.37) has suspended masses of 0.25 kg and 0.20 kg. Under ideal conditions, what will be the acceleration of the smaller mass?

70. ■■■ One mass, $m_1 = 0.215$ kg , of an ideal Atwood machine (see Fig. 4.37) rests on the floor 1.10 m below the other mass, $m_2 = 0.255$ kg. (a) If the masses are released from rest, how long does it take m_2 to reach the floor? (b) How high will mass m_1 ascend from the floor? [*Hint*: When m_2 hits the floor, m_1 continues to move upward.]

71. ■■■ A 0.20-kg ball is released from a height of 10 m above the beach; the impression the ball makes in the sand is 5.0 cm deep. What is the average force acting on the ball by the sand?

72. ■■■ In the ideal apparatus shown in ▼Fig. 4.38, $m_1 = 2.0$ kg. What is m_2 if both masses are at rest? How about if both masses are moving at constant velocity?

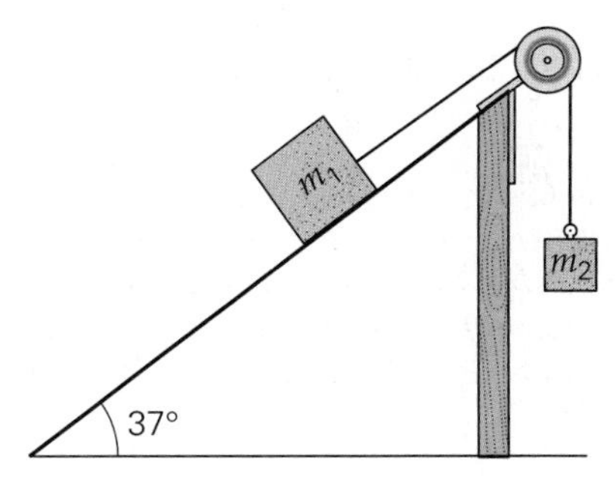

▲ **FIGURE 4.38 Inclined Atwood machine** See Exercises 72, 73, and 99.

73. ■■■ In the ideal setup shown in Fig. 4.38, $m_1 = 3.0$ kg and $m_2 = 2.5$ kg. (a) What is the acceleration of the masses? (b) What is the tension in the string?

4.6 Friction

Note: Neglect air resistance, unless otherwise stated.

74. In general, the frictional force (a) is greater for smooth than rough surfaces, (b) depends on sliding speeds, (c) is proportional to the normal force, or (d) depends significantly on the surface area of contact.

75. CQ Identify the direction of the friction force in the following cases: (a) a book sitting on a table; (b) a box sliding on a horizontal surface; (c) a car making a turn on a flat road; (d) the initial motion of a machine part delivered on a conveyor belt in an assembly line.

76. The coefficient of kinetic friction, μ_k (a) is usually greater than the coefficient of static friction, μ_s; (b) usually equals μ_s; (c) is usually smaller than μ_s; or (d) equals the applied force that exceeds the maximum static force.

77. CQ The purpose of a car's antilock brakes is to prevent the wheels from locking up so as to keep the car rolling rather than sliding. Why would rolling decrease the stopping distance as compared with sliding?

78. CQ Is it easier to push or pull a lawn mower at an angle? Draw a free-body diagram, and explain.

79. CQ ▼Fig. 4.39 shows the front and rear wings of an Indy racing car. These wings generate *down force*, the vertical downward force produced by the air moving over the car. Why is such a down force desired? An Indy car can create a down force equal to twice its weight. Why not simply make the cars heavier?

▲ **FIGURE 4.39 Down force** See Exercise 79.

80. CQ (a) We commonly say that friction opposes motion. Yet, when we walk, the frictional force is in the direction of our motion (Fig. 4.18). Is there an inconsistency in terms of Newton's second law? Explain. (b) What effects would wind have on air resistance? [*Hint*: The wind can blow in different directions.]

81. CQ Why are drag-racing tires wide and smooth, whereas passenger-car tires are narrower and have tread (►Fig. 4.40)? Are there frictional and/or safety considerations? Does this difference between the tires contradict the fact that friction is independent of surface area?

82. ■ In moving a 35.0-kg desk from one side of a classroom to the other, a professor finds that a horizontal force of 275 N is necessary to set the desk in motion, and a force of 195 N is necessary to keep it in motion at a constant speed. What are the coefficients of (a) static and (b) kinetic friction between the desk and the floor?

83. ■ A 40-kg crate is at rest on a level surface. If the coefficient of static friction between the crate and the surface is 0.69, what horizontal force is required to get the crate moving?

▲ **FIGURE 4.40 Racing tires versus passenger-car tires: safety** See Exercise 81.

84. IE ■ A 20-kg box sits on a rough horizontal surface. When a horizontal force of 120 N is applied, the object accelerates at 1.0 m/s^2. (a) If the applied force is doubled, the acceleration will (1) increase, but less than double; (2) also double; or (3) increase, but more than double. Why? (b) Calculate the acceleration to prove your answer to (a).

85. ■ The coefficients of static and kinetic friction between a 50-kg box and a horizontal surface are 0.60 and 0.40, respectively. (a) What is the acceleration of the object if a 250-N horizontal force is applied to the box? (b) What is the acceleration if the applied force is 350 N?

86. ■■ A 1500-kg automobile travels at a speed of 90 km/h along a straight concrete highway. Faced with an emergency situation, the driver jams on the brakes, and the car skids to a stop. What will be the car's stopping distance for (a) dry pavement and (b) wet pavement, respectively?

87. ■■ A hockey player hits a puck with his stick, giving the puck an initial speed of 5.0 m/s. If the puck slows uniformly and comes to rest in a distance of 20 m, what is the coefficient of kinetic friction between the ice and the puck?

88. ■■ A packing crate is placed on a 20° inclined plane. If the coefficient of static friction between the crate and the plane is 0.65, will the crate slide down the plane? Justify your answer.

89. ■■ In Exercise 58 and Fig. 4.33, if the coefficient of kinetic friction between the box and the surface is 0.03 (waxed wood box on snow), what is the acceleration of the box?

90. ■■ Suppose the slope conditions for the skier shown in ►Fig. 4.41 are such that the skier travels at a constant velocity. From the photo, could you find the coefficient of kinetic friction between the snowy surface and the skis? If so, describe how this would be done.

91. ■■ A 5.0-kg wooden block is placed on an adjustable wooden inclined plane. (a) What is the angle of incline above which the block will *start* to slide down the plane?

▲ **FIGURE 4.41 A downslope run** See Exercise 90.

(b) At what angle of incline will the block then slide down the plane at a constant speed?

92. ■■ A block that has a mass of 2.0 kg and is 10 cm wide on each side just begins to slide down an inclined plane with a 30° angle of incline (▼Fig. 4.42). Another block of the same height and same material has base dimensions of 20 cm × 10 cm and thus a mass of 4.0 kg. (a) At what critical angle will the more massive block start to slide down the plane? Why? (b) Estimate the coefficient of static friction between the block and the plane.

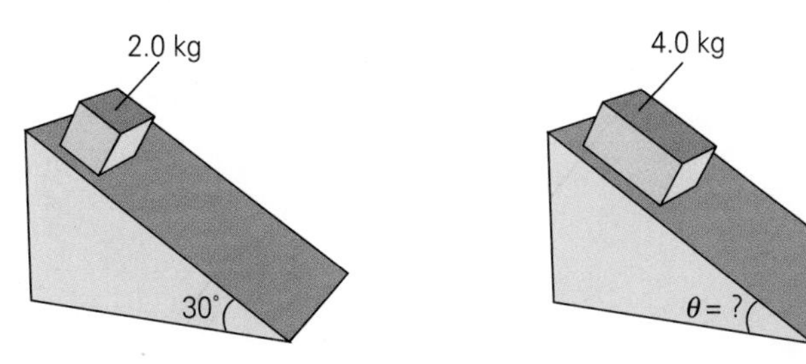

▲ **FIGURE 4.42 At what angle will it begin to slide?** See Exercise 92.

93. ■■ While being unloaded from a truck, a 10-kg suitcase is placed on a flat ramp inclined at 37°. When released from rest, the suitcase accelerates down the ramp at 0.15 m/s^2. What is the coefficient of kinetic friction between the suitcase and the ramp?

94. ■■ For the situation shown in Fig. 4.29, what is the minimum coefficient of static friction between the block and the surface that will keep the block from moving? ($F_1 = 5.0$ N, $F_2 = 4.0$ N , and $m = 5.0$ kg.)

95. ■■ For the system illustrated in Fig. 4.35, if $\mu_s = 0.45$ and $\mu_k = 0.35$ between the blocks and the surface, what applied forces will (a) set the blocks in motion and (b) move the blocks at a constant velocity?

96. ■■ In the apparatus shown in ▶Fig. 4.43, $m_1 = 10$ kg and the coefficients of static and kinetic friction between m_1 and the table are 0.60 and 0.40, respectively. (a) What mass of m_2 will set the system in motion? (b) After the system moves, what is the acceleration?

97. ■■■ For the apparatus in Fig. 4.36, what is the minimum value of the coefficient of static friction between the block (m_3) and the table that would keep the system at rest if $m_1 = 0.25$ kg, $m_2 = 0.50$ kg , and $m_3 = 0.75$ kg? (Assume ideal conditions for the string and pulleys.)

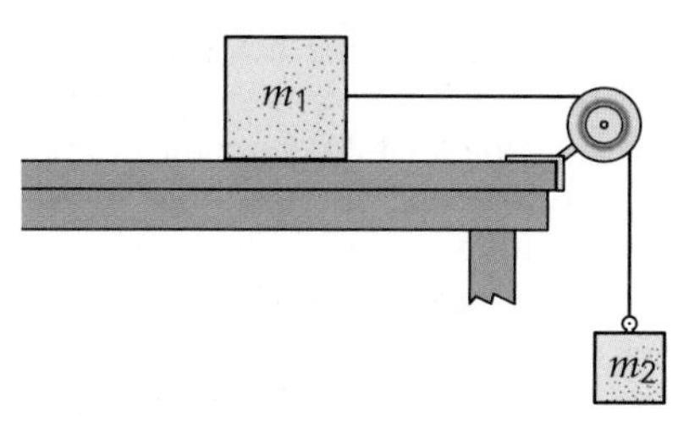

▲ **FIGURE 4.43 Friction and motion** See Exercise 96.

98. ■■■ If the coefficient of kinetic friction between the block and the table in Fig. 4.36 is 0.560, and $m_1 = 0.150$ kg and $m_2 = 0.250$ kg, (a) what should m_3 be if the system is to move with a constant speed? (b) If $m_3 = 0.100$ kg, what is the magnitude of the acceleration of the system? (Assume ideal conditions for the string and pulleys.)

99. ■■■ In the apparatus shown in Fig. 4.38, $m_1 = 2.0$ kg and the coefficients of static and kinetic friction between m_1 and the inclined plane are 0.30 and 0.20, respectively. (a) What is m_2 if both masses are at rest? (b) What is m_2 if both masses are moving at constant velocity? Neglect all friction.

Additional Exercises

100. ■■ At the end of most landing runways in airports, an extension of the runway is constructed using a special substance called *formcrete*. Formcrete can support the weight of cars, but crumbles under the weight of airplanes, so as to slow them down if they run off the end of a runway. If a plane of mass 2.00×10^5 kg is to stop from a speed of 25.0 m/s on a 100-m-long stretch of formcrete, what is the average force exerted on the plane by the formcrete?

101. A rifle weighs 50.0 N, and its barrel is 0.750 m long. It shoots a 25.0-g bullet, which leaves the barrel at a speed (muzzle velocity) of 300 m/s after being uniformly accelerated. What is the magnitude of the force exerted on the rifle by the bullet?

102. The maximum load that can safely be supported by a rope in an overhead hoist is 400 N. What is the maximum acceleration that can safely be given to a 25-kg object being hoisted vertically upward?

103. The coefficient of static friction between a 9.0-kg object and a horizontal surface is 0.45. Would a force of 35 N applied 20° above the horizontal cause the object to move from rest? If so, what would be the object's acceleration?

104. A 2.0-kg object travels at a constant velocity of 4.8 m/s northward. It is then acted on by forces of 6.5 N to the north and 8.5 N to the south. (a) How far will the object travel before coming to rest? (b) What will be the object's position 1.5 s after it comes momentarily to rest, with the forces still acting?

105. In the operation of a machine, a 5.0-kg steel part is to move on a horizontal steel surface. Force is applied to the part downward at an angle of 30° from the horizontal. (a) What is the magnitude of the applied force required to set the part in motion if the surface is dry? (b) If the surface is lubricated, by what factor is the force reduced?

106. A crate weighing 9.80×10^3 N is pulled up a 37° incline by a force parallel to the plane. If the coefficient of kinetic friction between the crate and the surface of the plane is 0.750, what is the magnitude of the applied force required to move the crate at a constant velocity?

107. For an Atwood machine (see Fig. 4.37) with suspended masses of 0.30 kg and 0.40 kg, the acceleration of the masses is measured as 0.95 m/s^2. What is the effective force of friction for the system?

108. A loaded jet plane with a weight of 2.75×10^6 N is ready for takeoff. If its engines supply 6.35×10^6 N of net thrust, how long a runway will the plane need to reach its minimum takeoff speed of 285 km/h?

109. A 0.45-kg shuffleboard puck is given an initial speed of 4.5 m/s down the flat playing surface. If the coefficient of sliding friction between the puck and the surface is 0.20, how far will the puck slide before coming to rest?

110. A 135-m-long ramp is to be built for a ski jump. If a skier starting from rest at the top is to have a speed no faster than 24 m/s at the bottom, what should be the maximum angle of inclination? Ignore friction.

111. A school bus pulls into an intersection as a car approaches at a speed of 25 km/h on an icy street. Seeing the bus from 26 m away, the driver of the car steps on and inadvertently locks the brakes, causing the car to slide toward the intersection. (The car does not have antilock brakes.) If the coefficient of kinetic friction between the car's tires and the icy road is 0.10, does the car hit the bus? Justify your answer.

112. While catching a baseball that is traveling horizontally at a speed of 15 m/s, a player's glove and arm move straight backward 25 cm from the time of contact to the time the ball comes to rest. If the ball has a mass of 0.14 kg, what is the average force on the ball during that interval?

Work and Energy

A description of pole vaulting might be as follows: An athlete runs with a pole, plants it into the ground, and tries to vault his body over a bar set at a certain height. However, a physicist might give a different description: The athlete has chemical potential energy stored in his body. He uses this potential energy to do work in running down the path to gain speed, or kinetic energy. When he plants the pole, most of his kinetic energy goes into elastic potential energy of the bent pole as shown in the photo. This potential energy is used to lift the vaulter or to do work against gravity, and is partially converted into gravitational potential energy. At the top, there is just enough kinetic energy left to carry the vaulter over the bar. On the way down, the gravitational potential energy is converted back to kinetic energy, which is absorbed by the mat in doing work to stop the fall. The pole vaulter participates in a game of work–energy give and take (see Fig. 5.28).

This chapter centers on these two concepts that are important in both science and everyday life—*work* and *energy*. We commonly think of work as being associated with doing or accomplishing something. Because work makes us physically (and sometimes mentally) tired, we have invented machines that we use to decrease the amount of effort we expend personally. Thinking about energy tends to bring to mind the cost of fuel for transportation and heating, or perhaps the food that supplies the energy our bodies need to carry out life processes and to do work.

Although these notions do not really define work and energy, they point us in the right direction. As you might have guessed, work and energy are closely related. In physics, as in everyday life, when something possesses energy, it has the ability to do work. For example, water rushing through the sluices of a dam has energy of motion, and this energy allows the water to do the work of driving a turbine or dynamo. Conversely, no work can be performed without energy.

Energy exists in various forms: There is mechanical energy, chemical energy, electrical energy, heat energy, nuclear energy, and so on. A transformation from one form to another may take place, but the total amount of energy is *conserved*, or always remains the same. This is the point that makes the concept of energy so useful. When a physically measurable quantity is conserved, it not only gives us an insight that leads to a better understanding of nature, but also usually provides another approach to practical problems. (You will be introduced to other conserved quantities during the course of our study of physics.)

5.1 Work Done by a Constant Force

OBJECTIVES: To (a) define mechanical work and (b) compute the work done in various situations.

The word *work* is commonly used in a variety of ways: We go to work; we work on projects; we work at our desks or on computers; we work problems. In physics, however, *work* has a very specific meaning. Mechanically, work involves force and displacement, and we use the word *work* to describe quantitatively what is accomplished when a force moves an object through a distance. In the simplest case of a *constant* force acting on an object, work is defined as follows:

Work—involves force and displacement

> The **work** done by a constant force acting on an object is equal to the product of the magnitudes of the displacement and the component of the force parallel to that displacement.

Note: The product of two vectors (force and displacement) in this case is a special type of vector multiplication and yields a scalar quantity equal to $(F \cos \theta)d$. Thus, work is a scalar—it does not have direction. It can, however, be positive, zero, or negative, depending on the angle.

Work then involves moving an object through a distance. A force may be applied, as in ▼Fig. 5.1a, but *if there is no motion (no displacement), then no work is done*. For a constant force F acting *in the same direction* as the displacement d (Fig. 5.1b), the work W is defined as the product of their magnitudes:

$$W = Fd \tag{5.1}$$

(As you might expect, when work is done in Fig. 5.1b, energy is expended. We shall discuss the relationship between work and energy in Section 5.3.)

In general, work is done on an object only by a force, or force *component*, parallel to the line of motion or displacement of the object (Fig. 5.1c). That is, if the force acts at an angle θ to the object's displacement, then $F_{\parallel} = F \cos \theta$ is the component of the force parallel to the displacement. Thus, a more general equation for work done by a constant force is

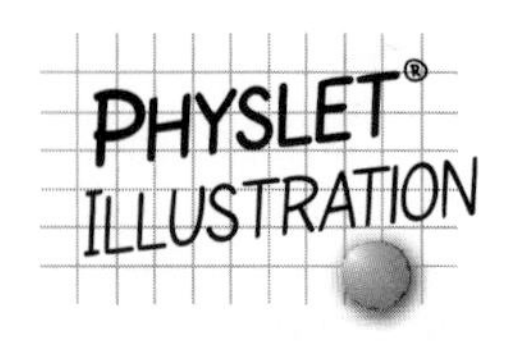

Work and Angles

$$W = F_{\parallel}d = (F \cos \theta)d \qquad \textit{work done by a constant force} \tag{5.2}$$

▼ **FIGURE 5.1 Work done by a constant force—the product of the magnitudes of the parallel component of force and the displacement** **(a)** If there is no displacement, no work is done: $W = 0$. **(b)** For a constant force in the same direction as the displacement, $W = Fd$. **(c)** For a constant force at an angle to the displacement, $W = (F \cos \theta)d$.

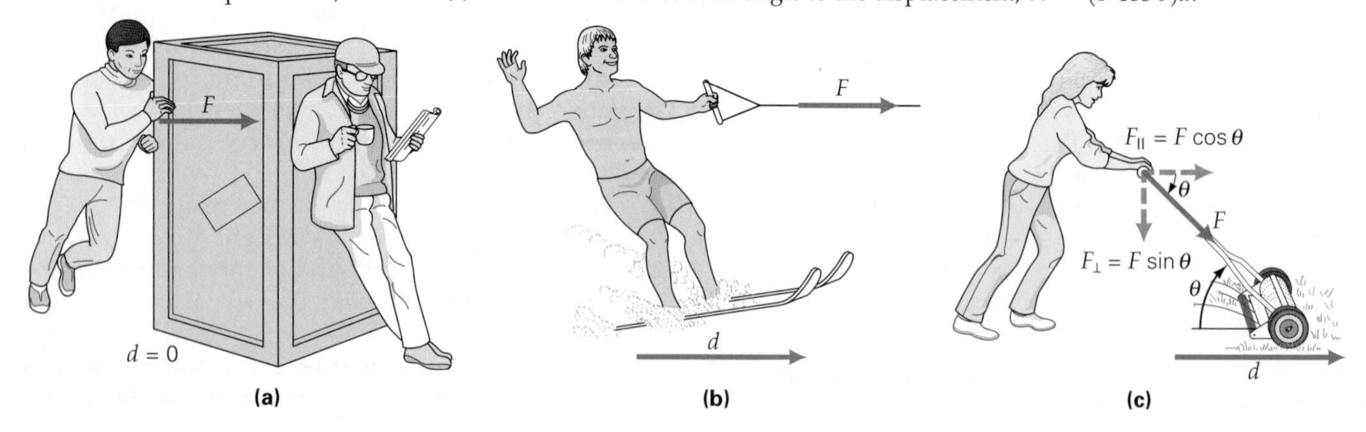

Notice that θ is the angle *between* the force and the displacement vectors. To remind yourself of this factor, you can write cos θ between the magnitudes of the force and displacement, as in Eq. 5.2. If $\theta = 0°$ (i.e., force and displacement are in the same direction as in Fig. 5.1b), then $W = F(\cos 0°)d = Fd$, so Eq. 5.2 reduces to Eq. 5.1. The perpendicular component of the force, $F_{\perp} = F \sin \theta$, does no work, since there is no displacement in this direction.

The units of work can be determined from the equation $W = Fd$. With force in newtons and displacement in meters, work has the SI unit of newton-meter $(\text{N} \cdot \text{m})$. This unit is given the special name *joule* (J):

$$Fd = W$$
$$1\ \text{N} \cdot \text{m} = 1\ \text{J}$$

For example, the work done by a force of 25 N on an object as the object moves through a parallel displacement of 2.0 m is $W = Fd = (25\ \text{N})(2.0\ \text{m}) = 50\ \text{N} \cdot \text{m}$, or 50 J.

From the previous displayed equation, we also see that in the British system, work would have the unit pound-foot. However, this name is commonly written in reverse: The British standard unit of work is the *foot-pound* (ft · lb). One ft · lb is equal to 1.36 J.

We can analyze work graphically. Suppose a constant force F acts on an object as it moves a distance x. Then $W = Fx$, and if F versus x is plotted, a straight-line graph is obtained such as shown in the Learn by Drawing figure. The area under the line is Fx, so this area is equal to the work done by the force over the given distance. We will consider a nonconstant, or variable, force later.*

Remember that *work is a scalar quantity* and, as such, may have a positive or negative value. In Fig. 5.1b, the work is positive, because the force acts in the same direction as the displacement (and cos 0° is positive). The work is also positive in Fig. 5.1c, because a force component acts in the direction of the displacement (and cos θ is positive).

However, if the force, or a force component, acts in the opposite direction of the displacement, the work is negative, since the cosine term is negative. For example, for $\theta = 180°$ (force opposite to the displacement), $\cos 180° = -1$, so the work is negative: $W = Fd = (F \cos 180°)d = -Fd$. An example is a braking force that slows down or decelerates an object. See Learn by Drawing on p. 144.

The joule (J), pronounced "jool," was named in honor of James Prescott Joule (1818–1889), a British scientist who investigated work and energy.

Learn by Drawing

Work: Area Under the F versus x Curve

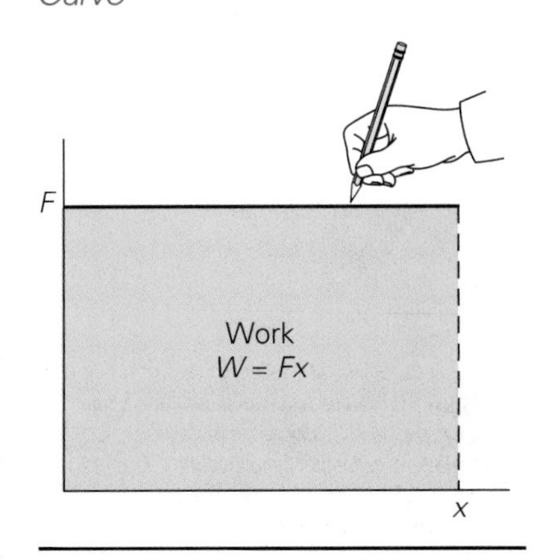

Example 5.1 ■ Applied Psychology: Mechanical Work

A student holds her psychology textbook, which has a mass of 1.5 kg, out of a second-story dormitory window until her arm is tired; then she releases it (▶Fig. 5.2). (a) How much work is done on the book by the student in simply holding it out the window? (b) How much work is done by the force of gravity during the time in which the book falls 3.0 m?

Thinking It Through. Analyze the situations in terms of the definition of work, keeping in mind that force and displacement are the key factors.

Solution. Listing the data, we have

Given: $v_o = 0$ (initially at rest)
$m = 1.5$ kg
$d = 3.0$ m

Find: (a) W (work done by student in holding)
(b) W (work done by gravity in falling)

(a) Even though the student gets tired (because work is performed within the body to maintain muscles in a state of tension), she does *no work on the book* in merely holding it stationary. She exerts an upward force on the book (equal in magnitude to its weight), but the displacement is zero in this case ($d = 0$). Thus, $W = Fd = F \times 0 = 0$ J.

(b) While the book is falling, the only force acting on it is the force of gravity, which is equal in magnitude to the weight of the book: $F = w = mg$ (neglecting air resistance).

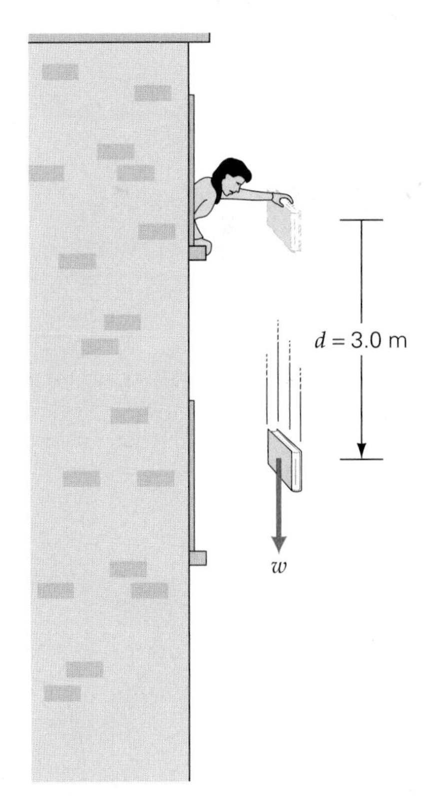

▲ **FIGURE 5.2 Mechanical work requires motion** See Example 5.1.

*Work is the area under the F versus x curve even if the curve is not a straight line. Finding the work in such cases generally requires advanced mathematics.

The displacement is in the same direction as the force ($\theta = 0°$) and has a magnitude of $d = 3.0$ m, so the work done by gravity is

$$W = F(\cos 0°)d = (mg)d = (1.5\ \text{kg})(9.8\ \text{m/s}^2)(3.0\ \text{m}) = +44\ \text{J}$$

Follow-up Exercise. A 0.20-kg ball is thrown upward. How much work is done on the ball by gravity as the ball rises between heights of 2.0 m and 3.0 m? *(Answers to all Follow-up Exercises are at the back of the text.)*

Learn by Drawing

Determining the Sign of Work

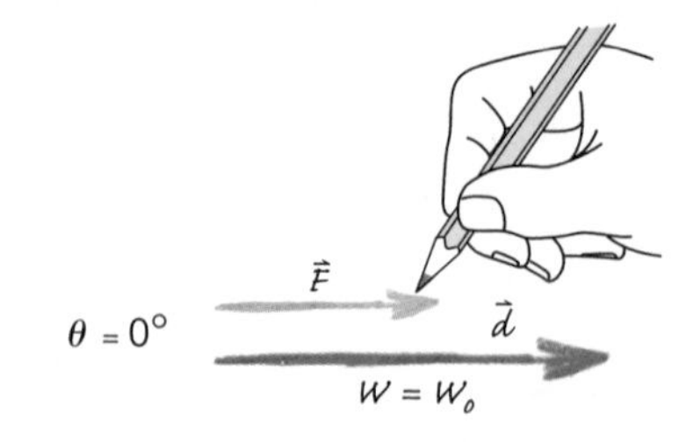

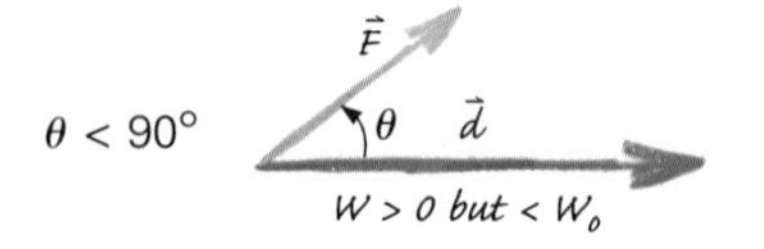

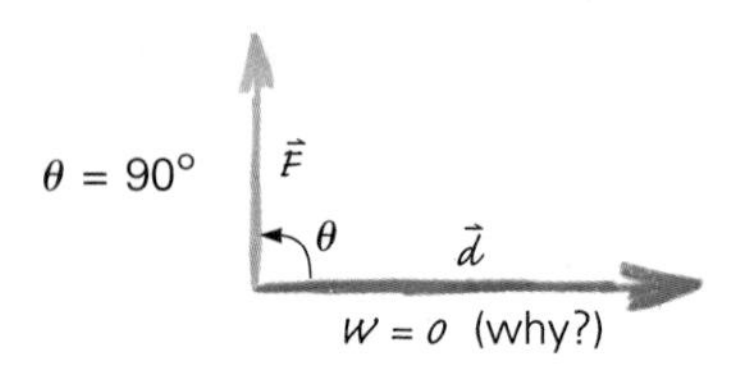

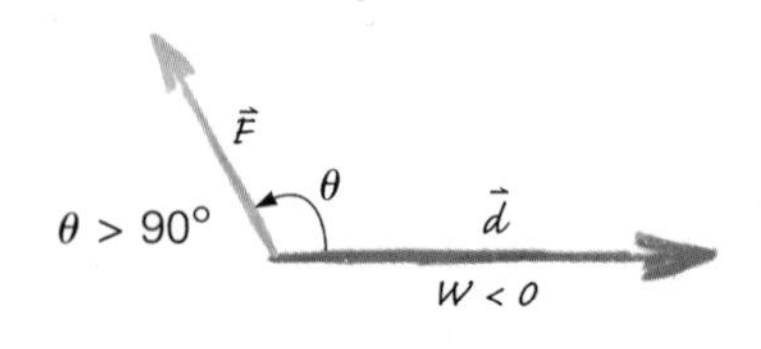

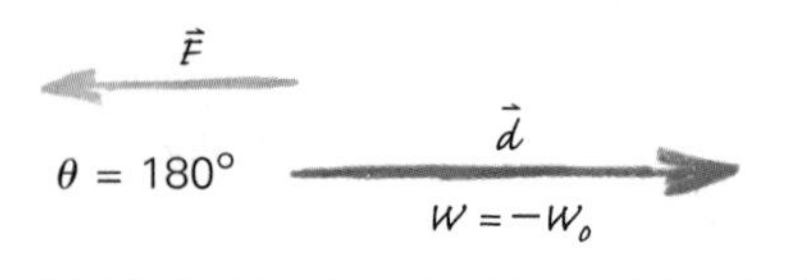

Example 5.2 ■ Yard Work: Parallel Component of a Force

If the person in Fig. 5.1c pushes on the lawn mower with a constant force of 90.0 N at an angle of 40° to the horizontal, how much work does she do in pushing it a horizontal distance of 7.50 m?

Thinking It Through. Only the component of the force parallel to the displacement does work on the mower. Clearly identify the angle between the force and the displacement.

Solution.

Given: $F = 90.0$ N, $\theta = 40°$, $d = 7.50$ m *Find:* W (work done by person pushing the mower)

Here, the horizontal component of the applied force, $F \cos \theta$, is parallel to the displacement, so Eq. 5.2 applies:

$$W = (F \cos 40°)d = (90.0\ \text{N})(0.766)(7.50\ \text{m}) = +517\ \text{J}$$

Work is done by the horizontal component of the force, but the vertical component does no work, because there is no vertical displacement.

Follow-up Exercise. When you push a wheelbarrow on a level surface, the force you apply has an upward component. Is work done on the wheelbarrow by this component?

We commonly specify which force is doing work *on* which object. For example, the force of gravity does work on a falling object, such as the book in Example 5.1. Also, when you lift an object, *you* do work *on* the object. We sometimes describe this as doing work *against* gravity, because the force of gravity acts in the direction opposite that of the applied lift force and opposes it. For example, an average-sized apple has a weight of about 1 N. So, if you lifted such an apple a distance of 1 m with a force equal to its weight, you would have done 1 J of work against gravity [$W = Fd = (1\ \text{N})(1\ \text{m}) = 1\ \text{J}$]. This example gives you an idea of how much work 1 J represents.

In both Examples 5.1 and 5.2, work was done by a single constant force. If more than one force acts on an object, the work done by each can be calculated separately:

Definition of net work

The *total*, or *net*, *work* is the work done by all the forces, or the scalar sum of those quantities of work.

This concept is illustrated in Example 5.3.

Example 5.3 ■ Total or Net Work

A 0.75-kg block slides with a uniform velocity down a 20° inclined plane (▶Fig. 5.3). (a) How much work is done by the force of friction on the block as it slides the total length of the plane? (b) What is the net work done on the block? (c) Discuss the net work done if the angle of incline is adjusted so that the block accelerates down the plane.

Thinking It Through. (a) The length of the plane can be found using trigonometry, so this part boils down to finding the force of friction. (b) The net work is the sum of all the

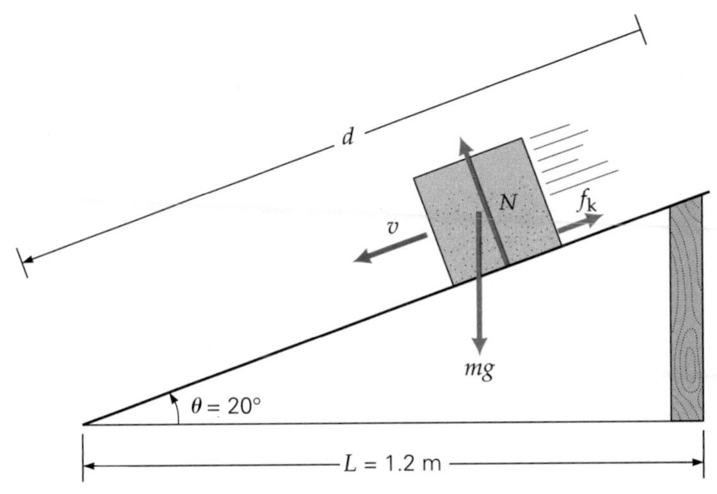

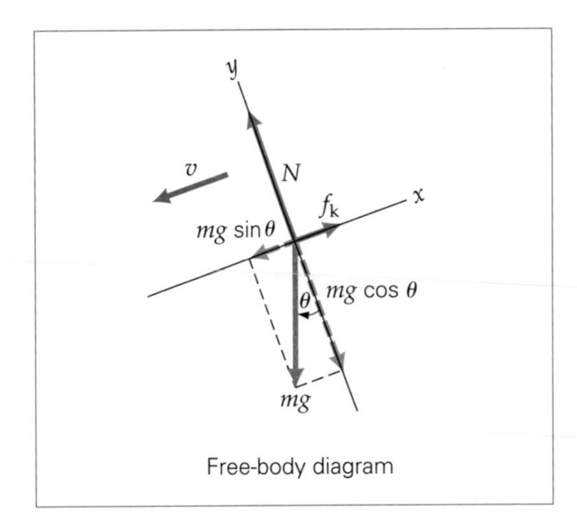

▲ **FIGURE 5.3 Total or net work** See Example 5.3.

work done by the individual forces. (*Note*: Since the block has a uniform, or constant, velocity, the net force on it is zero. This observation should tell you the answer, but it will be shown explicitly in the solution.) (c) If there is acceleration, Newton's second law applies, which involves a net force, so there will be net work.

Solution. We list the information that is given. In addition, it is equally important that we list specifically what is to be found.

Given:	*Find:*
$m = 0.75\text{kg}$	(a) W_f (work done on the block by friction)
$\theta = 20°$	(b) W_{net} (net work on the block)
$L = 1.2$ m (from Fig. 5.3)	(c) W (discuss net work with block accelerating)

(a) Note from Fig. 5.3 that only two forces do work, because there are only two forces parallel to the motion: f_k, the force of kinetic friction, and $mg \sin\theta$, the component of the block's weight acting down the plane. The normal force N and $mg\cos\theta$, the components of the block's weight acting perpendicular to the plane, do no work on the block. (Why?)

We first find the work done by the frictional force:

$$W_f = f_k(\cos 180°)d = -f_k d = -\mu_k N d$$

Note: Recall the discussion of friction in Section 4.6.

The angle 180° indicates that the force and displacement are in opposite directions. (It is common in such cases to write $W_f = -f_k d$ directly, since kinetic friction typically opposes motion.) The distance d the block slides down the plane can be found by using trigonometry. Note that $\cos\theta = L/d$, so

$$d = \frac{L}{\cos\theta}$$

We know that $N = mg\cos\theta$, but what is μ_k? It would appear that we are lacking some information. When this situation occurs, you should look for another approach to solve the problem. As noted earlier, there are only two forces parallel to the motion, and they are opposite, so with a constant velocity their magnitudes are equal, $f_k = mg\sin\theta$. Thus,

$$W_f = -f_k d = -(mg\sin\theta)\left(\frac{L}{\cos\theta}\right) = -mgL\tan 20°$$
$$= -(0.75\text{ kg})(9.8\text{ m/s}^2)(1.2\text{ m})(0.364) = -3.2\text{ J}$$

(b) To find the net work, we need to calculate the work done by gravity and then add it to our result in part (a). Since $F_\parallel$ for gravity is just $mg\sin\theta$, we have

$$W_g = F_\parallel d = (mg\sin\theta)\left(\frac{L}{\cos\theta}\right) = mgL\tan 20° = +3.2\text{ J}$$

where the calculation is the same as in (a) except for the sign. Then,

$$W_{\text{net}} = W_g + W_f = +3.2\text{ J} + (-3.2\text{ J}) = 0$$

Remember that work is a scalar quantity, so scalar addition is used to find net work.

(c) If the block accelerates down the plane, then from Newton's second law, we have $F_{\text{net}} = mg\sin\theta - f_k = ma$. The component of the gravitational force ($mg\sin\theta$) is greater than the opposing frictional force (f_k), so there is net work done on the block, because now $|W_g| > |W_f|$. You may be wondering what the effect of nonzero net work is. As you will learn shortly, nonzero net work causes a change in the amount of energy an object has.

Follow-up Exercise. In part (c) of this Example, is it possible for the frictional work to be greater in magnitude than the gravitational work? What would this condition mean in terms of the block's speed?

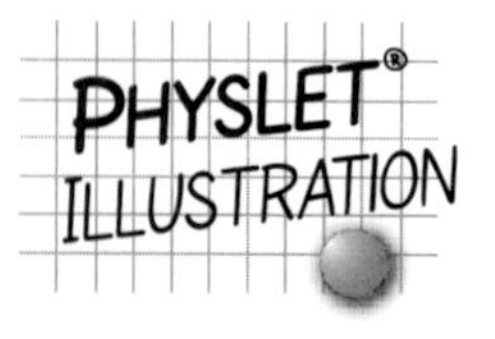

Work on an Incline

Problem-Solving Hint

Note how in part (a) of Example 5.3, the equation for W_f was simplified by using the algebraic expressions for N and d instead of by computing these quantities initially. It is a good rule of thumb not to plug numbers into an equation until you have to. Simplifying an equation through cancellation is easier with symbols and saves computation time.

5.2 Work Done by a Variable Force

OBJECTIVES: To (a) differentiate between work done by constant and variable forces and (b) compute the work done by a spring force.

The discussion in the preceding section was limited to work done by constant forces. In general, however, forces are variable; that is, they change in magnitude and/or angle with time and/or position. For example, someone might push harder and harder on an object to overcome the force of static friction, until the applied force exceeds $f_{s_{\max}}$. However, the force of static friction does no work, because there is no motion or displacement.

An example of a variable force that does work is illustrated in ▸Fig. 5.4, which depicts a spring being stretched. As the spring is stretched (or compressed) farther and farther, its restoring force (the force that opposes the stretching or compression) becomes greater, and an increased applied force is required. For most springs, the applied force F is directly proportional to the change in length of the spring from its unstretched length. In equation form, this relationship is expressed as

$$F = k\Delta x = k(x - x_o)$$

or, if we choose $x_o = 0$, then

$$F = kx$$

where x now represents the distance the spring is stretched (or compressed) from its unstretched length. As can be seen, the force varies with x. We describe this relationship by saying that the *force is a function of position*.

The k in this equation is a constant of proportionality and is commonly called the **spring constant**, or **force constant**. The greater the value of k, the stiffer or stronger is the spring. As you should be able to prove to yourself, the SI unit of k is newton per meter (N/m).

Note: In Fig. 5.4, the hand applies a variable force F in stretching the spring. At the same time, the spring exerts an equal and opposite force F_s on the hand.

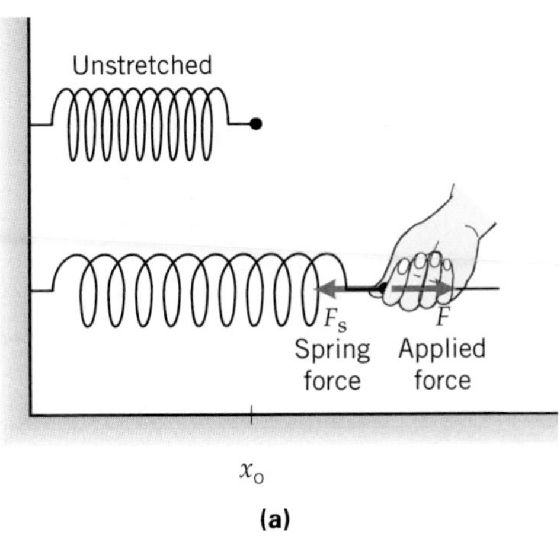

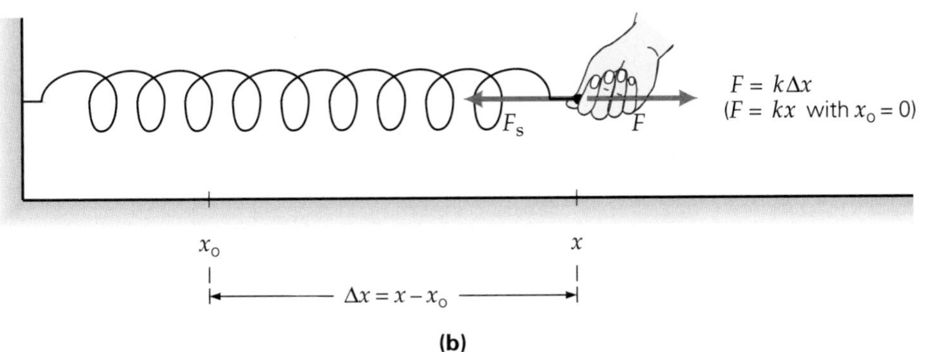

◀ **FIGURE 5.4 Spring force** **(a)** An applied force F stretches the spring, and the spring exerts an equal and opposite force F_s on the hand. **(b)** The magnitude of the force depends on the change Δx spring's length. This change is often referenced to the end of the unstretched spring, x_o.

The relationship expressed by the equation $F = kx$ holds only for ideal springs. Real springs approximate this linear relationship between force and displacement within certain limits. If a spring is stretched beyond a certain point, called its *elastic limit*, the spring will be permanently deformed, and $F = kx$ will no longer apply.

Note that a spring exerts a force that is equal and opposite to the external applied force F. Thus,

$$F_s = -k\Delta x = -k(x - x_o)$$

or, if $x_o = 0$,

$$F_s = -kx \qquad \textit{ideal spring force} \tag{5.3}$$

The minus sign indicates that the spring force acts in the direction opposite to the displacement when the spring is either stretched or compressed. Equation 5.3 is a form of what is known as *Hooke's law*, named after Robert Hooke, a contemporary of Newton.

To compute the work done by variable forces generally requires calculus. But we are fortunate in that the spring force is a special case that can be computed by using the average force. We examined an analogous case involving average velocity, $\bar{v} = (v + v_o)/2$, in our study of kinematics in Chapter 2, and it is instructive to explore this analogy graphically.

Plots of F versus x and of v versus t are shown in ▸Fig. 5.5. The graphs have straight-line slopes of k and a, respectively, with $F = kx$ and $v = at$. [The applied force F, rather than the spring force F_s, is plotted to avoid a negative slope ($F_s = -kx$) and thereby allow analogous graphs.]

By the same reasoning given for v in Section 2.3, the average force $\bar{F}$ can be expressed as

$$\bar{F} = \frac{F + F_o}{2}$$

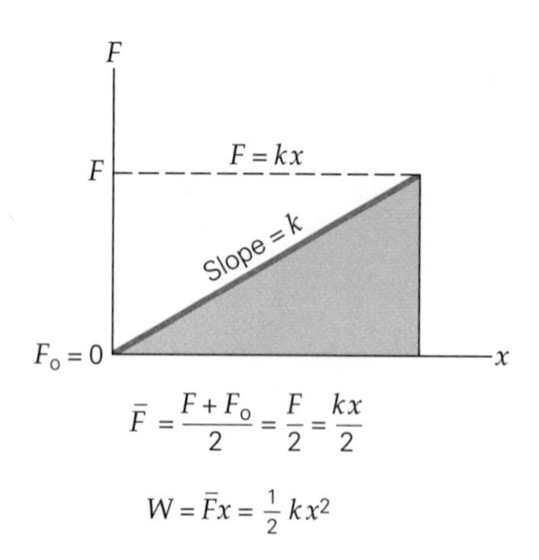

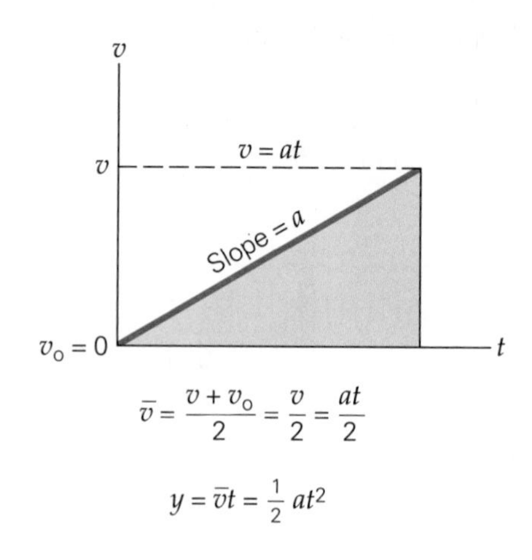

▶ **FIGURE 5.5 Work done by a uniformly variable force** The work done by a uniformly varying force of the form $F = kx$ is $W = \frac{1}{2}kx^2$. A plot of this special case of a variable force is graphically analogous to a plot of v versus t for a uniformly varying velocity starting at rest ($v_o = 0$): $v = at$. The work W and the distance y are equal to the areas under the respective straight lines.

or, since $F_o = 0$ (why?), as

$$\bar{F} = \frac{F}{2}$$

Thus, the work done in stretching or compressing the spring an amount x from its unstretched length is

$$W = \bar{F}x = \frac{Fx}{2}$$

Since $F = kx$, the work done is

$$W = \tfrac{1}{2}kx^2 \qquad \textit{work done in stretching (or compressing) a spring from } x_o = 0 \qquad (5.4)$$

Note that the work done is just the area under the curve in Fig. 5.5.

Example 5.4 ■ Determining the Spring Constant

A 0.15-kg mass is attached to a vertical spring and descends a distance of 4.6 cm below its original position. It then hangs at rest (▶Fig. 5.6). An additional 0.50-kg mass is then suspended from the first mass. What is the total extension of the spring? (Neglect the mass of the spring.)

Thinking It Through. The spring constant k appears in Eq. 5.3. Therefore, to find the value of k for a particular instance, the spring force and distance the spring is stretched (or compressed) must be known.

Solution. The data given are as follows:

Given: $m_1 = 0.15$ kg
$x_1 = 4.6$ cm $= 0.046$ m
$m_2 = 0.50$ kg

Find: x (total stretch distance)

The total stretch distance is given by $x = F/k$, where F is the applied force, which in this case is the weight of the mass suspended on the spring. However, the spring constant k is not given. This quantity may be found from the data pertaining to the suspension of m_1 and resulting displacement x_1. (This method is commonly used to determine spring constants.) As seen in Fig. 5.6a, the magnitudes of the weight force and the restoring spring force are equal, since $a = 0$, so we may equate them (with the directional minus signs omitted):

$$F_s = kx_1 = m_1 g$$

Solving for k, we obtain

$$k = \frac{m_1 g}{x_1} = \frac{(0.15 \text{ kg})(9.8 \text{ m/s}^2)}{0.046} = 32 \text{ N/m}$$

Then, knowing k, we find the total extension of the spring from the balanced-force situation shown in Fig. 5.6b:

$$F_s = (m_1 + m_2)g = kx$$

Thus,

$$x = \frac{(m_1 + m_2)g}{k} = \frac{(0.15 \text{ kg} + 0.50 \text{ kg})(9.8 \text{ m/s}^2)}{32 \text{ N/m}} = 0.20 \text{ m (or 20 cm)}$$

Follow-up Exercise. How much work is done by gravity in stretching the spring through both displacements in Example 5.4?

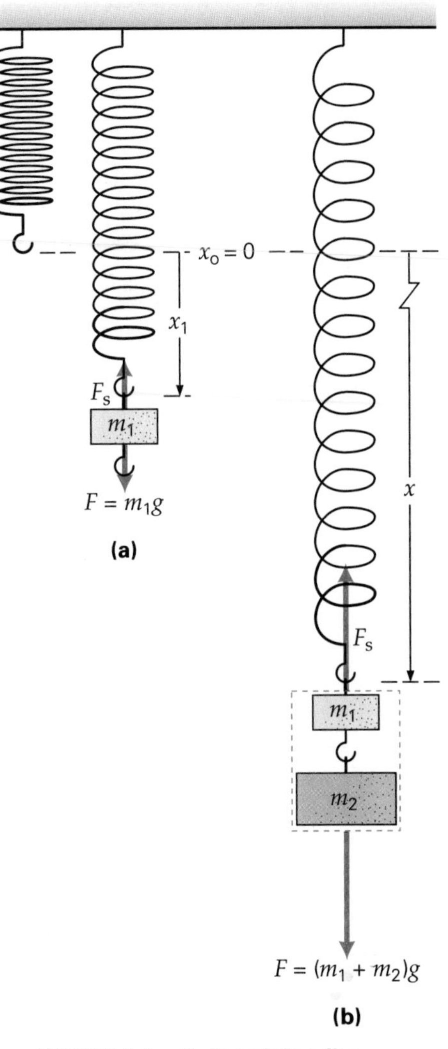

▲ **FIGURE 5.6 Determining the spring constant and the work done in stretching a spring** See Example 5.4.

Problem-Solving Hint

The reference position x_o for the change in length of a spring is arbitrary and is usually chosen for convenience. *The important quantity in computing work is the difference in position, Δx, or the net change in the length of the spring from its unstretched length.* As shown in ▼Fig. 5.7 for a mass suspended on a spring, x_o can be referenced to the unloaded length of the spring or to the loaded position, which may be taken as the zero position for convenience. In Example 5.4, x_o was referenced to the end of the unloaded spring. Also, with the displacement only in one direction, downward can be designated as the $+x$-direction in order to avoid minus signs.

When the net force on the suspended mass is zero, the mass is said to be at its *equilibrium position* (as in Fig. 5.7a with m_1 suspended). This position, rather than the unloaded length, may be taken as a zero reference ($x = x_o = 0$; see Fig. 5.7b). The equilibrium position is a convenient reference point for cases in which the mass oscillates up and down on the spring. Notice that, in general, there are both positive and negative directions. The chosen signs are arbitrary, but must be adhered to for the entire solution to the problem. Also, since the displacement is in the vertical direction, the x's are often replaced by y's.

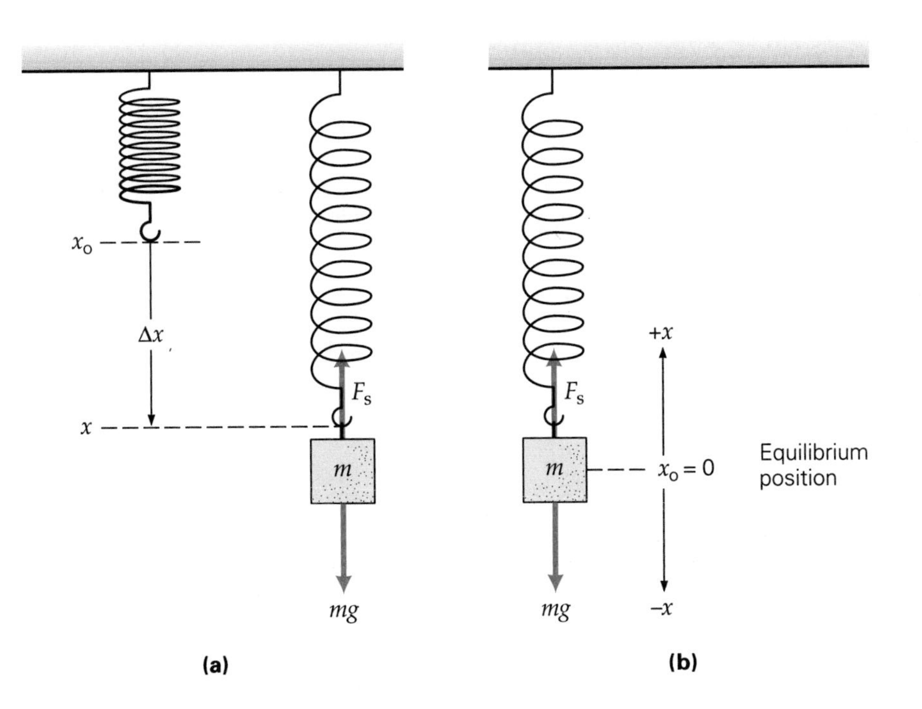

◀ **FIGURE 5.7 Displacement reference** The reference position x_o is arbitrary and is usually chosen for convenience. It may be **(a)** at the end of the spring at its unloaded position or **(b)** at the equilibrium position when a mass is suspended on the spring. The latter is particularly convenient in cases in which the mass oscillates up and down on the spring.

5.3 The Work–Energy Theorem: Kinetic Energy

OBJECTIVES: To (a) study the work–energy theorem and (b) apply it in solving problems.

Now that we have an operational definition of work, we are ready to look at how work is related to energy. Energy is one of the most important concepts in science. We describe it as a quantity that objects or systems possess. Basically, work is something that is *done on* objects, whereas energy is something that objects *have*—the ability to do work.

One form of energy that is closely associated with work is *kinetic energy*. (Another form of energy, *potential energy*, will be described in Section 5.4.) Consider an object at rest on a frictionless surface. Let a horizontal force act on the object and set it in motion. Work is done *on* the object, but where does the work "go," so to speak? It goes into setting the object into motion, or changing its *kinetic* conditions. Because of its motion, we say the object has gained energy—kinetic energy, which gives it the capability to do work.

For a constant net force doing work on a moving object, as illustrated in ▾Fig. 5.8, the force does an amount of work $W = Fx$. But what are the kinematic effects? The force causes the object to accelerate, and from Eq. 2.12, $v^2 = v_o^2 + 2ax$ (with $x_o = 0$),

$$a = \frac{v^2 - v_o^2}{2x}$$

where v_o may or may not be zero. Writing the magnitude of the force in Newton's second law form ($F = ma$, where $F = F_{net}$) and then substituting in the expression for a from the previous equation gives

$$F = ma = m\left(\frac{v^2 - v_o^2}{2x}\right)$$

Using this expression in the equation for work, we have

$$W = Fx = m\left(\frac{v^2 - v_o^2}{2x}\right)x$$

$$= \tfrac{1}{2}mv^2 - \tfrac{1}{2}mv_o^2$$

Definition of kinetic energy—the energy of motion

It is convenient to define $\frac{1}{2}mv^2$ as the **kinetic energy** K of the moving object:

$$K = \tfrac{1}{2}mv^2 \quad \textit{kinetic energy} \tag{5.5}$$

SI unit of energy: joule (J)

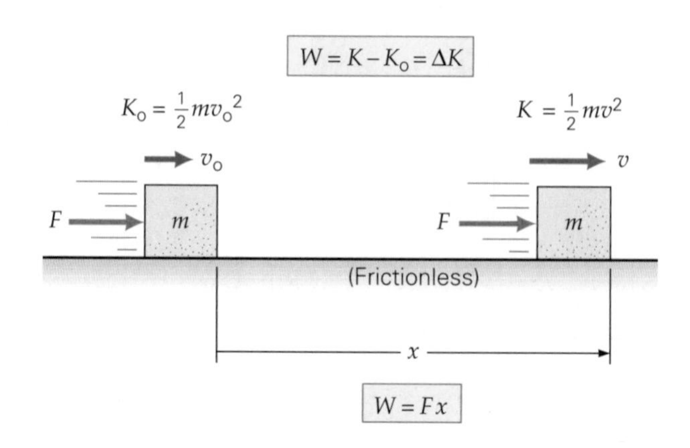

▶ **FIGURE 5.8 The relationship of work and kinetic energy** The work done on a block in moving it along a horizontal frictionless surface is equal to the change in the block's kinetic energy: $W = \Delta K$.

Kinetic energy is often called the *energy of motion*. Note that it is directly proportional to the square of the (instantaneous) speed of a moving object, and therefore cannot be negative.

Then, in terms of kinetic energy, the previous expression for work can be written as

Work–energy theorem

$$W = \tfrac{1}{2}mv^2 - \tfrac{1}{2}mv_o^2 = K - K_o = \Delta K$$

or

$$W = \Delta K \tag{5.6}$$

where it is understood that W is the net work if more than one force acts on the object, as shown in Example 5.3. This equation is called the **work–energy theorem**; it relates the work done on an object to the change in the object's kinetic energy. That is, *the net work done on a body by all the forces acting on it is equal to the change in kinetic energy of the body*. Both work and energy have the units of joules, and both are *scalar* quantities. Keep in mind that the work–energy theorem is true in general for varying forces and not just for the special case considered in deriving Eq. 5.6.

To illustrate that net work is equal to the change in kinetic energy, recall that in Example 5.1 the force of gravity did +44 J of work on a book that fell from rest through a distance of $y = 3.0$ m. At that position and instant, the falling book had 44 J of kinetic energy. Since $v_o = 0$ in this case, $\tfrac{1}{2}mv^2 = mgy$, and $gy = v^2/2$. Substituting this expression into the equation for the work done on the falling book by gravity, we get

$$W = Fd = mgy = \frac{mv^2}{2} = K = \Delta K$$

where $K_o = 0$. Thus the kinetic energy gained by the book is equal to the net work done on it: 44 J in this case. (As an exercise, confirm this fact by calculating the speed of the book and evaluating its kinetic energy.)

What the work–energy theorem tells us is that when work is done, there is a change in or a transfer of energy. In general, then, we might say that *work is a measure of the transfer of kinetic energy*. For example, a force doing work on an object that causes the object to speed up gives rise to an increase in the object's kinetic energy. Conversely, (negative) work done by the force of kinetic friction may cause a moving object to slow down and decrease its kinetic energy. So, for an object to have a change in its kinetic energy, there must be net work done on the object, as Eq. 5.6 tells us.

When an object is in motion, it possesses kinetic energy and has the capability to do work. For example, a moving automobile has kinetic energy and can do work in crumpling a fender in a fenderbender—not *useful* work in that case, but still work. Another example of work done by kinetic energy is shown in ▸Fig. 5.9.

▲ **FIGURE 5.9 Kinetic energy and work** A moving object, such as a wrecking ball, possesses kinetic energy and thus can do work.

Example 5.5 ■ A Game of Shuffleboard: The Work–Energy Theorem

A shuffleboard player (▸Fig. 5.10) pushes a 0.25-kg puck that is initially at rest such that a constant horizontal force of 6.0 N acts on it through a distance of 0.50 m. (Neglect friction.) (a) What are the kinetic energy and the speed of the puck when the force is removed? (b) How much work would be required to bring the puck to rest?

Thinking It Through. Apply the work–energy theorem. If you can find the amount of work done, you know the change in kinetic energy, and vice versa.

Solution. Listing the given data as usual, we have

Given: $m = 0.25$ kg, $F = 6.0$ N, $d = 0.50$ m, $v_o = 0$

Find: (a) K (kinetic energy), v (speed); (b) W (work done in stopping puck)

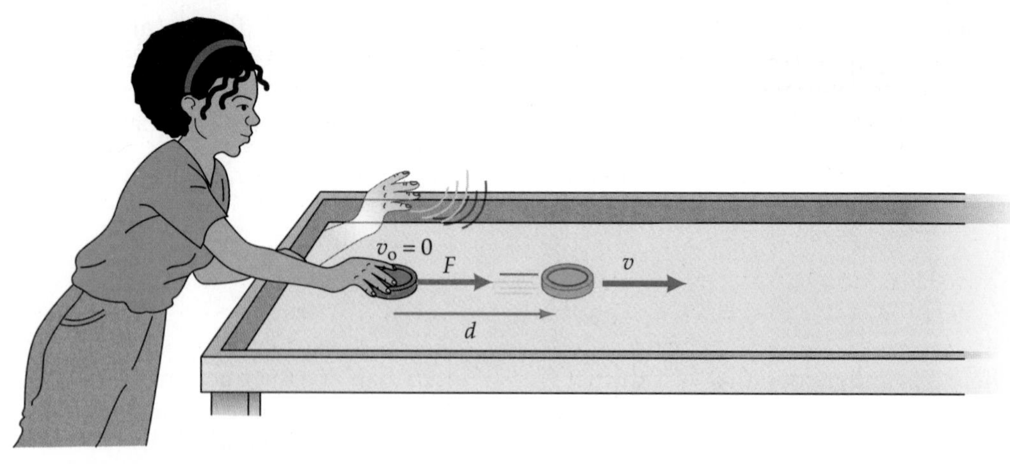

▲ **FIGURE 5.10 Work and kinetic energy** See Example 5.5.

(a) Since the speed is not known, we cannot compute the kinetic energy ($K = \frac{1}{2}mv^2$) directly. However, kinetic energy is related to work by the work–energy theorem. The work done on the puck is

$$W = Fd = (6.0\,\text{N})(0.50\,\text{m}) = +3.0\,\text{J}$$

Then, by the work–energy theorem, we obtain

$$W = \Delta K = K - K_o = +3.0\,\text{J}$$

But $K_o = \frac{1}{2}mv_o^2 = 0$, because $v_o = 0$, so

$$K = 3.0\,\text{J}$$

The speed can be found from the kinetic energy. Since $K = \frac{1}{2}mv^2$, we have

$$v = \sqrt{\frac{2K}{m}} = \sqrt{\frac{2(3.0\,\text{J})}{0.25\,\text{kg}}} = 4.9\,\text{m/s}$$

(b) As you might guess, the work required to bring the puck to rest is equal to the puck's kinetic energy (i.e., the amount of energy that must be "removed" from the puck to stop its motion). To confirm this equality, we essentially perform the reverse of the previous calculation, with $v_o = 4.9\,\text{m/s}$ and $v = 0$:

$$W = K - K_o = 0 - K_o = -\tfrac{1}{2}mv_o^2 = -\tfrac{1}{2}(0.25\,\text{kg})(4.9\,\text{m/s})^2 = -3.0\,\text{J}$$

The minus sign indicates that the puck loses energy as it slows down. The work is done *against* the motion of the puck; that is, the opposing force is in a direction opposite that of the motion. (In a real-life situation, the opposing force could be friction.)

Follow-up Exercise. Suppose the puck in this Example had twice the final speed when released. Would it then take twice as much work to stop the puck? Justify your answer numerically.

Problem-Solving Hint

Notice how work–energy considerations were used to find speed in Example 5.5. This operation can be done in another way as well. First, the acceleration could be found from $a = F/m$, and then the kinematic equation $v^2 = v_o^2 + 2ax$ could be used to find v (where $x = d = 0.50\,\text{m}$).

The point is that many problems can be solved in different ways, and finding the fastest and most efficient way is often the key to success. As our discussion of energy progresses, you will see how useful and powerful the notions of work and energy are, both as theoretical concepts and as practical tools for solving many kinds of problems.

Conceptual Example 5.6 ■ Kinetic Energy: Mass versus Speed

In a football game, a 140-kg guard runs at a speed of 4.0 m/s, and a 70-kg free safety moves at 8.0 m/s. In this situation, it is correct to say that (a) both players have the same kinetic energy, (b) the safety has twice as much kinetic energy as the guard, (c) the guard has twice as much kinetic energy as the safety, or (d) the safety has four times as much kinetic energy as the guard.

Reasoning and Answer. The kinetic energy of a body depends on both its mass and its speed. You might think that, with half the mass but twice the speed, the safety would have the same kinetic energy as the guard, but this is not the case. As we can observe from the relationship $K = \frac{1}{2}mv^2$, kinetic energy is directly proportional to the mass, but it is also proportional to the *square* of the speed. Thus, halving the mass decreases the kinetic energy by a factor of two; so if the two athletes had equal speeds, the safety would have had half as much kinetic energy as the guard.

However, doubling the speed increases the kinetic energy, not by a factor of 2 but by a factor of 2^2, or 4. Thus, the safety, with half the mass but twice the speed, would have $\frac{1}{2} \times 4 = 2$ times as much kinetic energy as the guard, and so the answer is (b).

Note that to answer this question, it was not necessary to calculate the kinetic energy of each player. We can do so, however, to verify our conclusions:

$$K_{\text{safety}} = \tfrac{1}{2}m_s v_s^2 = \tfrac{1}{2}(70\text{ kg})(8.0\text{ m/s})^2 = 2.2 \times 10^3\text{ J}$$
$$K_{\text{guard}} = \tfrac{1}{2}m_g v_g^2 = \tfrac{1}{2}(140\text{ kg})(4.0\text{ m/s})^2 = 1.1 \times 10^3\text{ J}$$

Thus, we see explicitly that our answer was correct.

Follow-up Exercise. Suppose that the safety's speed were only 50 percent greater than the guard's, or 6.0 m/s. Which athlete would then have the greater kinetic energy, and how many times greater?

Problem-Solving Hint

Note that the work–energy theorem relates the work done to the *change* in the kinetic energy. Often, we have $v_o = 0$ and $K_o = 0$, so $W = \Delta K = K$. But take care! You *cannot* simply use the square of the change in speed, $(\Delta v)^2$, to calculate ΔK, as you might at first think. In terms of speed, we have

$$W = \Delta K = K - K_o = \tfrac{1}{2}mv^2 - \tfrac{1}{2}mv_o^2 = \tfrac{1}{2}m(v^2 - v_o^2)$$

But $v^2 - v_o^2$ is not the same as $(v - v_o)^2 = (\Delta v)^2$, since $(v - v_o)^2 = v^2 - 2vv_o + v_o^2$. Hence, the work, or change in kinetic energy, is *not* equal to $\frac{1}{2}m(v - v_o)^2 = \frac{1}{2}m(\Delta v)^2$.

What this observation means is that to calculate work, or the charge in kinetic energy, you must compute the kinetic energy of an object at one point or time (using the instantaneous speed to get the instantaneous kinetic energy) and also at another point or time. Then the quantities are subtracted to find the change in kinetic energy, or the work. Alternatively, you can find the difference of the *squares* of the speeds $(v^2 - v_o^2)$ first in computing the change, but do not use the square of the difference of the speeds. To see this hint in action, take a look at Conceptual Example 5.7.

Conceptual Example 5.7 ■ An Accelerating Car: Speed and Kinetic Energy

A car traveling at 5.0 m/s speeds up to 10 m/s, with an increase in kinetic energy that requires work W_1. Then the car's speed increases from 10 m/s to 15 m/s, requiring additional work W_2. Which of the following relationships accurately compares the two works (a) $W_1 > W_2$; (b) $W_1 = W_2$; (c) $W_2 > W_1$.

Reasoning and Answer. As noted previously, the work–energy theorem relates the work done to the *change* in the kinetic energy. Since the speeds have the same increment in each case ($\Delta v = 5.0$ m/s), it might appear that (b) would be the answer. However, keep in mind that the work is equal to the *change* in kinetic energy and involves $v_2^2 - v_1^2$, *not* $(\Delta v)^2 = (v_2 - v_1)^2$.

So, the greater the speed of an object, the greater is its kinetic energy, and we would expect the *difference* in kinetic energy in changing speeds (or the work required to change speed) to be greater for higher speeds for the same Δv. Thus, (c) is the answer.

The main point is that the Δv values are the same, but more work is required to increase the kinetic energy of an object at higher speeds.

Follow-up Exercise. Suppose the car speeds up a third time, from 15 m/s to 20 m/s, a change requiring work W_3. How does the work done in this increment compare with W_2? Justify your answer numerically. (*Hint*: Use a ratio.)

(a)

(b)

▲ **FIGURE 5.11 Potential energy** Potential energy has many forms. **(a)** Work must be done to bend the bow, giving it potential energy. That energy is converted into kinetic energy when the arrow is released. **(b)** Gravitational potential energy is converted into kinetic energy when an object falls. (Where did the gravitational potential energy of the water and the diver come from?)

5.4 Potential Energy

OBJECTIVES: To (a) define and understand potential energy and (b) learn about gravitational potential energy.

An object in motion has kinetic energy. However, whether an object is in motion or not, it may have another form of energy—potential energy. As the name implies, an object having potential energy has the *potential* to do work. You can probably think of many examples: a compressed spring, a drawn bow, water held back by a dam, a wrecking ball poised to drop. In all such cases, the potential to do work derives from the *position* or *configuration* of bodies. The spring has energy because it is compressed, the bow because it is drawn, the water and the ball because they have been lifted above the surface of the Earth (◂Fig. 5.11). Consequently, **potential energy** U, is often called the energy of position (and/or configuration).

In a sense, potential energy can be thought of as stored work, just as kinetic energy can. You have already seen an example of potential energy in Section 5.2 when work was done in compressing a spring from its equilibrium position. Recall that the work done in such a case is $W = \frac{1}{2}kx^2$ (with $x_o = 0$). Note that the amount of work done depends on the amount of compression (x). Because work is done, there is a *change* in potential energy (ΔU), which is equal to the work done *by the applied force* in compressing (or stretching) the spring:

$$W = \Delta U = U - U_o = \tfrac{1}{2}kx^2 - \tfrac{1}{2}kx_o^2$$

Thus, with $x_o = 0$ and $U_o = 0$, as they are commonly taken for convenience, the *potential energy of a spring* is

$$U = \tfrac{1}{2}kx^2 \qquad \textit{potential energy of a spring} \qquad (5.7)$$

SI unit of energy: joule (J)

[*Note*: Since the potential energy varies as x^2, the previous problem-solving hint also applies. That is, when $x_o \neq 0$, then $x^2 - x_o^2 \neq (x - x_o)^2$.]

Perhaps the most common type of potential energy is **gravitational potential energy**. In this case, position refers to the height of an object above some reference point, such as the floor or the ground. Suppose that an object of mass m is lifted a distance Δy (▸Fig. 5.12). Work is done against the force of gravity, and an applied force at least equal to the object's weight is necessary to lift the object: $F = w = mg$. The work done in lifting is then equal to the change in potential

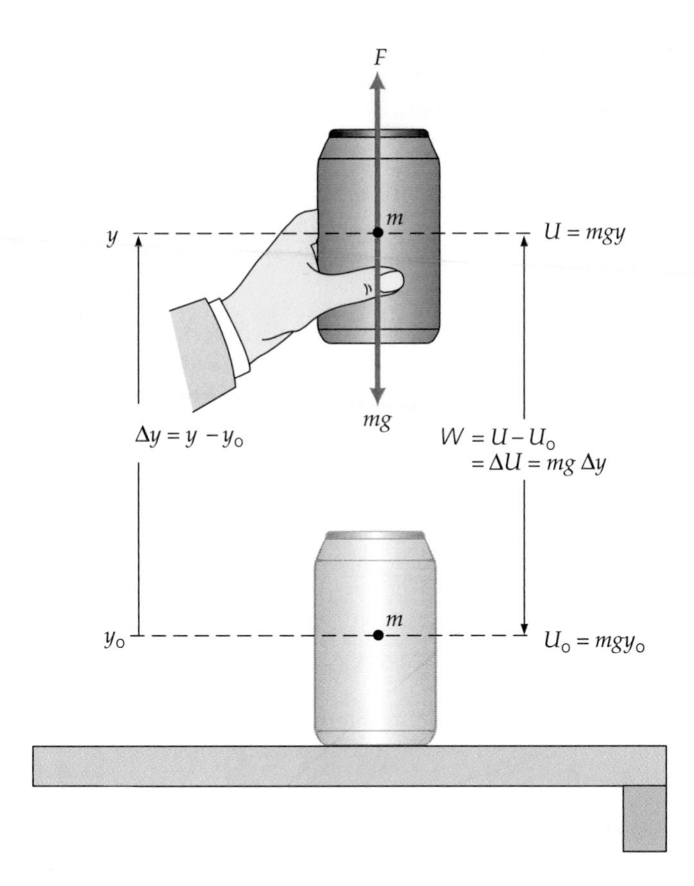

◀ **FIGURE 5.12 Gravitational potential energy** The work done in lifting an object is equal to the change in gravitational potential energy: $W = F\Delta y = mg(y - y_o)$.

energy. Expressing this relationship in equation form, since there is no overall change in kinetic energy, we have

work done by external force = change in gravitational potential energy

or

$$W = F\Delta y = mg(y - y_o) = mgy - mgy_o = \Delta U = U - U_o$$

where y is used as the vertical coordinate and, with the common choices of $y_o = 0$ and $U_o = 0$, the **gravitational potential energy** is

$$U = mgy \tag{5.8}$$

SI unit of energy: joule (J)

Definition of: Gravitational potential energy

(Eq. 5.8 represents the gravitational potential energy on or near the Earth's surface where g is considered to be constant.

Example 5.8 ■ A Thrown Ball: Kinetic Energy and Gravitational Potential Energy

A 0.50-kg ball is thrown vertically upward with an initial velocity of 10 m/s (▶Fig. 5.13). (a) What is the change in the ball's kinetic energy between the starting point and the ball's maximum height? (b) What is the change in the ball's potential energy between the starting point and the ball's maximum height? (Neglect air resistance.)

Thinking It Through. Kinetic energy is lost and gravitational potential energy is gained as the ball travels upward.

Solution. Studying Fig. 5.13 and listing the data, we have

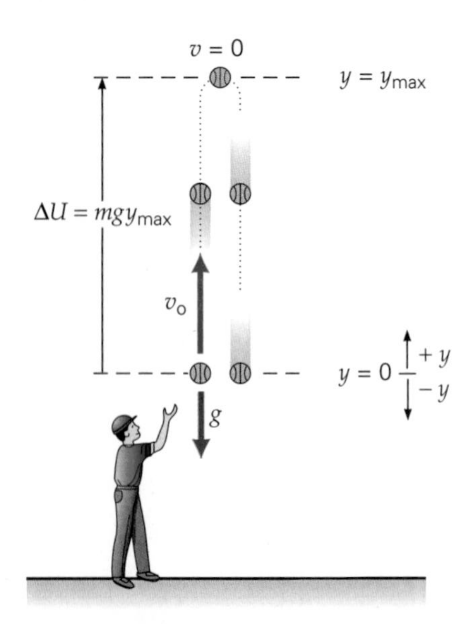

▲ **FIGURE 5.13 Kinetic and potential energies** See Example 5.8. (The ball is displaced sideways for clarity.)

Given: $m = 0.50$ kg, $v_o = 10$ m/s, $a = g$

Find: (a) ΔK (the change in kinetic energy)
(b) ΔU (the change in potential energy between y_o and y_{max})

(a) To find the *change* in kinetic energy, we first compute the kinetic energy at each point. We know the initial velocity v_o, and at the maximum height, $v = 0$, so $K = 0$. Thus,

$$\Delta K = K - K_o = 0 - K_o = -\tfrac{1}{2}mv_o^2 = -\tfrac{1}{2}(0.50 \text{ kg})(10 \text{ m/s})^2 = -25 \text{ J}$$

That is, the ball loses 25 J of kinetic energy as negative work is done on it by the force of gravity. (The gravitational force and the ball's displacement are in opposite directions.)
(b) To find the change in potential energy, we need to know the ball's height above its starting point when $v = 0$. Using Eq. 2.11′, $v^2 = v_o^2 - 2gy$ (with $y_o = 0$) to find y_{max},

$$y_{max} = \frac{v_o^2}{2g} = \frac{(10 \text{ m/s})^2}{2(9.8 \text{ m/s}^2)} = 5.1 \text{ m}$$

Then, with $y_o = 0$ and $U_o = 0$, $\Delta U = U - U_o = U - 0$, and

$$\Delta U = U = mgy_{max} = (0.50 \text{ kg})(9.8 \text{ m/s}^2)(5.1 \text{ m}) = +25 \text{ J}$$

The potential energy increases by 25 J, as might be expected. Notice that this value is the change in potential energy with respect to the release point, which was taken as the zero reference point ($y_o = 0$).

Follow-up Exercise. In this Example, what are the overall changes in the ball's kinetic and potential energies when the ball returns to the starting point?

Zero Reference Point

An important point is illustrated in Example 5.8, namely, the choice of a zero reference point. Potential energy is the energy of *position*, and the potential energy at a particular position (U) is referenced to the potential energy at some other position (U_o). The reference position or point is arbitrary, as is the origin of a set of coordinate axes for analyzing a system. Reference points are usually chosen with convenience in mind—for example, $y_o = 0$. The value of the potential energy at a particular position depends on the reference point used. However, the *difference, or change, in potential energy associated with two positions is the same regardless of the reference position.*

If, in Example 5.8, ground level had been taken as the zero reference point, then U_o at the release point would not have been zero. However, U at the maximum height would have been greater, and $\Delta U = U - U_o$ would have been the same. This concept is illustrated in ▸Fig. 5.14. Note that the potential energy can be negative. When an object has a negative potential energy, it is said to be in a potential-energy *well*, which is analogous to being in an actual well: Work is needed to raise the object to a higher position in the well or to get it out of the well.

Also, for gravitational potential energy, the path by which an object is raised (or lowered) makes no difference (▸Fig. 5.15). That is, *the change in gravitational potential energy is independent of path.* As illustrated in Fig. 5.15, an object raised to a height y has a change in potential energy of $\Delta U = mgy$ no matter whether it is lifted vertically or moved along an inclined plane. The change in potential energy is the same for both cases because the force of gravity always acts downward, and only vertical displacement (or the vertical component) is involved in doing work against gravity and changing the potential energy.

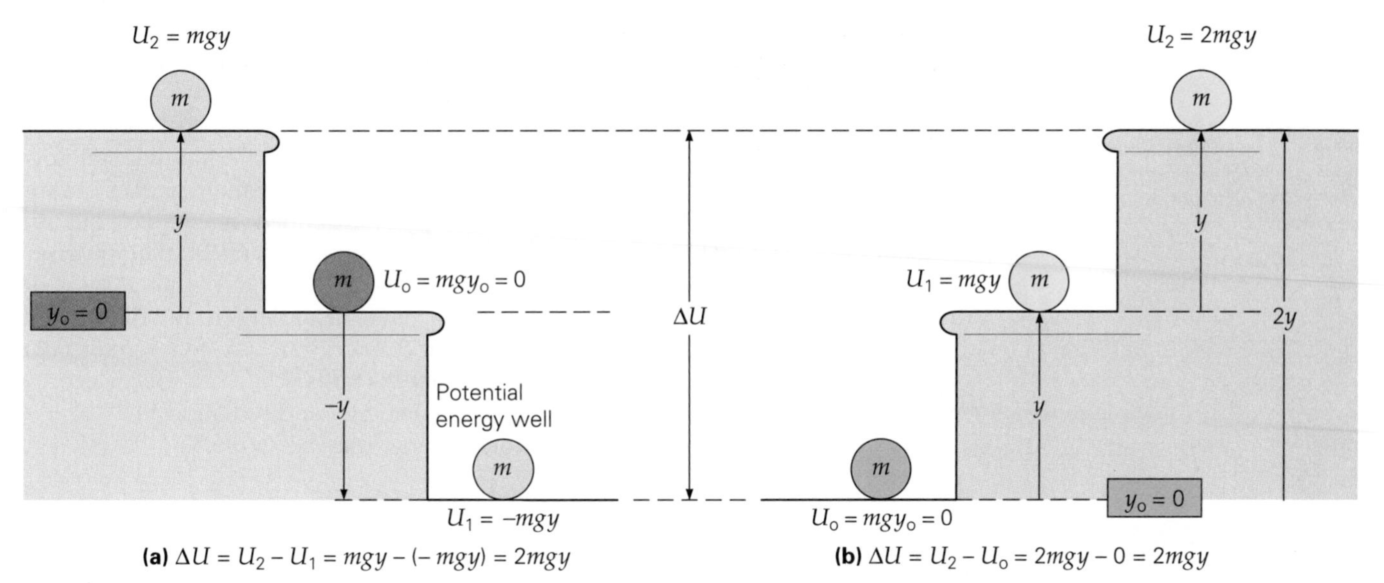

▲ **FIGURE 5.14 Reference point and change in potential energy** **(a)** The choice of a reference point (zero height) is arbitrary and may give rise to a negative potential energy. An object is said to be in a potential-energy well in this case. **(b)** The well may be avoided by selecting a new zero reference. Note that the difference, or *change*, in potential energy (ΔU) associated with the two positions is the same, regardless of the reference point. There is no physical difference, even though there are two coordinate systems and two different zero reference points.

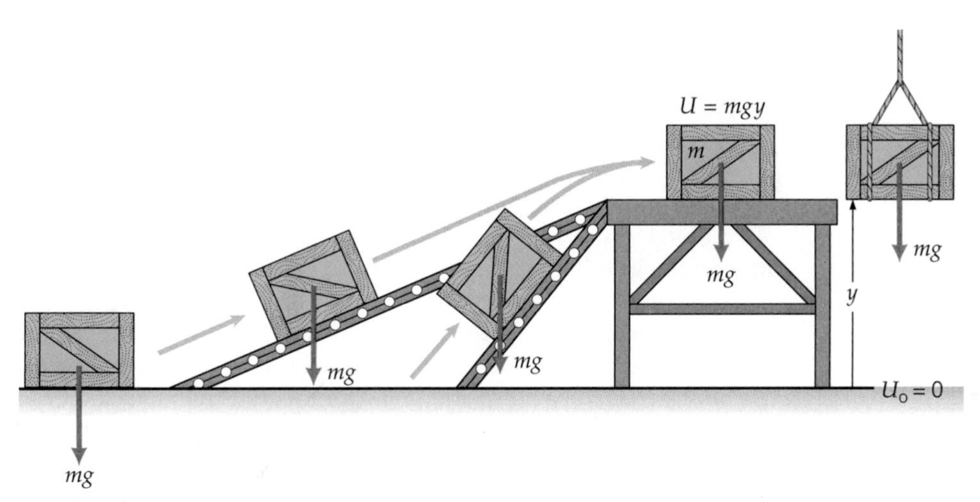

▲ **FIGURE 5.15 Path independence of the change in gravitational potential energy** When it is resting on the table, the crate has the same potential energy relative to the floor, regardless of how it got on the table. Only the vertical component of the force that moves the crate does work against gravity in lifting the crate vertically or moving it up an inclined plane or ramp.

5.5 The Conservation of Energy

OBJECTIVES: **To (a) distinguish between conservative and nonconservative forces and (b) explain their effects on the conservation of energy.**

Conservation laws are the cornerstones of physics, both theoretically and practically. Most scientists would probably name the conservation of energy as the most profound and far reaching of these important laws. When we say that a physical quantity is *conserved*, we mean that it is constant, or has a constant value. Because so many things continually change in physical processes, conserved quantities are extremely helpful in our attempts to understand and describe the universe. Keep in mind, though, that quantities are generally conserved only under special conditions.

Note: A system is a physical situation with real or imaginary boundaries. A classroom might be considered a system, and so might an arbitrary cubic meter of air.

One of the most important conservation laws is that concerning conservation of energy. (You may have seen this topic coming in Example 5.8.) A familiar statement is that the total energy of the universe is conserved. This statement is true, because the whole universe is taken to be a system. A *system* is defined as a definite quantity of matter enclosed by boundaries, either real or imaginary. In effect, the universe is the largest possible closed, or isolated, system we can imagine. Within a *closed system*, particles can interact with each other, but have absolutely no interaction with anything outside. In general, then, the amount of energy in a system remains constant when no mechanical work is done on or by the system, and no energy is transmitted to or from the system (including thermal energy and radiation).

Conservation of total energy

Thus, the **law of conservation of total energy** may be stated as follows:

> The total energy of an isolated system is always conserved.

Within such a system, energy may be converted from one form to another, but the total amount of all forms of energy is constant, or unchanged. Total energy can never be created or destroyed.

Conservative and Nonconservative Forces

Note: Friction is discussed in Section 4.6.

We can make a general distinction among systems by considering two categories of forces that may act within them: conservative and nonconservative forces. You have already been introduced to a couple of conservative forces: the force due to gravity and the spring force. We considered a classic nonconservative force, friction, in Chapter 4. A conservative force is defined as follows:

Conservative force—work independent of path

> A force is said to be conservative if the work done by or against it in moving an object is independent of the object's path.

What this definition means is that the work done by a **conservative force** depends only on the initial and final positions of an object.

The concept of conservative and nonconservative forces is sometimes difficult to comprehend at first. Because this concept is so important in the conservation of energy, let's consider some illustrative examples to increase our understanding.

First, what does *independent of path* mean? An example of path independence was given in Fig. 5.15, where work was done against the *conservative force of gravity*. The figure illustrates that the work done in moving a crate onto a table does not depend on the *path* of the crate, but only on the initial and final positions of the crate. The magnitude of the work done is equal to the change in potential energy (under frictionless conditions only), and in fact, *the concept of potential energy is associated only with conservative forces*. A change in potential energy can be defined in terms of the work done by a conservative force.

Conversely, a **nonconservative force** *does* depend on path.

Nonconservative force—work dependent on path

> A force is said to be nonconservative if the work done by or against it in moving an object does depend on the object's path.

Friction is a nonconservative force. For example, given the same frictional conditions for each case in Fig. 5.15, it would take more work (against friction) to move the crate up the longer ramp, so the work would depend on path—the longer the path, the more frictional work is done. It should therefore be evident that the *total work* done is not equal to a change in potential energy. Some work was done against a nonconservative force, in addition to the conservative gravitational force. In this case, the energy associated with the work done against friction would be converted to heat energy. Hence, in a sense, a conservative force allows you to conserve or store all of the energy as potential energy, whereas a nonconservative force does not.

To further highlight this idea, consider moving the crate around the tabletop. Here, work is done only against the nonconservative frictional force. (Why?) Certainly the work done in moving the crate between two points depends on the path taken. The work would be greater, for example, if we were to move the crate around the table's edges before coming to the destination point than if we were to take a straight-line path.

Another approach to explain the distinction between conservative and nonconservative forces is through an equivalent statement of the previous definition of conservative force:

> A force is conservative if the work done by or against it in moving an object through a round-trip is zero.

Another way of describing a conservative force

Consider a book resting on a table. It has gravitational potential energy $U = mgy$, relative to some reference point $y_o = 0$. You could drop the book on the floor, pick it up, and place it back at its original position; or, you could pick it up from the table, carry it around with you all day, and then place it back at its original position. Both sets of circumstances are round-trips, and the potential energy of the book is the same when it is returned to its original position as it was before the book was moved. Thus, the change in the book's potential energy, or the work done by the conservative force of gravity, is $\Delta U = W = 0$. However, if you were to push the book around on the tabletop and eventually back to its original position, the work done against the nonconservative force of friction would depend on the path (i.e., the longer the path, the more work is done). The work done would not be stored, but would instead be lost as heat and sound.

Notice that for the *conservative* gravitational force, the force and displacement are sometimes in the same direction (in which case positive work is done by the force) and sometimes in opposite directions (in which case negative work is done by the force) during a round-trip. Think of the simple case of the book falling to the floor and being placed back on the table. With positive and negative work, the total work done by gravity can be zero.

However, for only a *nonconservative* force like that of kinetic friction, which always opposes the motion or is in the opposite direction to the displacement, the total work done in a round-trip can *never* be zero and is always negative (i.e., energy is lost). But don't get the idea that nonconservative forces only take energy away from a system. On the contrary, we often supply nonconservative pushes and pulls (forces) that add to the energy of a system, such as when you push a stalled car.

Conservation of Total Mechanical Energy

The idea of a conservative force allows us to extend the conservation of energy to the special case of mechanical energy, which greatly helps us better analyze many physical situations. The sum of the kinetic and potential energies is called the **total mechanical energy**:

Total mechanical energy—kinetic plus potential

$$\underset{\substack{\textit{total}\\\textit{mechanical}\\\textit{energy}}}{E} = \underset{\substack{\textit{kinetic}\\\textit{energy}}}{K} + \underset{\substack{\textit{potential}\\\textit{energy}}}{U} \tag{5.9}$$

For a **conservative system** (i.e., a system in which only conservative forces do work) the total mechanical energy is constant, or conserved; that is,

$$E = E_o$$

Substituting for E and E_o from Eq. 5.9,

$$K + U = K_o + U_o \tag{5.10a}$$

or

$$\tfrac{1}{2}mv^2 + U = \tfrac{1}{2}mv_o^2 + U_o \tag{5.10b}$$

Conservation of mechanical energy

Equation 5.10b is a mathematical statement of the **law of the conservation of mechanical energy**:

> In a conservative system, the sum of all types of kinetic energy and potential energy is constant and equals the total mechanical energy of the system.

The kinetic and potential energies in a conservative system may change, but their sum is always constant. This concept is illustrated in ▼Fig. 5.16a.

Notice for a conservative system that when work is done and energy is transferred within a system, we can write Eq. 5.10a as

$$(K - K_o) + (U - U_o) = 0 \tag{5.11a}$$

or as

$$\Delta K + \Delta U = 0 \tag{5.11b}$$

(for a conservative system)

This expression tells us that these quantities are related in a seesaw fashion: If there is a decrease in potential energy, then the kinetic energy must increase by an equal amount to keep the sum of the changes equal to zero. However, in a nonconservative system, mechanical energy is usually lost (for example, to the heat of friction), and thus $\Delta K + \Delta U < 0$. Such a situation is illustrated in Fig. 5.16b. In terms of the total mechanical energy, $\Delta E = E - E_o < 0$, where ΔE is the amount of energy lost from the system. But, keep in mind, as pointed out previously, a nonconservative force may instead add energy to a system (or have no effect at all).

Examples 5.9 through 5.11 illustrate the conservation of mechanical energy for some conservative systems.

▼ **FIGURE 5.16 Conservative and nonconservative systems** **(a)** The work done by a conservative force exchanges energy between kinetic and potential forms; that is, $\Delta K + \Delta U = 0$. This relationship means that $K_o + U_o = K + U$, or $E_o = E$, and the total mechanical energy is conserved (i.e., no mechanical energy is lost or gained). **(b)** For a nonconservative force, not all the work goes into the exchange of mechanical energy; some energy (ΔE) is lost, for example, if friction acts. The mechanical energy is not conserved in this case. **(c)** A graphical energy summary for the nonconservative case. (Keep in mind that a nonconservative force doing work may instead add energy to a system, rather than subtracting it.) How would the energy summary for a conservative system look?

$K_o + U_o$ (Work) $K + U$ $\quad K_o + U_o = K + U$, $E_o = E$

Initial total mechanical energy, E_o

Final total mechanical energy, E

(a) Conservative system

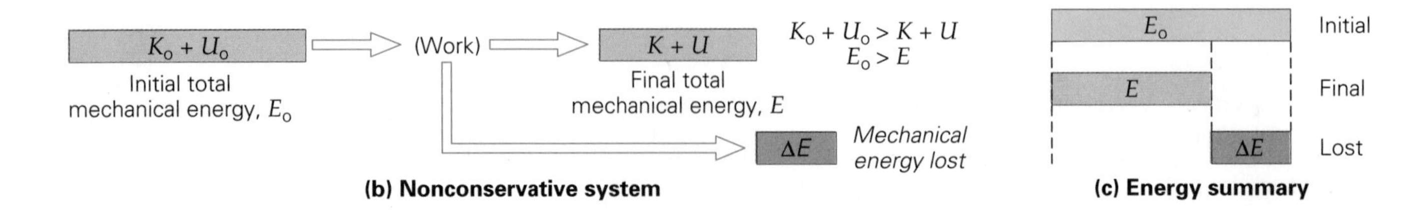

Example 5.9 ■ Look Out Below! Conservation of Mechanical Energy

A painter on a scaffold drops a 1.50-kg can of paint from a height of 6.00 m. (a) What is the kinetic energy of the can when the can is at a height of 4.00 m? (b) With what speed will the can hit the ground? (Neglect air resistance.)

Thinking It Through. Total mechanical energy is conserved, since only the conservative force of gravity acts on the system (the can). The initial total mechanical energy can be found, and potential energy decreases as kinetic energy (as well as speed) increases.

Solution. Listing what is given and what we are to find, we have:

Given: $m = 1.50$ kg, $y_o = 6.00$ m, $y = 4.00$ m, $v_o = 0$

Find: (a) K (kinetic energy at $y = 4.00$ m)
(b) v (speed hitting the ground)

(a) First, it is convenient to find the can's total mechanical energy, since this quantity is conserved while the can is falling (why?). Initially, with $v_o = 0$, the can's total mechanical energy is all potential energy. Taking the ground as the zero reference point, we have

$$E = K_o + U_o = 0 + mgy_o = (1.50\text{ kg})(9.80\text{ m/s}^2)(6.00\text{ m}) = 88.2\text{ J}$$

The relation $E = K + U$ continues to hold while the can is falling, but now we know what E is. Rearranging the equation, we have $K = E - U$ and can find U at $y = 4.00$ m:

$$K = E - U = E - mgy = 88.2\text{ J} - (1.50\text{ kg})(9.80\text{ m/s}^2)(4.00\text{ m}) = 29.4\text{ J}$$

Alternatively, we could have computed the change in (in this case, the loss of) potential energy, ΔU. Whatever potential energy was lost must have been gained as kinetic energy (Eq. 5.11). Then,

$$\Delta K + \Delta U = 0$$

$$(K - K_o) + (U - U_o) = (K - K_o) + (mgy - mgy_o) = 0$$

With $K_o = 0$ (since $v_o = 0$), we obtain

$$K = mg(y_o - y) = (1.50\text{ kg})(9.8\text{ m/s}^2)(6.00\text{ m} - 4.00\text{ m}) = 29.4\text{ J}$$

(b) Just before the can strikes the ground ($y = 0, U = 0$), the total mechanical energy is all kinetic energy, or

$$E = K = \tfrac{1}{2}mv^2$$

Thus,

$$v = \sqrt{\frac{2E}{m}} = \sqrt{\frac{2(88.2\text{ J})}{1.50\text{ kg}}} = 10.8\text{ m/s}$$

Basically, all of the potential energy of a free-falling object released from some height y is converted into kinetic energy just before the object hits the ground, so

$$|\Delta K| = |\Delta U|$$

Thus,

$$\tfrac{1}{2}mv^2 = mgy$$

or

$$v = \sqrt{2gy}$$

Note that the mass cancels and is not a consideration. This result is also obtained from the kinematic equation $v^2 = 2gy$ (Eq. 2.11′), with $v_o = 0$ and $y_o = 0$.

Follow-up Exercise. A fellow painter on the ground wishes to toss a paintbrush vertically upward a distance of 5.0 m to his partner on the scaffold. Use methods of conservation of mechanical energy to determine the minimum speed that he must give to the brush.

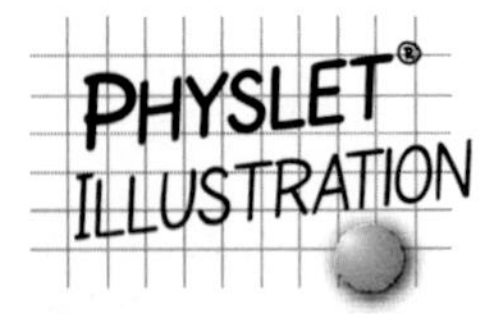

Roller Coaster

Conceptual Example 5.10 ■ A Matter of Direction? Speed and Conservation of Energy

Three balls of equal mass m are projected with the same speed in different directions, as shown in ▾Fig. 5.17. If air resistance is neglected, which ball would you expect to strike the ground with the greatest speed? (a) ball 1; (b) ball 2; (c) ball 3; (d) all balls strike with the same speed.

Reasoning and Answer. All of the balls have the same initial kinetic energy $K_o = \frac{1}{2}mv_o^2$. (Recall that energy is a scalar quantity, and the different directions of projection do not produce any difference in the kinetic energies.) Regardless of their trajectories, all of the balls ultimately descend a distance y relative to their common starting point, so they all lose the same amount of potential energy. (Recall that U is energy of *position* and thus is *independent* of path—see Fig. 5.15.)

By the law of conservation of mechanical energy, the amount of potential energy each ball loses is equal to the amount of kinetic energy it gains. Since all of the balls start with the same amount of kinetic energy and gain the same amount of kinetic energy, all three will have equal kinetic energies just before striking the ground. This means that their speeds must be equal, so the answer is (d).

Note that although balls 1 and 2 are projected at 45° angles, this factor is not relevant. Since the change in potential energy is independent of path, it is independent of the projection angle. The vertical distance between the starting point and the ground is the same (y) for projectiles at any angle. (*Note*: Although the strike speeds are equal, the *times* it takes the balls to reach the ground are different. Refer to Conceptual Example 3.11 for another approach.)

Follow-up Exercise. Would the balls strike the ground with different speeds if their masses were different? (Neglect air resistance.)

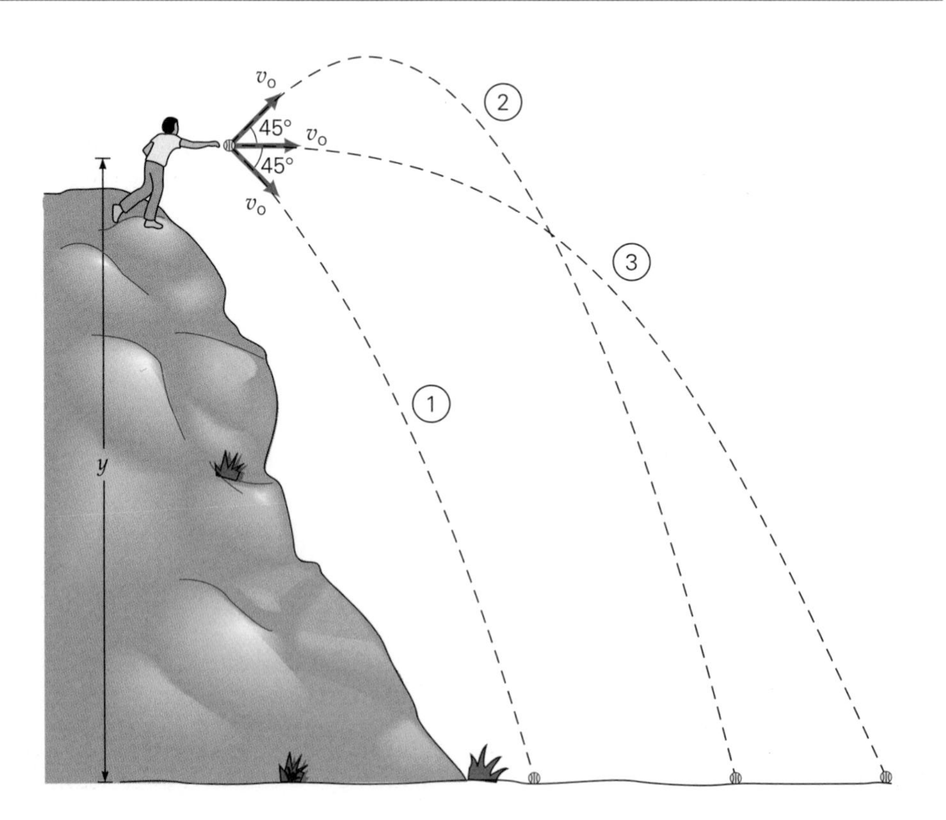

▶ **FIGURE 5.17 Speed and energy** See Conceptual Example 5.10.

Example 5.11 ■ Conservative Forces: Mechanical Energy of a Spring

A 0.30-kg block sliding on a horizontal frictionless surface with a speed of 2.5 m/s, as depicted in ▸Fig. 5.18, strikes a light spring that has a spring constant of 3.0×10^3 N/m. (a) What is the total mechanical energy of the system? (b) What is the kinetic energy K_1 of the block when the spring is compressed a distance $x_1 = 1.0$ cm? (Assume that no energy is lost in the collision.)

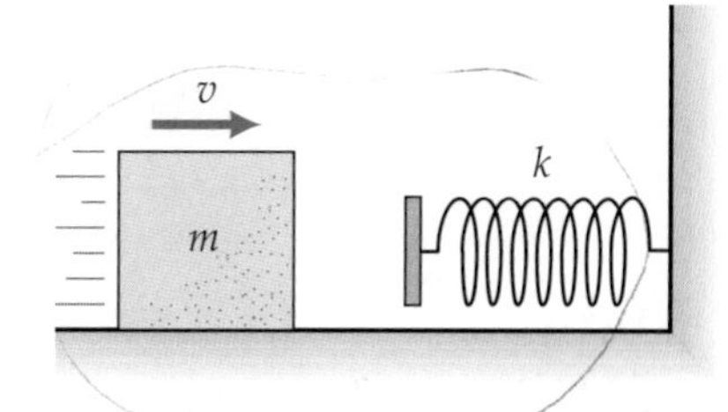

▲ **FIGURE 5.18 Conservative force and the mechanical energy of a spring** See Example 5.11.

Thinking It Through. (a) Initially, the total mechanical energy is all kinetic energy. (b) The total energy is the same as in (a), but it is now divided between kinetic energy and spring potential energy.

Solution.

Given: $m = 0.30$ kg
$v_o = 2.5$ m/s
$k = 3.0 \times 10^3$ N/m
$x_1 = 1.0$ cm $= 0.010$ m

Find: (a) E (total mechanical energy)
(b) K_1 (kinetic energy)

(a) Before the block makes contact with the spring, the total mechanical energy of the system is all in the form of kinetic energy; therefore,

$$E = K_o = \tfrac{1}{2}mv_o^2 = \tfrac{1}{2}(0.30\text{ kg})(2.5\text{ m/s})^2 = 0.94\text{ J}$$

Since the system is conservative (i.e., no mechanical energy is lost), this quantity is the total mechanical energy at any time.

(b) When the spring is compressed a distance x_1, it has potential energy $U_1 = \tfrac{1}{2}kx_1^2$, and

$$E = K_1 + U_1 = K_1 + \tfrac{1}{2}kx_1^2$$

Solving for K_1, we have

$$K_1 = E - \tfrac{1}{2}kx_1^2$$

$$= 0.94\text{ J} - \tfrac{1}{2}(3.0 \times 10^3\text{ N/m})(0.010\text{ m})^2 = 0.94\text{ J} - 0.15\text{ J} = 0.79\text{ J}$$

Follow-up Exercise. How far will the spring in Example 5.11 be compressed when the block comes to a stop? (Solve using energy principles.)

See the Learn by Drawing on the next page for another example of energy exchange.

Total Energy and Nonconservative Forces

In the preceding examples, we ignored the force of friction, which is probably the most common nonconservative force. In general, both conservative and nonconservative forces can do work on objects. However, as you know, when some nonconservative forces do work, the total mechanical energy is not conserved. Mechanical energy is "lost" through the work done by nonconservative forces, such as friction.

You might think that we can no longer use an energy approach to analyze problems involving such nonconservative forces, since mechanical energy can be lost or dissipated (▸Fig. 5.19). However, in some instances, we can use the total energy to find out how much energy was lost to the work done by a nonconservative force. Suppose an object initially has mechanical energy and that nonconservative

▲ **FIGURE 5.19 Nonconservative force and energy loss** Friction is a nonconservative force—when friction is present and does work, mechanical energy is not conserved. Can you tell from the photo what is happening to the work being done by the motor on the grinding wheel after the work is converted into rotational kinetic energy? (Note that the worker is wisely wearing a face shield rather than just goggles as the sign in the background suggests.)

Learn by Drawing

Energy Exchanges: A Falling Ball

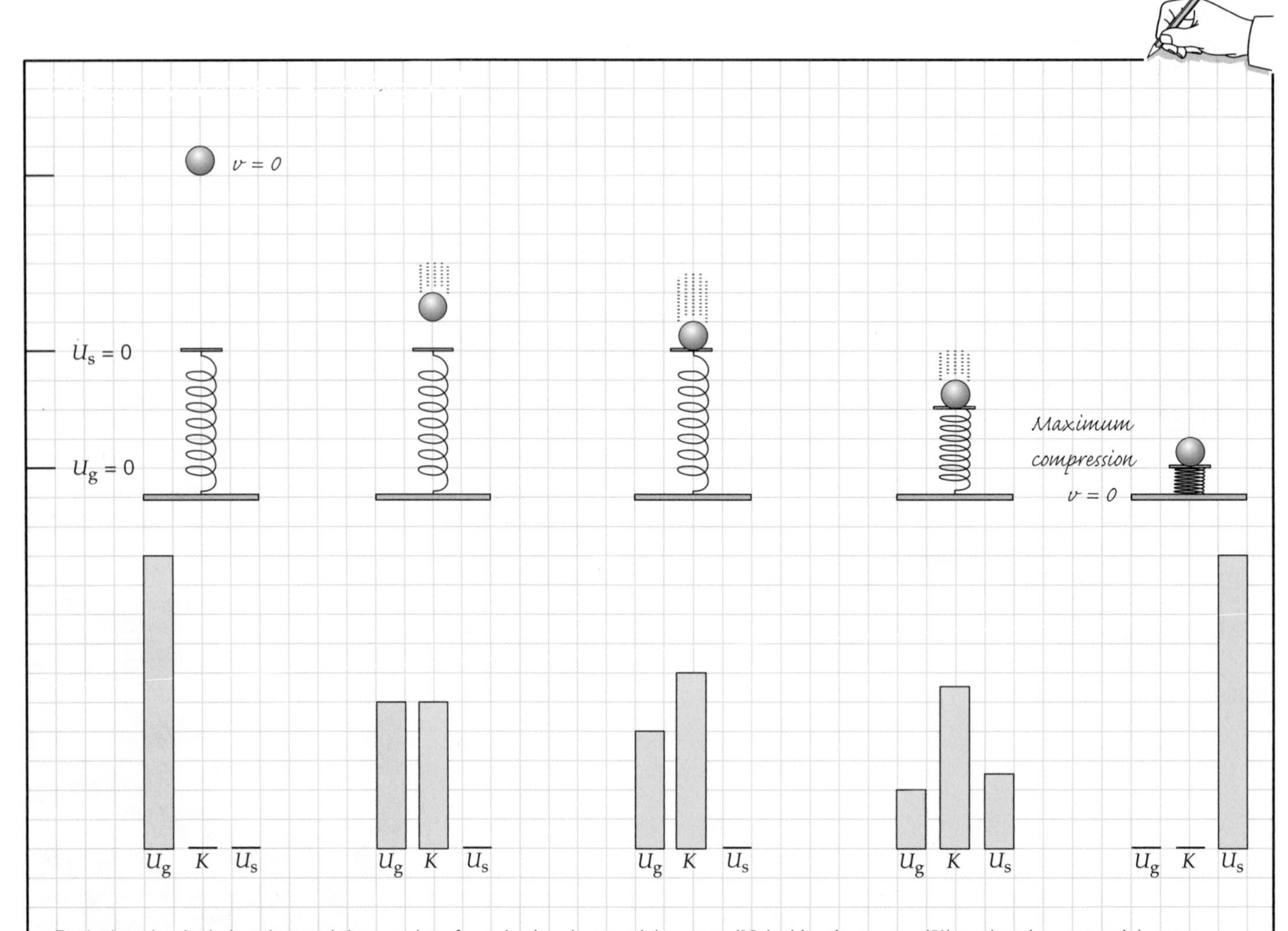

Both the physical situation and the graphs of gravitational potential energy (U_g), kinetic energy (K), and spring potential energy (U_s) are drawn to scale. (Air resistance, the mass of the spring, and any energy loss in the collision are assumed to be negligible.) Why is the spring energy only one-quarter of the total when the spring is halfway compressed?

forces do an amount of work W_{nc} on it. Starting with the work–energy theorem, we have

$$W = \Delta K = K - K_o$$

In general, the net work (W) may be done by both conservative forces (W_c) and nonconservative forces (W_{nc}), so we may write

$$W_c + W_{nc} = K - K_o \tag{5.12}$$

But recall that the work done by conservative forces is equal to $-\Delta U$, or $W_{nc} = U_o - U$, and Eq. 5.12 then becomes

$$\begin{aligned} W_{nc} &= K - K_o - (U_o - U) \\ &= (K + U) - (K_o + U_o) \end{aligned}$$

Therefore,

$$W_{nc} = E - E_o = \Delta E \qquad (5.13)$$

Hence, the work done by the nonconservative forces acting on a system is equal to the change in mechanical energy. Notice that for dissipative forces, $E_o > E$. Thus, the change is negative, indicating a decrease in mechanical energy. This condition agrees in sign with W_{nc}, which, for friction, would also be negative. Example 5.12 illustrates this concept.

Example 5.12 ■ Downhill Racer: Nonconservative Force

A skier with a mass of 80 kg starts from rest at the top of a slope and skis down from an elevation of 110 m (▼Fig. 5.20). The speed of the skier at the bottom of the slope is 20 m/s. (a) Show that the system is nonconservative. (b) How much work is done by the nonconservative force of friction?

Thinking It Through. (a) If the system is nonconservative, then $E_o \neq E$, and these quantities can be computed. (b) We cannot determine the work from force–distance considerations, but W_{nc} is equal to the difference in total energies (Eq. 5.13).

Solution.

Given: $m = 80$ kg, $v_o = 0$, $v = 20$ m/s, $y_o = 110$ m

Find: (a) Show that E is not constant. (b) W_{nc} (work done by friction)

(a) If the system is conservative, the total mechanical energy is constant. Taking $U_o = 0$ at the bottom of the hill, we find the initial energy at the top of the hill to be

$$E_o = U = mgy_o = (80\text{ kg})(9.8\text{ m/s}^2)(110\text{ m}) = 8.6 \times 10^4\text{ J}$$

Then we find the energy at the bottom of the slope to be

$$E = K = \tfrac{1}{2}mv^2 = \tfrac{1}{2}(80\text{ kg})(20\text{ m/s})^2 = 1.6 \times 10^4\text{ J}$$

Therefore, $E_o \neq E$, so this system is not conservative.

(b) The amount of work done by the nonconservative force of friction is equal to the change in the mechanical energy, or to the amount of mechanical energy lost (Eq. 5.13):

$$W_{nc} = E - E_o = (1.6 \times 10^4\text{ J}) - (8.6 \times 10^4\text{ J}) = -7.0 \times 10^4\text{ J}$$

This quantity is over 80% of the initial energy. (Where did this energy actually go?)

Follow-up Exercise. In free fall, air resistance is neglected, but for skydivers, air resistance has a very practical effect. Typically, a skydiver descends about 450 m before reaching a terminal velocity (Section 4.6) of 60 m/s. (a) What is the percentage of energy

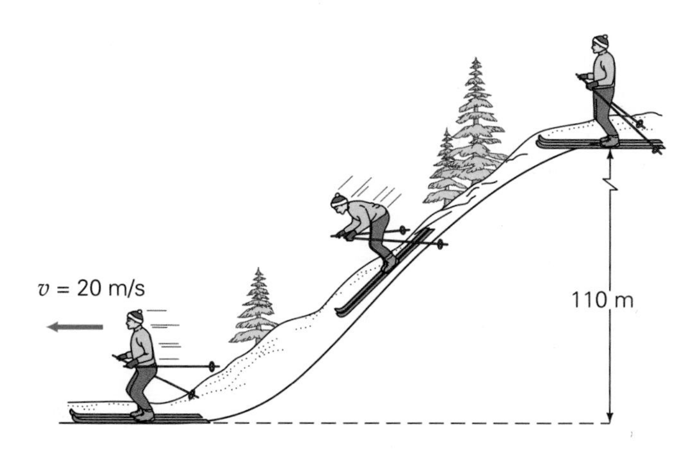

◀ **FIGURE 5.20 Work done by a nonconservative force** See Example 5.12.

loss to nonconservative forces during this descent? (b) Show that after terminal velocity is reached, the rate of energy loss is given by $60mg$ J/s, where m is the mass of the skydiver.

Integrated Example 5.13 ■ Nonconservative Force: One More Time

A 0.75-kg block slides on a frictionless surface with a speed of 2.0 m/s. It then slides over a rough area 1.0 m in length and onto another frictionless surface. The coefficient of kinetic friction between the block and the rough surface is 0.17. (a) Make a sketch of the situation, with the regions labelled with regard to energy, work, and speed. (b) What is the speed of the block after it passes across the rough surface?

(a) Conceptual Reasoning. The block originally has energy E_o and speed v_o, loses energy (W_{nc}), and slows down in the rough area, and emerges with energy E and speed v. Assuming that the motion is in the $+x$-direction, the sketch would look like that shown in ▼Fig. 5.21.

(b) Thinking It Through. The task of finding the final speed implies that we use equations involving kinetic energy, where the final kinetic energy can be found by using the conservation of *total* energy. Note that the initial and final energies are kinetic energies, since there is no change in gravitational potential energy. Listing the data as usual, we have the following:

Given: $m = 0.75$ kg
$x = 1.0$ m
$\mu_k = 0.17$
$v_o = 2.0$ m/s

Find: v (final speed of block)

For this nonconservative system we have from Eq. 5.13,

$$W_{nc} = E - E_o = K - K_o$$

In the rough area, the block loses energy, because of the work done against friction (W_{nc}), and thus

$$W_{nc} = -f_k x = -\mu_k N x = -\mu_k mgx$$

[negative because f_k and the displacement x are in opposite directions, i.e., $(f_k \cos 180°)x = -f_k x$].

Then, rearranging the energy equation and writing the terms out in detail, we have

$$K = K_o + W_{nc}$$

or

$$\tfrac{1}{2}mv^2 = \tfrac{1}{2}mv_o^2 - \mu_k mgx$$

Simplifying yields

$$v = \sqrt{v_o^2 - 2\mu_k gx} = \sqrt{(2.0\text{ m/s})^2 - 2(0.17)(9.8\text{ m/s}^2)(1.0\text{ m})} = 0.82\text{ m/s}$$

Note that the mass of the block was not needed. And, it can be easily shown that the block lost over 80% of its energy to friction.

Follow-up Exercise. Suppose the coefficient of kinetic friction between the block and the rough surface were 0.25. What would happen to the block in this case?

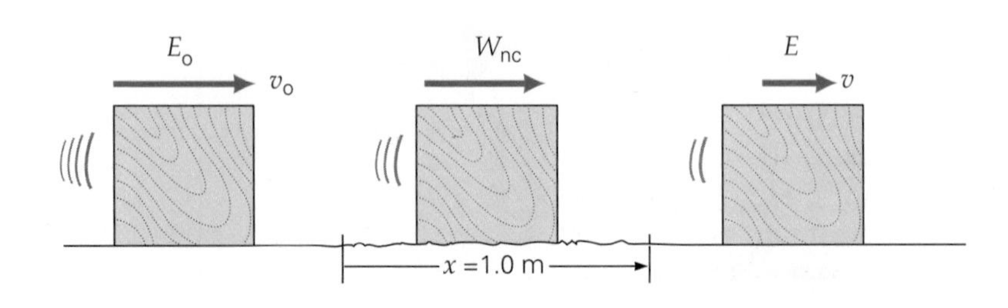

▶ **FIGURE 5.21 A nonconservative rough spot** See Integrated Example 5.13.

Note that in a nonconservative system, the *total energy* (*not* the total mechanical energy) is conserved (including nonmechanical forms of energy, such as heat), but not all of it is available for mechanical work. For a conservative system, you get back what you put in, so to speak. That is, if you do work on the system, the transferred energy is available to do work. But keep in mind that conservative systems are idealizations, because most all real systems are nonconservative to some degree. However, working with ideal conservative systems gives us an understanding of the conservation of energy.

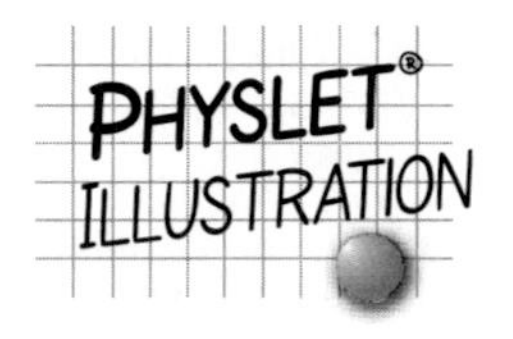

Work Done by Friction

Total energy is always conserved. During this course of study, you will learn about other forms of energy, such as thermal, electrical, nuclear, and chemical energies. In general, on the microscopic and submicroscopic levels, these forms of energy can be described in terms of kinetic energy and potential energy. Also, you will learn that mass is a form of energy and that the law of the conservation of energy must take this form into account in order to be applied to the analysis of nuclear reactions.

5.6 Power

OBJECTIVES: To (a) define power and (b) describe mechanical efficiency.

A particular task may require a certain amount of work, but that work might be done over different lengths of time or at different rates. For example, suppose that you have to mow a lawn. This task takes a certain amount of work, but you might do the job in a half hour, or you might take an hour or two. There's a practical distinction to be made here. There is usually not only an interest in the amount of work done, but also an interest in how fast it is done—that is, the rate at which it is done. *The time rate of doing work* is called **power**.

Definition of power: the time rate of doing work

The average power is the work done divided by the time it takes to do the work, or work per unit of time:

$$\overline{P} = \frac{W}{t} \tag{5.14}$$

If we are interested in the work (and power) done by a constant force of magnitude F acting while an object moves through a parallel displacement of magnitude d, then

$$\overline{P} = \frac{W}{t} = \frac{Fd}{t} = F\left(\frac{d}{t}\right) = F\overline{v} \tag{5.15}$$

SI unit of power: J/s or watt (W)

where it is assumed that the force is in the direction of the displacement. Here, $\overline{v}$ is the magnitude of the average velocity. If the velocity is constant, then $\overline{P} = P = Fv$. If the force and displacement are not in the same direction, then we can write

$$\overline{P} = \frac{F(\cos\theta)d}{t} = F\,\overline{v}\cos\theta \tag{5.16}$$

where θ is the angle between the force and the displacement.

As you can see from Eq. 5.15, the SI unit of power is joules per second (J/s), but this unit is given another name, the **watt** (**W**):

$$1\ \text{J/s} = 1\ \text{watt (W)}$$

The SI unit of power is named in honor of James Watt (1736–1819), a Scottish engineer who developed one of the first practical steam engines. A common unit of electrical power is the *kilowatt* (kW).

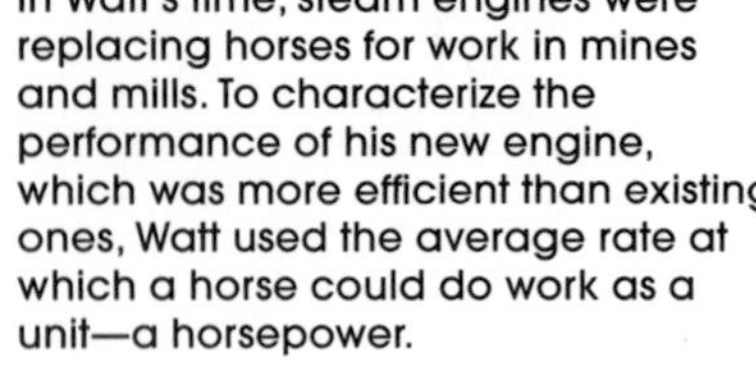
In Watt's time, steam engines were replacing horses for work in mines and mills. To characterize the performance of his new engine, which was more efficient than existing ones, Watt used the average rate at which a horse could do work as a unit—a horsepower.

The British unit of power is foot-pound per second (ft · lb/s). However, a larger unit, the **horsepower (hp)**, is more commonly used:

$$1\text{ hp} = 550\text{ ft}\cdot\text{lb/s} = 746\text{ W}$$

Power tells you how fast work is being done *or* how fast energy is transferred. For example, motors have power ratings commonly given in horsepower. A 2-hp motor can do a given amount of work in half the time that a 1-hp motor would take, or twice the work in the same amount of time. That is, a 2-hp motor is twice as "powerful" as a 1-hp motor.

Example 5.14 ■ A Crane Hoist: Work and Power

A crane hoist like the one shown in ◂Fig. 5.22 lifts a load of 1.0 metric ton a vertical distance of 25 m in 9.0 s at a constant velocity. How much useful work is done by the hoist each second?

▲ **FIGURE 5.22 Power delivery** See Example 5.14.

Thinking It Through. The useful work done each (i.e., per) second is the power output, so this quantity is what is to be found.

Solution.

Given: $m = 1.0$ metric ton $= 1.0 \times 10^3$ kg, $y = 25$ m, $t = 9.0$ s

Find: W per second ($=$ power, P)

Keep in mind that the work per unit time (work per second) is power, so this quantity is what we need to compute. Since the load moves with a constant velocity, $\overline{P} = P$. (Why?) The work is done against gravity, so $F = mg$, and

$$P = \frac{W}{t} = \frac{Fd}{t} = \frac{mgy}{t} = \frac{(1.0 \times 10^3\text{ kg})(9.8\text{ m/s}^2)(25\text{ m})}{9.0\text{ s}} = 2.7 \times 10^4\text{ W (or 27 kW)}$$

Thus, since a watt (W) is a joule per second (J/s), the hoist did 2.7×10^4 J of work each second. Note that the velocity has a magnitude of $v = d/t = 25\text{ m}/9.0\text{ s} = 2.8\text{ m/s}$, and the power could be found using $P = Fv$.

Follow-up Exercise. If the hoist motor of the crane in this Example is rated at 70 hp, what percentage of this power output goes into useful work?

Example 5.15 ■ Cleaning Up: Work and Time

The motors of two vacuum cleaners have net power outputs of 1.00 hp and 0.500 hp, respectively. (a) How much work in joules can each motor do in 3.00 min? (b) How long does it take for each motor to do 97.0 kJ of work?

Thinking It Through. (a) Since power is work/time ($P = W/t$), the work can be computed. Note that power is given in horsepower units. (b) This part of the problem is another application of Eq. 5.15.

Solution.

Given: $P_1 = 1.00\text{ hp} = 746\text{ W}$, $P_2 = 0.500\text{ hp} = 373\text{ W}$, $t = 3.00\text{ min} = 180\text{ s}$, $W = 97.0\text{ kJ} = 97.0 \times 10^3\text{ J}$

Find: (a) W (work for each) (b) t (time for each)

(a) Since $P = W/t$,

$$W_1 = P_1 t = (746\text{ W})(180\text{ s}) = 1.34 \times 10^5\text{ J}$$

and

$$W_2 = P_2 t = (373\text{ W})(180\text{ s}) = 0.67 \times 10^5\text{ J}$$

Note that in the same amount of time, the smaller motor does half the work as the larger one, as you would expect.

(b) The times are given by $t = W/P$, and for the same amount of work,

$$t_1 = \frac{W}{P_1} = \frac{97.0 \times 10^3\ \text{J}}{746\ \text{W}} = 130\ \text{s}$$

and

$$t_2 = \frac{W}{P_2} = \frac{97.0 \times 10^3\ \text{J}}{373\ \text{W}} = 260\ \text{s}$$

Note that the smaller motor takes twice as long as the larger one to do the same amount of work.

Follow-up Exercise. (a) A 10-hp motor breaks down and is temporarily replaced with a 5-hp motor. What can you say about the rate of work output? (b) Suppose the situation were reversed—a 5-hp motor is replaced with a 10-hp motor. What can you say about the rate of work output for this case?

A real-life example of power, energy, and physics is given in the Insight at the end of this section.

Efficiency

Machines and motors are commonly used items in our daily lives, and we often talk about their efficiency. Efficiency involves work, energy, and/or power. Both simple and complex machines that do work have mechanical parts that move, so some input energy is always lost because of friction or some other cause (perhaps in the form of sound). Thus, not all of the input energy goes into doing useful work.

Mechanical efficiency is essentially a measure of what you get out for what you put in—that is, the *useful* work output compared with the energy input. **Efficiency** ε is given as a fraction (or percentage):

$$\varepsilon = \frac{\text{work output}}{\text{energy input}} (\times 100\%) = \frac{W_{\text{out}}}{E_{\text{in}}} (\times 100\%) \tag{5.17}$$

Efficiency is a unitless quantity

For example, if a machine has a 100-joule (energy) input and a 40-joule (work) output, then its efficiency is

$$\varepsilon = \frac{W_{\text{out}}}{E_{\text{in}}} = \frac{40\ \text{J}}{100\ \text{J}} = 0.40\ (\times 100\%) = 40\%$$

An efficiency of 0.40, or 40%, means that 60% of the energy input is lost because of friction or some other cause and doesn't serve its intended purpose. Note that if both terms of the ratio in Eq. 5.17 are divided by time t, we obtain $W_{\text{out}}/t = P_{\text{out}}$ and $E_{\text{in}}/t = P_{\text{in}}$. So, we can also write efficiency in terms of power P:

$$\varepsilon = \frac{P_{\text{out}}}{P_{\text{in}}} (\times 100\%) \tag{5.18}$$

Example 5.16 ■ Home Improvement: Mechanical Efficiency and Work Output

The motor of an electric drill with an efficiency of 80% has a power input of 600 W. How much useful work is done by the drill in a time of 30 s?

Thinking It Through. This example is an application of Eq. 5.18 and the definition of power.

Solution.

Given: $\varepsilon = 80\% = 0.80$
$P_{in} = 600\text{ W}$
$t = 30\text{ s}$

Find: W_{out} (work output)

Given the efficiency and power input, we can readily find the power output P_{out} from Eq. 5.18, and this quantity is related to the work output ($P_{out} = W_{out}/t$). First, we rearrange Eq. 5.18:

$$P_{out} = \varepsilon P_{in} = (0.80)(600\text{ W}) = 4.8 \times 10^2\text{ W}$$

Then, substituting this value into the equation relating power output and work output, we obtain

$$W_{out} = P_{out}t = (4.8 \times 10^2\text{ W})(30\text{ s}) = 1.4 \times 10^4\text{ J}$$

Follow-up Exercise. (a) Is it possible to have a mechanical efficiency of 100%? (b) What would an efficiency of greater than 100% imply?

TABLE 5.1 Typical Efficiencies of Some Machines

Machine	*Efficiency (approximate %)*
Compressor	85
Electric motor	70–95
Automobile	20
Human muscle*	20–25
Steam locomotive	5–10

*Technically not a machine, but used to perform work.

Table 5.1 lists the typical efficiencies of some machines. You may be surprised by the relatively low efficiency of the automobile. Much of the energy input (from gasoline combustion) is lost as exhaust heat and through the cooling system (more than 60%), and friction accounts for a great deal more. About 20% of the input energy is converted to useful work that goes into propelling the vehicle. Air conditioning, power steering, radio, and tape and CD players are nice, but they also use energy and also contribute to the car's decrease in efficiency.

INSIGHT

More Broken Records: The Clap Skate

At the 1998 Winter Olympics in Nagano, Japan, speed skating records were broken and new ones set—largely because of an innovation in ice skates (and applied physics). This new skate technology, invented by Dutch researchers in biomechanics, is commonly called the *clap skate*. The skates are designed to increase the amount of time they are in contact with the ice and therefore also the length of the skater's stride.

The new skates have a spring-loaded hinge on the toe that allows the blade to pull away from the heel (Fig. 1). With a longer stride, the amount of work done by the skater's leg muscle is increased, providing more kinetic energy and speed. Toward the end of the stride, the blade returns to the boot with a "clap" sound when the foot is lifted off the ice—hence, the name *clap skate*. (The skates' inventors called the skates "slap skates," because the skates enable a skater to "slap on" an extra amount of work with each stride.)

Traditional skates require skaters to push from side to side. However, with claps, a new skating technique must be learned, with an emphasis on pushing straight back during the stride to keep the blade on the ice longer. Will the clap skate replace the traditional skate? Probably not completely. On a long track against the clock, the clapping is no more than an annoyance. But on a relatively short curved track, where skaters compete against each other, a surprise move to pass another skater would be well announced—clap, clap, clap—no surprise.

Related Exercise: 35

FIGURE 1 Clap, clap, clap The new clap skate is helping skaters set records. A hinge allows the heel to lift off the blade so that the blade stays on the ice longer, thus providing the skater with more kinetic energy and speed.

Chapter Review

Important Concepts and Equations

- **Work done by a constant force** is the product of the magnitude of the displacement and the component of the force parallel to the displacement:

$$W = (F\cos\theta)d \qquad (5.2)$$

- Calculating work done by a variable force requires advanced mathematics. An example of a variable force is the **spring force**, given by *Hooke's law*:

$$F_s = -kx \qquad (5.3)$$

The **work done by a spring force** is given by

$$W = \tfrac{1}{2}kx^2 \qquad (5.4)$$

- **Kinetic energy** is the energy of motion and is given by

$$K = \tfrac{1}{2}mv^2 \qquad (5.5)$$

- By the **work–energy theorem**, the net work done on an object is equal to the change in the kinetic energy of the object:

$$W = K - K_o = \Delta K \qquad (5.6)$$

- **Potential energy** is the energy of position and/or configuration. The elastic **potential energy of a spring** is given by

$$U = \tfrac{1}{2}kx^2 \quad (\text{with } x_o = 0) \qquad (5.7)$$

The most common type of potential energy is **gravitational potential energy**, associated with the gravitational attraction near the Earth's surface.

$$U = mgy \quad (\text{with } y_o = 0) \qquad (5.8)$$

- **Conservation of energy**: The total energy of the universe or of an isolated system is always conserved.

Conservation of mechanical energy: The total mechanical energy (kinetic plus potential) is constant in a conservative system:

$$\tfrac{1}{2}mv^2 + U = \tfrac{1}{2}mv_o^2 + U_o \qquad (5.10b)$$

- In systems with **nonconservative forces**, where mechanical energy is lost, the work done by a nonconservative force is given by

$$W_{nc} = E - E_o = \Delta E \qquad (5.13)$$

- **Power** is the time rate of doing work (or expending energy). **Average power** is given by

$$\overline{P} = \frac{W}{t} = \frac{Fd}{t} = F\overline{v} \qquad (5.15)$$

(constant force in direction of d and v)

$$\overline{P} = \frac{F(\cos\theta)d}{t} = F\overline{v}\cos\theta \qquad (5.16)$$

(constant force acts at an angle θ between d and v)

- **Efficiency** relates work output to energy (work) input as a percent:

$$\varepsilon = \frac{W_{out}}{E_{in}}\ (\times 100\%) \qquad (5.17)$$

$$\varepsilon = \frac{P_{out}}{P_{in}}\ (\times 100\%) \qquad (5.18)$$

Exercises

5.1 Work Done by a Constant Force

1. The units of work are (a) N · m, (b) kg · m²/s², (c) J, or (d) all of the preceding.

2. CQ If you push against the wall of a building, are you doing any work? Explain.

3. CQ When you catch a basketball, are you doing positive, negative, or zero work on the ball? Explain.

4. CQ Can the work done by a frictional force on an object be positive? If yes, give an example.

5. CQ (a) As a weightlifter strains to lift a barbell from the floor (▶Fig. 5.23a), is he doing work? Why or why not? (b) In raising the barbell above his head, is he doing work? Explain. (c) In holding the barbell above his head (Fig. 5.23b), is he doing more work, less work, or the same amount of work as in lifting the barbell? Explain. (d) If the weightlifter drops the barbell, is work done on the barbell? Explain what happens in this situation.

(a)

(b)

▲ **FIGURE 5.23 Man at work?** See Exercise 5.

6. CQ You are carrying a backpack across campus. What is the work done by your vertical carrying force on the backpack? Explain.

7. CQ A jet plane flies in a vertical circular loop. In what regions of the loop is the work done by the plane's weight positive and/or negative? Is the work constant? If not, are there maximum and minimum instantaneous values? Explain.

8. ■ If a person does 50 J of work in moving a 30-kg box over a 10-m distance on a horizontal surface, what is the minimum force required?

9. ■ A 5.0-kg box slides a 10-m distance on ice. If the coefficient of kinetic friction is 0.20, what is the work done by the friction force?

10. ■ A passenger at an airport pulls a rolling suitcase by its handle. If the force used is 10 N and the handle makes an angle of 25° to the horizontal, what is the work done by the pulling force after the passenger walks 200 m?

11. ■ A college student earning some summer money pushes a lawn mower on a level lawn with a constant force of 250 N at an angle of 30° downward from the horizontal. How far does the student push the mower in doing 1.44×10^3 J of work?

12. ■■ A 3.00-kg block slides down a frictionless plane inclined 20° to the horizontal. If the length of the plane's surface is 1.50 m, how much work is done, and by what force?

13. ■■ Suppose the coefficient of kinetic friction between the block and the plane in Exercise 12 is 0.275. What would be the net work done in this case?

14. ■■ The formula for work is sometimes written $W = F_{\parallel}d$, where $F_{\parallel}$ is the component of the force parallel to the displacement. Show that work is also given by $Fd_{\parallel}$, where $d_{\parallel}$ is the component of the displacement parallel to the force.

15. IE ■■ A hot-air balloon ascends at a constant rate. (a) The weight of the balloon does (1) positive work, (2) negative work, or (3) no work. Why? (b) A hot-air balloon with a mass of 500 kg ascends at a constant rate of 1.50 m/s for 20.0 s. How much work is done by the upward buoyant force? (Neglect air resistance.)

16. ■■ A father pulls his young daughter on a sled with a constant velocity on a level surface through a distance of 10 m, as illustrated in ▸Fig. 5.24a. If the total mass of the sled and the girl is 35 kg and the coefficient of kinetic friction between the sled runners and the snow is 0.20, how much work does the father do?

17. ■■ A father pushes horizontally on his daughter's sled to move it up a snowy incline, as illustrated in Fig. 5.24b. If the sled moves up the hill with a constant velocity, how much work is done by the father in moving it from the bottom to the top of the hill? (Some necessary data are given in Exercise 16.)

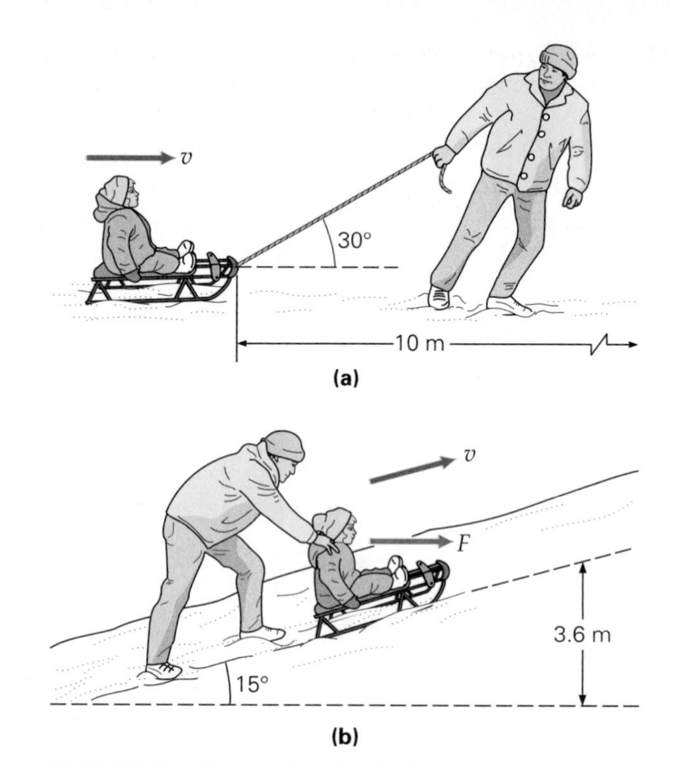

▲ **FIGURE 5.24 Fun and work** See Exercises 16 and 17.

18. ■■ A boy pulls a 20-kg box with a 50-N force at 37° above a horizontal surface. The coefficient of kinetic friction between the box and the horizontal surface is 0.15, and the box is pulled over a distance of 25 m. (a) What is the work done by the boy? (b) What is the work done by the frictional force? (c) What is the net work done on the box?

19. ■■■ A 500-kg helicopter ascends from the ground with an acceleration of 2.00 m/s². Over a 5.00-s interval, what is (a) the work done by the lifting force, (b) the work done by the gravitational force, and (c) the net work done on the helicopter?

20. IE ■■■ A student could either pull or push, at an angle of 30° from the horizontal, a 50-kg crate on a horizontal surface, where the coefficient of kinetic friction between the crate and surface is 0.20. The crate is to be moved a horizontal distance of 15 m. (a) Compared with pushing, pulling requires the student to do (1) less, (2) the same, or (3) more work. (b) Calculate the minimum work required for both pulling and pushing.

5.2 Work Done by a Variable Force

21. The work done by a variable force of the form $F = kx$ is equal to (a) kx^2, (b) kx, (c) $\frac{1}{2}kx^2$, or (d) none of the preceding.

22. CQ Does it take the same amount of work to stretch a spring two centimeters from its equilibrium position as it does to stretch it one centimeter? Explain.

23. CQ If a spring is compressed 2.0 cm from its equilibrium position and then compressed an additional 2.0 cm, how much more work is done in the second compression than in the first? Explain.

24. ■ To measure the spring constant of a certain spring, a student applies a 4.0-N force, and the spring stretches by 5.0 cm. What is the spring constant?

25. ■ If a 10-N force is used to compress a spring with a spring constant of 4.0×10^2 N/m, what is the resulting spring compression?

26. ■ A spring has a spring constant of 40 N/m. How much work is required to stretch the spring 2.0 cm from its equilibrium position?

27. ■ If it takes 400 J of work to stretch a spring 8.00 cm, what is the spring constant?

28. IE ■ A certain amount of work is required to stretch a spring from its equilibrium position. (a) If twice the work is performed on the spring, the spring will stretch more by a factor of (1) $\sqrt{2}$, (2) 2, (3) $1/\sqrt{2}$, or (4) $\frac{1}{2}$? Why? (b) If 100 J of work is done to pull a spring 1.0 cm, what work is required to stretch it 3.0 cm?

29. ■■ When a 75-g mass is suspended from a vertical spring, the spring is stretched from a length of 4.0 cm to a length of 7.0 cm. If the mass is then pulled downward an additional 10 cm, what is the total work done against the spring force in joules?

30. ■■ A particular spring has a force constant of 2.5×10^3 N/m. (a) How much work is done in stretching the relaxed spring by 6.0 cm? (b) How much more work is done in stretching the spring an additional 2.0 cm?

31. ■■ For the spring in Exercise 30, how much mass would have to be suspended from the vertical spring to stretch it (a) the first 6.0 cm and (b) the additional 2.0 cm?

32. ■■ A particular force is described by the equation $\mathbf{F} = (60 \text{ N/m})x\,\hat{\mathbf{x}}$. How much work is done when this force pushes a box horizontally between (a) $x_o = 0$ and $x = 0.15$ m, and (b) $x_o = 0.15$ m and $x = 0.25$ m?

33. ■■ Compute the work done by the variable force in the graph of F versus x in ▸Fig. 5.25. [*Hint*: The area of a triangle is $A = \frac{1}{2}$ altitude × base.]

5.3 The Work–Energy Theorem: Kinetic Energy

34. If the angle between the net force and the displacement of an object is greater than 90°, (a) kinetic energy increases, (b) kinetic energy decreases, (c) kinetic energy remains the same, or (d) the object stops.

35. CQ ▸Fig. 5.26 shows a close-up of the clap skate discussed in the Insight in this chapter. The skates have a spring-loaded hinged toe at the front of the boot and a plunger system at the heel. As the skater strides, the heel lifts from the blade—unlike with traditional skates—lengthening the skater's stride. Explain how these skates can improve performance.

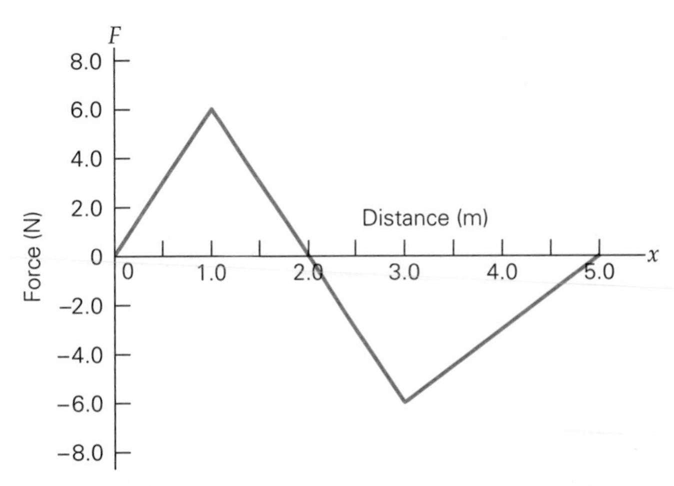

▲ **FIGURE 5.25 How much work is done?** See Exercise 33.

▲ **FIGURE 5.26 Clap to records** See Exercise 35.

36. CQ Which of the following objects has the smallest kinetic energy? (a) an object of mass $4m$ and speed v; (b) an object of mass $3m$ and speed $2v$; (c) an object of mass $2m$ and speed $3v$; (d) an object of mass m and speed $4v$.

37. CQ You want to decrease the kinetic energy of an object as much as you can, and you can do so by either reducing the mass by half or reducing the speed by half. Which option should you pick, and why?

38. CQ A certain amount of work W is required to accelerate a car from rest to a speed v. How much work is required to accelerate the car from rest to a speed of $2v$?

39. CQ A certain amount of work W is required to accelerate a car from rest to a speed v. If an amount of work equal to $2W$ is done on the car, what is the car's speed?

40. CQ Two identical cars traveling at 55 mph collide head on. A third identical car crashes into a wall at 55 mph. Which car has more damage? Explain.

41. IE ■ A 0.20-kg object with a horizontal speed of 10 m/s 10 m/s hits a wall and bounces directly back with only half the original speed. (a) The percentage of lost kinetic energy compared with the object's original kinetic energy is (1) 25%, (2) 50%, or (3) 75%. (b) How much kinetic energy is lost in the ball's collision with the wall?

42. ■ A 1200-kg automobile travels at a speed of 90 km/h. (a) What is its kinetic energy? (b) What is the net work that would be required to bring it to a stop?

43. ■ A constant net force of 75 N acts on an object initially at rest through a parallel distance of 0.60 m. (a) What is the final kinetic energy of the object? (b) If the object has a mass of 0.20 kg, what is its final speed?

44. ■ A 3.0-g bullet traveling at 350 m/s hits a tree and slows down uniformly to a stop while penetrating a distance of 12 cm into the tree's trunk. What was the force exerted on the bullet in bringing it to rest?

45. ■■ The stopping distance of a vehicle is an important safety factor. Assuming a constant braking force, use the work–energy theorem to show that a vehicle's stopping distance is proportional to the square of its initial speed. If an automobile traveling at 45 km/h is brought to a stop in 50 m, what would be the stopping distance for an initial speed of 90 km/h?

46. IE ■■ A large car of mass $2m$ travels at speed v, and a small car of mass m travels with a speed $2v$. Both skid to a stop with the same coefficient of friction. (a) The small car will have (1) a longer, (2) the same, or (3) a shorter stopping distance. (b) Calculate the ratio of the stopping distance of the small car to that of the large car. (Use the work–energy theorem, not Newton's laws.)

47. ■■■ If the work required to speed a car up from 10 km/h to 20 km/h is 5.0×10^3 J, what would be the work required to increase the car's speed from 20 km/h to 30 km/h?

5.4 Potential Energy

48. A change in gravitational potential energy (a) is always positive, (b) depends on the reference point, (c) depends on the path, or (d) depends only on the initial and final positions.

49. CQ If a spring changes its position from x_o to x, the change in potential energy is then proportional to what? (Express the quantity in terms of x_o and x.)

50. Sketch a plot of U versus x for a mass oscillating on a spring between the limits of $-A$ and $+A$.

51. ■ What is the gravitational potential energy, relative to the ground, of a 1.0-kg box at the top of a 50-m building?

52. ■ To store exactly 1.0 J of potential energy in a spring for which $k = 2.0 \times 10^4$ N/m, how much would the spring have to be stretched beyond its equilibrium length? How about to store 4.0 J?

53. ■ How much more gravitational potential energy does a 1.0-kg hammer have when it is on a shelf 1.5 m high than when it is on a shelf 0.90 m high?

54. IE ■ You are told that the gravitational potential energy of a 2.0-kg object has decreased by 10 J. (a) With this information, you can determine (1) the object's initial height, (2) the object's final height, (3) both the initial and the final height, or (4) only the difference between the two heights. Why? (b) What can you say has physically happened to the object?

55. ■■ A 0.20-kg stone is thrown vertically upward with an initial velocity of 7.5 m/s from a starting point 1.2 m above the ground. (a) What is the potential energy of the stone at its maximum height relative to the ground? (b) What is the change in the potential energy of the stone between its launch point and its maximum height?

56. ■■ A 60-kg diver dives off a board that is 5.0 m above the surface of the water in a swimming pool; he touches the bottom of the pool 3.0 m below the water's surface. (a) What are the respective potential energies of the diver relative to the surface of the water when he is on the board and at the bottom of the swimming pool? (b) What is the change in the diver's potential energy relative to the board, to the surface of the water, and to the bottom of the swimming pool?

57. IE ■■ The floor of the basement of a house is 3.0 m below ground level, and the floor of the attic is 4.5 m above ground level. (a) If an object in the attic were brought to the basement, the change in potential energy will be greatest relative to which floor, (1) attic, (2) ground, (3) basement, or (4) all the same? Why? (b) What are the respective potential energies of 1.5-kg objects in the basement and attic, relative to ground level? (c) What is the change in potential energy if the object in the attic is brought to the basement?

58. ■■■ A student has six textbooks, each with a thickness of 4.0 cm and a weight of 30 N. What is the minimum work the student would have to do to place all the books in a single vertical stack, starting with all the books on the surface of the table?

5.5 The Conservation of Energy

59. If a nonconservative force acts on an object, (a) the object's kinetic energy is conserved, (b) the object's potential is conserved, (c) the mechanical energy is conserved, or (d) the mechanical energy is not conserved.

60. The speed of a pendulum is greatest (a) when the pendulum's kinetic energy is a minimum, (b) when the pendulum's acceleration is a maximum, (c) when the pendulum's potential energy is a minimum, or (d) none of the preceding.

61. CQ For a classroom demonstration, a bowling ball suspended from a ceiling is displaced from the vertical position to one side and released from rest just in front of the nose of a student (▼Fig. 5.27). If the student doesn't move, why won't the bowling ball hit his nose?

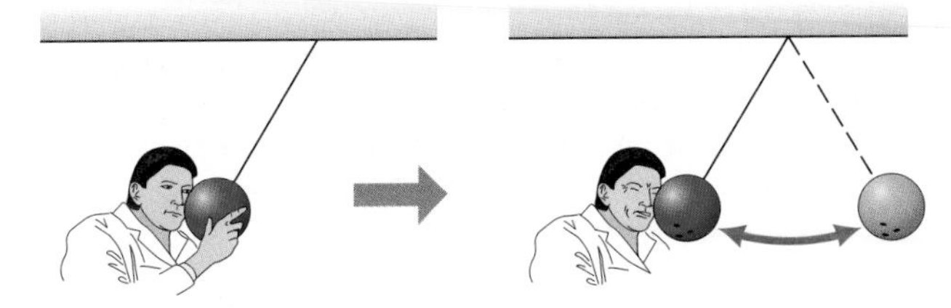

▲ **FIGURE 5.27 In the face?** See Exercise 61.

62. CQ Discuss all the different energy conversions that are involved in a pole vault, as shown in ▼Fig. 5.28. (Include the vaulter's running start. Where does the energy for this action come from?)

▲ **FIGURE 5.28 Energy conversion(s)** See Exercise 62.

63. CQ Here's an energy-transfer question: When jumping straight upward from the ground, you can achieve only the same maximum height with each jump. However, on a trampoline, you can jump higher and higher with each bounce. Why? However, there's a limit on the trampoline, too. What determines this limit?

64. CQ When you throw an object into the air, is its initial velocity the same as its velocity just before it returns to your hand? Explain by applying the concept of the conservation of mechanical energy.

65. CQ A rubber ball dropped on a floor will bounce back to a height lower than its original height. Is this phenomenon a violation of the conservation of energy? Discuss some of the energy conversions that take place in the process.

66. ■ A person standing on a bridge at a height of 115 m above a river drops a 0.250-kg rock. (a) What is the rock's mechanical energy at the time of release relative to the surface of the river? (b) What are the rock's kinetic, potential, and mechanical energies after it has fallen 75.0 m? (c) Just before the rock hits the water, what are its speed and total mechanical energy? (d) Answer parts (a)–(c) for a reference point ($y = 0$) at the elevation where the rock is released. (Neglect air resistance.)

67. ■ A 0.300-kg ball is thrown vertically upward with an initial speed of 10.0 m/s. If the initial potential energy is taken as zero, find the ball's kinetic, potential, and mechanical energies (a) at its initial position, (b) at 2.50 m above the initial position, and (c) at its maximum height.

68. ■ What is the maximum height reached by the ball in Exercise 67?

69. ■■ A 0.50-kg ball thrown vertically upward has an initial kinetic energy of 80 J. (a) What are its kinetic and potential energies when it has traveled three fourths of the distance to its maximum height? (b) What is the ball's speed at this point? (c) What is its potential energy at the maximum height? (Assume a reference is chosen to be zero at the launch point.)

70. IE ■■ A girl swings back and forth on a swing with ropes that are 4.00 m long. The maximum height she reaches is 2.00 m above the ground. At the lowest point of the swing, she is 0.500 m above the ground. (a) The girl attains the maximum speed (1) at the top, (2) in the middle, or (3) at the bottom of the swing. Why? (b) What is the girl's maximum speed?

71. ■■ When a certain rubber ball is dropped from a height of 1.25 m onto a hard surface, it loses 18.0% of its mechanical energy on each bounce. (a) How high will the ball bounce on the first bounce? (b) How high will it bounce on the second bounce? (c) With what speed would the ball have to be thrown downward to make it reach its original height on the first bounce?

72. ■■ A skier coasts down a very smooth, 10-m-high slope similar to the one shown in Fig. 5.20. If the speed of the skier on the top of the slope is 5.0 m/s, what is his speed at the bottom of the slope?

73. ■■ A roller coaster travels on a frictionless track as shown in ▸Fig. 5.29. (a) If the speed of the roller coaster at point A is 5.0 m/s, what is its speed at point B? (b) Will it reach point C? (c) What speed at point *A* is required for the roller coaster to reach point C?

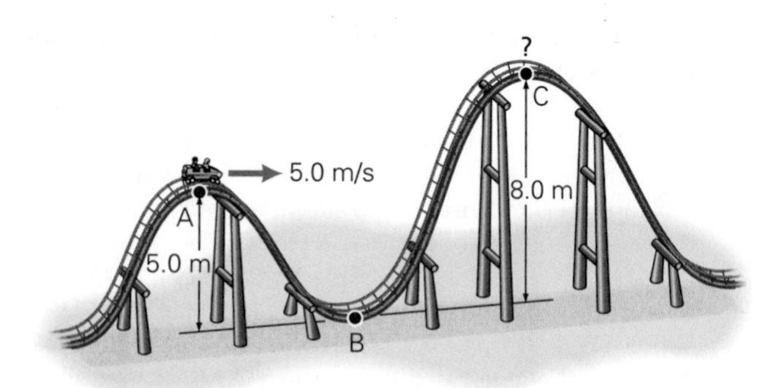

▲ **FIGURE 5.29 Enough energy?** See Exercise 73.

74. ■■ A simple pendulum has a length of 0.75 m and a bob whose mass is 0.15 kg. The bob is released from an angle of 25° relative to a vertical reference line (▼Fig. 5.30). (a) Show that the vertical height of the bob when it is released is $h = L(1 - \cos 25°)$. (b) What is the kinetic energy of the bob when the string is at an angle of 9.0°? (c) What is the speed of the bob at the bottom of the swing? (Neglect friction and the mass of the string.)

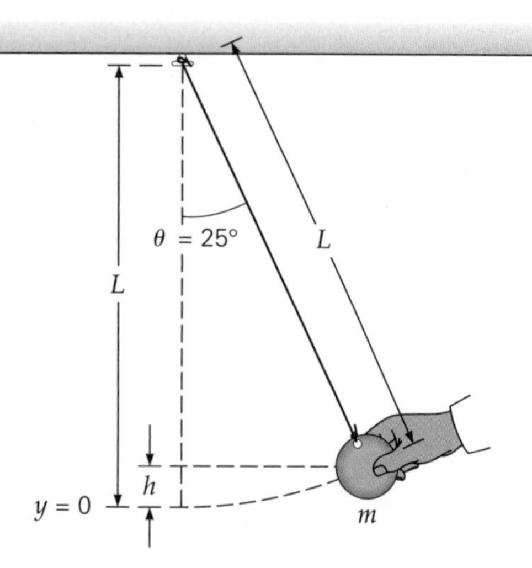

▲ **FIGURE 5.30 A pendulum swings** See Exercise 74.

75. ■■ Suppose the simple pendulum in Exercise 74 were released from an angle of 60°. (a) What would be the speed of the bob at the bottom of the swing? (b) To what height would the bob swing on the other side? (c) What angle of release would give half the speed of that for the 60° release angle at the bottom of the swing?

76. ■■ A 1.5-kg box that is sliding on a frictionless surface with a speed of 12 m/s approaches a horizontal spring. (See Fig. 5.18.) The spring has a spring constant of 2000 N/m. (a) How far will the spring be compressed in stopping the box? (b) How far will the spring be compressed when the box's speed is reduced to half of its initial speed?

77. ■■ A 28-kg child slides down a playground slide from a height of 3.0 m above the bottom of the slide. If her speed at the bottom is 2.5 m/s, what is the work done by nonconservative forces?

78. IE ■■ A 50-kg student on a sled starts from rest at a vertical height of 20 m above the horizontal base of a hill and slides down. (a) If the sled and the student have a speed of 10 m/s at the bottom of the hill, this system is (1) conservative, (2) nonconservative, or (3) none of the preceding. Why? (b) What is the work done by the nonconservative force?

79. ■■■ In Exercise 72, if the skier has a mass of 60 kg and the force of friction retards his motion by doing 2500 J of work, what is his speed at the bottom of the slope?

5.6 Power

80. Which of the following is not a unit of power? (a) J/s; (b) W · s; (c) W; (d) hp.

81. CQ If you check your electricity bill, you will note that you are paying the power company for so many kilowatt-hours (kWh). Are you really paying for power? Explain. Also, convert 2.5 kWh to J.

82. CQ (a) Does efficiency describe how fast work is done? Explain. (b) Does a more powerful machine always perform more work than a less powerful one? Explain.

83. CQ Two students who weigh the same start at the same ground-floor location at the same time to go to the same classroom on the third floor by different routes. If they arrive at different times, which student will have expended more power? Explain.

84. ■ What is the power in watts of a motor rated at $\frac{1}{4}$ hp?

85. ■ A girl consumes 8.4×10^6 J (2000 food calories) of energy per day while maintaining a constant weight. What is the average power she produces in a day?

86. ■ A 1500-kg race car can go from 0 to 90 km/h in 5.0 s. What average power is required to do this?

87. ■ The two 0.50-kg weights of a cuckoo clock descend 1.5 m in a three-day period. At what rate is gravitational potential energy decreased?

88. ■ A 60-kg woman runs up a staircase 15 m high (vertically) in 20 s. (a) How much power does she expend? (b) What is her horsepower rating?

89. ■■ An electric motor with a 2.0-hp output drives a machine with an efficiency of 45%. What is the energy output of the machine per second?

90. ■■ Water is lifted out of a well 30.0 m deep by a motor rated at 1.00 hp. Assuming 90% efficiency, how many kilograms of water can be lifted in 1 min?

91. ■■ The Gossamer Albatross, a human-powered aircraft that requires the pilot to pedal, flew across the English Channel on June 12, 1979, in 2 h and 49 min . If the average power needed to keep the aircraft flying is 0.30 hp, how much energy did the pilot use during the flight?

92. ■■■ A 3250-kg aircraft takes 12.5 min to achieve its cruising altitude of 10.0 km and cruising speed of 850 km/h. If the plane's engines deliver, on average, 1500 hp of power during this time, what is the efficiency of the engines?

93. ■■■ A sleigh and driver with a total mass of 120 kg is pulled up a hill with a 15° incline by a horse, as illustrated in ▼Fig. 5.31. (a) If the overall retarding frictional force is 950 N and the sled moves up the hill with a constant velocity of 5.0 km/h, what is the power output of the horse? (Express in horsepower, of course. Note the magnitude of your answer, and explain.) (b) Suppose that in a spurt of energy, the horse accelerates the sled uniformly from 5.0 km/h to 20 km/h in 5.0 s. What is the horse's maximum instantaneous power output? Assume the same force of friction.

▲ **FIGURE 5.31 A one-horse open sleigh** See Exercise 93.

Additional Exercises

94. It is estimated that a 60-kg Olympic sprinter in the 100-m dash can achieve a kinetic energy of 3.0×10^3 J during the race. What is the sprinter's speed at this time?

95. A large electric motor with an efficiency of 75% has a power output of 1.5 hp. If the motor is run steadily and the cost of electricity is \$0.12/kWh, how much does it cost, to the nearest penny, to run the motor for 2.0 h?

96. In planing a piece of wood 35 cm long, a carpenter applies a force of 40 N to a plane at a downward angle of 25° to the horizontal. How much work is done by the carpenter?

97. IE A spring with a force constant of 50 N/m is to be stretched from 0 to 20 cm. (a) The work required to stretch the spring from 10 cm to 20 cm is (1) more than, (2) the same as, or (3) less than that required to stretch it from 0 to 10 cm. (b) Compare the two work values to prove your answer to (a).

98. A 120-kg sleigh is pulled by one horse at a constant velocity for a distance of 0.75 km on a level snowy surface. The coefficient of kinetic friction between the sleigh runners and the snow is 0.25. (a) Calculate the work done by the horse. (b) Calculate the work done by friction.

99. A water slide has a height of 4.0 m. The people coming down the slide shoot out horizontally at the bottom, which is a distance of 1.5 m above the surface of the water in the swimming pool. (a) If a person starts down the slide from rest, neglecting frictional losses, how far from a point directly below the bottom of the slide does the person land? (b) Does it make any difference whether the person is a small child or an adult?

100. A hiker plans to swing on a rope across a ravine in the mountains, as illustrated in ▼Fig. 5.32, and to drop when she is just above the far edge. (a) At what horizontal speed should she be moving when she starts to swing? (b) At what point would she be in danger of falling into the ravine? Explain.

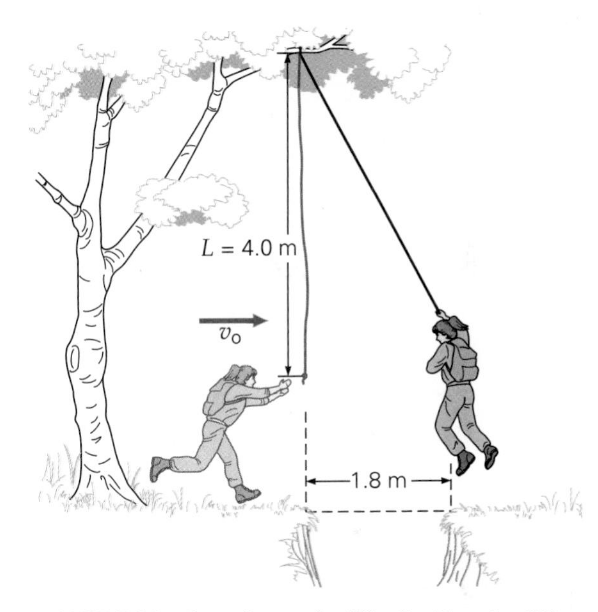

▲ **FIGURE 5.32 Can she make it?** See Exercise 100.

101. A tractor pulls a wagon from rest with a constant force of 700 N, eventually giving the wagon a constant speed of 20.0 km/h. (a) How much work is done by the tractor in 3.50 min ? (b) What is the tractor's power output?

102. A sports car weighs one third as much as a large luxury car. (a) If the sports car is traveling at a speed of 90 km/h, at what speed would the larger car have to travel to have the same kinetic energy? (b) Suppose that the large car is traveling at a speed that gives it half the kinetic energy of the sports car. What is the speed of the more massive car?

103. A ball with a mass of 0.360 kg is dropped from a height of 1.20 m above the top of a fixed vertical spring whose force constant is 350 N/m. (a) What is the maximum distance the spring is compressed by the ball? (Neglect energy loss due to the collision.) (b) What is the speed of the ball when the spring has been compressed 5.00 cm?

104. A constant horizontal force of 30 N moves a box with a constant speed along a rough surface. If the force does work at a rate of 50 W, (a) what is the box's speed, and (b) how much work is done by the force in 2.5 s?

105. In a time of 10 s, a 70-kg student runs up two flights of stairs whose combined vertical height is 8.0 m. Compute the student's power output in doing work against gravity in (a) watts and (b) horsepower.

106. ■■■ A 50-kg crate slides down a 5.0-m loading ramp that is inclined at an angle of 25° to the horizontal. A worker pushes on the crate parallel to the surface of the ramp so that the crate slides down with a constant velocity. If the coefficient of kinetic friction between the crate and the ramp is 0.33, how much work is done by (a) the worker, (b) the force of friction, and (c) the force of gravity? (d) What is the net work done on the crate?

Linear Momentum and Collisions

Tomorrow, the sportscasters may say that the momentum of the entire game changed as a result of this clutch hit. One team gained momentum and went on to win the game, while its opponents lost it. But regardless of the effect on the team, it's clear that the momentum of the *ball* must have changed dramatically in the instant before this photograph was taken. The ball was traveling from right to left, probably at a pretty good rate of speed—and thus with lots of momentum. But a collision with several pounds of hardwood—with plenty of momentum of its own—changed the ball's trajectory in a fraction of a second. A fan might say that the batter turned the ball around. After studying Chapter 4, you might say that the force he applied gave it a large negative acceleration, reversing its velocity (momentum) vector. Yet, if you summed up the momentum of the ball and bat just before the collision and just afterward, you'd discover that although both the ball and the bat had momentum changes, the total momentum never changed!

If you were bowling and the ball bounced off the pins and rolled back toward you, you would probably be very surprised. But why? What leads us to expect that the ball will send the pins flying and continue on its way, rather than rebounding? You might say that the momentum of the ball carries it onward even after the collision (and you would be right)—but what does that really mean? In this chapter, you will study the concept of *momentum* and learn how it is particularly useful in analyzing motion and collisions.

6.1 Linear Momentum

OBJECTIVE: To compute linear momentum and the components of momentum.

The term *momentum* may bring to mind a football player running down the field, knocking down players who are trying to stop him. Or you might have heard someone say that a team lost its momentum (and so lost the game). Such everyday usages give some insight into the meaning of momentum. They suggest the idea of mass in motion and therefore of inertia. We tend to think of heavy or massive objects in motion as having a great deal of momentum, even if they move very slowly. However, according to the technical definition of momentum, a light object can have just as much momentum as a heavier one, and sometimes more.

Newton referred to what modern physicists term **linear momentum** as "the quantity of motion . . . arising from velocity and the quantity of matter conjointly." In other words, the momentum of a body is proportional to both its mass and its velocity. By definition,

Definitiion of: linear momentum

the linear momentum of an object is the product of its mass and velocity:

Note: The momentum vector of a single object is in the direction of the object's velocity.

$$\mathbf{p} = m\mathbf{v} \tag{6.1}$$

SI unit of momentum: kilogram-meter per second (kg · m/s)

It is common to refer to linear momentum as simply *momentum*. From Eq. 6.1, you can see that the SI units for momentum are kilogram-meters per second. Momentum is a vector quantity that has the same direction as the velocity, and x–y components with magnitudes of $p_x = mv_x$ and $p_y = mv_y$, respectively.

Equation 6.1 expresses the momentum of a single object or particle. For a system of more than one particle, the **total linear momentum** of the system is the vector sum of the momenta (plural of *momentum*) of the individual particles:

Note: Total linear momentum—a vector sum

$$\mathbf{P} = \mathbf{p}_1 + \mathbf{p}_2 + \mathbf{p}_3 + \mathbf{p}_4 = \Sigma \mathbf{p}_i \tag{6.2}$$

(*Note*: **P** signifies the *total* momentum, while **p** signifies an *individual* momentum.)

Example 6.1 ■ Momentum: Mass *and* Velocity

A 100-kg football player runs with a velocity of 4.0 m/s straight down the field. A 1.0-kg artillery shell leaves the barrel of a gun with a muzzle velocity of 500 m/s. Which has the greater momentum (magnitude), the football player or the shell?

Thinking It Through. Given the mass and velocity of an object, the momentum can be calculated from Eq. 6.1.

Solution. As usual, we first list the given data and what we are to find, using the subscripts "p" and "s" to refer to the player and shell, respectively.

Given: $m_p = 100$ kg
$v_p = 4.0$ m/s
$m_s = 1.0$ kg
$v_s = 500$ m/s

Find: p_p and p_s (magnitudes of the momenta)

The magnitude of the momentum of the football player is

$$p_p = m_p v_p = (100\text{ kg})(4.0\text{ m/s}) = 4.0 \times 10^2\ \text{kg}\cdot\text{m/s}$$

and that of the shell is

$$p_s = m_s v_s = (1.0\text{ kg})(500\text{ m/s}) = 5.0 \times 10^2\ \text{kg}\cdot\text{m/s}$$

Thus, the less massive shell has the greater momentum. Remember, the magnitude of momentum depends on *both* the mass *and* the magnitude of the velocity.

Follow-up Exercise. What would the football player's speed have to be for his momentum to have the same magnitude as the artillery shell's momentum? Would this speed be realistic? *(Answers to all Follow-up Exercises are at the back of the text.)*

Integrated Example 6.2 ■ Linear Momentum: Some Ballpark Comparisons

Consider the three objects shown in ▸Fig. 6.1—a .22-caliber bullet, a cruise ship, and a glacier. Assuming each to be moving at its normal speed, (a) which would you expect to have the (1) greatest linear momentum and (2) the least linear momentum? (b) Estimate the masses and velocities and compute order-of-magnitude values of the linear momentum of the objects.

(a) Conceptual Reasoning. Certainly the bullet travels the fastest and the glacier the slowest, with the cruise ship in between. But, momentum, $p = mv$, is equally dependent on mass and velocity. The fast bullet has a tiny mass compared with that of the ship and the glacier. The slow glacier has a huge mass that greatly overshadows that of the bullet, but not so much that of the ship. The cruise ship weighs a great deal and thus has considerable mass. Which object has the greater momentum also depends on the relative speeds. The glacier "creeps" along compared with the ship, so the very slow speed of the glacier counterbalances its huge mass to make its momentum less than might be expected. Assuming the speed difference to be greater than the mass difference for the ship and glacier, the ship would have the larger momentum. Similarly, because of the fast bullet's relatively tiny mass, it would be expected to have the least momentum. So, with this reasoning, the largest momentum goes to the ship and the smallest momentum to the bullet.

(b) Thinking It Through. With no physical data given, you are asked to estimate the masses and velocities (speeds) of the objects so as to be able to compute their momenta [which will verify the reasoning in part (a)]. As is often the case in real-life problems, you may have difficulty estimating the values, so you would try to look up approximate values for the various quantities. For this example, we will provide these estimates. (Note that the units given in references vary, and it is important to convert units correctly.)

Given: Estimates (given below) of weight (mass) and speed for the bullet, cruise ship, and glacier.

Find: The approximate magnitudes of the momenta for the bullet (p_b), cruise ship (p_s), and glacier (p_g).

Bullet: A typical .22-caliber bullet has a weight of about 30 grains and a muzzle velocity of about 1300 ft/s. (A grain, abbreviated gr, is an old British unit. It was once commonly used for pharmaceuticals, such as 5-grain aspirin tablets; 1 lb = 7 000 gr.)

Ship: A ship like the one shown in Fig. 6.1 would have a weight of about 70 000 tons and a speed of about 20 knots. (A knot is another old unit, still commonly used in nautical contexts; 1 knot = 1.15 mi/h.)

Glacier: The glacier might be 1 km wide, 10 km long, and 250 m deep and move at a rate of 1 m per day. (There is much variation among glaciers. Therefore, these figures must involve more assumptions and rougher estimates than those for the bullet or ship. For example, we are assuming a uniform, rectangular cross-sectional area for the glacier. The depth is particularly difficult to estimate from a photograph; a minimum value is given by the fact that glaciers must be at least 50–60 m thick before they can "flow." Observed speeds range from a few centimeters to as much as 40 m a day for valley glaciers such as the one shown in Fig. 6.1c. The value chosen here is considered a typical one.)

(a)

(b)

(c)

▲ **FIGURE 6.1 Three moving objects: a comparison of momenta and kinetic energies** **(a)** A .22-caliber bullet shattering a ballpoint pen; **(b)** a cruise ship; **(c)** a glacier, Glacier Bay, Alaska. See Example 6.2.

Then, converting the data to metric units and giving orders of magnitude yields the following:

Bullet: $$m_b = 30\text{ gr}\left(\frac{1\text{ lb}}{7000\text{ gr}}\right)\left(\frac{1\text{ kg}}{2.2\text{ lb}}\right) = 0.0019\text{ kg} \approx 10^{-3}\text{ kg}$$

$$v_b = 1.3 \times 10^3\text{ ft/s}\left(\frac{0.305\text{ m/s}}{\text{ft/s}}\right) = 4.0 \times 10^2\text{ m/s} \approx 10^2\text{ m/s}$$

Ship: $$m_s = 7.0 \times 10^4\text{ ton}\left(\frac{2.0 \times 10^3\text{ lb}}{\text{ton}}\right)\left(\frac{1\text{ kg}}{2.2\text{ lb}}\right) = 6.4 \times 10^7\text{ kg} \approx 10^8\text{ kg}$$

$$v_s = 20\text{ knots}\left(\frac{1.15\text{ mi/h}}{\text{knot}}\right)\left(\frac{0.447\text{ m/s}}{\text{mi/h}}\right) = 10\text{ m/s} = 10^1\text{ m/s}$$

Glacier: width $\approx 10^3$ m, length $\approx 10^4$ m, depth $\approx 10^2$ m

$$v_g = 1\text{ m/day}\left(\frac{1\text{ day}}{86\,400\text{ s}}\right) = 1.2 \times 10^{-5}\text{ m/s} \approx 10^{-5}\text{ m/s}$$

We have all the speeds and masses except for m_g, the mass of the glacier. To compute this value, we need to know the density of ice, since $m = \rho V$ (Eq. 1.1). The density of ice is less than that of water (ice floats in water), but the two are not very different, so we will use the density of water, $1.0 \times 10^3\text{ kg/m}^3$, to simplify the calculations. (The actual density of ice is $0.92 \times 10^3\text{ kg/m}^3$, but most of our other data in this Example are also approximations or estimates, so this shortcut should produce results that are good enough for our present purposes.)

Thus, the mass of the glacier is approximated as

$$m_g = \rho V = \rho(l \times w \times d)$$
$$\approx (10^3\text{ kg/m}^3)[(10^4\text{m})(10^3\text{m})(10^2\text{m})] = 10^{12}\text{ kg}$$

Then, calculating the magnitudes of the momenta of the objects, we have

Bullet: $$p_b = m_b v_b \approx (10^{-3}\text{ kg})(10^2\text{ m/s}) = 10^{-1}\text{ kg}\cdot\text{m/s}$$

Ship: $$p_s = m_s v_s \approx (10^8\text{ kg})(10^1\text{ m/s}) = 10^9\text{ kg}\cdot\text{m/s}$$

Glacier: $$p_g = m_g v_g \approx (10^{12}\text{ kg})(10^{-5}\text{ m/s}) = 10^7\text{ kg}\cdot\text{m/s}$$

So, the ship does have the largest momentum, and the bullet has the smallest.

Follow-up Exercise. Which of the objects in Example 6.2 has (1) the greatest kinetic energy and (2) the least kinetic energy? Justify your choices using order-of-magnitude calculations. (Notice here that the dependence is on the *square* of the velocity, $K = \frac{1}{2}mv^2$.)

Example 6.3 ■ Total Momentum: A Vector Sum

What is the total momentum for each of the systems of particles illustrated in ▶ Fig. 6.2?

Thinking It Through. The total momentum is the vector sum of the individual momenta (Eq. 6.2). This quantity can be computed using the components of each vector.

Solution.

Given: Magnitudes and directions of momenta from Fig. 6.2	*Find:* (a) Total momentum (**P**) for Fig. 6.2a (b)Total momentum (**P**) for Fig. 6.2b

(a) The total momentum of a system is the vector sum of the momenta of the individual particles, so

$$\mathbf{P} = \mathbf{p}_1 + \mathbf{p}_2 = (2.0\text{ kg}\cdot\text{m/s})\hat{\mathbf{x}} + (3.0\text{ kg}\cdot\text{m/s})\hat{\mathbf{x}} = (5.0\text{ kg}\cdot\text{m/s})\hat{\mathbf{x}} \quad (+x\text{-direction})$$

(b) Computing the total momenta in the x- and y-directions gives

Note: Review Example 4.4 and Fig. 4.10.

$$\mathbf{P}_x = \mathbf{p}_1 + \mathbf{p}_2 = (5.0\text{ kg}\cdot\text{m/s})\hat{\mathbf{x}} + (-8.0\text{ kg}\cdot\text{m/s})\hat{\mathbf{x}}$$
$$= -(3.0\text{ kg}\cdot\text{m/s})\hat{\mathbf{x}} \quad (-x\text{-direction})$$

$$\mathbf{P}_y = \mathbf{p}_3 = (4.0\text{ kg}\cdot\text{m/s})\hat{\mathbf{y}} \quad (+y\text{-direction})$$

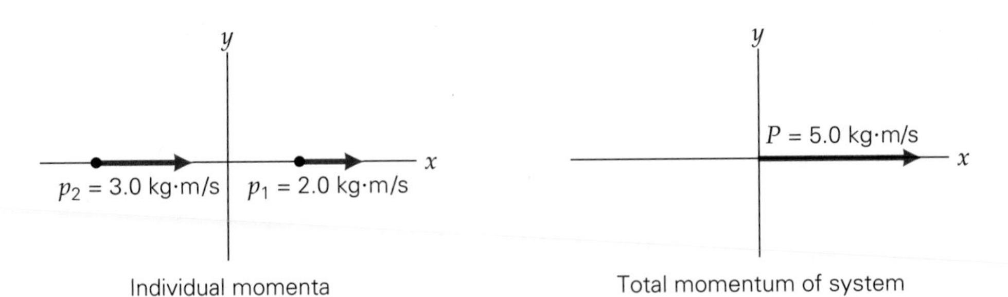

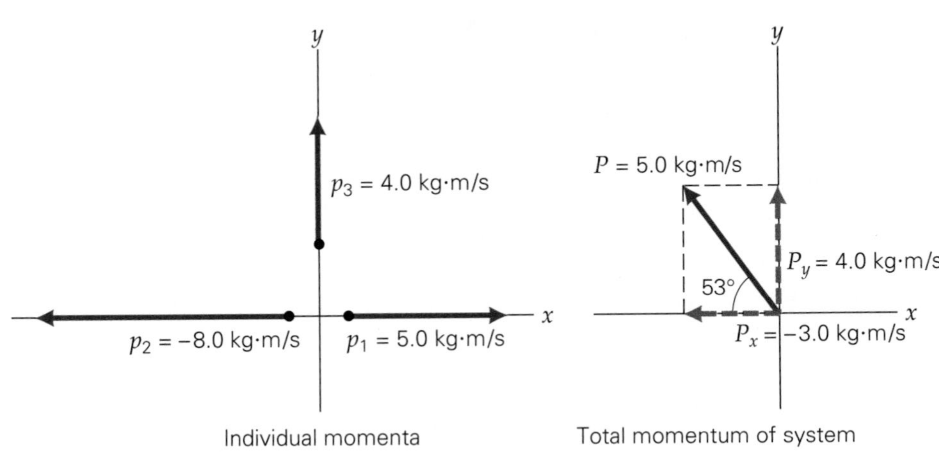

◀ **FIGURE 6.2 Total momentum** The total momentum of a system of particles is the vector sum of the particles' individual momenta. See Example 6.3.

Then

$$\mathbf{P} = \mathbf{P}_x + \mathbf{P}_y = (-3.0\ \text{kg}\cdot\text{m/s})\hat{\mathbf{x}} + (4.0\ \text{kg}\cdot\text{m/s})\hat{\mathbf{y}}$$

Follow-up Exercise. In this Example, if $\mathbf{p}_1$ and $\mathbf{p}_2$ in part (a) were added to $\mathbf{p}_2$ and $\mathbf{p}_3$ in part (b), what would be the total momentum?

In Example 6.3a, the momenta were along the coordinate axes and thus were added straightforwardly. If the motion of one (or more) of the particles is not along an axis, its momentum vector may be broken up, or resolved, into rectangular components, and individual components can then be added to find the components of the total momentum, just as you learned to do with force components in Chapter 4.

Since momentum is a vector, a change in momentum can result from a change in magnitude and/or direction. Examples of changes in the momenta of particles because of changes of direction on collision are illustrated in ▶ Fig. 6.3. In the figure, the magnitude of a particle's momentum is taken to be the same both before and after collision (as indicated by the arrows of equal length). Figure 6.3a illustrates a direct rebound—a 180° change in direction. Note that the change in momentum ($\Delta\mathbf{p}$) is the vector difference and that directional signs for the vectors are important. Figure 6.3b shows a glancing collision, for which the change in momentum is given by analyzing the x- and y-components.

Two-Dimensional Collisions

Force and Momentum

As you know from Chapter 4, if an object has a change in velocity (an acceleration), a net force must be acting on it. Similarly, since momentum is directly related to velocity (as well as mass), a change in momentum also requires a force. In fact, Newton originally expressed his second law of motion in terms of momentum rather than acceleration. The force–momentum relationship may be seen by

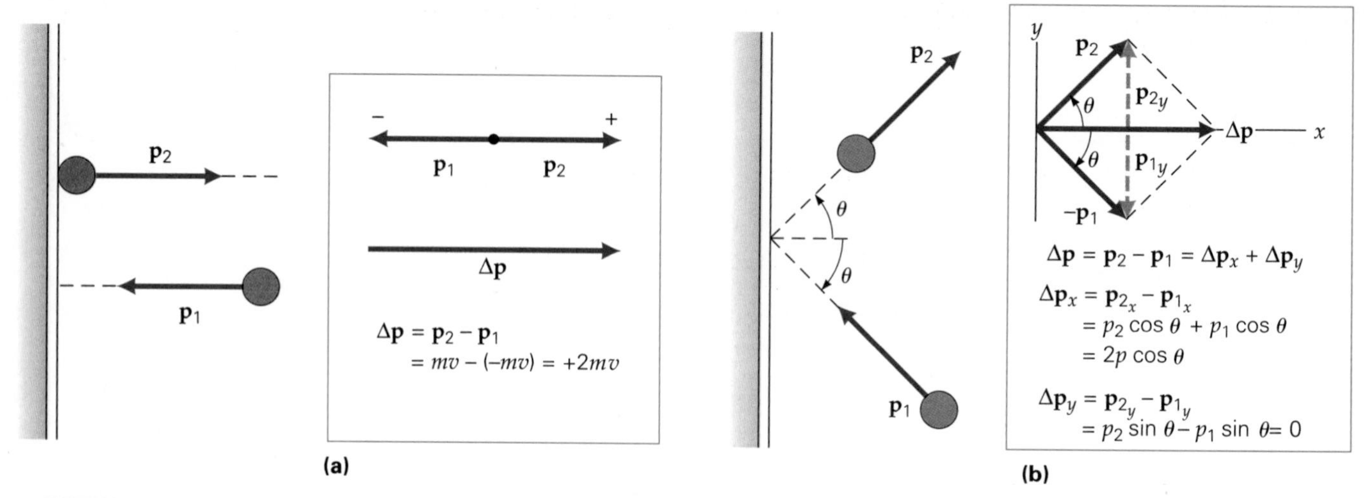

▲ **FIGURE 6.3 Change in momentum** The change in momentum is given by the *difference* in the momentum vectors. **(a)** Here, the vector sum is zero, but the vector *difference*, or change in momentum, is not. (The particles are displaced for convenience.) **(b)** The change in momentum is found by computing the change in the components.

starting with $\mathbf{F}_{\text{net}} = m\mathbf{a}$ and using $\mathbf{a} = (\mathbf{v} - \mathbf{v}_o)/\Delta t$, where the mass is assumed to be constant. Thus,

$$\mathbf{F}_{\text{net}} = m\mathbf{a} = \frac{m(\mathbf{v} - \mathbf{v}_o)}{\Delta t} = \frac{m\mathbf{v} - m\mathbf{v}_o}{\Delta t} = \frac{\mathbf{p} - \mathbf{p}_o}{\Delta t} = \frac{\Delta \mathbf{p}}{\Delta t}$$

or

Newton's second law of motion in terms of momentum

$$\mathbf{F}_{\text{net}} = \frac{\Delta \mathbf{p}}{\Delta t} \tag{6.3}$$

where $\mathbf{F}_{\text{net}}$ is the *average* net force on the object if the acceleration is not constant (or the *instantaneous* net force if Δt goes to zero).

Expressed in this form, Newton's second law states that *the net external force acting on an object is equal to the time rate of change of the object's momentum*. It is easily seen from the development of Eq. 6.3 that the equations $\mathbf{F}_{\text{net}} = m\mathbf{a}$ and $\mathbf{F}_{\text{net}} = \Delta\mathbf{p}/\Delta t$ are equivalent if the mass is constant. In some situations, however, the mass may vary. This factor will not be a consideration here in our discussion of particle collisions, but a special case will be given later in the chapter. The more general form of Newton's second law, Eq. 6.3, is true even if the mass varies.

Just as the equation $\mathbf{F}_{\text{net}} = m\mathbf{a}$ indicates that an acceleration is evidence of a net force, the equation $\mathbf{F}_{\text{net}} = \Delta\mathbf{p}/\Delta t$ indicates that *a change in momentum is evidence of a net force*. For example, as illustrated in ▾Fig. 6.4, the momentum of a projectile is tangential to the projectile's parabolic path and changes in both magnitude and direction. The change in momentum indicates that there is a net force acting on the projectile, which you know is the force of gravity. Changes in momentum were il-

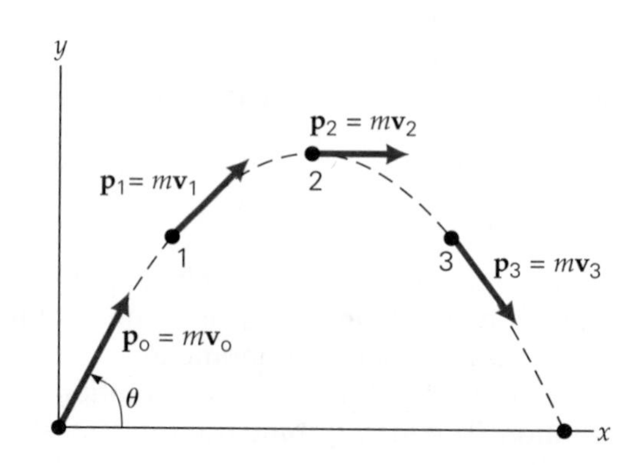

▸ **FIGURE 6.4 Change in the momentum of a projectile** The total momentum vector of a projectile is tangential to the projectile's path (as is its velocity); this vector changes in magnitude and direction, because of the action of an external force (gravity). The x-component of the momentum is constant. (Why?)

lustrated in Fig. 6.3. Can you identify the forces in these cases? Think in terms of Newton's third law.

6.2 Impulse

OBJECTIVES: **To relate (a) impulse and momentum, and (b) kinetic energy and momentum.**

When two objects—such as a hammer and a nail, a golf club and a golf ball, or even two cars—collide, they can exert large forces on one another for a short period of time (▸Fig. 6.5a). The force is not constant in this case. However, Newton's second law in momentum form is still useful for analyzing such situations by using average values. Written in this form, the law states that the net *average* force is equal to the time rate of change of momentum: $\bar{\mathbf{F}} = \Delta \mathbf{p}/\Delta t$ (Eq. 6.3). Rewriting the equation to express the change in momentum, we have (with only one force acting on the object)

$$\bar{\mathbf{F}}\Delta t = \Delta \mathbf{p} = \mathbf{p} - \mathbf{p}_o \quad (6.4)$$

The term $\bar{\mathbf{F}}\Delta t$ is known as the **impulse** of the force:

$$\text{Impulse} = \bar{\mathbf{F}}\Delta t = \Delta \mathbf{p} = m\mathbf{v} - m\mathbf{v}_o \quad (6.5)$$

SI unit of impulse and momentum: newton-second (N · s)

Thus, *the impulse exerted on a body is equal to the change in the body's momentum.* This statement is referred to as the **impulse–momentum theorem**. Impulse has units of newtons-second (N · s), which are also units of momentum by Eq. 6.4 and Eq. 6.1 ($1\ \text{kg}\cdot\text{m/s} = 1\ \text{N}\cdot\text{s}$).

In Chapter 5, you learned that by the work–energy theorem ($W_{net} = F_{net}\Delta x = \Delta K$), the area under an F_{net} versus x curve is equal to the net work, or change in kinetic energy. Similarly, the area under an F_{net} versus t curve is equal to the impulse, or the change in momentum (Fig. 6.5b). An impulse force usually varies with time and is therefore not a constant force. However, in general, it is convenient to talk about the equivalent *constant* average force $\bar{\mathbf{F}}$ acting over a time interval Δt to give the same impulse (same area under the force-versus-time curve), as shown in ▸Fig. 6.6.

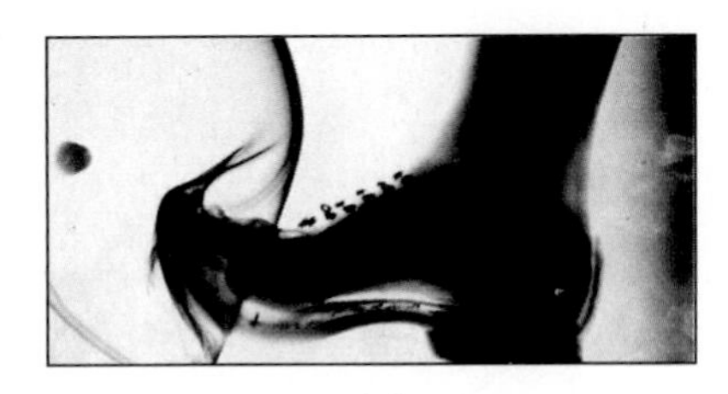

(a)

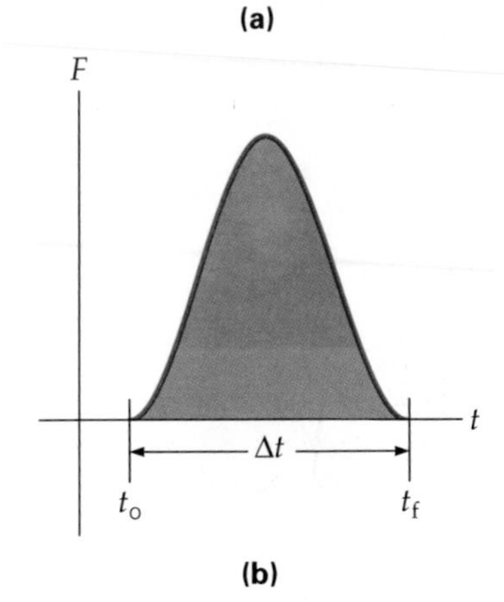

(b)

▲ **FIGURE 6.5 Collision impulse** **(a)** Collision impulse causes the football to be deformed. **(b)** The impulse is the area under the curve of an *F*-versus-*t* graph. Note that the impulse force on the ball is not constant, but rises to a maximum.

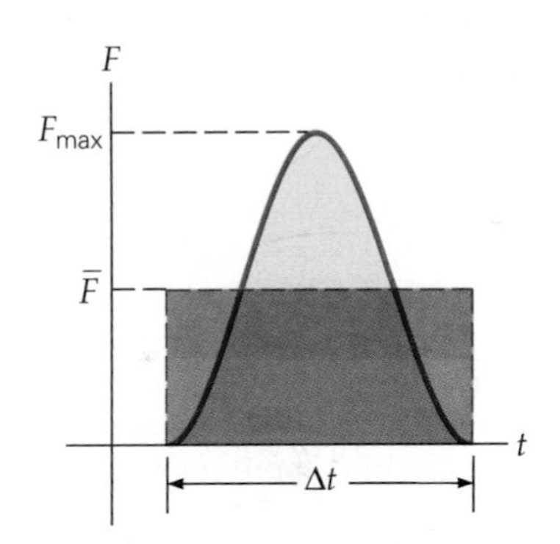

▲ **FIGURE 6.6 Average impulse force** The area under the average-force curve ($\bar{F}\Delta t$, within the dashed red lines) is the same as the area under the *F* versus *t* curve, which is usually difficult to evaluate.

Example 6.4 ■ Teeing Off: The Impulse-Momentum Theorem

A golfer drives a 0.10-kg ball from an elevated tee, giving the ball an initial horizontal speed of 40 m/s (about 90 mi/h). The club and the ball are in contact for 1.0 ms (millisecond). What is the average force exerted by the club on the ball during this time?

Thinking It Through. The average force is equal to the time rate of change of momentum (Eq. 6.5 rearranged).

Solution.

Given: $m = 0.10$ kg
$v = 40$ m/s
$v_o = 0$
$\Delta t = 1.0\ \text{ms} = 1.0 \times 10^{-3}$ s

Find: $\bar{F}$ (average force)

Notice that the mass and the initial and final velocities are given, so the change in momentum can be found. Then, the average force can be computed from the impulse–momentum theorem:

$$\bar{F}\Delta t = p - p_o = mv - mv_o$$

Thus,

$$\bar{F} = \frac{mv - mv_o}{\Delta t} = \frac{(0.10\ \text{kg})(40\ \text{m/s}) - 0}{1.0 \times 10^{-3}\ \text{s}} = 4000\ \text{N (or 900 lb)}$$

[This a very large force compared with the weight of the ball, $w = mg = (0.10\ \text{kg})(9.8\ \text{m/s}^2) = 0.98\ \text{N}$.] The force is in the direction of the acceleration and is the *average* force. The instantaneous force is even greater near the midpoint of the time interval of the collision (Δtin Fig. 6.6).

Follow-up Exercise. Suppose the golfer in this Example drives the ball with the same average force, but "follows through" on the swing so as to increase the contact time to 1.5 ms. What effect would this change have on the initial horizontal speed of the drive?

(a)

(b)

▲ **FIGURE 6.7 Adjust the impulse** **(a)** The change in momentum in catching the ball is a constant mv_o. If the ball is stopped quickly (small Δt), the impulse force is large (big $\bar{F}$) and stings the catcher's bare hands. **(b)** Increasing the contact time (large Δt) by moving the hands with the ball reduces the impulse force and makes catching more enjoyable.

Example 6.4 illustrates the large forces that colliding objects can exert on one another during short contact times. However, in some instances, the impulse may be manipulated to reduce the force. Suppose there is a fixed change in momentum in a given situation. Then, since $\Delta p = \bar{F}\Delta t$, if Δt could be made longer, the average impulse force $\bar{F}$ would be reduced.

You have probably tried to minimize the impulse force on occasion. For example, when jumping from a height onto a hard surface, you try not to land stiff legged. The abrupt stop (small Δt) would apply a large impulse force to your leg bones and joints and could cause injury. If you bend your knees as you land, the impulse is vertically upward, opposite your velocity ($\bar{F}\Delta t = \Delta p = -mv_o$, with the final velocity being zero). Thus, increasing the time interval Δt makes the impulse force smaller.

Similarly, in catching a hard, fast-moving ball, you quickly learn not to catch it with your arms rigid, but rather to move your hands with the ball. This movement increases the contact time and reduces the impulse force and the "sting" (◂Fig. 6.7).

Another example in which the contact time is increased to decrease the impulse force is given in the Insight in this chapter.

In other instances, the *applied* impulse force may be relatively constant and the contact time (Δt) deliberately increased to produce a greater impulse, and thus a greater change in momentum($\bar{F}\Delta t = \Delta p$). This is the principle of "following through" in sports, for example, when hitting a ball with a bat or racquet, or driving a golf ball. In the latter case (▸Fig. 6.8a), assuming that the golfer supplies the same average force with each swing, the longer the contact time, the greater will be the impulse or the momentum the ball receives. That is, with $\bar{F}\Delta t = mv$ (since $v_o = 0$), the greater the value ofΔt, the greater will be the final velocity of the ball. (This principle is illustrated in the Follow-up Exercise in Example 6.4.) As you learned in Section 3.4, a greater projection velocity gives a projectile a greater range. (Ideally, at what angle of projection should a golfer try to achieve when driving the ball on a level fairway? Remember from Chapter 3?)

In some instances, a long follow-through that increases the contact time may be used to improve control of the ball's direction (Fig. 6.8b).

The word *impulse* implies that the impulse force acts only briefly or quickly (like an "impulsive" person), and this is true in many instances. However, the definition of *impulse* places no limit on the time interval over which the force may act. Technically, a comet at its closest approach to the Sun is involved in a collision, because in physics, collision forces do not have to be contact forces. Basically, a **collision** is an interaction of objects in which there is an exchange of momentum and energy. As you might expect from the work–energy theorem and the impulse–momentum theorem, momentum and kinetic energy are directly related. A little algebraic manipulation of the equation for kinetic energy (Eq. 5.5) allows us to express kinetic energy in terms of the *magnitude* of momentum:

$$K = \tfrac{1}{2}mv^2 = \frac{(mv)^2}{2m} = \frac{p^2}{2m} \qquad (6.6)$$

Thus, kinetic energy and momentum are intimately related. The conservation of these quantities is important in collisions, as we shall see later in the chapter.

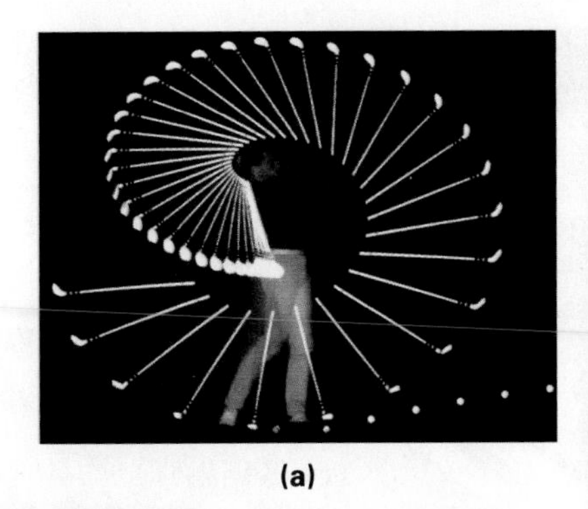

(a)

(b)

▲ **FIGURE 6.8 Increasing the contact time** **(a)** A golfer follows through on a drive swing. One reason he does so is to increase the contact time so that the ball receives greater impulse and momentum. **(b)** The follow-through on a long putt increases the contact time for greater impulse and momentum, but the main reason is for directional control. Notice that the putter is in contact with the ball for a time equivalent to about four flash intervals.

6.3 The Conservation of Linear Momentum

OBJECTIVES: To (a) explain the condition for the conservation of linear momentum and (b) apply them to physical situations.

Like total mechanical energy, the momentum of a body or system is a conserved quantity under certain conditions. This fact allows us to analyze a wide range of situations and solve many problems readily. The conservation of momentum is one of the most important principles in physics. In particular, it is used to analyze the collision of objects ranging from subatomic particles to automobiles in traffic accidents.

For the linear momentum of an object to be conserved (i.e., to remain constant with time), one condition must hold that is apparent from the momentum form of Newton's second law (Eq. 6.3). If the net force acting on a particle is zero, that is,

$$\mathbf{F}_{\text{net}} = \frac{\Delta \mathbf{p}}{\Delta t} = 0$$

then

$$\Delta \mathbf{p} = 0 = \mathbf{p} - \mathbf{p}_{\text{o}}$$

where $\mathbf{p}_{\text{o}}$ is the initial momentum and $\mathbf{p}$ is the momentum at some later time. Since these two values are equal, the momentum is conserved:

$$\mathbf{p} = \mathbf{p}_{\text{o}} \tag{6.7}$$

or

$$m\mathbf{v} = m\mathbf{v}_{\text{o}}$$

Note that this conservation is consistent with Newton's first law: An object remains at rest ($\mathbf{p} = 0$), or in motion with a *uniform* velocity (constant $\mathbf{p}$), unless acted on by a net external force.

The conservation of momentum can be extended to a system of particles if we write Newton's second law in terms of the net force acting on the system and of the momenta of the particles: $\mathbf{F}_{\text{net}} = \Sigma \mathbf{F}_i$ and $\mathbf{P} = \Sigma \mathbf{p}_i = \Sigma m\, \mathbf{v}_i$.

Note: A lowercase "**p**" means individual momentum. A capital "**P**" means total system momentum. Both are vectors.

Since $\mathbf{F}_{\text{net}} = \Delta \mathbf{P}/\Delta t$, and if there is no net external force acting *on the system*, then $\mathbf{F}_{\text{net}} = 0$, and $\Delta \mathbf{P} = 0$; so $\mathbf{P} = \mathbf{P}_{\text{o}}$, and the total momentum is conserved. This generalized condition is referred to as the law of **conservation of linear momentum**:

Conservation of momentum—no net external force

$$\mathbf{P} = \mathbf{P}_{\text{o}}$$

INSIGHT

The Automobile Air Bag

A dark, rainy night—a car goes out of control and hits a big tree head on! But the driver walks away with only minor injuries, because he had his seatbelt buckled and was in a car equipped with air bags. Air bags, along with seatbelts, are safety devices designed to prevent (or lessen) injuries to passengers in the front seat in automobile collisions.

When a car collides with something basically immovable, such as a tree or a bridge abutment, or has a head-on collision with another vehicle, it stops almost instantaneously. If the front-seat passengers have not buckled up (and there are no air bags), they keep moving until acted on by an external force (Newton's first law). For the driver, this force is supplied by the steering wheel and column, and for the passenger by the dashboard and/or windshield.

Even when everyone has buckled up, there can be injuries. Seatbelts absorb energy by stretching, and they spread the force over a wider area. However, if a car is going fast enough and hits something truly immovable, there may be too much energy for the belts to absorb. This is where the air bag comes in. The bag inflates automatically on hard impact (Fig. 1), cushioning the driver (and front-seat passenger if both sides are equipped with air bags). In terms of impulse, the air bag increases the stopping contact time—the fraction of a second it takes your head to sink into the inflated bag is many times longer than the instant in which your head would be stopped by the dashboard. A longer contact time means a reduced average impact force and thus much less likelihood of an injury. (Because the bag is large, the total impact force is also spread over a greater area of the body, so the force on any one part of the body is also less.)

An interesting point is the inflating mechanism of an air bag. Think of how little time elapses between the front-end impact and the driver hitting the steering column in the collision of a fast-moving automobile. We say such a collision takes place instantaneously, yet during this time the air bag must be inflated! How is this done?

FIGURE 1 Impulse and safety An automobile air bag increases the contact time over what a person in a crash would experience with the dashboard or windshield, thereby decreasing the impulse force that could cause injury.

First, the air bag is equipped with sensors that detect the sharp deceleration associated with a head-on collision the instant it begins. If the deceleration exceeds the sensors' threshold settings, an electric current in an igniter in the air bag sets off a chemical explosion that generates gas to inflate the bag. The complete process from sensing to full inflation takes only on the order of 25 *thousandths* of a second (0.025 s).

The sensors' signals go first to a control unit, which determines whether a frontal collision rather than a system malfunction is occurring. (Accidental deployment could be dangerous as well as costly.) Typically, the control unit com-

Thus, the total linear momentum of a system, $\mathbf{P} = \Sigma \mathbf{p}_i$, is conserved if the net external force acting on the system is zero.

There are other ways to express this condition. For example, recall from Chapter 5 that a *closed*, or *isolated*, system is one on which no net external force acts, so the total linear momentum of an isolated system is conserved.

Note: Third-law force pairs were discussed in Section 4.4.

Within a system, internal forces are acting, for example, when particles collide. These are force pairs of Newton's third law, and there is a good reason that such forces are not explicitly referred to in the condition for the conservation of momentum: By Newton's third law, these internal forces are equal and opposite and vectorially cancel each other. Thus, the net internal force of a closed system is always zero.

An important point to understand, however, is that the momenta of *individual* particles or objects within a system may change. But in the absence of a net external force, the *vector sum* of all the momenta (the total system momentum $\mathbf{P}$) remains the same. If the objects are initially at rest (i.e., the total momentum is zero) and then are set in motion as the result of internal forces, the total momentum must still add to zero. This principle is illustrated in ▶Fig. 6.9 and analyzed in Example 6.5. Objects in an isolated system may transfer momentum among them-

INSIGHT

pares signals from two different sensors for collision verification. The unit is equipped with its own power source, since the car's battery and alternator are usually destroyed in a hard front-end collision. Sensing a collision, the control unit completes the circuit to the air-bag igniter. It initiates a chemical reaction in a sodium-azide (NaN_3) propellant. Gas (mostly nitrogen) is generated at an explosive rate, which inflates the air bag. The bag itself is made of thin nylon that is covered with cornstarch. The cornstarch acts as a lubricant to help the bag unfold smoothly on inflation.

Not only is sodium azide explosive, but it is also poisonous. Thus, you should not open a collapsed air bag, and if a car is junked, undeployed air bags must be disposed of properly. Other, nonpoisonous compounds are being developed for use as air-bag inflators.

In general, air bags offer protection only if the occupants are thrown forward, because the bags are designed to deploy only in front-end collisions. They are of little use in side-impact crashes. Side air bags, however, are now available in many new automobile models.

Recent Concerns

In some cases, however, the deployment of air bags has been shown to cause injuries and deaths. An air bag is not a soft, fluffy pillow. When activated, it is ejected out of its compartment at speeds up to 320 km/h(200 mi/h) and could hit a person close by with enough force to cause severe injury and even death. Adults are advised to sit at least 13 cm (10 in.) from the air-bag compartment to allow a margin of safety from the 5–8 cm (2–3-in.) injury "risk zone." Seats should be adjusted to allow the proper safety distance.*

*Guidelines from the National Highway Traffic Safety Administration (www.nhtsa.dot.gov).

FIGURE 2 The wrong way

The most serious concern involves children. Children may get too close to the dashboard if they are not buckled in or not buckled in securely with an adjustable shoulder harness. Using a rear-facing child seat in the front passenger seat is also dangerous if the air bag inflates (Fig. 2). According to government recommendations, (1) *children 12 years old and younger should ride buckled up in the back seat*, and (2) *a rear-facing child seat should never be put in front of an air bag*. The next generation of "smart" air bags will be designed to sense the severity of an accident and inflate accordingly, and to base inflation on the weight of the occupant. For example, if sensors detect the weight of a child, or a child in a safety seat, in the passenger seat, the air bag won't deploy.

There may be specific problems in some instances, but air bags do save many lives. All new passenger cars are now required to have dual air bags. But even if your car is equipped with air bags, *always* remember to buckle up. (Maybe we should make that Newton's fourth law of motion!)

Related Exercise: 41

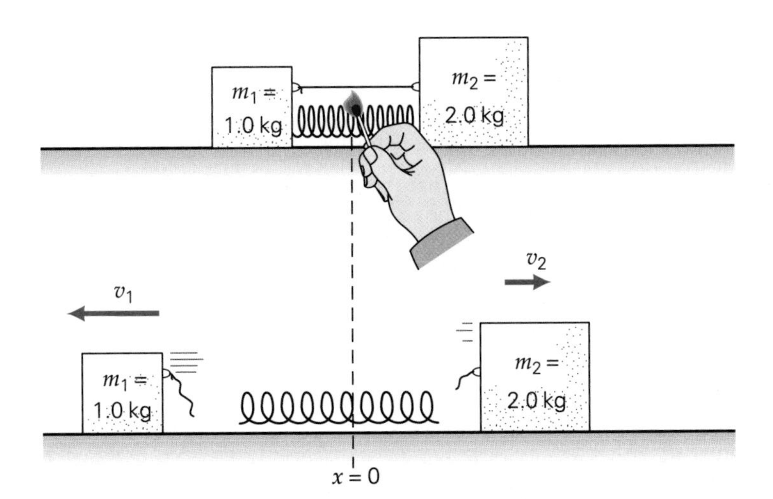

◀ **FIGURE 6.9 An internal force and the conservation of momentum** The spring force is an internal force, so the momentum of the system is conserved. See Example 6.5.

selves, but the total momentum after the changes must add up to the initial value, assuming that friction is zero.

The conservation of momentum is often a powerful and convenient tool for analyzing situations involving motion. Its application is illustrated in the following

Examples. (Notice that conservation of momentum, in many cases, bypasses the need to know the forces involved.)

Example 6.5 ■ Before and After: Conservation of Momentum

Two masses, $m_1 = 1.0$ kg and $m_2 = 2.0$ kg, are held on either side of a light compressed spring by a light string joining them, as shown in Fig. 6.9. The string is burned (negligible external force), and the masses move apart on the frictionless surface, with m_1 having a velocity of 1.8 m/s to the left. What is the velocity of m_2?

Thinking It Through. With no net external force (the weights are canceled by normal forces), the total momentum of the system is conserved. It is initially zero, so after the string is burned, the momentum of m_2 must be *equal to* and opposite that of m_1. (Vector addition gives zero total momentum. Also, note that the term *light* indicates that the masses of the spring and string can be ignored.)

Solution. Listing the masses and speed given, we have

Given: $m_1 = 1.0$ kg *Find:* v_2 (velocity—speed and direction)
$m_2 = 2.0$ kg
$v_1 = 1.8$ m/s (left)

Here, the system consists of the two masses and the spring. Since the spring force is internal to the system, the momentum of the system is conserved. It should be apparent that the initial total momentum of the system ($\mathbf{P}_o$) is zero, and therefore the final momentum must also be zero. Thus, we may write

$$\mathbf{P}_o = \mathbf{P} = 0 \quad \text{and} \quad \mathbf{P} = \mathbf{p}_1 + \mathbf{p}_2 = 0$$

(The momentum of the spring does not come into the equations, because its velocity is zero.) Thus,

$$\mathbf{p}_2 = -\mathbf{p}_1$$

which means that the momenta of m_1 and m_2 are equal and opposite. Using directional signs (with $+x$ indicating the direction to the right in the figure), we get

$$p_2 - p_1 = m_2 v_2 - m_1 v_1 = 0$$

or, in terms of magnitudes,

$$m_2 v_2 = m_1 v_1$$

and

$$v_2 = \left(\frac{m_1}{m_2}\right) v_1 = \left(\frac{1.0 \text{ kg}}{2.0 \text{ kg}}\right)(1.8 \text{ m/s}) = 0.90 \text{ m/s}$$

Thus, the velocity of m_2 is 0.90 m/s in the positive x-direction, or to the right in the figure. This value is half of v_1, as you might have expected, since m_2 has twice the mass of m_1.

Follow-up Exercise. (a) Suppose that the large block in Fig. 6.9 were attached to the Earth's surface so that the block could not move when the string was burned. Would momentum be conserved in this case? Explain. (b) Two girls, each having a mass of 50 kg, stand at rest on skateboards with negligible friction. The first girl tosses a 2.5-kg ball to the second. If the speed of the ball is 10 m/s, what is the speed of each girl after the ball is caught, and what is the momentum of the ball before it is tossed, while it is in the air, and after it is caught?

Integrated Example 6.6 ■ Conservation of Linear Momentum: Fragments and Components

A 30-g bullet with a speed of 400 m/s strikes a glancing blow to a target brick of mass 1.0 kg. The brick breaks into two fragments. The bullet deflects at an angle of 30° and has a reduced speed of 100 m/s. One piece of the brick (with mass 0.75 kg) goes off to the right, or in the initial direction of the bullet, with a speed of 5.0 m/s. (a) Make "before" and "after" sketches of the situation, along with a momentum vector diagram for the after-collision condition. (b) Determine the speed and direction of the other piece of the brick immediately after collision (where gravity can be neglected).

(a) Conceptual Reasoning. The idea here is to apply the conservation of linear momentum because there is no net external force (gravity neglected) on the system, bullet + brick. Adding the linear momentum vectors should be facilitated by a sketch. Could you have come up with something like ▼Fig. 6.10?

(b) Thinking It Through. There is one momentum before collision (that of the bullet), and three momenta afterwards (for the bullet and two fragments). By the conservation of linear momentum, the total (vector) momentum after collision equals that before collision. This quantity may be expressed in component form (Fig. 6.10), which should allow the velocity (speed and direction) of the fragment to be determined.

Given: $m_b = 30\text{ g} = 0.030\text{ kg}$
$v_{b_o} = 400\text{ m/s}$ (initial bullet speed)
$v_b = 100\text{ m/s}$ (final bullet speed)
$\theta_b = 30°$ (final bullet angle)
$M = 1.0\text{ kg}$ (brick mass)
$m_1 = 0.75\text{ kg}$ and $\theta_1 = 0°$ (mass and angle of the large fragment)
$v_1 = 5.0\text{ m/s}$
$m_2 = 0.25\text{ kg}$ (mass of small fragment)

Find: v_2 (speed of the smaller brick fragment) and θ_2 (direction of the fragment relative to the original direction of the bullet)

With no external forces (gravity neglected), the linear total momentum is conserved. Therefore, we can write both the x- and y-components of the total momentum, before and after, as follows (see Fig. 6.10):

$$\begin{aligned} & \quad\text{before} \qquad\qquad\qquad \text{after} \\ x:&\quad m_b v_{b_o} = m_b v_b \cos\theta_b + m_1 v_1 + m_2 v_2 \cos\theta_2 \\ y:&\quad 0 = m_b v_b \sin\theta_b - m_2 v_2 \sin\theta_2 \end{aligned}$$

The x equation can be rearranged to solve for the magnitude of the x velocity of the smaller fragment:

$$x:\quad v_2\cos\theta_2 = \frac{m_b v_{b_o} - m_b v_b \cos\theta_b - m_1 v_1}{m_2}$$

$$= \frac{(3.0\times10^{-2}\text{ kg})(4.0\times10^{2}\text{ m/s}) - (3.0\times10^{-2}\text{ kg})(10^{2}\text{ m/s})(0.866) - (0.75\text{ kg})(5.0\text{ m/s})}{0.25\text{ kg}} = 23\text{ m/s}$$

Similarly, the y equation can be solved for the magnitude of the y velocity component of the smaller fragment:

$$y:\quad v_2\sin\theta_2 = \frac{m_b v_b \sin\theta_b}{m_2} = \frac{(3.0\times10^{-2}\text{ kg})(10^{2}\text{ m/s})(0.50)}{0.25\text{ kg}} = 6.0\text{ m/s}$$

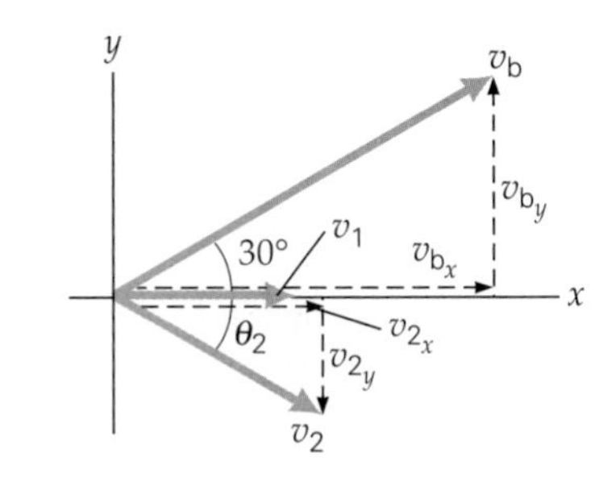

Before

After

v_{b_o} v_b 30° θ_2 v_1 v_2

◀ **FIGURE 6.10 A glancing collision** Momentum is conserved in an isolated system. The motion in two dimensions may be analyzed in terms of the components of momentum, which are also conserved. See Integrated Example 6.6.

Forming a ratio of the equations (y:/x:),

$$\frac{v_2 \sin\theta_2}{v_2 \cos\theta_2} = \frac{6.0 \text{ m/s}}{23 \text{ m/s}} = 0.26 = \tan\theta_2 \quad \left(\text{where the } v_2 \text{ terms cancel, and } \frac{\sin\theta_2}{\cos\theta_2} = \tan\theta_2\right)$$

and

$$\theta_2 = \tan^{-1}(0.26) = 15°$$

Then from the x equation,

$$v_2 = \frac{23 \text{ m/s}}{\cos 15°} = \frac{23 \text{ m/s}}{0.97} = 24 \text{ m/s}$$

Follow-up Exercise. Is the kinetic energy conserved for the collision in Exercise 6.6? If not, where did the energy go?

Example 6.7 ■ Physics on Ice

A physicist is lowered from a helicopter to the middle of a smooth, level, frozen lake, the surface of which has negligible friction, and challenged to make her way off the ice. Walking is out of the question. (Why?) As she stands there pondering her predicament, she decides to use the conservation of momentum by throwing her heavy, identical mittens, which will provide her with the momentum to get herself to shore. To get to the shore more quickly, which should this sly physicist do, throw both mittens at once or throw them separately, one after the other?

Thinking It Through. The initial momentum of the system (physicist and mittens) is zero. With no net external force, by the conservation of momentum, this remains zero, so if the mittens are thrown in one direction, she will go in the opposite direction (because momenta vectors in opposite directions can add to zero). So, which way of throwing gives greater speed? If both the mittens were thrown together, the magnitude of their momentum would be $2mv$, where v is relative to the ice and m is the mass of one mitten.

When thrown separately, the first mitten would have a momentum of mv. The physicist and the second mitten would then be in motion, and throwing the second mitten would add some more momentum to the physicist and increase her speed, but would the speed now be greater than that if both mittens were thrown simultaneously? Let's analyze the conditions of the second throw. After throwing the first mitten, the physicist "system" would have less mass. With less mass, the second throw would produce a greater acceleration and speed things up. But, on the other hand, after the first throw, the second mitten is moving with the person, and when thrown in the opposite direction, the mitten would have a velocity less than v relative to the ice (or to a stationary observer).

So, which effect would be greater? What do you think? Sometimes situations are difficult to analyze intuitively, and you must apply scientific principles to figure them out.

Solution.

Given: m = mass of single mitten
M = mass of physicist
v = velocity of thrown mitten(s)
V_p = velocity of physicist

Find: Which method of mitten throwing gives the physicist the greater speed

When the mittens are thrown together, by the conservation of momentum (V_p positive and v negative),

$$0 = 2m(-v) + MV_p \quad \text{and} \quad V_p = \frac{2mv}{M} \qquad \text{(Thrown together) (1)}$$

When they are thrown separately,

$$\text{First throw: } 0 = m(-v) + (M + m)V_{p_1} \text{ and } V_{p_1} = \frac{mv}{M + m} \qquad \text{(Thrown separately) (2)}$$

$$\text{Second throw: } (M + m)V_{p_1} = m(V_{p_1} - v) + MV_{p_2}$$

Note that in the m term, the velocity of the mitten is that relative to the ice. With an initial velocity of $+V_{P_1}$ when the first mitten is thrown in the negative direction, we have $V_{P_1} - v$. (Recall relative velocities from Chapter 3.)

Solving for V_{P_2}

$$V_{P_2} = V_{P_1} + \left(\frac{m}{M}\right)v = \frac{mv}{M + m} + \left(\frac{m}{M}\right)v = \left(\frac{m}{M + m} + \frac{m}{M}\right)v \quad (3)$$

where Eq. 2 was substituted for V_{P_1} of the first throw.

Now, when the mittens are thrown together,

$$V_P = \left(\frac{2m}{M}\right)v$$

(Eq. 1), so the question is whether the result of Eq. 3 is greater or less than that of Eq. 1. Notice that with a greater denominator for the $m/(M + m)$ term in Eq. 3, is less than the m/M term. So,

$$\left(\frac{m}{M + m} + \frac{m}{M}\right) < \frac{2m}{M}$$

and $V_P > V_{P_2}$, or (thrown together) > (thrown separately).

Follow-up Exercise. Suppose the second throw were in the direction of the physicist's velocity from the first throw. Would this throw bring her to a stop?

The conservation of momentum is one of the most important principles in physics. As mentioned previously, it is used to analyze the collisions of objects ranging from subatomic particles to automobiles in traffic accidents. In many instances, however, external forces may be acting on the objects, which means that the momentum is not conserved.

But, as you will learn in the next section, the conservation of momentum often allows a good approximation *over the short time of a collision*, because the internal forces, for which momentum is conserved, are much greater than the external forces. For example, external forces such as gravity and friction also act on colliding objects, but are often relatively small compared with the internal forces. (This concept was implied in Example 6.6.) Therefore, if the objects interact for only a brief time, the effects of the external forces may be negligible compared with those of the large internal forces during that time.

6.4 Elastic and Inelastic Collisions

OBJECTIVE: **To describe the conditions on kinetic energy and momentum in elastic and inelastic collisions.**

Taking a closer look at collisions in terms of the conservation of momentum is simpler if we consider an isolated system, such as a system of particles (or balls) involved in head-on collisions. For simplicity, we will consider only collisions in one dimension. Such collisions can also be analyzed in terms of the conservation of energy. On the basis of what happens to the total kinetic energy, we can define two types of collisions: *elastic* and *inelastic*.

In an **elastic collision**, the total kinetic energy is conserved. That is, the *total* kinetic energy of all the objects of the system after the collision is the same as their *total* kinetic energy before the collision (▸ Fig. 6.11a). Kinetic energy may be traded between objects of a system, but the total kinetic energy in the system remains constant. Therefore,

Elastic collision—total kinetic energy conserved, as is momentum

total K after = total K before

$$K_f = K_i \quad \textit{(elastic collision)} \quad (6.8)$$

During such a collision, some or all of the initial kinetic energy is temporarily converted to potential energy as the objects are deformed. But, after the maximum

(a)

(b)

▶ **FIGURE 6.11 Collisions**
(a) Approximate elastic collisions.
(b) An inelastic collision.

deformations occur, the objects *elastically* spring back to their original shapes, and the system regains all of its original kinetic energy. For example, two steel balls or two billiard balls may have a nearly elastic collision, with each ball having the same shape afterward as before; that is, there is no permanent deformation.

Inelastic collision—total kinetic energy not conserved, but momentum is

In an **inelastic collision** (Fig. 6.11b), total kinetic energy is *not* conserved. For example, one or more of the colliding objects may not spring back to its original shape, or heat or sound may be generated. In such interactions, work is done by nonconservative forces (Section 5.5), such as friction, and some kinetic energy is lost:

$$\begin{gathered}\text{total } K \text{ after} = \text{total } K \text{ before} \\ K_{\mathrm{f}} < K_{\mathrm{i}}\end{gathered} \qquad \textit{(condition for an inelastic collision)} \qquad (6.9)$$

Note: In reality, only atoms and subatomic particles have truly elastic collisions, but some larger hard objects have nearly elastic collisions in which the kinetic energy is approximately conserved.

For example, a hollow aluminum ball that collides with a solid steel ball may be dented. Permanently deformation of the ball takes work, and that work is done at the expense of the original kinetic energy of the system. Everyday collisions are inelastic.

For isolated systems, momentum is conserved in both elastic and inelastic collisions. *For an inelastic collision, only an amount of kinetic energy consistent with the conservation of momentum may be lost.* It may seem strange that kinetic energy can be lost and momentum still be conserved, but this fact provides insight into the difference between scalar and vector quantities.

Energy and Momentum in Inelastic Collisions

To see how momentum can remain constant while the kinetic energy changes (decreases) in inelastic collisions, consider the examples illustrated in ▶Fig. 6.12. In Fig. 6.12a, two balls of equal mass ($m_1 = m_2$) approach each other with equal and opposite velocities ($v_{1_o} = -v_{2_o}$). Hence, the total momentum before the collision is (vectorially) zero, but the (scalar) total kinetic energy is *not* zero. After the collision, the balls are stuck together and stationary, so the total momentum is unchanged—still zero. Momentum is conserved because the forces of collision are internal to the system of the two balls; thus, there is no net external force on the system. The total kinetic energy, however, has decreased to zero. In this case, some of the kinetic energy went into the work done in permanently deforming the balls. Some energy may also have gone into doing work against friction (producing heat) or may have been lost in some other way (for example, in producing sound).

It should be noted that the balls need not come to rest after collision. In a less inelastic collision, the balls may recoil in opposite directions at reduced, but equal, speeds. The momentum would be conserved (still equal to zero—why?), but the kinetic energy would again not be conserved. Under all conditions, the amount of kinetic energy lost must be consistent with the conservation of momentum.

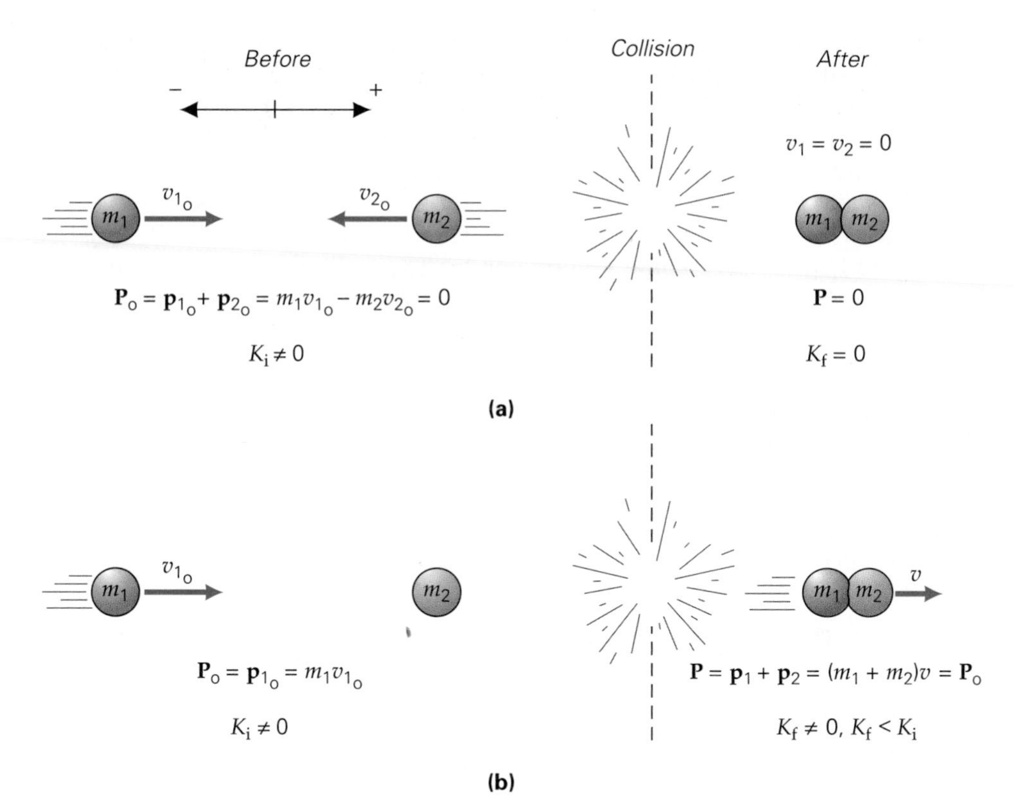

FIGURE 6.12 Inelastic collisions In inelastic collisions, momentum is conserved, but kinetic energy is not. Collisions like the ones shown here, in which the objects stick together, are called *completely* or *totally inelastic collisions*. The maximum amount of kinetic energy lost is consistent with the law of conservation of momentum. (The equations are first provided in boldface (vector) notation and then in sign-magnitude notation.)

In Fig. 6.12b, one ball is initially at rest as the other approaches. The balls stick together after collision, but are still in motion. Both of these cases are examples of a **completely inelastic collision**, in which the objects stick together, and hence both objects have the same velocity after colliding. The coupling of colliding railroad cars is a practical example of a completely inelastic collision.

Assume that the balls in Fig. 6.12b have different masses. Since the momentum is conserved even in inelastic collisions,

$$\overset{\textit{before}}{m_1 v_{1_o}} = \overset{\textit{after}}{(m_1 + m_2)v}$$

and

$$v = \left(\frac{m_1}{m_1 + m_2}\right) v_{1_o} \quad \begin{array}{l}(m_2 \textit{ initially at rest,} \\ \textit{completely inelastic} \\ \textit{collision only})\end{array} \qquad (6.10)$$

Thus, v is less than v_{1_o}, since $m_1/(m_1 + m_2)$ must be less than one. Now let us consider how much kinetic energy has been lost. Initially, $K_i = \frac{1}{2} m_1 v_o^2$; finally, after the collision,

$$K_f = \tfrac{1}{2}(m_1 + m_2)v^2$$

Substituting for v from Eq. 6.10 and simplifying the result, we have

$$K_f = \tfrac{1}{2}(m_1 + m_2)\left(\frac{m_1 v_{1_o}}{m_1 + m_2}\right)^2 = \frac{\frac{1}{2} m_1^2 v_{1_o}^2}{m_1 + m_2} = \left(\frac{m_1}{m_1 + m_2}\right)\tfrac{1}{2} m_1 v_{1_o}^2 = \left(\frac{m_1}{m_1 + m_2}\right) K_i$$

and

$$\frac{K_f}{K_i} = \frac{m_1}{m_1 + m_2} \quad \begin{array}{l}(m_2 \textit{ initially at rest,} \\ \textit{completely inelastic} \\ \textit{collision only})\end{array} \qquad (6.11)$$

Equation 6.11 gives the fractional amount of the initial kinetic energy that the system has after a completely inelastic collision. For example, if the masses of the balls are equal ($m_1 = m_2$), then $m_1/(m_1 + m_2) = \frac{1}{2}$ and $K_f/K_i = \frac{1}{2}$, or $K_f = K_i/2$. That is, only half of the initial kinetic energy is lost.

Note that not all of the kinetic energy can be lost in this case, no matter what the masses of the balls are. The total momentum after collision cannot be zero, since it was not zero initially. Thus, after the collision, the balls must be moving and must have some kinetic energy ($K_f \neq 0$). *In a completely inelastic collision, the maximum amount of kinetic energy is lost, consistent with the conservation of momentum.*

Example 6.8 ■ Stuck Together: Completely Inelastic Collision

A 1.0-kg ball with a speed of 4.5 m/s strikes a 2.0-kg stationary ball. If the collision is completely inelastic, (a) what are the speeds of the balls after the collision? (b) What percentage of the initial kinetic energy do the balls have after the collision? (c) What is the total momentum after the collision?

Thinking It Through. Recall the definition of a *completely inelastic collision*. The balls stick together after collision; kinetic energy is *not* conserved, but total momentum is.

Solution. Using the labeling as in the preceding discussion, we have

Given: $m_1 = 1.0\ \text{kg}$, $m_2 = 2.0\ \text{kg}$, $v_o = 4.5\ \text{m/s}$

Find: (a) v (speed after collision)
(b) $\dfrac{K_f}{K_i}$ ($\times$ 100%)
(c) $\mathbf{P}_f$ (total momentum after collision)

(a) The momentum is conserved and

$$\mathbf{P}_f = \mathbf{P}_o$$

or

$$(m_1 + m_2)v = m_1 v_o$$

The balls stick together and have the same speed after collision. This speed is then

$$v = \left(\frac{m_1}{m_1 + m_2}\right)v_o = \left(\frac{1.0\ \text{kg}}{1.0\ \text{kg} + 2.0\ \text{kg}}\right)(4.5\ \text{m/s}) = 1.5\ \text{m/s}$$

(b) The fractional part of the initial kinetic energy that the balls have after the completely inelastic collision is given by Eq. 6.11. Notice that this fraction, as given by the masses, is the same as that for the speeds (Eq. 6.10) in this special case. By inspection, we can write

$$\frac{K_f}{K_i} = \frac{m_1}{m_1 + m_2} = \frac{1.0\ \text{kg}}{1.0\ \text{kg} + 2.0\ \text{kg}} = \frac{1}{3} = 0.33\ (\times\ 100\%) = 33\%$$

Let's show this relationship explicitly:

$$\frac{K_f}{K_i} = \frac{\frac{1}{2}(m_1 + m_2)v^2}{\frac{1}{2}m_1 v_o^2} = \frac{\frac{1}{2}(1.0\ \text{kg} + 2.0\ \text{kg})(1.5\ \text{m/s})^2}{\frac{1}{2}(1.0\ \text{kg})(4.5\ \text{m/s})^2} = 0.33\ (=33\%)$$

Keep in mind that Eq. 6.11 applies *only* to *completely* inelastic collisions. For other types of collisions, the initial and final values of the kinetic energy must be computed explicitly.

(c) The total momentum is conserved in all collisions (in the absence of external forces), so the total momentum after collision is the same as before collision. That value is the momentum of the incident ball, with a magnitude of

$$P_f = p_{1_o} = m_1 v_o = (1.0\ \text{kg})(4.5\ \text{m/s}) = 4.5\ \text{kg}\cdot\text{m/s}$$

and the same direction as that of the incoming ball. Also, $P_f = (m_1 + m_2)v = 4.5\ \text{kg}\cdot\text{m/s}$.

Follow-up Exercise. A small hard-metal ball of mass m collides with a larger, stationary, soft-metal ball of mass M. A *minimum* amount of work W is required to make a dent in the larger ball. If the smaller ball initially has kinetic energy $K = W$, will the larger ball be dented in a completely inelastic collision between the two balls?

Energy and Momentum in Elastic Collisions

For a general *elastic* collision of two objects,

$$\text{Conservation of } K\text{:}\quad \overbrace{\tfrac{1}{2}m_1v_{1_o}^2 + \tfrac{1}{2}m_2v_{2_o}^2}^{\textit{before}} = \overbrace{\tfrac{1}{2}m_1v_1^2 + \tfrac{1}{2}m_2v_2^2}^{\textit{after}} \tag{6.12a}$$

Linear momentum is conserved even if the collision is inelastic, so we can write

$$\text{Conservation of } \mathbf{P}\text{:}\quad m_1\mathbf{v}_{1_o} + m_2\mathbf{v}_{2_o} = m_1\mathbf{v}_1 + m_2\mathbf{v}_2 \tag{6.12b}$$

Thus, for head-on elastic collisions, knowing the masses of the objects and the initial velocities allows you to find the final velocities.

A common collision situation is that in which one of the objects is initially stationary and then is hit head on by the other (▾ Fig. 6.13). Assume that the motion of both of the balls after the collision is to the right, or in the positive direction, as shown in the figure. If this is not the case, the math will tell you. (How?)

This situation is one dimensional. The condition for an elastic, head-on collision in this situation is

$$\tfrac{1}{2}m_1v_{1_o}^2 = \tfrac{1}{2}m_1v_1^2 + \tfrac{1}{2}m_2v_2^2 \tag{6.13a}$$

and conservation of linear momentum gives

$$m_1v_{1_o} = m_1v_1 + m_2v_2 \tag{6.13b}$$

Rearranging these equations gives

$$m_1(v_{1_o}^2 - v_1^2) = m_2v_2^2 \tag{6.13a$'$}$$

and

$$m_1(v_{1_o} - v_1) = m_2v_2 \tag{6.13b$'$}$$

Then, using the algebraic relationship $x^2 - y^2 = (x + y)(x - y)$ and dividing Eq. 6.13a′ by Eq. 6.13b′, we get

$$\frac{m_1(v_{1_o} + v_1)(v_{1_o} - v_1)}{m_1(v_{1_o} - v_1)} = \frac{m_2v_2^2}{m_2v_2} \quad \frac{\text{(Eq. 6.13a}')}{\text{(Eq. 6.13b}')} \quad (\textit{divide})$$

or

$$v_{1_o} + v_1 = v_2 \tag{6.14}$$

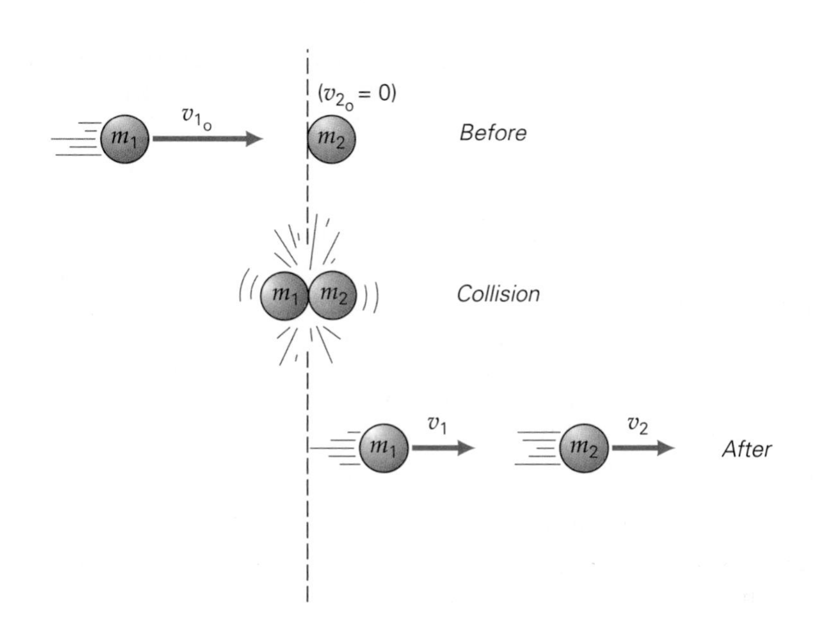

◀ **FIGURE 6.13 Elastic collision** For an elastic collision between two bodies, one of which is initially at rest, the velocities after the collision depend on the relative masses of the bodies.

Equation 6.14 can now be used to eliminate v_1 or v_2 from Eq. 6.13b. Thus, each of these final velocities can be expressed in terms of the initial velocity (v_{1_o}):

$$v_1 = \left(\frac{m_1 - m_2}{m_1 + m_2}\right)v_{1_o} \quad (6.15)$$

$$v_2 = \left(\frac{2m_1}{m_1 + m_2}\right)v_{1_o} \quad (6.16)$$

(final velocities for elastic, head-on collision with m_2 initially stationary)

Note that the final velocities depend on mass *ratios* of the objects. Looking at Eq. 6.15, you can see that if m_1 is greater than m_2, then v_1 is positive, or in the same direction as the initial velocity of the incoming ball, as was assumed in Fig. 6.13. However, if m_2 is greater than m_1, then v_1 is negative, and the incoming ball recoils in the opposite direction after collision. Equation 6.16 shows that v_2 is always in the same direction as the velocity of the incoming ball.

You can also get some general ideas about what happens after such a collision by considering three possible situations for the relative masses of the objects, illustrated in ▸Fig. 6.14:

Case 1. $m_1 = m_2$ (Fig. 6.14a). From Eqs. 6.15 and 6.16,

$$v_1 = 0 \quad \text{and} \quad v_2 = v_{1_o}$$

That is, if the masses of the colliding objects are equal, the objects simply exchange momentum and energy. The incoming ball is stopped on collision, and the originally stationary ball moves off with the same velocity as that of the incoming ball, thus obviously conserving the system's kinetic energy and momentum. (A real-world example would be two billiard balls colliding along a straight line.)

Case 2. $m_1 \gg m_2$ (m_1 very much greater than m_2; Fig. 6.14b). In this case, m_2 can be ignored in the addition and subtraction with m_1 in Eqs. 6.15 and 6.16, and

$$v_1 \approx v_{1_o} \quad \text{and} \quad v_2 \approx 2v_{1_o}$$

This pair of relationships tells you that if a very massive object collides with a stationary light object, the massive object is slowed down only slightly by the collision, and the light object is knocked away with a velocity almost twice that of the initial velocity of the massive object. (Think of a bowling ball hitting a pin.)

Case 3. $m_1 \ll m_2$ (m_1 very much less than m_2; Fig. 6.14c). Here, m_1 can be ignored in the addition and subtraction with m_2 in Eqs. 6.15 and 6.16, and

$$v_1 \approx -v_{1_o} \quad \text{and} \quad v_2 \approx 0$$

(In the second equation, the approximation $m_1/m_2 \approx 0$ is made.) Thus, if a light object collides with a massive stationary one, the massive object remains *almost* stationary, and the light object recoils backward with approximately the same speed it had before collision. An extreme case of this type is similar to a particle striking a solid, immovable wall. (See Fig. 6.3.) If the wall is anchored to the ground, then the Earth and wall recoil together, but this effect is totally unnoticeable. (Why?) Total momentum, however, is still conserved. For the case in Fig. 6.14c, the massive ball must move a bit after the collision to conserve momentum. (Think of throwing a small rubber ball at a stationary bowling ball.)

Remember, these special cases give you a general idea about what might happen for similar, but not exact, situations. Here are some examples that demonstrate such cases.

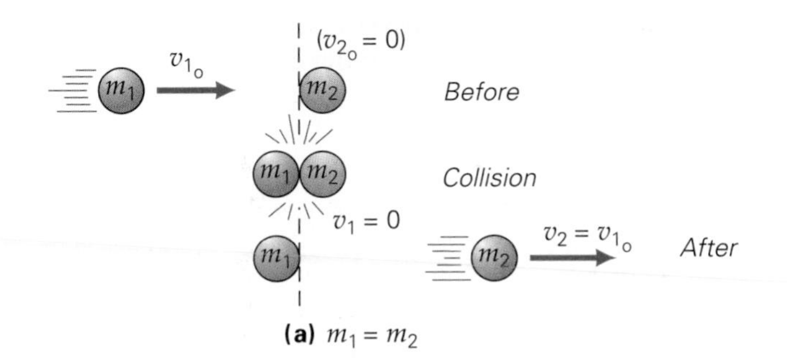

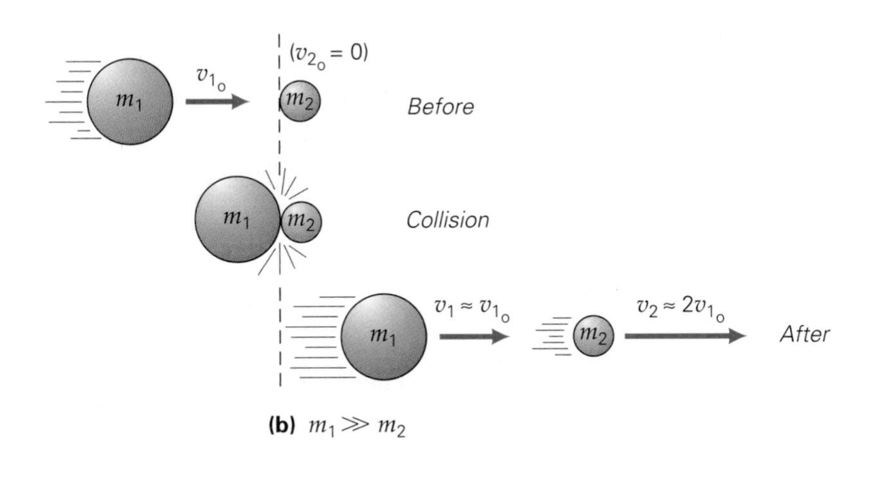

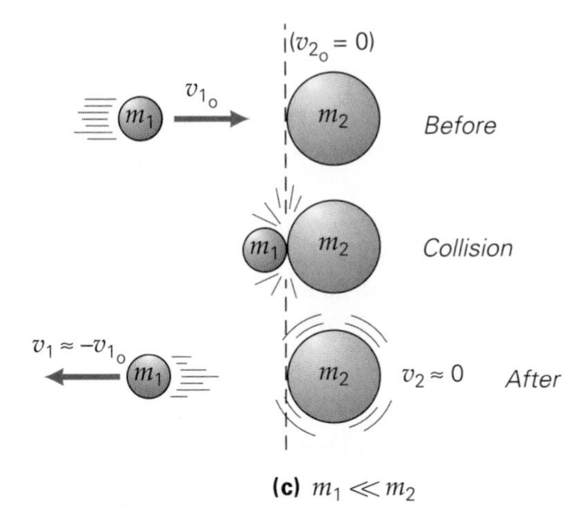

◀ **FIGURE 6.14 Special cases of head-on elastic collisions**
(a) When a moving object collides elastically with a stationary object of equal mass, there is a complete exchange of momentum and energy. **(b)** When a very massive moving object collides elastically with a much less massive stationary object, the very massive object continues to move essentially as before, and the less massive object is given a velocity of almost twice the initial velocity of the large mass. **(c)** When a moving object of small mass collides elastically with a very massive stationary object, the incoming object recoils in the opposite direction with approximately the same speed as its initial speed, and the very massive object remains essentially stationary.

Example 6.9 ■ Elastic Collision: Conservation of Momentum and Kinetic Energy

A 0.30-kg object with a speed of 2.0 m/s in the positive x-direction has a head-on elastic collision with a stationary 0.70-kg object located at $x = 0$. What is the distance separating the objects 2.5 s after the collision?

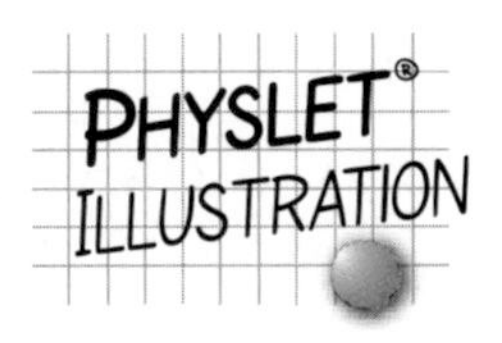

Elastic and Inelastic Collisions

Thinking It Through. The incoming object is less massive than the stationary one. However, it is not extremely less massive, so we might expect the objects to separate in opposite directions after collision, as in Case 1. Equations 6.15 and 6.16 will give the velocities; knowing the time, we can find the distances traveled or the separation distance after collision.

Solution. Using the notation used previously, we have

Given: $m_1 = 0.30$ kg   **Find:** $\Delta x = x_2 - x_1$ (separation distance 2.5 s after collision)
$v_{1_o} = 2.0$ m/s
$m_2 = 0.70$ kg
$v_{2_o} = 0$
$t = 2.5$ s

From Eqs. 6.15 and 6.16, the velocities after collision are

$$v_1 = \left(\frac{m_1 - m_2}{m_1 + m_2}\right)v_{1_o} = \left(\frac{0.30\text{ kg} - 0.70\text{ kg}}{0.30\text{ kg} + 0.70\text{ kg}}\right)(2.0\text{ m/s}) = -0.80\text{ m/s}$$

$$v_2 = \left(\frac{2m_1}{m_1 + m_2}\right)v_{1_o} = \left[\frac{2(0.30\text{ kg})}{0.30\text{ kg} + 0.70\text{ kg}}\right](2.0\text{ m/s}) = 1.2\text{ m/s}$$

Here, m_1 is less than m_2, but not *so much* less that it could be ignored, as was done in Fig. 6.14c.

The objects are separating after collision, and their positions relative to the collision point ($x_o = 0$) are

$$x_1 = v_1 t = (-0.80\text{ m/s})(2.5\text{ s}) = -2.0\text{ m}$$
$$x_2 = v_2 t = (1.2\text{ m/s})(2.5\text{ s}) = 3.0\text{ m}$$

So,

$$\Delta x = x_2 - x_1 = 3.0\text{ m} - (-2.0\text{ m}) = 5.0\text{ m}$$

The objects are 5.0 m apart at that time.

Follow-up Exercise. Suppose the objects in this Example had equal masses. What would be the separation distance 2.5 s after collision in this case?

Example 6.10 ■ Spare! Conservation of Momentum and Kinetic Energy

A 7.1-kg bowling ball with a speed of 6.0 m/s has a head-on elastic collision with a stationary 1.6-kg pin. (a) What is the velocity of each object after the collision? (b) What is the total momentum after the collision?

Thinking It Through. If the ball and the pin have an elastic collision, then Eqs. 6.15 and 6.16 apply and will give the velocities. (The ball is quite a bit more massive than the pin, so one might expect that the ball and the pin will go in same direction after collision, as in Fig. 6.14b.) The total momentum is conserved, so we can calculate it from the initial total momentum. (Why?)

Solution. Listing the data, we have

Given: $m_1 = 7.1$ kg   **Find:** (a) $\mathbf{v}_1$ and $\mathbf{v}_2$ (velocities after collision)
$v_{1_o} = 6.0$ m/s   (b) $\mathbf{P}$ (total momentum after collision)
$m_2 = 1.6$ kg
$v_{2_o} = 0$

(a) The velocities are given directly by Eqs. 6.15 and 6.16, and the direction of the incoming ball is taken as positive:

$$v_1 = \left(\frac{m_1 - m_2}{m_1 + m_2}\right)v_{1_o} = \left(\frac{7.1\text{ kg} - 1.6\text{ kg}}{7.1\text{ kg} + 1.6\text{ kg}}\right)(6.0\text{ m/s}) = 3.8\text{ m/s}$$

$$v_2 = \left(\frac{2m_1}{m_1 + m_2}\right)v_{1_o} = \left[\frac{2(7.1\text{ kg})}{7.1\text{ kg} + 1.6\text{ kg}}\right](6.0\text{ m/s}) = 9.8\text{ m/s}$$

So both objects move in the same direction. Here, m_1 is greater than m_2, but not *so much* greater that m_2 could be ignored, as was done in Fig. 6.14b.

(b) Momentum is conserved in elastic (and inelastic) collisions, so the total momentum afterward is the same as that before the collision. Thus, the total momentum is that of the incident ball, in the same direction and with a magnitude of

$$P_f = p_{1_o} = m_1 v_{1_o} = (7.1\text{ kg})(6.0\text{ m/s}) = 43\text{ kg}\cdot\text{m/s}$$

Follow-up Exercise. In general, for head-on, elastic collisions with one of the objects initially stationary, is it possible for the velocities of the objects to be the same after collision as they were before it? Explain.

Example 6.11 ■ An Elastic Collision on a Small Scale

An electron has an elastic, head-on collision with a stationary hydrogen atom. What fraction of the electron's initial kinetic energy is transferred to the hydrogen atom? (The mass of the hydrogen atom is 1840 times the mass of the electron.)

Thinking It Through. This is certainly a case of an object hitting a much more massive, stationary object (similar to Fig. 6.14c). You may notice immediately that we are not given any initial velocity, only a ratio of masses. Right away, this should make you think of a solution involving a ratio—that of the kinetic energies, which would be a fractional representation.

Solution.

Given: $M_H = 1840\, m_e$ or $M_H/m_e = 1840$ *Find:* Fraction of kinetic energy transfer

Since no initial velocity for the electron is given, we take it to be v_{1_o}. After the collision, the hydrogen atom would have a velocity given by Eq. 6.16. These values may be used to compute kinetic energies. Then, the ratio K_H/K_{e_o} (K of the H atom after collision/K of the electron before collision) is the fraction of the kinetic energy transferred to the hydrogen atom, since initially, the total kinetic energy is that of the electron. So, using Eq. 6.16, we have

$$\frac{K_H}{K_{e_o}} = \frac{\frac{1}{2}M_H v^2}{\frac{1}{2}m_e v_{1_o}^2} = \frac{\frac{1}{2}M_H\left(\frac{2m_e}{m_e + M_H}\right)^2 v_{1_o}^2}{\frac{1}{2}m_e v_{1_o}^2} = \left(\frac{M_H}{m_e}\right)\left[\frac{2}{1 + \left(\frac{M_H}{m_e}\right)}\right]^2$$

$$= (1840)\left[\frac{4}{(1 + 1840)^2}\right] \approx \left(\frac{4}{1840}\right) = 0.0022$$

where an approximation was made in the last step. (Is it reasonable?) So, a little over $\frac{2}{1000}$ of the electron's kinetic energy is transferred to the hydrogen atom, which means that the more massive atom doesn't move very fast after collision.

Follow-up Exercise. What would be the kinetic-energy transfer if a moving hydrogen atom collided with a stationary electron?

Conceptual Example 6.12 ■ Two In, One Out?

A novelty collision device, as shown in ▸Fig. 6.15, consists of five identical metal balls. When one ball swings in, after multiple collisions, one ball swings out at the other end of the row of balls. When two balls swing in, two swing out; when three swing in, three swing out, and so on—always the same number out as in.

Suppose that two balls, each of mass m, swing in at velocity v and collide with the next ball. Why doesn't one ball swing out at the other end with a velocity $2v$?

Reasoning and Answer. The collisions along the horizontal row of balls are approximately elastic. The case of two balls swinging in and one ball swinging out with twice the velocity wouldn't violate the conservation of momentum: $(2m)v = m(2v)$. However, there's another condition that applies if we assume elastic collisions—the conservation of kinetic energy. Let's check to see if this condition is upheld for this case:

▲ **FIGURE 6.15 One in, one out** See Conceptual Example 6.12.

$$\begin{aligned} &\textit{before} \quad \textit{after} \\ K_i &= K_f \\ \tfrac{1}{2}(2m)v^2 &\stackrel{?}{=} \tfrac{1}{2}m\,(2v)^2 \\ mv^2 &\neq 2mv^2 \end{aligned}$$

Hence, the kinetic energy would *not* be conserved if this happened, and the equation is telling us that this situation violates established physical principles and does not occur. Note that there's a big violation—more energy out than in.

Follow-up Exercise. Suppose the first ball of mass m were replaced with a ball of mass $2m$. When this ball is pulled back and allowed to swing in, how many balls will swing out? [*Hint*: Think about the analogous situation in Fig. 6.14, and remember that the balls in the row are actually colliding. It may help to think of them as being separated.]

6.5 Center of Mass

OBJECTIVES: **To (a) explain the concept of the center of mass and compute its location for simple systems, and (b) describe how the center of mass and center of gravity are related.**

The conservation of total momentum gives us a method of analyzing a "system of particles." Such a system may be virtually anything—for example, a volume of gas, water in a container, or a baseball. Another important concept, the center of mass, allows us to analyze the overall motion of a system of particles. It involves representing the whole system as a single particle or point mass. This concept will be introduced here and applied in more detail in the upcoming chapters.

We have seen that if no net external force acts on a particle, the particle's linear momentum is constant. Similarly, if no net external force acts on a *system* of particles, the linear momentum of the system is constant. This similarity implies that a system of particles might be represented by an *equivalent* single particle. Moving rigid objects, such as balls, automobiles, and so forth, are essentially systems of particles and can be effectively represented by equivalent single particles when we analyze motion. Such representation is done through the concept of the **center of mass (CM)**:

> The center of mass is the point at which all of the mass of an object or system may be considered to be concentrated, for the purposes of linear or translational motion only.

Even if a rigid object is rotating, an important result (beyond the scope of this text to derive) is that the center of mass moves as though it were a particle (▸Fig. 6.16). The center of mass is sometimes described as the *balance point* of a solid object. For example, if you balance a meterstick on your finger, the center of mass of the stick is located directly above your finger, and all of the mass (or weight) seems to be concentrated there.

An expression similar to Newton's second law for a single particle applies to a *system* when the center of mass is used:

$$\mathbf{F}_{\text{net}} = M\mathbf{A}_{\text{CM}} \tag{6.17}$$

Here, $\mathbf{F}_{\text{net}}$ is the net external force on the system, M is the total mass of the system or the sum of the masses of the particles of the system ($M = m_1 + m_2 + m_3 + \cdots + m_n$, where the system has n particles), and $\mathbf{A}_{\text{CM}}$ is the acceleration of the center of mass of the system. In words, Eq. 6.17 says that the *center of mass* of a system of particles moves as though all the mass of the system were concentrated there and acted on by the resultant of the external forces. Note that the movement of the individual parts of the system is *not* predicted by Eq. 6.17.

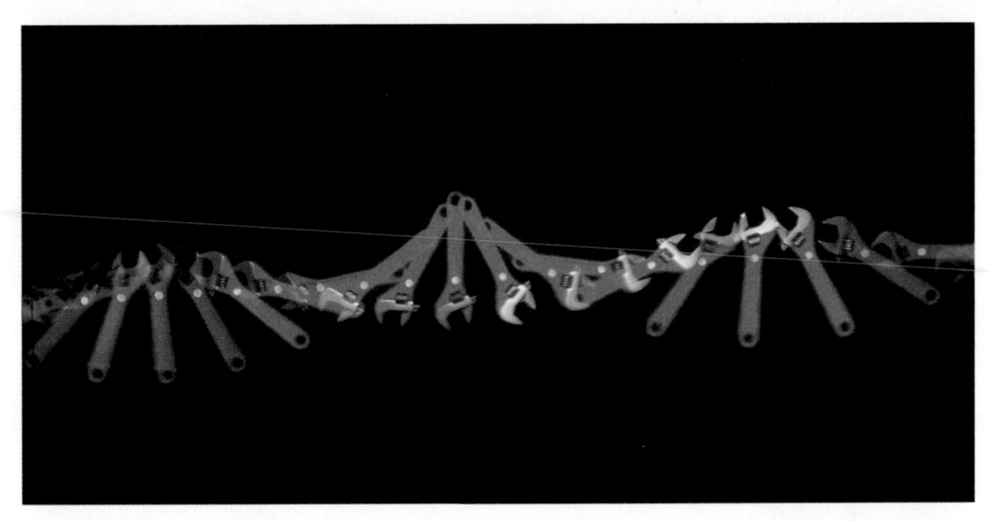

▲ **FIGURE 6.16 Center of mass** The center of mass of this sliding wrench moves in a straight line as though it were a particle. Note the white dot on the wrench that marks the center of mass.

It follows that *if the net external force on a system is zero*, the total linear momentum of the center of mass is conserved (i.e., stays constant), because

$$\mathbf{F}_{\text{net}} = M\mathbf{A}_{\text{CM}} = M(\Delta\mathbf{V}_{\text{CM}}/\Delta t) = \Delta(M\mathbf{V}_{\text{CM}})/\Delta t = \Delta\mathbf{P}/\Delta t = 0 \qquad (6.18)$$

Then, $\Delta\mathbf{P}/\Delta\text{t} = 0$, which means that there is no change in **P** during a time Δt, or the total momentum of the system, $\mathbf{P} = M\mathbf{V}_{\text{CM}}$, is constant (but not necessarily zero). Since M is constant (why?), $\mathbf{V}_{\text{CM}}$ is a constant in this case. Thus, the center of mass either moves with a constant velocity or remains at rest.

Although you may more readily visualize the center of mass of a solid object, the concept of the center of mass applies to any system of particles or objects, even a quantity of gas. For a system of n particles arranged in one dimension, along the x-axis (▸Fig. 6.17), the location of the center of mass is given by

$$X_{\text{CM}} = \frac{m_1\mathbf{x}_1 + m_2\mathbf{x}_2 + m_3\mathbf{x}_3 + \cdots + m_n\mathbf{x}_n}{m_1 + m_2 + m_3 + \cdots + m_n} \qquad (6.19)$$

That is, X_{CM} is the x-coordinate of the center of mass of a system of particles. In shorthand notation (using signs to indicate vector directions in one dimension), this relationship is expressed as

$$X_{\text{CM}} = \frac{\Sigma m_i x_i}{M} \qquad (6.20)$$

where Σ is the summation of the products $m_i x_i$ for n particles ($i = 1, 2, 3, \ldots, n$). If $\Sigma m_i x_i = 0$, then $X_{\text{CM}} = 0$, and the center of mass of the one-dimensional system is located at the origin.

Other coordinates of the center of mass for systems of particles are similarly defined. For a two-dimensional distribution of masses, the coordinates of the center of mass are $(X_{\text{CM}}, Y_{\text{CM}})$.

Example 6.13 ■ Finding the Center of Mass: A Summation Process

Three masses, 2.0 kg, 3.0 kg, and 6.0 kg, are located at positions (3.0, 0), (6.0, 0), and (−4.0, 0), respectively, in meters from the origin (Fig. 6.17). Where is the center of mass of this system?

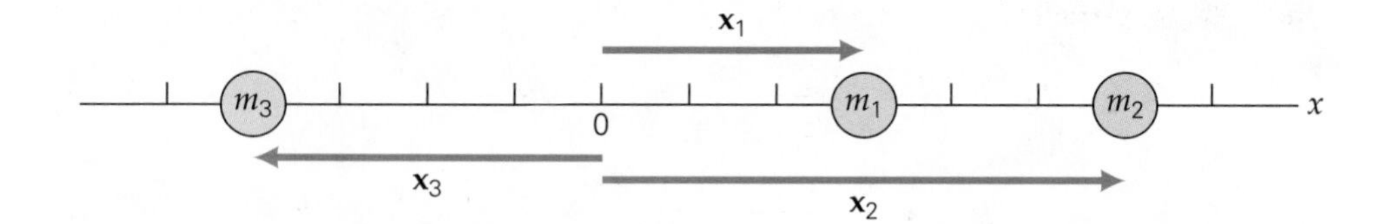

▶ **FIGURE 6.17 System of particles in one dimension** Where is the system's center of mass? See Example 6.13.

Thinking It Through. The masses and the positions are given, so the definition of X_{CM} (Eq. 6.20) applies. However, keep in mind that the positions are located by vector displacements from the origin and are indicated in one dimension by the appropriate signs (+ or −).

Solution.

Given: $m_1 = 2.0\ \text{kg}$
$m_2 = 3.0\ \text{kg}$
$m_3 = 6.0\ \text{kg}$
$x_1 = 3.0\ \text{m}$
$x_2 = 6.0\ \text{m}$
$x_3 = -4.0\ \text{m}$

Find: X_{CM} (CM coordinate)

Then, simply performing the summation as indicated in Eq. 6.20 yields

$$X_{CM} = \frac{\Sigma_i m_i x_i}{M}$$

$$= \frac{(2.0\ \text{kg})(3.0\ \text{m}) + (3.0\ \text{kg})(6.0\ \text{m}) + (6.0\ \text{kg})(-4.0\ \text{m})}{2.0\ \text{kg} + 3.0\ \text{kg} + 6.0\ \text{kg}} = 0$$

The center of mass is at the origin.

Follow-up Exercise. Describe a single particle that could replace the system in this Example in order for us to be able to analyze the motion of the CM.

Example 6.14 ■ A Dumbbell: Center of Mass Revisited

A dumbbell (▼Fig. 6.18) has a connecting bar of negligible mass. Find the location of the center of mass (a) if m_1 and m_2 are each 5.0 kg and (b) if m_1 is 5.0 kg and m_2 is 10.0 kg.

Thinking It Through. This Example shows how the location of the center of mass depends on the distribution of mass. In (b), you might expect the center of mass to be located closer to the more massive end of the dumbbell.

Solution. Listing the data, with the coordinates from Eq. 6.18

Given: $x_1 = 0.20\ \text{m}$
$x_2 = 0.90\ \text{m}$
$y_1 = y_2 = 0.10\ \text{m}$
(a) $m_1 = m_2 = 5.0\ \text{kg}$
(b) $m_1 = 5.0\ \text{kg}$
$m_2 = 10.0\ \text{kg}$

Find: (a) (X_{CM}, Y_{CM}) (CM coordinates), with $m_1 = m_2$
(b) (X_{CM}, Y_{CM}), with $m_1 \neq m_2$

Note that each mass is considered to be a particle located at the center of the sphere (its center of mass).

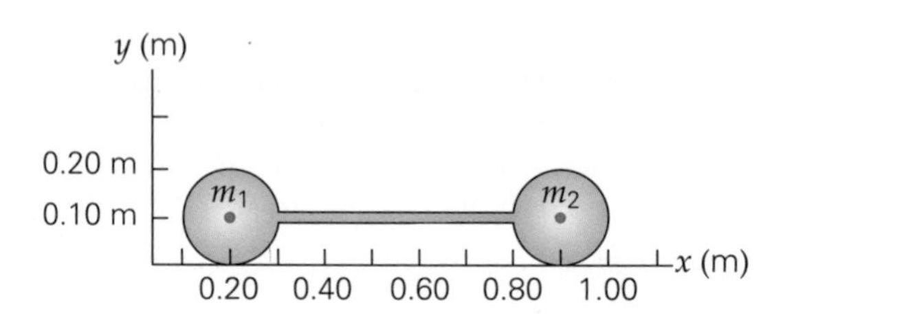

▶ **FIGURE 6.18 Location of the center of mass** See Example 6.14.

(a) X_{CM} is given by

$$X_{CM} = \frac{m_1x_1 + m_2x_2}{m_1 + m_2}$$

$$= \frac{(5.0\ \text{kg})(0.20\ \text{m}) + (5.0\ \text{kg})(0.90\ \text{m})}{5.0\ \text{kg} + 5.0\ \text{kg}} = 0.55\ \text{m}$$

Similarly, we find that $Y_{CM} = 0.10$ m. (You might have seen this right away, since each center of mass is at this height.) The center of mass of the dumbbell is then located at $(X_{CM}, Y_{CM}) = (0.55\ \text{m}, 0.10\ \text{m})$, or midway between the end masses.

(b) With $m_2 = 10.0$ kg,

$$X_{CM} = \frac{m_1x_1 + m_2x_2}{m_1 + m_2}$$

$$= \frac{(5.0\ \text{kg})(0.20\ \text{m}) + (10.0\ \text{kg})(0.90\ \text{m})}{5.0\ \text{kg} + 10.0\ \text{kg}} = 0.67\ \text{m}$$

which is two thirds of the way between the masses. (Note that the distance of the CM from the center of m_1 is $\Delta x = 0.67\ \text{m} - 0.20\ \text{m} = 0.47$ m. With the distance $L = 0.70$ m between the centers of the masses, $\Delta x/L = 0.47\ \text{m}/0.70\ \text{m} = 0.67$, or $\frac{2}{3}$.) You might expect the balance point of the dumbbell in this case to be closer to m_2. The y-coordinate of the center of mass is again $Y_{CM} = 0.10$ m, as you can prove for yourself.

Follow-up Exercise. In part (b) of this Example, take the origin of the coordinate axes to be at the point where m_1 touches the x-axis. What are the coordinates of the CM in this case, and how does its location compare with that found in the Example?

In Example 6.14, when the value of one of the masses changed, the x-coordinate of the center of mass changed. You might have expected the y-coordinate to change also. However, the centers of the end masses were still at the same height, and Y_{CM} remained the same. To increase Y_{CM}, one or both of the end masses would have to be in a higher position.

Now let's see how the concept of the center of mass can be applied to a realistic situation.

Example 6.15 ■ Internal Motion: Where's the Center of Mass?

A 75.0-kg man stands in the far end of a 50.0-kg boat 100 m from the shore, as illustrated in ▾Fig. 6.19. If he walks to the other end of the 6.00-m-long boat, how far is he from the shore? Neglect friction, and assume that the center of mass of the boat is at its midpoint.

Thinking It Through. The answer is *not* 100 m − 6.00 m = 94.0 m, because the boat moves as the man walks. Why? With no net external force, the acceleration of the center of mass of the man–boat system is zero (Eq. 6.17), and so is the total momentum by Eq. 6.18

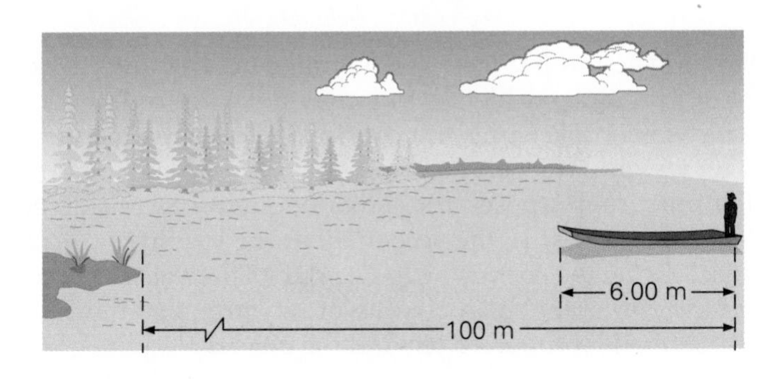

◀ **FIGURE 6.19 Walking toward shore** See Example 6.15.

($\mathbf{P} = M\mathbf{V}_{CM} = 0$). Hence, the velocity of the center of mass of the system is zero, or the center of mass is stationary and remains so to conserve system momentum; that is, X_{CM} (initial) $= X_{CM}$ (final).

Solution. Taking the shore as the origin ($x = 0$), we have

Given: $m_m = 75.0$ kg
$x_{m_i} = 100$ m
$m_b = 50.0$ kg
$x_{b_i} = 94.0\text{ m} + 3.00\text{ m} = 97.0$ m (CM position)
(where the location of the boat is taken at its center of mass)

Find: x_{m_f} (distance of man from shore)

Note that if we take the man's final position to be a distance x_{m_f} from the shore, then the final position of the boat's center of mass will be $x_{b_f} = x_{m_f} + 3.00$ m, since the man will be at the front of the boat.

Then initially,

$$X_{CM_i} = \frac{m_m x_{m_i} + m_b x_{b_i}}{m_m + m_b}$$

$$= \frac{(75.0\text{ kg})(100\text{ m}) + (50.0\text{ kg})(97.0\text{ m})}{75.0\text{ kg} + 50.0\text{ kg}} = 98.8\text{ m}$$

And finally,

$$X_{CM_f} = \frac{m_m x_{m_f} + m_b x_{b_f}}{m_m + m_b}$$

$$= \frac{(75.0\text{ kg})x_{m_f} + (50.0\text{ kg})(x_{m_f} + 3.00\text{ m})}{75.0\text{ kg} + 50.0\text{ kg}} = 98.8\text{ m}$$

Here, $X_{CM_f} = 98.8\text{ m} = X_{CM_i}$, since the CM does not move. Then, solving for x_{m_f}, we get

$$(125\text{ kg})(98.8\text{ m}) = (125\text{ kg})x_{m_f} + (50.0\text{ kg})(3.00\text{ m})$$

and

$$x_{m_f} = 97.6\text{ m}$$

from the shore.

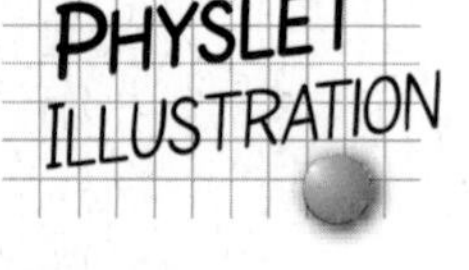

Where Is the Center of Mass

Follow-up Exercise. Suppose the man then walks back to his original position at the opposite end of the boat. Would he then be 100 m from shore again?

Center of Gravity

As you know, mass and weight are related. Closely associated with the concept of the center of mass is the concept of the **center of gravity (CG)**, the point where all of the weight of an object may be considered to be concentrated when the object is represented as a particle. If the acceleration due to gravity is constant both in magnitude and direction over the extent of the object, Eq. 6.20 can be rewritten as (with all $g_i = g$)

$$MgX_{CM} = \Sigma_i m_i g x_i \qquad (6.21)$$

Then, the weight Mg acts as if it were concentrated at X_{CM}, and the center of mass and the center of gravity coincide. As you may have noticed, the location of the center of gravity was implied in some previous figures in Chapter 4, where the vector arrows for weight ($\mathbf{w} = m\mathbf{g}$) were drawn from a point at or near the center of an object. For practical purposes, the center of gravity is considered to coincide with the center of mass. That is, the acceleration due to gravity is constant for all parts of the object. (Note the constant g in Eq. 6.21.) There would be a difference in the locations of the two points if an object were so large that the acceleration due to gravity were different at different parts of the object.

In some cases, the center of mass or the center of gravity of an object may be located by symmetry. For example, for a spherical object that is homogeneous (i.e., the mass is distributed evenly throughout), the center of mass is at the geometrical center (or center of symmetry). In Example 6.14(a), where the end masses of the dumbbell were equal, it was probably apparent that the center of mass was midway between them.

The location of the center of mass or center of gravity of an irregularly shaped object is not so evident and is usually difficult to calculate (even with advanced mathematical methods that are beyond the scope of this book). In some instances, the center of mass may be located experimentally. For example, the center of mass of a flat, irregularly shaped object can be determined experimentally by suspending it freely from different points (▼Fig. 6.20). A moment's thought should convince you that the center of mass (or center of gravity) always lies vertically below the point of suspension. Since the center of mass is defined as the point at which all the mass of a body can be considered to be concentrated, this is analogous to a particle of mass suspended from a string. Suspending the object from two or more points and marking the vertical lines on which the center of mass must lie locates the center of mass as the intersection of the lines.

The center of mass (or center of gravity) of an object may lie outside the body of the object (▶Fig. 6.21). For example, the center of mass of a homogeneous ring is at the ring's center. The mass in any section of the ring is compensated for by the mass in an equivalent section directly across the ring, and by symmetry, the center of mass is at the center of the ring. For an L-shaped object with equal legs, the center of mass lies on a line that makes a 45° angle with both legs. Its location can easily be determined by suspending the L from a point on one of the legs and noting where a vertical line from that point intersects the diagonal line.

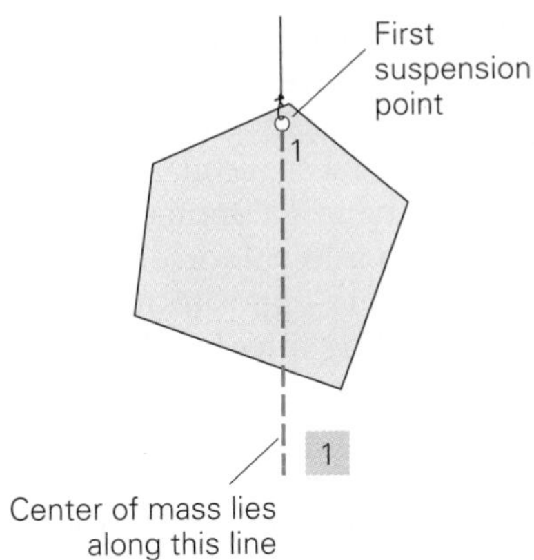

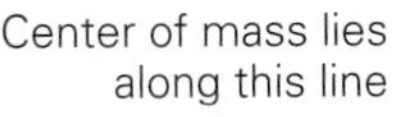

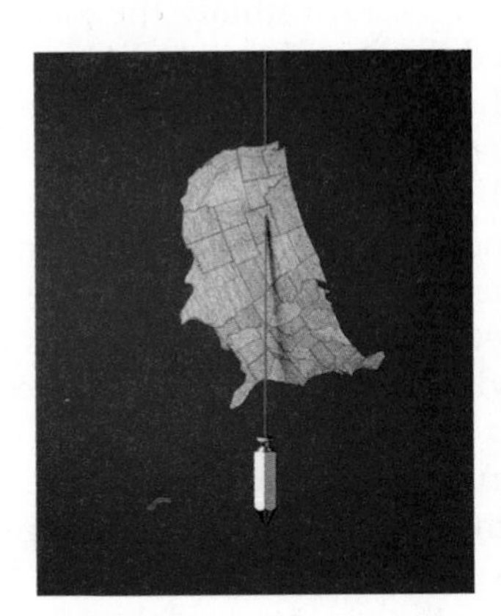

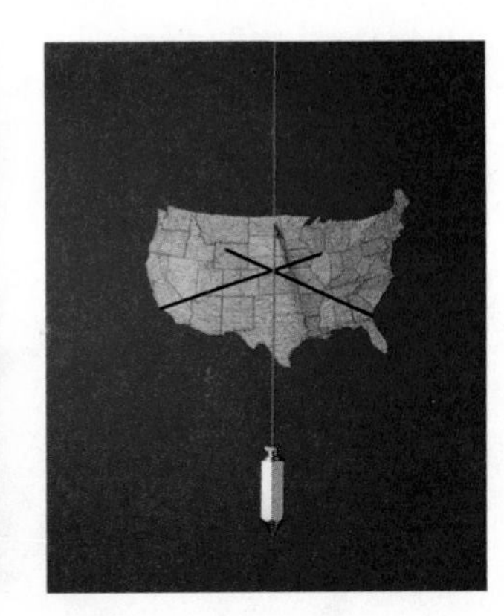

(b)

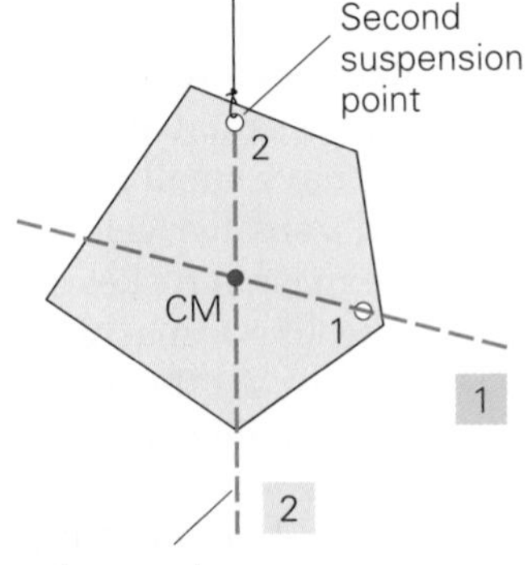

(a)

▲ **FIGURE 6.20 Location of the center of mass by suspension** **(a)** The center of mass of a flat, irregularly shaped object can be found by suspending the object from two or more points. The CM (and CG) lies on a vertical line under any point of suspension, so the intersection of two such lines marks its location midway through the thickness of the body. The sheet could be balanced horizontally at this point. Why? **(b)** The process is illustrated with a cutout map of the United States. Note that a plumb line dropped from any other point (third photo) does in fact pass through the CM as located in the first two photos.

(a)

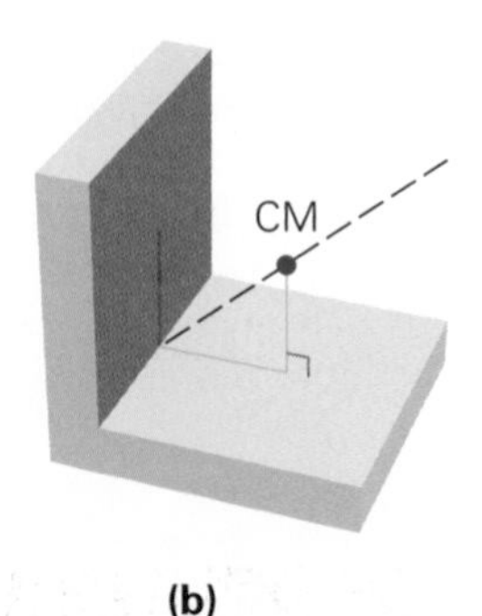

(b)

▲ **FIGURE 6.21 The center of mass may be located outside of a body** The center of mass (and center of gravity) may lie either inside or outside of a body, depending on the distribution of that object's mass. **(a)** For a uniform ring, the center of mass is at the center of the ring. **(b)** For an L-shaped object, if the mass distribution is uniform and the legs are of equal length, the center of mass lies on the diagonal between the legs.

▲ **FIGURE 6.22 Center of gravity** By arching his body, this high jumper can get over the bar even though his center of gravity passes beneath it.

Keep in mind that the location of the center of mass or center of gravity of an object depends on the distribution of mass. Therefore, for a flexible object such as the human body, the position of the center of gravity changes as the object changes configuration (distribution of mass). For example, when a person raises both arms overhead, his or her center of gravity is raised several centimeters. For a high jumper going over a bar, the center of gravity lies outside the arched body (▼Fig. 6.22). In fact, the center of gravity passes *beneath* the bar. This configuration is made purposefully, because work must be done to raise the center of gravity, and only the jumper's body has to clear the bar, not the CG.

*6.6 Jet Propulsion and Rockets

OBJECTIVE: **To apply the conservation of momentum in the explanation of jet propulsion and the operation of rockets.**

The word *jet* is sometimes used to refer to a stream of liquid or gas emitted at a high speed—for example, a jet of water from a fountain or a jet of air from an automobile tire. **Jet propulsion** is the application of such jets to the production of motion. This concept usually brings to mind jet planes and rockets, but squid and octopi propel themselves by squirting jets of water.

You have probably tried the simple application of blowing up a balloon and releasing it. Lacking any guidance or rigid exhaust system, the balloon zigzags around, driven by the escaping air. In terms of Newton's third law, the air is forced out by the contraction of the stretched balloon—that is, the balloon exerts a force on the air. Thus, there must be an equal and opposite reaction force exerted by the air on the balloon. It is this force that propels the balloon on its erratic path.

Jet propulsion is explained by Newton's third law, and in the absence of external forces, the conservation of momentum also applies. You may understand this concept better by considering the recoil of a rifle, taking the rifle and the bullet as an isolated system (▸Fig. 6.23). Initially, the total momentum of this system is zero. When the rifle is fired (by remote control to avoid external forces), the expansion of the gases from the exploding charge accelerates the bullet down the barrel. These gases push backward on the rifle as well, producing a recoil force (the "kick" experienced by a person firing a weapon). Since the initial momentum of the system is zero and the force of the expanding gas is an internal force, the momenta of the bullet and of the rifle must be exactly equal and opposite at any instant. After the bullet leaves the barrel, there is no propelling force, so the bullet and the rifle move with constant velocities (unless acted on by a net external force such as gravity or air resistance).

Similarly, the thrust of a rocket is created by exhausting the gas from burning fuel out the rear of the rocket. The expanding gas exerts a net force on the rocket that propels the rocket in the forward direction (▸Fig. 6.24a and b). The rocket exerts a reaction force on the gas, so all of the gas is directed out the exhaust nozzle. If the rocket is at rest when the engines are turned on and there are no external forces (as in deep space, where friction is zero and gravitational forces are negligible), then the instantaneous momentum of the exhaust gas is equal and opposite to that of the rocket. The numerous exhaust-gas molecules have small masses and high velocities, and the rocket has a much larger mass and a smaller velocity.

Unlike a rifle firing a single shot, which has negligible mass, a rocket continuously loses mass when burning fuel. (The rocket is more like a machine gun). Thus, the rocket is a system for which the mass is not constant. As the mass of the rocket decreases, it accelerates more easily. Multistage rockets take advantage of this fact. The hull of a burnt-out stage is jettisoned to give a further in-flight reduction in mass (Fig. 6.24c). The payload (cargo) is typically a very small part of the initial mass of rockets for space flights.

Suppose that the purpose of a space flight is to land a payload on the Moon. At some point on the journey, the gravitational attraction of the Moon will become

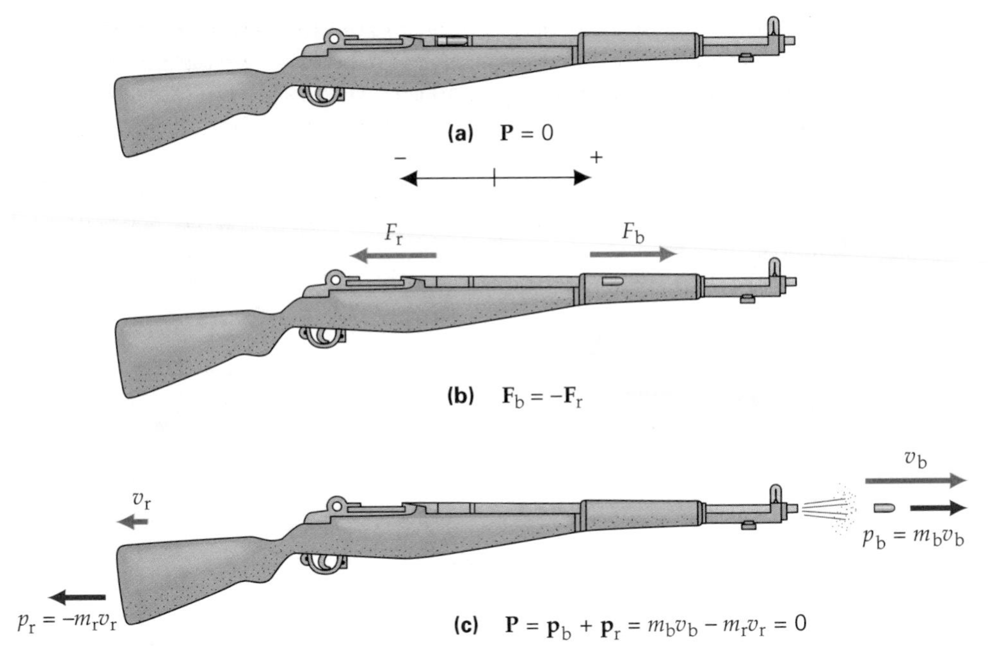

◀ **FIGURE 6.23 Conservation of momentum** **(a)** Before the rifle is fired, the total momentum of the rifle and bullet (as an isolated system) is zero. **(b)** During firing, there are equal and opposite internal forces, and the instantaneous total momentum of the rifle–bullet system remains zero (neglecting external forces, such as arise when a rifle is being held). **(c)** When the bullet leaves the barrel, the total momentum of the system is still zero. (The vector equation is written in boldface (vector) notation and then in sign–magnitude notation so as to indicate directions.)

greater than that of the Earth, and the spacecraft will accelerate toward the Moon. A soft landing is desirable, so the spacecraft must be slowed down enough to go into orbit around the Moon. This slowing down is accomplished by using the rocket engines to apply a *reverse thrust*, or braking thrust. The spacecraft is maneuvered through a 180° angle, or turned around, which is quite easy to do in space. The rocket engines are then fired, expelling the exhaust gas toward the Moon and supplying a braking action.

You have experienced a reverse-thrust effect if you have flown in a commercial jet. In this instance, however, the craft is not turned around. Instead, after touchdown, the jet engines are revved up, and a braking action can be felt. Ordinarily, revving up the engines accelerates the plane forward. The reverse thrust is accomplished by activating thrust reversers in the engines that deflect the exhaust gases forward (▸Fig. 6.25). The gas experiences an impulse force and a change in momentum in the forward direction (see Fig. 6.3b), and the engine and the aircraft have an equal and opposite momentum change and braking impulse force.

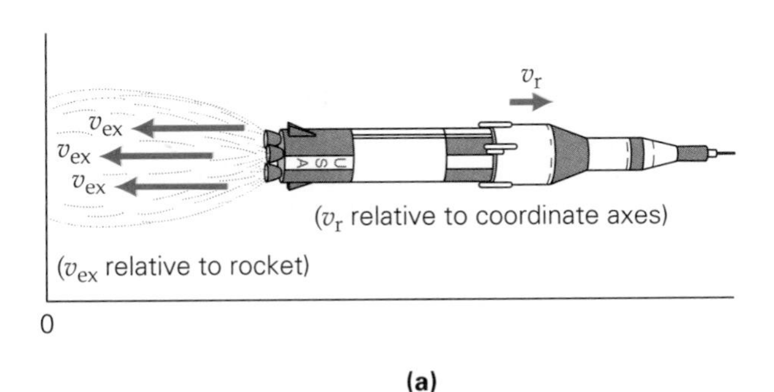

(a)

(b)

(c)

▲ **FIGURE 6.24 Jet propulsion and mass reduction** **(a)** A rocket burning fuel is continuously losing mass and thus becomes easier to accelerate. The resulting force on the rocket (the thrust) depends on the product of the rate of change of its mass with time and the velocity of the exhaust gases: $(\Delta m/\Delta t)\mathbf{v}_{ex}$. Since the mass is decreasing, $\Delta m/\Delta t$ is negative, and the thrust is opposite $\mathbf{v}_{ex}$. **(b)** The space shuttle uses a multistage rocket. Both the two booster rockets and the huge external fuel tank are jettisoned in flight. **(c)** The first and second stages of a *Saturn V* rocket separating after 148 s of burn time.

Rocket

Question: There are no end-of-chapter exercises on the material covered in this section, so test your knowledge with this one: Astronauts use handheld maneuvering devices (small rockets) to move around on space walks. Describe how these rockets are used. Is there any danger on an untethered space walk?

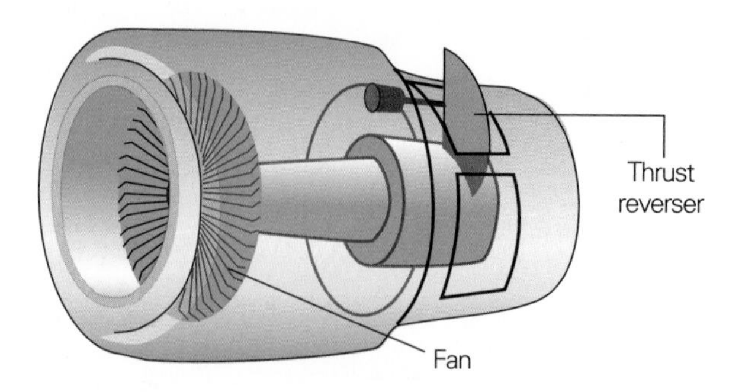

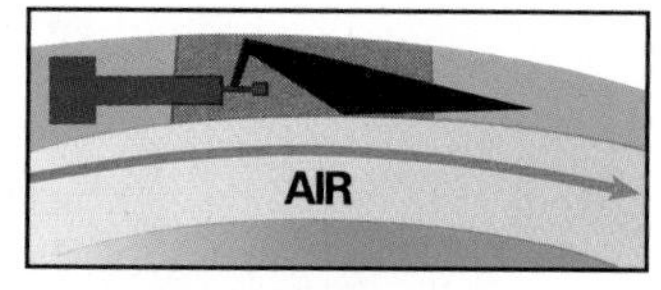

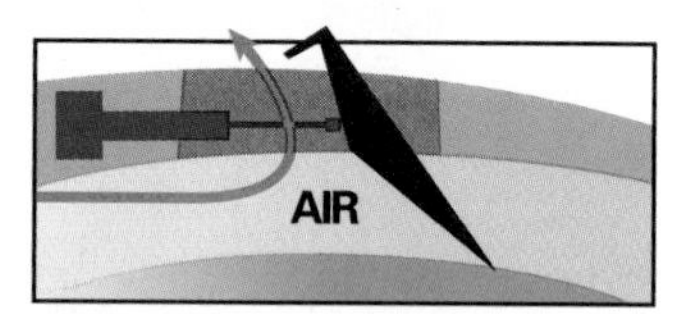

▶ **FIGURE 6.25 Reverse thrust** Thrust reversers are activated on jet engines during landing to help slow the plane. The gas experiences an impulse force and a change in momentum in the forward direction, and the plane experiences an equal and opposite momentum change and a braking impulse force.

Chapter Review

Important Concepts and Equations

- The **linear momentum (p)** of a particle is a vector and is defined as the product of mass and velocity.

$$\mathbf{p} = m\mathbf{v} \quad (6.1)$$

- The **total linear momentum (P)** of a system is the vector sum of the momenta of the individual particles:

$$\mathbf{P} = \mathbf{p}_1 + \mathbf{p}_2 + \mathbf{p}_3 + \cdots = \Sigma \mathbf{p}_i \quad (6.2)$$

- **Newton's second law in terms of momentum (for a particle):**

$$\mathbf{F}_{\text{net}} = \frac{\Delta \mathbf{p}}{\Delta t} \quad (6.3)$$

- **Conservation of linear momentum:** In the absence of a net external force, the total linear momentum of a system is conserved.

- The **impulse–momentum theorem** relates the impulse acting on an object to its change in momentum:

$$\text{Impulse} = \overline{\mathbf{F}}\Delta t = \Delta \mathbf{p}_{\text{o}} = m\mathbf{v} - m\mathbf{v}_{\text{o}} \quad (6.5)$$

- **In an elastic collision, the total kinetic energy of the system is conserved.**

- **Momentum is conserved in both elastic and inelastic collisions.** In a completely inelastic collision, objects stick together after impact.

- **Conditions for an elastic collision:**

$$\mathbf{P}_{\text{f}} = \mathbf{P}_{\text{i}}$$
$$K_{\text{f}} = K_{\text{i}} \quad (6.8)$$

- **Conditions for an inelastic collision:**

$$\mathbf{P}_{\text{f}} = \mathbf{P}_{\text{i}}$$
$$K_{\text{f}} < K_{\text{i}} \quad (6.9)$$

- **Final velocities in head-on, two-body elastic collisions** $(v_{2_{\text{o}}} = 0)$:

$$v_1 = \left(\frac{m_1 - m_2}{m_1 + m_2}\right) v_{1_{\text{o}}} \quad (6.15)$$

$$v_2 = \left(\frac{2m_1}{m_1 + m_2}\right) v_{1_{\text{o}}} \quad (6.16)$$

- The **center of mass** is the point at which all of the mass of an object or system may be considered to be concentrated. (The **center of gravity** is the point at which all the weight may be considered to be concentrated.)
Coordinates of the center of mass (using signs for directions):

$$X_{\text{CM}} = \frac{\Sigma_i m_i x_i}{M} \quad (6.20)$$

Exercises

6.1 Linear Momentum

1. Linear momentum has units of (a) N/m, (b) kg·m/s, (c) N/s, or (d) all of the preceding.

2. Linear momentum is (a) always conserved, (b) a scalar quantity, (c) a vector quantity, or (d) unrelated to force.

3. **CQ** Does a fast-running running back always have more linear momentum than a slow-moving, more massive lineman? Explain.

4. **CQ** Both the kinetic energy and the linear momentum of an object depend on the mass and velocity of the object. Explain the differences between kinetic energy and linear momentum.

5. **CQ** If two objects have the same linear momentum, will they have the same kinetic energy? Explain.

6. ■ If a 60-kg woman is riding in a car traveling at 90 km/h, what is her linear momentum relative to (a) the ground and (b) the car?

7. ■ The linear momentum of a runner in a 100-m dash is 7.5×10^2 kg·m/s. If the runner's speed is 10 m/s, what is his mass?

8. ■ Find the magnitude of the linear momentum of (a) a 7.1-kg bowling ball traveling at 12 m/s and (b) a 1200-kg automobile traveling at 90 km/h.

9. **IE** ■ In a football game, a lineman usually has more mass than a running back. (a) Will a lineman always have greater linear momentum than a running back? Why? (b) Who has greater linear momentum, a 75-kg running back running at 8.5 m/s or a 120-kg lineman moving at 5.0 m/s?

10. ■ How fast would a 1200-kg car travel if it had the same linear momentum as a 1500-kg truck traveling at 90 km/h?

11. ■ A ball of mass 3.0 kg has a linear momentum of 12 kg·m/s. What is the kinetic energy of the ball?

12. ■■ A 0.150-kg baseball traveling with a horizontal speed of 4.50 m/s is hit by a bat and then moves with a speed of 34.7 m/s in the opposite direction. What is the change in the ball's momentum?

13. ■■ A 15.0-g rubber bullet hits a wall with a speed of 150 m/s. If the bullet bounces straight back with a speed of 120 m/s, what is the change in momentum of the bullet?

14. **IE** ■■ Two protons approach each other with different speeds. (a) Will the magnitude of the total momentum of the two-proton system be (1) greater than the magnitude of the momentum of either proton, (2) equal to the difference between the magnitudes of momenta of the two protons, or (3) equal to the sum of the magnitudes of momenta of the two protons? Why? (b) If the speeds of the two protons are 340 m/s and 450 m/s, respectively, what is the total momentum of the two-proton system? [*Hint*: Find the mass of a proton in one of the tables inside the backcover.]

15. ■■ If a 0.50-kg ball is dropped from a height of 10 m, what is the momentum of the ball (a) 0.75 s after being released and (b) just before it hits the ground?

16. ■■ Taking the density of air to be 1.29 kg/m^3, what is the magnitude of the linear momentum of a cubic meter of air moving with a wind speed of (a) 36 km/h and (b) 74 mi/h (the wind speed at which a tropical storm becomes a hurricane)?

17. ■■ Two runners of mass 70 kg and 60 kg, respectively, have a total linear momentum of 350 kg·m/s. The heavier runner is running at 2.0 m/s. Determine the possible speeds of the lighter runner.

18. ■■ A 0.20-kg billiard ball traveling at a speed of 15 m/s strikes the side rail of a pool table at an angle of 60° (▼Fig. 6.26). If the ball rebounds at the same speed and angle, what is the change in its momentum?

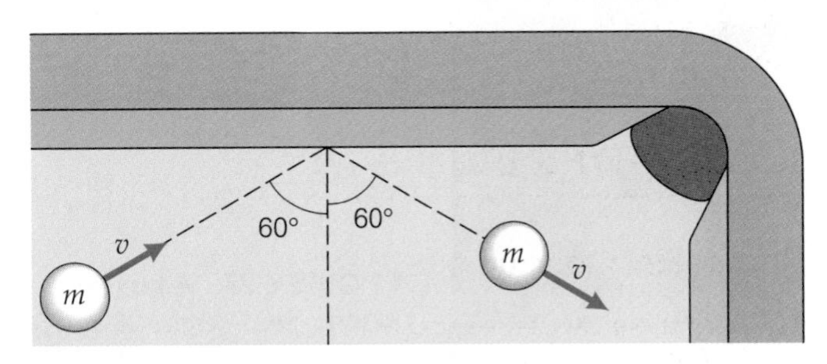

▲ **FIGURE 6.26 Glancing collision** See Exercises 18, 19, and 40.

19. ■■ Suppose that the billiard ball in Fig. 6.26 approaches the rail at a speed of 15 m/s and an angle of 60°, as shown, but rebounds at a speed of 10 m/s and an angle of 50°. What is the change in momentum in this case? [*Hint*: Use components.]

20. ■■ A person pushes a 10-kg box from rest and accelerates it to a speed of 4.0 m/s with a constant force. If the box is pushed for a time of 2.5 s, what is the force exerted by the person?

21. ■■ A loaded tractor-trailer with a total mass of 5000 kg traveling at 3.0 km/h hits a loading dock and comes to a stop in 0.64 s. What is the magnitude of the average force exerted on the truck by the dock?

22. ■■ A 2.0-kg mud ball drops from rest at a height of 15 m. If the impact between the ball and the ground lasts 0.50 s, what is the average net force exerted by the ball on the ground?

23. ■■■ At a basketball game, a 120-lb cheerleader is tossed vertically upward with a speed of 4.50 m/s by a male cheerleader. (a) What is the cheerleader's change in momentum from the time she is released to just before being caught if she is caught at the height at which she was released? (b) Would there be any difference if she were caught 0.25 m below the point of release? If so, what is the change then?

6.2 Impulse

24. Impulse is equal to (a) $F\Delta x$, (b) the change in kinetic energy, (c) the change in momentum, or (d) $\Delta p/\Delta t$.

25. CQ "Follow-through" is very important in many sports, such as in serving a tennis ball. Explain how follow-through can increase the speed of the tennis ball when it is served.

26. CQ A karate student tries *not* to follow through in order to break a board, as shown in ▼Fig. 6.27. How can the abrupt stop of the hand (with no follow-through) generate so much force?

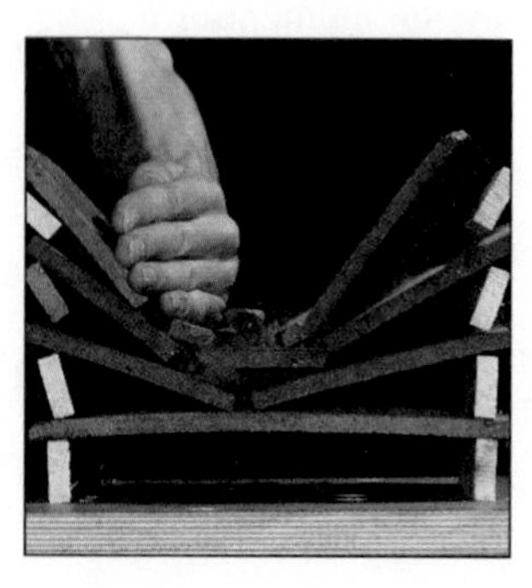

◀ **FIGURE 6.27 A karate punch** See Exercise 26 and 33.

27. CQ Explain the difference for each of the following pairs of actions in terms of impulse: (a) a golfer's long drive and a short chip shot; (b) a boxer's jab and knock-out punches; (c) a baseball player's bunting action and home-run swing.

28. CQ Explain the principle behind (a) the use of Styrofoam as packing material to prevent objects from breaking, (b) the use of shoulder pads of football players to prevent injuries, and (c) the thicker glove used by a baseball catcher than by his teammates in the field.

29. CQ Will a greater force always generate a greater impulse? Explain.

30. ■ When tossed upward and hit horizontally by a batter, a 0.20-kg softball receives an impulse of 3.0 N · s. With what horizontal speed does the ball move away from the bat?

31. ■ An automobile with a linear momentum of 3.0×10^4 kg · m/s is brought to a stop in 5.0 s. What is the magnitude of the average braking force?

32. ■ A pool player imparts an impulse of 3.2 N · s to a stationary 0.25-kg cue ball with a cue stick. What is the speed of the ball just after impact?

33. ■■ For the karate punch in Exercise 26, assume that the hand has a mass of 0.35 kg and that the speeds of the hand just before and just after hitting the board are 10 m/s and 0, respectively. What is the average force exerted by the fist on the board if (a) the fist follows through, so the contact time is 3.0 ms, and (b) the fist stops abruptly, so the contact time is only 0.30 ms?

34. IE ■■ When bunting, a baseball player uses the bat to change both the speed and direction of the baseball. (a) Will the magnitude of the change in momentum of the baseball before and after the bunt be (1) greater than the magnitude of the momentum of the baseball either before or after the bunt, (2) equal to the difference between the magnitudes of momenta of the baseball before and after the bunt, or (3) equal to the sum of the magnitudes of momenta of the baseball before and after the bunt? Why? (b) The baseball has a mass of 0.16 kg; its speeds before and after the bunt are 15 m/s and 10 m/s, respectively; and the bunt lasts 0.025 s. What is the change in momentum of the baseball? (c) What is the average force on the ball by the bat?

35. IE ■■ A volleyball is traveling toward you. (a) Which action will require a greater force on the volleyball, your catching the ball or your hitting the ball back? Why? (b) A 0.45-kg volleyball travels with a horizontal velocity of 4.0 m/s over the net. You jump up and hit the ball back with a horizontal velocity of 7.0 m/s. If the contact time is 0.040 s, what was the average force on the ball?

36. ■■ A 1.0-kg ball is thrown horizontally with a velocity of 15 m/s against a wall. If the ball rebounds horizontally with a velocity of 13 m/s and the contact time is 0.020 s, what is the force exerted on the ball by the wall?

37. ■■ A boy catches—with bare hands and his arms rigidly extended—a 0.16-kg baseball coming directly toward him at a speed of 25 m/s. He emits an audible "ouch!", because the ball stings his hands. He learns quickly to move his hands with the ball as he catches it. If the contact time of the collision is increased from 3.5 ms to 8.5 ms in this way, how do the magnitudes of the average impulse forces compare?

38. ■■ A one-dimensional impulse force acts on a 3.0-kg object as diagrammed in ▼Fig. 6.28. Find (a) the magnitude of the impulse given to the object, (b) the magnitude of the average force, and (c) the final speed if the object had an initial speed of 6.0 m/s.

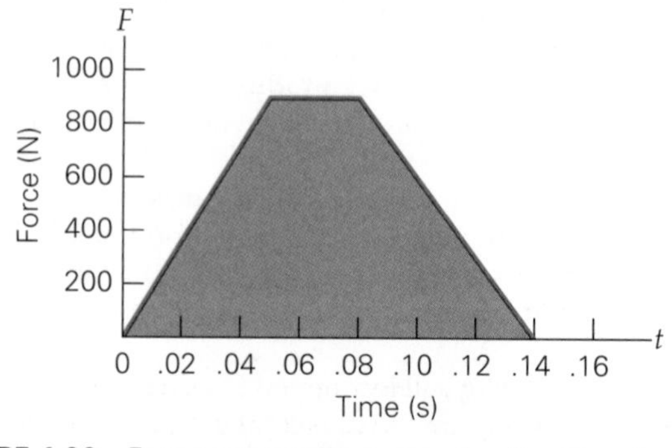

▲ **FIGURE 6.28 Force versus time graph** See Exercise 38.

39. ■■ A 0.35-kg piece of putty is dropped from a height of 2.5 m above a flat surface. When it hits the surface, the putty comes to rest in 0.30 s. What is the average force exerted on the putty by the surface?

40. ■■ If the billiard ball in Fig. 6.26 is in contact with the rail for 0.010 s, what is the magnitude of the average force exerted on the ball? (See Exercise 18.)

41. ■■■ In a simulated head-on crash test, a car impacts a wall at 25 mi/h (40 km/h) and comes abruptly to rest. A 120-lb passenger dummy (with a mass of 55 kg), without a seat belt, is stopped by an air bag, which exerts a force on the dummy of 2400 lb. How long was the dummy in contact with the air bag while coming to a stop?

6.3 The Conservation of Linear Momentum

42. The linear momentum of an object is conserved if (a) the force acting on the object is conservative; (b) there is a single, unbalanced internal force acting on the object; (c) the mechanical energy is conserved; or (d) none of the preceding.

43. Internal forces do not affect the conservation of momentum because (a) they cancel each other, (b) their effects are canceled by external forces, (c) they can never produce a change in velocity, or (d) Newton's second law is not applicable to them.

44. CQ An airboat of the type used in swampy and marshy areas is shown in ▼Fig. 6.29. Explain the principle of its propulsion. Using the concept of conservation of linear momentum, determine what would happen to the boat if a sail were installed behind the fan?

▲ **FIGURE 6.29 Fan propulsion** See Exercise 44.

45. CQ Imagine yourself standing in the middle of a frozen lake. The ice is so smooth that it is frictionless. How could you get to shore? (You couldn't walk. Why?)

46. CQ A stationary object receives a direct hit by another object moving toward it. Is it possible for both objects to be at rest after the collision? Explain.

47. CQ When a golf ball is driven off the tee, its speed is often much greater than the speed of the golf club. Explain how this situation can happen.

48. ■ A 60-kg astronaut floating at rest in space outside a space capsule throws his 0.50-kg hammer such that it moves with a speed of 10 m/s relative to the capsule. What happens to the astronaut?

49. ■ In a pairs figure-skating competition, a 65-kg man and his 45-kg female partner stand facing each other on skates on the ice. If they push apart and the woman has a velocity of 1.5 m/s eastward, what is the velocity of her partner? (Neglect friction.)

50. ■ To get off a frozen, frictionless lake, a 70.0-kg person takes off a 0.150-kg shoe and throws it horizontally, directly away from the shore with a speed of 2.00 m/s. If the person is 5.00 m from the shore, how long does it take for him to reach it?

51. ■■ A 100-g bullet is fired horizontally into a 14.9-kg block of wood resting on a horizontal surface, and the bullet becomes embedded in the block. If the muzzle velocity of the bullet is 250 m/s, what is the speed of the block immediately after the impact? (Neglect surface friction.)

52. IE ■■ An object initially at rest explodes and splits into three fragments. The first fragment flies off to the west, and the second fragment flies off to the south. The third fragment will fly off toward a general direction of (1) southwest, (2) north of east, or (3) either due north or due east. Why? (b) If the object has a mass of 3.0 kg, the first fragment has a mass of 0.50 kg and a speed of 2.8 m/s, and the second fragment has a mass of 1.3 kg and a speed of 1.5 m/s, what are the speed and direction of the third fragment?

53. ■■ Suppose that the 3.0-kg object in Exercise 52 is initially traveling at a speed of 2.5 m/s in the positive x-direction. What will be the speed and direction of the third fragment in this case?

54. ■■ Two identical cars hit each other and lock bumpers. In each of the following cases, what are the speeds of the cars immediately after coupling bumpers? (a) a car moving with a speed of 90 km/h approaches a stationary car; (b) two cars approach each other with speeds of 90 km/h and 120 km/h, respectively; (c) two cars travel in the same direction with speeds of 90 km/h and 120 km/h, respectively.

55. ■■ A 1200-kg car moving to the right with a speed of 25 m/s collides with a 1500-kg truck and locks bumpers with the truck. Calculate the velocity of the combination after the collision if the truck is initially (a) at rest, (b) moving to the right with a speed of 20 m/s, and (c) moving to the left with a speed of 20 m/s.

56. ■■ A 10-g bullet moving horizontally at 400 m/s penetrates a 3.0-kg wood block resting on a horizontal surface. If the bullet slows down to 300 m/s after emerging from

the block, what is the speed of the block immediately after the bullet emerges (▼Fig. 6.30)?

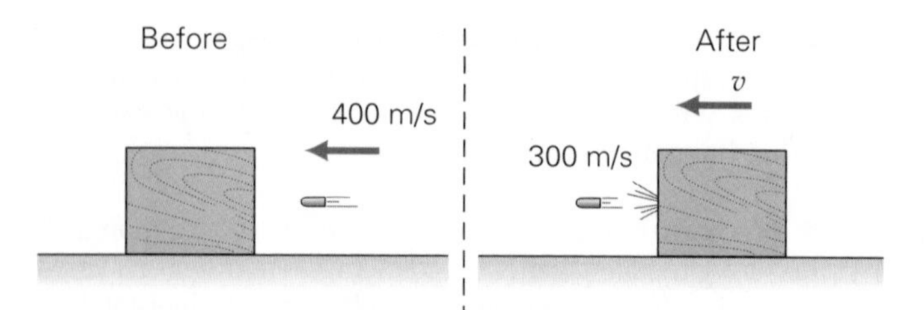

▲ **FIGURE 6.30 Momentum transfer?** See Exercise 56.

57. ■■ A 1600-kg (empty) truck rolls with a speed of 2.5 m/s under a loading bin, and a mass of 3500 kg is deposited in the truck. What is the truck's speed immediately after loading?

58. ■■■ A projectile that is fired from a gun has an initial velocity of 90.0 km/h at an angle of 60.0° above the horizontal. When the projectile is at the top of its trajectory, an internal explosion causes it to separate into two fragments of equal mass. One of the fragments falls straight downward as though it had been released from rest. How far from the gun does the other fragment land?

59. ■■■ A moving shuffleboard puck has a glancing collision with a stationary puck of the same mass, as shown in ▼Fig. 6.31. If friction is negligible, what are the speeds of the pucks after the collision?

60. ■■■ A *ballistic pendulum* is a device used to measure the velocity of a projectile—for example, the muzzle velocity of a rifle bullet. The projectile is shot horizontally into, and becomes embedded in, the bob of a pendulum, as illustrated in ►Fig. 6.32. The pendulum swings upward to some height h, which is measured. The masses of the block and the bullet are known. Using the laws of momentum and energy, show that the initial velocity of the projectile is given by $v_o = [(m + M)/m]\sqrt{2gh}$.

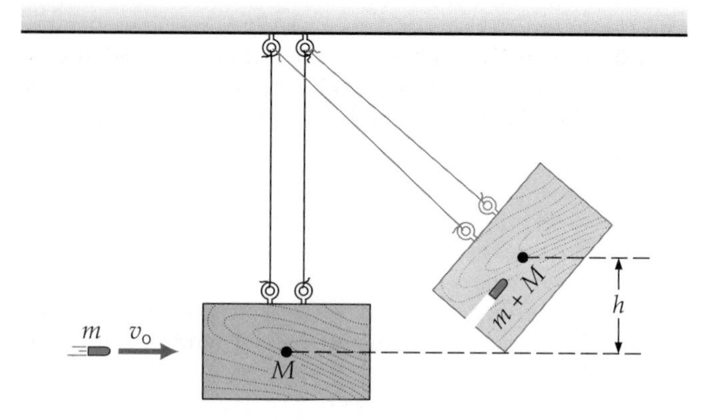

▲ **FIGURE 6.32 A ballistic pendulum** See Exercises 60, 78, and 79.

6.4 Elastic and Inelastic Collisions

61. Which of the following is *not* conserved in an inelastic collision? (a) momentum, (b) mass, (c) kinetic energy, or (d) total energy.

62. In a head-on elastic collision, mass m_1 strikes a stationary mass m_2. There is a complete transfer of energy if (a) $m_1 = m_2$, (b) $m_1 \gg m_2$, (c) $m_1 \ll m_2$, or (d) the masses stick together.

63. CQ Since $K = p^2/2m$, how can kinetic energy be lost in an inelastic collision while the total momentum is still conserved? Explain.

64. CQ Discuss the common and different characteristics of an elastic collision and an inelastic collision.

65. CQ If a rubber ball hits a wall and bounces back with the same speed, is the collision elastic or inelastic? Explain.

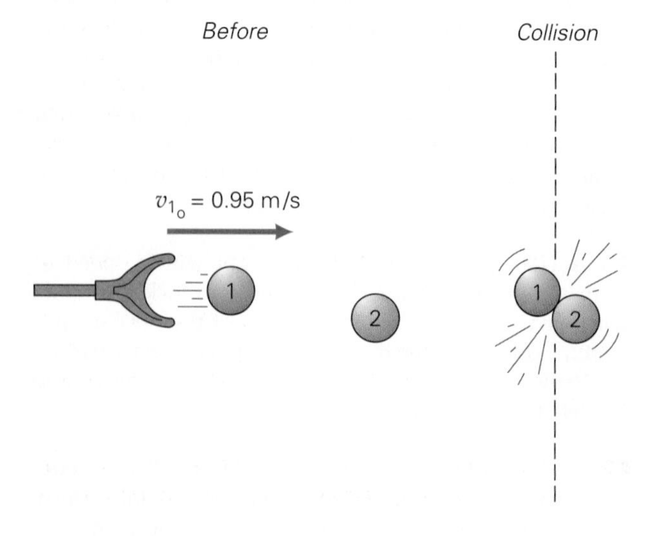

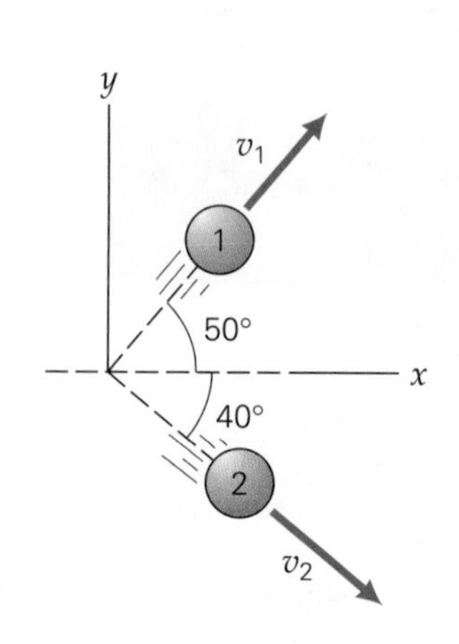

◄ **FIGURE 6.31 Another glancing collision** See Exercise 59.

66. ■■ A 4.0-kg ball with a velocity of 4.0 m/s in the $+x$-direction collides head on elastically with a stationary 2.0-kg ball. What are the velocities of the balls after the collision?

67. ■■ A ball with a mass of 0.10 kg is traveling with a velocity of 0.50 m/s in the $+x$-direction and collides head on with a 5.0-kg ball that is at rest. Find the velocities of the balls after the collision. Assume that the collision is elastic.

68. IE ■■ For the apparatus in Fig. 6.15, one ball swinging in at a speed of $2v_o$ will not cause two balls to swing out with speeds v_o. (a) Which law of physics precludes this situation from happening, the law of conservation of momentum or the law of conservation of mechanical energy? (b) Prove this law mathematically.

69. ■■ A proton of mass m moving with a speed of 3.0×10^6 m/s undergoes a head-on elastic collision with an alpha particle of mass $4m$, which is initially at rest. What are the velocities of the two particles after the collision?

70. ■■ Two balls with masses of 2.0 kg and 6.0 kg travel toward each other at speeds of 12 m/s and 4.0 m/s, respectively. If the balls have a head-on, inelastic collision and the 2.0-kg ball recoils with a speed of 8.0 m/s, how much kinetic energy is lost in the collision?

71. IE ■■ ▼Fig. 6.33 shows a bird catching a fish. Assume that initially the fish jumps up and that the bird coasts horizontally and does not touch water with its feet or flap its wings. (a) Is this kind of collision (1) elastic, (2) inelastic, or (3) completely inelastic? Why? (b) If the mass of the bird is 5.0 kg, the mass of the fish is 0.80 kg, and the bird coasts with a speed of 6.5 m/s before grabbing, what is the speed of the bird after grabbing the fish?

▲ **FIGURE 6.33 Elastic or inelastic?** See Exercise 71.

72. ■■ Two balls approach each other as shown in ▶Fig. 6.34, where $m = 2.0$ kg, $v = 3.0$ m/s, $M = 4.0$ kg, and $V = 5.0$ m/s. If the balls collide and stick together at the origin, (a) what are the components of the velocity v of the balls after collision, and (b) what is the angle θ?

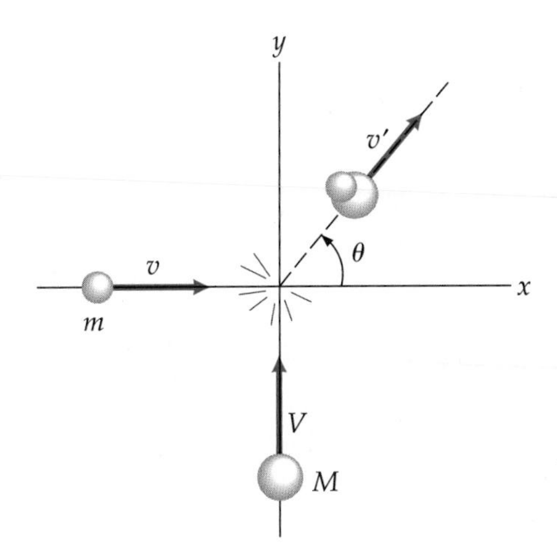

▲ **FIGURE 6.34 A completely inelastic collision** See Exercise 72.

73. IE ■■ A car traveling east and a minivan traveling south collide in a completely inelastic collision at a perpendicular intersection. (a) Right after the collision, will the car and minivan move toward a general direction (1) southeast, (2) north of west, or (3) either due south or due east? Why? (b) If the initial speed of the 1500-kg car was 90.0 km/h and the initial speed of the 3000-kg minivan was 60.0 km/h, what is the velocity of the vehicles immediately after collision?

74. ■■ In a pool game, a cue ball traveling at 0.75 m/s hits the stationary eight ball. The eight ball moves off with a velocity of 0.25 m/s at an angle of 37° relative to the cue ball's initial direction. Assuming that the collision is inelastic, at what angle will the cue ball be deflected, and what will be its speed?

75. ■■ A fellow student states that the total momentum of a three-particle system ($m_1 = 0.25$ kg, $m_2 = 0.20$ kg, and $m_3 = 0.33$ kg) is initially zero, and he calculates that after an inelastic triple collision, the particles have velocities of 4.0 m/s at 0°, 6.0 m/s at 120°, and 2.5 m/s at 230°, respectively, measured from the $+x$-direction. Do you agree with his calculations? If not, assuming the first two answers to be correct, what should be the momentum of the third particle so the total momentum is zero?

76. ■■ A freight car with a mass of 25 000 kg rolls down an inclined track through a vertical distance of 2.5 m. At the bottom of the incline, on a level track, the car collides and couples with an identical freight car that was at rest. What percentage of the initial kinetic energy is lost in the collision?

77. ■■■ In an elastic head-on collision with a stationary target particle, a moving particle recoils at one third of its

incident speed. (a) What is the ratio of the particles' masses (m_1/m_2)? (b) What is the speed of the target particle after the collision in terms of the initial speed of the incoming particle?

78. ■■■ Show that the fraction of kinetic energy lost in a ballistic-pendulum collision (as in Fig. 6.32) is equal to $M/(m + M)$.

79. ■■■ A 10-g bullet is fired horizontally into, and becomes embedded in, a suspended block of wood whose mass is 0.890 kg. (See Fig. 6.32.) (a) How does the speed of the block with the embedded bullet immediately after the collision compare with the initial speed of the bullet (v_o)? (b) If the block with the embedded bullet swings upward and its center of mass is raised 0.40 m, what was the initial speed of the bullet? (c) Was the collision elastic? If not, what percentage of the initial kinetic energy was lost?

80. ■■■ A moving billiard ball collides with an identical stationary one, and the incoming ball is deflected at an angle of 45° from its original direction. Show that if the collision is elastic, both balls will have the same speed afterward and will move at a right angle (90°) relative to each other.

81. ■■■ (a) For an elastic, two-body head-on collision, show that, in general, $v_2 - v_1 = -(v_{2_o} - v_{1_o})$. That is, the relative speed of recession after the collision is the same as the relative speed of approach before it. (b) In general, a collision is either completely inelastic, completely elastic, or somewhere in between. The degree of elasticity is sometimes expressed as the *coefficient of restitution* (e), which is defined as the ratio of the relative velocities of recession and approach: $v_2 - v_1 = -e(v_{2_o} - v_{1_o})$. What are the values of e for an elastic collision and a completely inelastic collision?

82. ■■■ The coefficient of restitution (see Exercise 81) for steel colliding with steel is 0.95. If a steel ball is dropped from a height h_o above a steel plate, to what height will the ball rebound?

6.5 Center of Mass

83. The center of mass of an object (a) always lies at the center of the object, (b) is at the location of the most massive particle in the object, (c) always lies within the object, or (d) none of the preceding.

84. CQ ▸Figure 6.35 shows a performer walking on a tightrope. The long pole he holds curves down at the ends. What effect does this pole have on the center of mass of the performer–pole system?

85. CQ ▸Figure 6.36 shows a flamingo standing on one of its two legs, with its other leg lifted. What can you say about the location of the flamingo's center of mass?

▲ **FIGURE 6.35 Tightrope walking** See Exercise 84.

▲ **FIGURE 6.36 Delicate balance** See Exercise 85.

86. CQ A spacecraft is initially at rest in free space, and then its rocket engines are fired. Describe the motion of the center of mass of the system after the firing.

87. ■ (a) The center of mass of a system consisting of two 0.10-kg particles is located at the origin. If one of the particles is at (0, 0.45 m), where is the other? (b) If the masses are moved so their center of mass is located at (0.25 m, 0.15 m), can you tell where the particles are located?

88. ■ The centers of a 4.0-kg sphere and a 7.5-kg sphere are separated by a distance of 1.5 m. Where is the center of mass of the two-sphere system?

89. ■ (a) Find the center of mass of the Earth–Moon system. [*Hint*: Use data from tables on the inside cover of the book, and consider the distance between the Earth and Moon to be measured from their centers.] (b) Where is that center of mass relative to the surface of the Earth?

90. ■■ Find the center of mass of a system composed of three spherical objects with masses of 3.0 kg, 2.0 kg, and 4.0 kg and centers located at (−6.0 m, 0), (1.0 m, 0), and (3.0 m, 0), respectively.

91. ■■ Rework Exercise 58, using the concept of the center of mass, and compute the distance the other fragment landed from the gun.

92. IE ■■ A 3.0-kg rod of length 5.0 m has at opposite ends point masses of 4.0 kg and 6.0 kg. (a) Will the center of mass of this system be (1) nearer to the 4.0-kg mass, (2) nearer to the 6.0-kg mass, or (3) at the center of the rod? Why? (b) Where is the center of mass of the system?

93. ■■ A piece of uniform sheet metal measures 25 cm by 25 cm. If a circular piece with a radius of 5.0 cm is cut from the center of the sheet, where is the sheet's center of mass now?

94. ■■ Locate the center of mass of the system shown in ▾Fig. 6.37 (a) if all of the masses are equal; (b) if $m_2 = m_4 = 2m_1 = 2m_3$; (c) if $m_1 = 1.0$ kg, $m_2 = 2.0$ kg, $m_3 = 3.0$ kg, and $m_4 = 4.0$ kg.

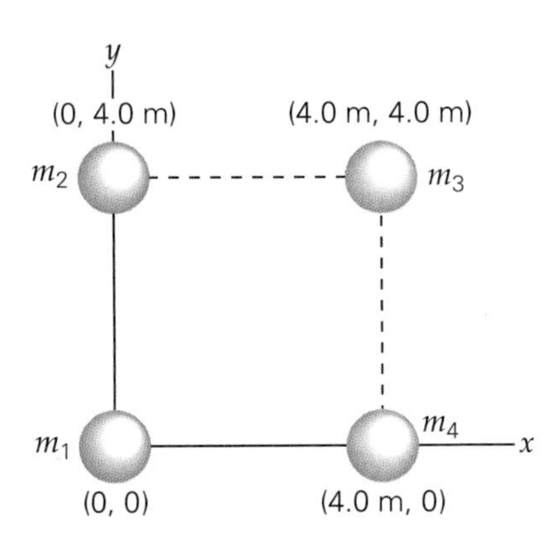

▲ **FIGURE 6.37 Where's the center of mass?** See Exercise 94.

95. ■■ A system of two masses has a center of mass given by X_{CM1}. A different system of three masses has a center of mass given by X_{CM2}. Show that if all five masses are considered to be one system, the center of mass of the combined system is not $X_{CM} = X_{CM1} + X_{CM2}$.

96. ■■ A 100-kg astronaut (mass includes space gear) on a space walk is 5.0 m from a 3000-kg space capsule and at the full length of her safety cord. To return to the capsule, she pulls herself along the cord. Where do the astronaut and capsule meet?

97. ■■ Two skaters with masses of 65 kg and 45 kg, respectively, stand 8.0 m apart, each holding one end of a piece of rope. (a) If they pull themselves along the rope until they meet, how far does each skater travel? (Neglect friction.) (b) If only the 45-kg skater pulls along the rope until she meets her friend (who just holds onto the rope), how far does each skater travel?

98. ■■■ Three particles, each with a mass of 0.25 kg, are located at (−4.0 m, 0), (2.0 m, 0), and (0, 3.0 m) and are acted on by forces $\mathbf{F}_1 = (-3.0\text{ N})\,\hat{\mathbf{y}}$, $\mathbf{F}_2 = (5.0\text{ N})\,\hat{\mathbf{y}}$, and $\mathbf{F}_3 = (4.0\text{ N})\,\hat{\mathbf{x}}$, respectively. Find the acceleration (magnitude and direction) of the center of mass of the system. [*Hint*: Consider the components of the acceleration.]

Additional Exercises

99. CQ Two objects have the same momentum. (a) Will they always have the same kinetic energy? (b) What can you say definitely about their motion?

100. A 1.0-kg object moving at 10 m/s collides with a stationary 2.0-kg object as shown in ▾Fig. 6.38. If the collision is perfectly inelastic, how far along the inclined plane will the combined system travel? Neglect friction.

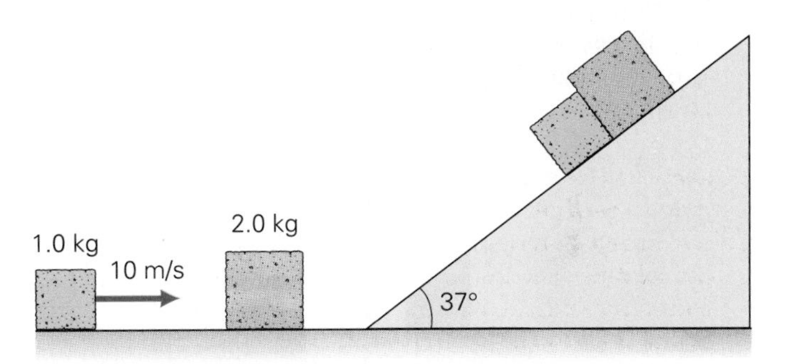

▲ **FIGURE 6.38 How far is up?** See Exercise 100.

101. A 1500-kg truck moving with a speed of 25 m/s runs into the rear of a 1200-kg stopped car. If the collision is perfectly inelastic, what is the kinetic energy lost in the collision?

102. Two balls of equal mass (0.50 kg) approach the origin along the positive *x*- and *y*-axes at the same speed (3.3 m/s). (a) What is the total momentum of the system? (b) Will the balls necessarily collide at the origin? What is the total momentum of the system after both balls have passed through the origin?

103. Two identical billiard balls approach each other at the same speed (2.0 m/s). At what speeds do they rebound after a head-on elastic collision?

104. A truck with a mass of 2400 kg travels at a constant speed of 90 km/h. (a) What is the magnitude of the truck's linear momentum? (b) What average force would be required to stop the truck in 8.0 s?

105. A 15 000-N automobile travels at a speed of 45 km/h northward along a street, and a 7500-N sports car travels at a speed of 60 km/h eastward along an intersecting street.

(a) If neither driver brakes and the cars collide at the intersection and lock bumpers, what will the velocity of the cars be immediately after the collision? (b) What percentage of the initial kinetic energy will be lost in the collision?

106. For a movie scene, a 75-kg stunt man drops from a tree onto a 50-kg sled that is moving on a frozen lake with a velocity of 10 m/s toward the shore. (a) What is the speed of the sled after the stunt man is on board? (b) If the sled hits the bank and stops, but the stunt man keeps on going, with what speed does he leave the sled? (Neglect friction.)

107. IE During a snowball fight, a snowball traveling horizontally hits a student in the back of the head and sticks there. (a) Is this collision elastic or inelastic? Why? (b) If the mass of the snowball is 0.15 kg and its initial speed is 14 m/s, what is the impulse? (c) If the contact time is 0.10 s, what is the average force on the student's head?

108. A 2.5-kg block sliding with a constant velocity of 6.0 m/s on a frictionless horizontal surface approaches a stationary 6.5-kg block. (a) If the blocks suffer a completely inelastic collision, what is their velocity after the collision? (b) How much mechanical energy is lost in the completely inelastic collision?

109. A 90-kg astronaut is stranded in space at a point 6.0 m from his spaceship, and he needs to get back in 4.0 minutes to control the spaceship. To get back, he throws a 0.50-kg piece of equipment so that it moves at a speed of 4.0 m/s directly away from the spaceship. (a) Does he get back in time? (b) How fast must he throw the piece of equipment so he gets back in time?

110. In nuclear reactors, subatomic particles called *neutrons* are slowed down by allowing them to collide with the atoms of a moderator material, such as carbon, which is 12 times more massive than neutrons. (a) In a head-on elastic collision with a carbon atom, what percentage of a neutron's energy is lost? (b) If the neutron has an initial speed of 1.5×10^7 m/s, what will be its speed after collision?

111. A 70-kg athlete achieves a height of 2.25 m in a high jump. Considering the jumper and the Earth as an isolated system, with what speed does the Earth initially move as the jumper launches himself upward?

112. A uniform, flat piece of metal is shaped like an equilateral triangle with sides that are 30 cm long. What are the coordinates of the center of mass in the xy-plane if one apex is at the origin and one side is along the y-axis?

Solids and Fluids

Like the person who is hang gliding, we exist at the intersection of three realms. We walk on the solid surface of the Earth and in our daily lives use solid objects of all sorts, from scissors to computers. But we are surrounded by fluids—liquids and gases—on which we are dependent. Without the water that we drink, we could survive only for a few days at most; without the oxygen in the air we breathe, we could not live for more than a few minutes. Indeed, we ourselves are not nearly as solid as we think. By far the most abundant substance in our bodies is water, and it is in the watery environment of our cells that all chemical processes on which life depends take place.

On the basis of general physical distinctions, matter is commonly divided into three phases: solid, liquid, and gas. A solid has a definite shape and volume. A liquid has a fairly definite volume, but assumes the shape of its container. A gas takes on the shape and volume of its container. Solids and liquids are sometimes called *condensed matter*. We will use a different classification scheme and consider matter in terms of solids and fluids. Liquids and gases are referred to collectively as fluids. A **fluid** is a substance that can flow; liquids and gases qualify, but solids do not.

A simplistic description of solids is that they are made up of particles called atoms that are held rigidly together by interatomic forces. Real solid bodies are not absolutely rigid and can be elastically deformed by external forces. Elasticity usually brings to mind a rubber band or spring that will resume its original dimensions even after being greatly deformed. In fact, all materials—even very hard steel—are elastic to some degree. But, as you will learn, such deformation has an *elastic limit*.

Fluids, however, have little or no elastic response to a force. Instead, the force merely causes an unconfined fluid to flow. This chapter pays particular attention to the behavior of fluids, shedding light on such questions as how hydraulic lifts work, why icebergs and ocean liners float, and what the 10W–30 on a can of motor oil means. You'll also discover why the person in the photo can neither float like a helium balloon nor fly like a hummingbird, yet, with the aid of a suitably shaped piece of plastic, can soar like an eagle.

Because of their fluidity, liquids and gases have many properties in common, and it is convenient to study them together. There are important differences as well. For example, liquids are not very compressible, whereas gases are easily compressed, as we will see shortly.

7.1 Solids and Elastic Moduli

OBJECTIVES: **To (a) distinguish between stress and strain and (b) use elastic moduli to compute dimensional changes.**

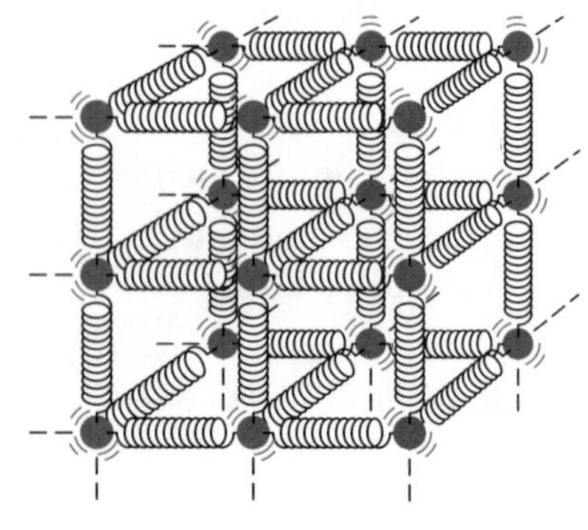

▲ **FIGURE 7.1 A springy solid** The elastic nature of interatomic forces is indicated by simplistically representing them as springs, which, like the forces, resist deformation.

As stated previously, all solid materials are elastic to some degree. That is, a body which is slightly deformed by an applied force will return to its original dimensions or shape when the force is removed. The deformation may not be noticeable for many materials, but it's there.

You may be able to visualize why materials are elastic if you think in terms of the simplistic model of a solid in ◀Fig. 7.1. The atoms of the solid substance are imagined to be held together by springs. The elasticity of the springs represents the resilient nature of the interatomic forces. The springs resist permanent deformation, as do the forces between atoms. The elastic properties of solids are commonly discussed in terms of stress and strain. **Stress** is a measure of the force causing a deformation. **Strain** is a relative measure of the deformation a stress causes. Quantitatively, *stress is the applied force per unit cross-sectional area*:

$$\text{stress} = \frac{F}{A} \tag{7.1}$$

SI unit of stress: newton per square meter (N/m^2)

Here, F is the magnitude of the applied force normal (perpendicular) to the cross-sectional area. Equation 7.1 shows that the SI units for stress are newtons per square meter (N/m^2).

As illustrated in ▼Fig. 7.2, a force applied to the ends of a rod gives rise to either a *tensile stress* (an elongating tension, $+\Delta L$) or a *compressional stress* (a shortening tension, $-\Delta L$), depending on the direction of the force. In both these cases,

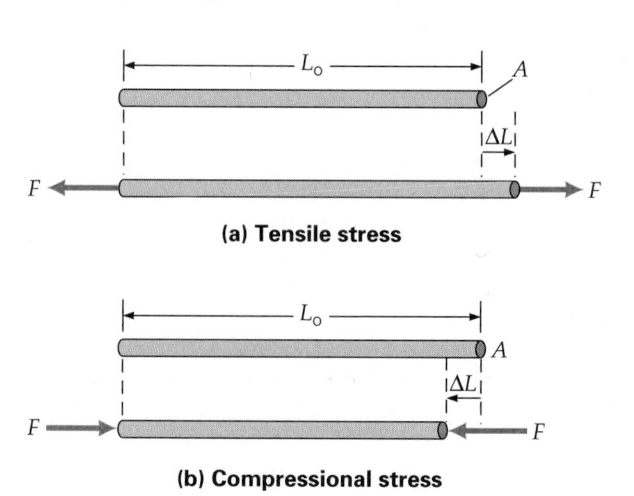

▶ **FIGURE 7.2 Tensile and compressional stress and strain** Tensile and compressional stresses are due to forces applied normally to the surface area of the ends of bodies. **(a)** A tension, or tensile stress, tends to increase the length of an object. **(b)** A compressional stress tends to shorten the length. $\Delta L = L - L_o$ can be positive, as in (a), or negative, as in (b). The sign is not needed in Eq. 7.2, so the absolute value, $|\Delta L|$, is used.

the *tensile strain* is the ratio of the change in length ($\Delta L = L - L_o$) to the original length (L_o), without regard to the sign, so we use the absolute value, $|\Delta L|$:

$$\text{strain} = \frac{\text{change in length}}{\text{original length}} = \frac{|\Delta L|}{L_o} = \frac{|L - L_o|}{L_o} \tag{7.2}$$

Strain is a positive unitless quantity

Thus the strain is the *fractional change* in length. For example, if the strain is 0.05, the length of the material has changed by 5% of the original length.

As might be expected, the resulting strain is proportional to the applied stress; that is, strain $\propto$ stress. For relatively small stresses, this is a direct proportion. The constant of proportionality, which depends on the nature of the material, is called the **elastic modulus**. Thus,

Definition of elastic modulus

$$\text{stress} = \text{elastic modulus} \times \text{strain}$$

or

$$\text{elastic modulus} = \frac{\text{stress}}{\text{strain}} \tag{7.3}$$

SI unit of elastic modulus: newton per square meter (N/m^2)

That is, the elastic modulus is the stress divided by the strain, and the elastic modulus has the same units as stress. (Why?)

Three general types of elastic moduli (plural of modulus) are associated with stresses that produce changes in length, shape, or volume. These are called *Young's modulus*, the *shear modulus*, and the *bulk modulus*, respectively.

Change in Length: Young's Modulus

▼Figure 7.3 is a graph of the tensile stress versus the strain for a typical metal rod. The curve is a straight line up to a point called the *proportional limit*. Beyond this point, the strain begins to increase more rapidly to another critical point called the **elastic limit**. If the tension is removed at this point, the material will return to its original length. If the tension is applied beyond the elastic limit and then removed, the material will recover somewhat, but will retain some permanent deformation.

The straight-line part of the graph shows a direct proportionality between stress and strain. This relationship, first formalized by Robert Hooke in 1678, is

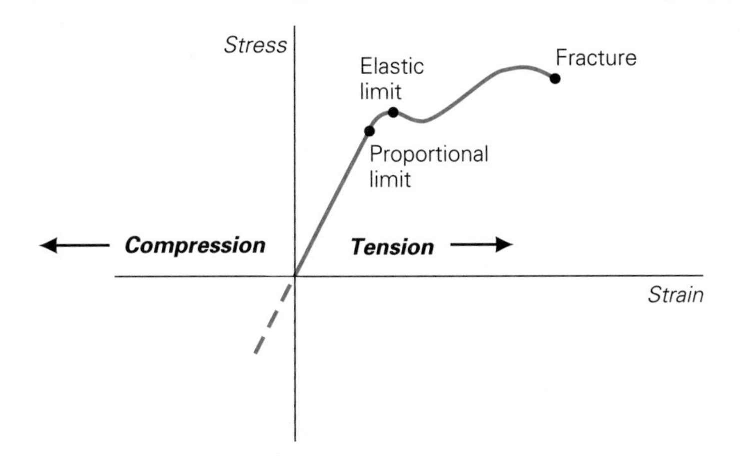

◀ **FIGURE 7.3 Stress versus strain** A plot of stress versus strain for a typical metal rod is a straight line up to the proportional limit. Then elastic deformation continues until the elastic limit is reached. Beyond that, the rod will be permanently deformed and will eventually fracture or break.

now known as *Hooke's law*. (It is the same general relationship as that given for a spring in Section 5.2—see Fig. 5.5.) The elastic modulus for a tension or a compression is called **Young's modulus** (Y):

$$\underbrace{\frac{F}{A}}_{\text{stress}} = Y\underbrace{\left(\frac{\Delta L}{L_o}\right)}_{\text{strain}} \quad \text{or} \quad Y = \frac{F/A}{\Delta L/L_o} \tag{7.4}$$

SI unit of Young's modulus: newton per square meter (N/m^2)

Thomas Young (1773–1829) was a British physicist who investigated the mechanical properties of materials, as well as optical phenomena.

The units of Young's modulus are the same as those of stress, newtons per square meter (N/m^2), since the strain is unitless. Some typical values of Young's modulus are given in Table 7.1.

To obtain a conceptual or physical understanding of Young's modulus, let's solve Eq. 7.4 for ΔL:

$$\Delta L = \left(\frac{FL_o}{A}\right)\frac{1}{Y} \quad \text{or} \quad \Delta L \propto \frac{1}{Y}$$

Hence, the larger the modulus of a material, the smaller its change in length (other parameters being equal).

Young's Modulus and Tensile Strength

Example 7.1 ■ Pulling My Leg: Under a Lot of Stress

The femur (upper leg bone) is the longest and strongest bone in the body. Taking a typical femur to be approximately circular with a radius of 2.0 cm, how much force would be required to extend the bone by 0.010%?

Thinking It Through. We can see that Eq. 7.4 should apply, but where does the percentage increase fit in? We can answer this question as soon as we recognize that the $\Delta L/L_o$ term is the *fractional* increase in length. For example, if you had a spring with a length of 10 cm (L_o), and you stretched it 1.0 cm (ΔL), then $\Delta L/L_o = 1.0\text{ cm}/10\text{ cm} = 0.10$. This ratio can readily be changed to a percentage, and we would say the spring's length was increased by 10%. So the percentage increase is really just the value of the $\Delta L/L_o$ term (multiplied by 100%).

Solution. Listing the data, we have the following:

Given: $r = 2.0\text{ cm} = 0.020\text{ m}$
$\Delta L/L_o = 0.010\% = 1.0 \times 10^{-4}$
$Y = 1.5 \times 10^{10}\text{ N/m}^2$ (for bone from Table 7.1)

Find: F (tensile force)

TABLE 7.1 Elastic Moduli for Various Materials (in N/m^2)

Substance	*Young's Modulus (Y)*	*Shear Modulus (S)*	*Bulk Modulus (B)*
Solids			
Aluminum	7.0×10^{10}	2.5×10^{10}	7.0×10^{10}
Bone (limb)	1.5×10^{10}	8.0×10^{10}	
Brass	9.0×10^{10}	3.5×10^{10}	7.5×10^{10}
Copper	11×10^{10}	3.8×10^{10}	12×10^{10}
Glass	5.7×10^{10}	2.4×10^{10}	4.0×10^{10}
Iron	15×10^{10}	6.0×10^{10}	12×10^{10}
Steel	20×10^{10}	8.2×10^{10}	15×10^{10}
Liquids			
Alcohol, ethyl			1.0×10^9
Glycerin			4.5×10^9
Mercury			26×10^9
Water			2.2×10^9

Using Eq. 7.4, we have

$$F = Y(\Delta L/L_o)A = Y(\Delta L/L_o)\pi r^2$$
$$= (1.5 \times 10^{10}\ \text{N/m}^2)(1.0 \times 10^{-4})\pi(0.020\ \text{m})^2 = 1.9 \times 10^3\ \text{N}$$

How much force is this? Quite a bit—in fact, more than 400 lb. The femur is a pretty strong bone.

Follow-up Exercise. A total mass of 16 kg is suspended from a 0.10-cm-diameter steel wire. (a) By what percentage does the length of the wire increase? (b)The tensile or ultimate strength of a material is the maximum stress the material can support before breaking or fracturing. If the tensile strength of the steel wire in (a) is $4.9 \times 10^8\ \text{N/m}^2$, how much mass could be suspended before the wire would break? *(Answers to all Follow-up Exercises are at the back of the text.)*

Change in Shape: Shear Modulus

Another way an elastic body can be deformed is by a *shear stress*. In this case, the deformation is due to an applied force that is tangential to the surface area (▸Fig. 7.4). A change in shape results without a change in volume. The *shear strain* is given by x/h, where x is the relative displacement of the faces and h is the distance between them.

The shear strain is sometimes defined in terms of the *shear angle* ϕ. As Fig. 7.4 shows, $\tan\phi = x/h$. But the shear angle is usually quite small, so a good approximation is $\tan\phi \approx \phi \approx x/h$, where ϕ is in radians. (If $\phi = 10°$, for example, there is only 1.0% difference between ϕ and $\tan\phi$.) The **shear modulus** (sometimes called the *modulus of rigidity*) is then

$$S = \frac{F/A}{x/h} \approx \frac{F/A}{\phi} \qquad (7.5)$$

SI unit of shear modulus: newton per square meter (N/m²)

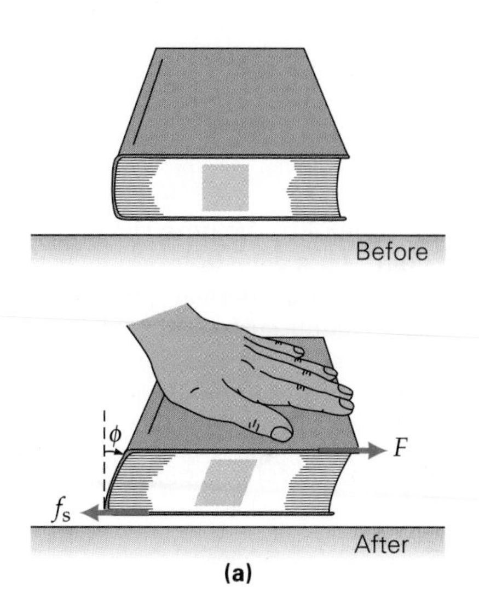

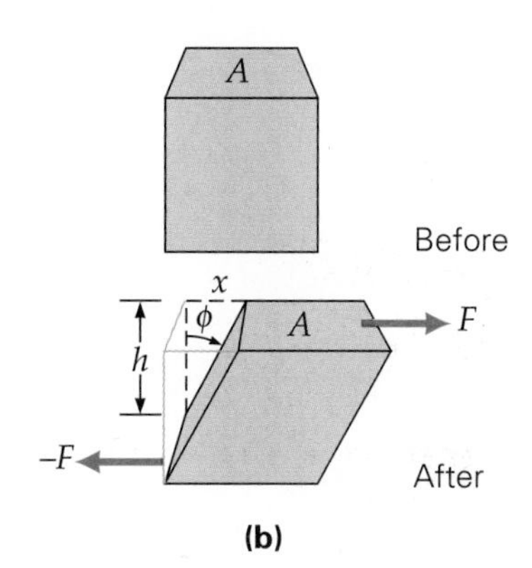

▲ **FIGURE 7.4 Shear stress and strain** A shear stress is produced when a force is applied tangentially to a surface area. The strain is measured in terms of the relative displacement of the object's faces, or the shear angle ϕ.

Note in Table 7.1 that the shear modulus is generally less than Young's modulus. In fact, S is approximately $Y/3$ for many materials, which indicates that there is a greater response to a shear stress than to a tensile stress. Note also the inverse relationship $\phi \approx 1/S$, similar to that pointed out previously for Young's modulus.

A shear stress may be of the torsional type, resulting from the twisting action of a torque. For example, a torsional shear stress may shear off the head of a bolt that is being tightened.

Liquids do not have shear moduli (or Young's moduli)—hence the gaps in Table 7.1. A shear stress cannot be effectively applied to a liquid or a gas. It is often said that *fluids cannot support a shear.* (Why?)

Change in Volume: Bulk Modulus

Suppose that a force directed inward acts over the entire surface of a body (▸Fig. 7.5). Such a *volume stress* is often applied by pressure transmitted by a fluid. An elastic material will be compressed by a volume stress; that is, the material will show a change in volume, but not in general shape, in response to a pressure change Δp. (Pressure is force per unit area, as we shall see in Section 7.2.) The change in pressure is equal to the volume stress, or $\Delta p = F/A$. The *volume strain* is the ratio of the volume change (ΔV) to the original volume (V_o). The **bulk modulus** is then

$$B = \frac{F/A}{-\Delta V/V_o} = -\frac{\Delta p}{\Delta V/V_o} \qquad (7.6)$$

SI unit of bulk modulus: newton per square meter (N/m²)

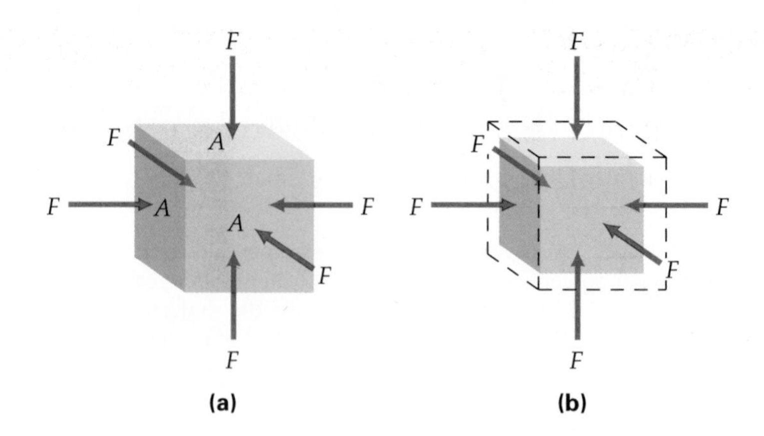

▶ **FIGURE 7.5 Volume stress and strain** **(a)** A volume stress is applied when a normal force acts over an entire surface area, as shown here for a cube. This type of stress most commonly occurs in gases. **(b)** The resulting strain is a change in volume.

The minus sign is introduced to make B a positive quantity, since $\Delta V = V - V_o$ is negative for an increase in external pressure (when Δp is positive). Similarly to the previous moduli relationships, $\Delta V \propto 1/B$.

Bulk moduli of solids and liquids are listed in Table 7.1. Gases also have bulk moduli, since they can be compressed. For a gas, it is common to talk about the reciprocal of the bulk modulus, which is called the **compressibility** (k):

$$k = \frac{1}{B} \quad \textit{(compressibility for gases)} \qquad (7.7)$$

The change in volume ΔV is thus directly proportional to the compressibility k.

Solids and liquids are relatively incompressible and thus have small values of compressibility. Conversely, gases are easily compressed and have large compressibilities, which vary with pressure and temperature.

Example 7.2 ■ Compressing a Liquid: Volume Stress and Bulk Modulus

By how much should the pressure on a liter of water be changed to compress it by 0.10%?

Thinking It Through. Similarly to the fractional change in length, $\Delta L/L_o$, the fractional change in volume is given by $-\Delta V/V_o$, which may be expressed as a percentage. The pressure change can then be found from Eq. 7.6. Compression implies a negative ΔV.

Solution. Listing the data, we have the following:

Given: $-\Delta V/V_o = 0.0010$ (or 0.10%)
$V_o = 1.0\ \text{L} = 1000\ \text{cm}^3$
$B_{H_2O} = 2.2 \times 10^9\ \text{N/m}^2$ (from Table 7.1)

Find: Δp

Note that $-\Delta V/V_o$ is the *fractional* change in the volume. With $V_o = 1000\ \text{cm}^3$, the reduction in volume is

$$-\Delta V = 0.0010\,V_o = 0.0010\,(1000\ \text{cm}^3) = 1.0\ \text{cm}^3$$

However, the change in volume is not needed. The fractional change, as listed in the given data, can be used directly in Eq. 7.6 to find the increase in pressure:

$$\Delta p = B\left(\frac{-\Delta V}{V_o}\right) = (2.2 \times 10^9\ \text{N/m}^2)(0.0010) = 2.2 \times 10^6\ \text{N/m}^2$$

(This increase is about 22 times normal atmospheric pressure!)

Follow-up Exercise. If an extra $1.0 \times 10^6\ \text{N/m}^2$ of pressure above normal atmospheric pressure is applied to a half liter of water, what is the change in the water's volume?

INSIGHT

Feat of Strength or Knowledge of Materials?

The breaking of wooden boards, concrete blocks, or similar materials with a bare hand or foot is an impressive demonstration often performed by martial arts experts (Fig. 1). The physics of this feat can be analyzed in terms of the properties of the materials involved.

In delivering the blow, the expert imparts a large impulse force (Chapter 6) to the top board or block, which bends under the pressure. Note that the objects are struck midway between the end supports. At the same time, the bones of the hand are being compressed as well. Fortunately, human bone can withstand more compressive force than can wood, tile, or concrete, which is why the expert's bones aren't damaged. The ultimate compressive strength of bone is at least four times greater than that of concrete.*

When each board or block is hit, the upper surface is compressed and the lower surface is elongated, or subjected to a tension force. Wood, tile, and concrete are weaker under tension than under compression. (The ultimate tensile strength of concrete is only about a twentieth of its ultimate compressive strength.) The board or block therefore begins to crack at the bottom surface first. The crack propagates from the underside *toward* the hand, widens, and becomes a complete break. Thus, the hand never actually "cuts through" the board or block.

The amount of force required to break a board or block in this way depends on several factors. For a wooden board, these include the type of wood, the width and thickness of the board or block, and the distance between the end supports. Also, the edge of the hand must strike the board parallel to the grain of the wood. Similar considerations apply for a tile or a concrete block. Because tile and concrete are more rigid than wood, more force is generally required to break these substances.

*Ultimate strength is the maximum strength a material can stand before it breaks or fractures.

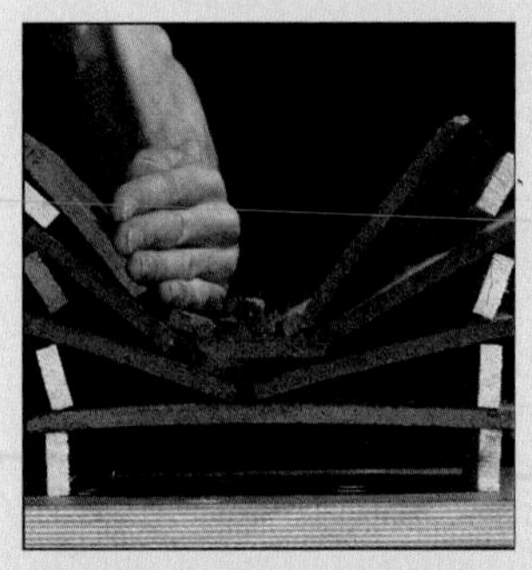

FIGURE 1 Feat of strength or knowledge of materials? Breaking wooden boards, concrete blocks, or roofing tiles (as shown here) with a karate blow depends on both the physical strength of the expert and the strength of the material. Wood, concrete, and tile have different maximum tensile and compressional stresses, but the maximum compressional strength of bone is greater than any of these. (This photo, from a high-speed photography sequence, was made toward the end of the blow.)

Some karate experts are able to break through a stack of boards or tiles and more than one concrete block. The force required does not increase by a factor equal to the number of objects. High-speed photography shows that the hand makes contact with only one or two boards or tiles at the top of the stack. Then, as each object breaks, it collides with and breaks through the one below it.

Even though the properties of the materials seem to guarantee the success of this demonstration, you should not attempt the feat unless you are an expert and know what you're doing. The board or block might win.

7.2 Fluids: Pressure and Pascal's Principle

OBJECTIVES: **To (a) explain the pressure-depth relationship and (b) state Pascal's principle and describe how it is used in practical applications.**

A force can be applied to a solid at a point of contact, but this won't work with a fluid, since a fluid cannot support a shear. With fluids, a force must be applied over an area. Such an application of force is expressed in terms of **pressure**, or the *force per unit area*:

Definition of pressure—force per unit area

$$p = \frac{F}{A} \qquad (7.8a)$$

SI unit of pressure: newton per square meter (N/m^2), or pascal (Pa)

The force in this equation is understood to be acting normally (perpendicularly) to the surface area. F may be the perpendicular component of a force that acts at an angle to the surface (▶Fig. 7.6).

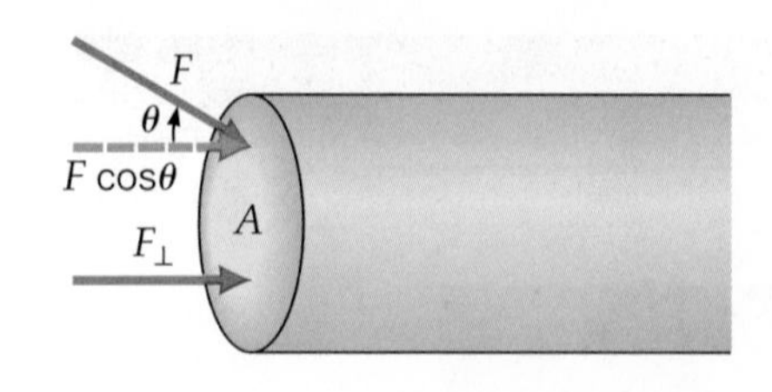

$$p = \frac{F_\perp}{A} = \frac{F\cos\theta}{A}$$

▲ **FIGURE 7.6 Pressure** Pressure is usually written $p = F/A$, where it is understood that F is the force or component of force normal to the surface. In general, then, $p = (F\cos\theta)/A$.

As Fig. 7.6 shows, in the more general case we should write

$$p = \frac{F_\perp}{A} = \frac{F\cos\theta}{A} \tag{7.8b}$$

Pressure is a scalar quantity (with magnitude only), even though the force producing it or the force produced within a fluid by a pressure does have direction and so is a vector.

Pressure has SI units of newton per square meter (N/m^2), or **pascal (Pa)**, in honor of the French scientist and philosopher Blaise Pascal (1623–1662), who studied fluids and pressure. By definition,

$$1\ \text{Pa} = 1\ \text{N/m}^2$$

In the British system, a common unit of pressure is pound per square inch (lb/in^2, or psi). Other units, some of which will be introduced later, are used in special applications. Before going on, here's a "solid" example of the relationship between force and pressure.

Conceptual Example 7.3 ■ Force and Pressure: Taking a Nap on a Bed of Nails

Suppose you are getting ready to take a nap, and you have a choice of lying stretched out on your back on (a) a bed of nails, (b) a hardwood floor, or (c) a couch. Which one would you choose, and *why*? (See Fig. 7.27.)

Reasoning and Answer. The comfortable choice is quite apparent—the couch. But here, the conceptual question is *why*.

First let's look at the prospect of lying on a bed of nails, an old trick that originated in India and used to be demonstrated in carnival sideshows. There is really no trick here, just physics—namely, force and pressure. It is the force per unit area, or pressure ($p = F/A$), that determines whether a nail will pierce the skin. The force is determined by the weight of the person lying on the nails. The area is determined by the *effective* area of the nails in contact with the skin (neglecting one's clothes). If there were only one nail, the person's weight on the area of its tip (pressure) would be very great—a situation in which the lone nail would pierce the skin. However, when a bed of nails is used, the same force (weight) is distributed over hundreds of nails, which gives a relatively large effective area of contact. The pressure is then reduced to a level at which the nails do not pierce the skin.

When you are lying on a hardwood floor, the area in contact with your body is appreciable and the pressure is reduced, but it still may be uncomfortable. Parts of your body, such as your neck and the small of your back, are *not* in contact with a surface, but they would be on a soft couch, making for a comfortable pressure—the lower the pressure, the more comfort (same force over a larger area). So (c) is the answer.

Follow-up Exercise. What are a couple of important considerations in constructing a bed of nails to lie on?

Now, let's take a quick review of density, which is an important consideration in the study of fluids. Recall from Chapter 1 that the density (ρ) of a substance is defined as (Eq. 1.1)

$$\text{density} = \frac{\text{mass}}{\text{volume}}$$

$$\rho = \frac{m}{V}$$

SI unit of density: kilogram per cubic meter (kg/m^3)
(common cgs unit: gram per cubic centimeter, or g/cm^3)

TABLE 7.2 Densities of Some Common Substances (in kg/m^3)

Solids	*Density* (ρ)	*Liquids*	*Density* (ρ)	*Gases**	*Density* (ρ)
Aluminum	2.7×10^3	Alcohol, ethyl	0.79×10^3	Air	1.29
Brass	8.7×10^3	Alcohol, methyl	0.82×10^3	Helium	0.18
Copper	8.9×10^3	Blood, whole	1.05×10^3	Hydrogen	0.090
Glass	2.6×10^3	Blood plasma	1.03×10^3	Oxygen	1.43
Gold	19.3×10^3	Gasoline	0.68×10^3	Water vapor (100°C)	0.63
Ice	0.92×10^3	Kerosene	0.82×10^3		
Iron (and steel)	7.8×10^3 (general value)	Mercury	13.6×10^3		
Lead	11.4×10^3	Seawater (4°C)	1.03×10^3		
Silver	10.5×10^3	Water, fresh (4°C)	1.00×10^3		
Wood, oak	0.81×10^3				

*At 0°C and 1 atm, unless otherwise specified.

That is, density is mass per *unit* volume. The densities of some common substances are given in Table 7.2.

Water has a density of 1.00×10^3 kg/m^3 (or 1.00 g/cm^3), from the original definition of the kilogram (Chapter 1). Mercury has a density of 13.6×10^3 kg/m^3 (or 13.6 g/cm^3). Hence, mercury is 13.6 times denser than water. Gasoline, however, is less dense than water. (See Table 7.2.) (*Note*: Be careful not to confuse the symbol for density, ρ, with that for pressure, p.)

We say that density is a measure of the compactness of the matter of a substance: The greater the density, the more matter or mass there is in a given volume. Notice how density quantifies the amount or mass per unit volume. It would be incorrect to say that mercury is "heavier" than water, because you could have a large volume of water that would be heavier than some much smaller volume of mercury.

Pressure and Depth

If you have gone scuba diving, you well know that pressure increases with depth, having felt the increased pressure on your eardrums. An opposite effect is commonly felt when you fly in a plane or ride in a car going up a mountain: With increasing altitude, your ears may "pop" because of *reduced* external air pressure.

How the pressure in a fluid varies with depth can be demonstrated by considering a container of liquid at rest. Imagine that you can isolate a rectangular column of water, as shown in ▼Fig. 7.7. Then the force on the bottom of the container below the column (or the hand) is equal to the weight of the liquid making up the

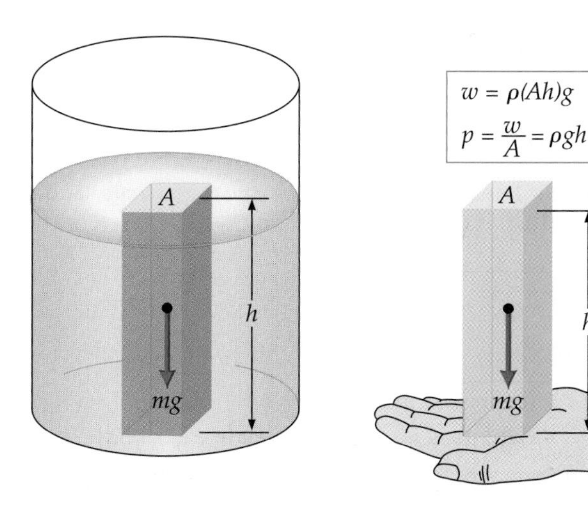

◀ **FIGURE 7.7 Pressure and depth** The extra pressure at a depth h in a liquid is due to the weight of the liquid above: $p = \rho gh$, where ρ is the density of the liquid (assumed to be constant). This is shown for an imaginary rectangular column of liquid.

column: $F = w = mg$. Since density is $\rho = m/V$, the mass in the column is equal to the density times the volume; that is, $m = \rho V$. (The liquid is assumed incompressible, so ρ is constant.)

The volume of the isolated liquid column is equal to the height of the column times the area of its base, or $V = hA$. Thus, we can write

$$F = w = mg = \rho V g = \rho g h A$$

With $p = F/A$, the pressure at a depth h due to the weight of the column is

$$p = \rho g h \tag{7.9}$$

This is a general result for incompressible liquids. The pressure is the same everywhere on a horizontal plane at a depth h (with ρ and g constant). Note that Eq. 7.9 is independent of the base area of the rectangular column: We could have taken the whole cylindrical column of the liquid in the container in Fig. 7.7 and gotten the same result.

The derivation of Eq. 7.9 did not take into account pressure being applied to the open surface of the liquid. This factor adds to the pressure at a depth h to give a *total* pressure of

Pressure-depth relationship

$$p = p_o + \rho g h \quad \textit{(incompressible fluid at constant density)} \tag{7.10}$$

where p_o is the pressure applied to the liquid surface (that is, the pressure at $h = 0$). For an open container, p_o is atmospheric pressure, or the weight (force) per unit area due to the gases in the atmosphere above the liquid's surface. The average atmospheric pressure at sea level is sometimes used as a unit, called an **atmosphere (atm)**:

$$1 \text{ atm} \equiv 101.325 \text{ kPa} = 1.01325 \times 10^5 \text{ N/m}^2 \approx 14.7 \text{ lb/in}^2.$$

The measurement of atmospheric pressure is described shortly.

Example 7.4 ■ A Scuba Diver: Pressure and Force

(a) What is the total pressure on the back of a scuba diver in a lake at a depth of 8.00 m? (b) What is the force on the diver's back due to the water alone, taking the surface of the back to be a rectangle 60.0 cm by 50.0 cm?

Thinking It Through. (a) This is a direct application of Eq. 7.10 in which p_o is taken as the atmospheric pressure p_a. (b) Knowing the area and the pressure due to the water, the force can be found from the definition of pressure, $p = F/A$.

Solution.

Given: $h = 8.00$ m
$A = 60.0 \text{ cm} \times 50.0 \text{ cm} = 0.600 \text{ m} \times 0.500 \text{ m} = 0.300 \text{ m}^2$
$\rho_{H_2O} = 1.00 \times 10^3 \text{ kg/m}^3$ (from Table 7.2)
$p_a = 1.01 \times 10^5 \text{ N/m}^2$

Find: (a) p (total pressure)
(b) F (force due to water)

(a) The total pressure is the sum of the pressure due to the water and the atmospheric pressure (p_a). By Eq. 7.10, this is

$$\begin{aligned} p &= p_a + \rho g h \\ &= (1.01 \times 10^5 \text{ N/m}^2) + (1.00 \times 10^3 \text{ kg/m}^3)(9.80 \text{ m/s}^2)(8.00 \text{ m}) \\ &= (1.01 \times 10^5 \text{ N/m}^2) + (0.784 \times 10^5 \text{ N/m}^2) = 1.79 \times 10^5 \text{ N/m}^2 \text{ (or Pa)} \end{aligned}$$

$$\text{(expressed in atmospheres)} \approx 1.8 \text{ atm}$$

(b) The pressure p_{H_2O} due to the water alone is the $\rho g h$ portion of the preceding equation, so $p_{H_2O} = 0.784 \times 10^5 \text{ N/m}^2$.

Then, $p_{H_2O} = F/A$, and

$$F = p_{H_2O}A = (0.784 \times 10^5 \text{ N/m}^2)(0.300 \text{ m}^2)$$
$$= 2.35 \times 10^4 \text{ N (or } 5.29 \times 10^3 \text{ lb—about 2.6 tons!)}$$

Follow-up Exercise. You might question the answer to part (b) of this Example—how could the diver support such a force? To get a better idea of the forces our bodies can support, what would be the force on the diver's back at the water surface from atmospheric pressure alone? How do you suppose our bodies can support such forces or pressures?

Pascal's Principle

When the pressure (for example, air pressure) is increased on the entire open surface of an incompressible liquid at rest, the pressure at any point in the liquid or on the boundary surfaces increases by the same amount. The effect is the same if pressure is applied to any surface of an enclosed fluid by means of a piston (▸Fig. 7.8). The transmission of pressure in fluids was studied by Pascal, and the observed effect is called **Pascal's principle**:

Pascal's principle

> Pressure applied to an enclosed fluid is transmitted undiminished to every point in the fluid and to the walls of the container.

For an incompressible liquid, the change in pressure is transmitted essentially instantaneously. For a gas, a change in pressure will generally be accompanied by a change in volume or temperature (or both), but after equilibrium has been reestablished, Pascal's principle remains valid.

Common practical applications of Pascal's principle include the hydraulic braking systems used on automobiles. Through tubes filled with brake fluid, a force on the brake pedal transmits a force to the wheel brake cylinder. Similarly, hydraulic lifts and jacks are used to raise automobiles and other heavy objects (▾Fig. 7.9).

Using Pascal's principle, we can show how such systems not only allow us to transmit force from one place to another, but also to multiply that force. The input pressure p_i supplied by compressed air for a garage lift, for example, gives an input force F_i on a small piston area A_i (Fig. 7.9). The full magnitude of the pressure is transmitted to the output piston, which has an area A_o. Since $p_i = p_o$, it follows that

$$\frac{F_i}{A_i} = \frac{F_o}{A_o}$$

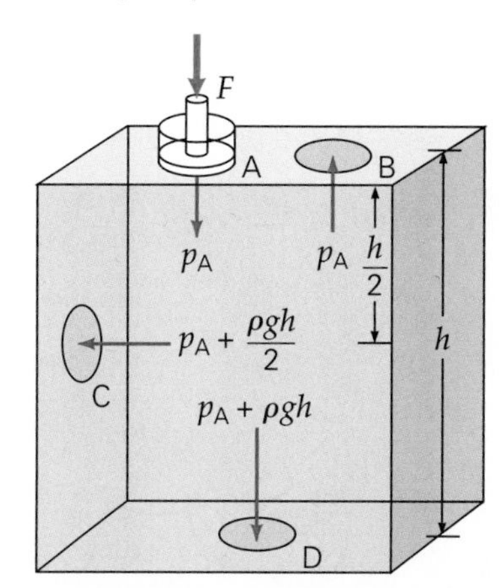

▲ **FIGURE 7.8 Pascal's principle** The pressure applied at point A is fully transmitted to all parts of the fluid and to the walls of the container. There is also pressure due to the weight of the fluid above at different depths (for instance, $\rho gh/2$ at C and ρgh at D).

▾ **FIGURE 7.9 The hydraulic lift and shock absorbers** **(a)** Because the input and output pressures are equal (Pascal's principle), a small input force gives a large output force proportional to the ratio of the piston areas. **(b)** A simplified exposed view of one type of shock absorber. (See Follow-up Exercise 7.5 for description.)

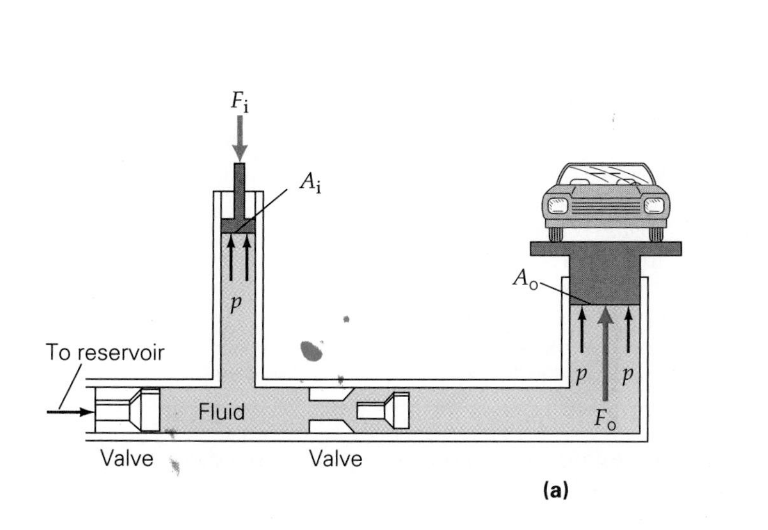

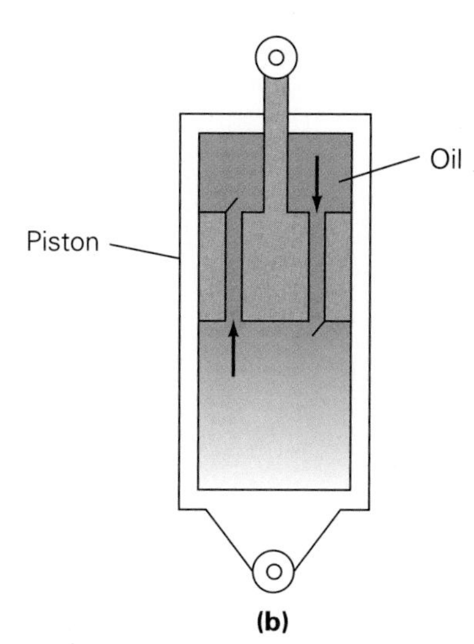

and

$$F_o = \left(\frac{A_o}{A_i}\right)F_i \quad \textit{hydraulic force multiplication} \tag{7.11}$$

With A_o larger than A_i, F_o will be larger than F_i. The input force is greatly multiplied if the input piston has a relatively small area.

Example 7.5 ■ The Hydraulic Lift: Pascal's Principle

A garage lift has input and lift (output) pistons with diameters of 10 cm and 30 cm, respectively. The lift is used to hold up a car with a weight of 1.4×10^4 N. (a) What is the force on the input piston? (b) What pressure is applied to the input piston?

Thinking It Through. (a) Pascal's principle, as expressed in the hydraulic Eq. 7.11, has four variables, and three are given (areas via diameters). (b) The pressure is simply $p = F/A$.

Solution.

Given: $d_i = 10\text{ cm} = 0.10\text{ m}$
$d_o = 30\text{ cm} = 0.30\text{ m}$
$F_o = 1.4 \times 10^4\text{ N}$

Find: (a) F_i (input force)
(b) p_i (input pressure)

(a) Rearranging Eq. 7.11 and using $A = \pi r^2 = \pi d^2/4$ for the circular piston ($r = d/2$) gives

$$F_i = \left(\frac{A_i}{A_o}\right)F_o = \left(\frac{\pi d_i^2/4}{\pi d_o^2/4}\right)F_o = \left(\frac{d_i}{d_o}\right)^2 F_o$$

or

$$F_i = \left(\frac{0.10\text{ m}}{0.30\text{ m}}\right)^2 F_o = \frac{F_o}{9} = \frac{1.4 \times 10^4\text{ N}}{9} = 1.6 \times 10^3\text{ N}$$

The input force is one-ninth of the output force; in other words, the force was multiplied by 9 (i.e., $F_o = 9F_i$).

(Note that we didn't really need to write the complete expressions for the areas. We know that the area of a circle is proportional to the square of the diameter of the circle. If the ratio of the piston diameters is 3 to 1, the ratio of their areas must therefore be 9 to 1, and we could have used this ratio directly in Eq. 7.11.)

(b) Then we apply Eq. 7.8a:

$$p_i = \frac{F_i}{A_i} = \frac{F_i}{\pi r_i^2} = \frac{F_i}{\pi (d_i/2)^2} = \frac{1.6 \times 10^3\text{ N}}{\pi (0.10\text{ m})^2/4}$$
$$= 2.0 \times 10^5\text{ N/m}^2\ (= 200\text{ kPa})$$

This pressure is about 30 lb/in^2, a common pressure used in automobile tires and about twice atmospheric pressure (which is approximately 100 kPa, or 15 lb/in^2.)

Follow-up Exercise. Pascal's principle is used in shock absorbers on automobiles and on the landing gear of airplanes. (The polished steel piston rods can be seen above the wheels on aircraft.) In these devices, a large force (the shock produced on hitting a bump in the road or an airport runway at high speed) must be reduced to a safe level by removing energy. Basically, fluid is forced by the motion of a large-diameter piston through small channels in the piston on each stroke cycle (Fig. 7.9b).

Note that the valves allow for fluid through the channel, which creates resistance to the motion of the piston (effectively the reverse of the situation in Fig. 7.9a). The piston goes up and down, dissipating the energy of the shock. This is called *damping*. Suppose that the input piston of a shock absorber on a jet plane has a diameter of 8.0 cm. What would be the diameter of an output channel that would reduce the force by a factor of 10?

As Example 7.5 shows, we can relate forces produced by pistons directly to their diameters: $F_i = (d_i/d_o)^2 F_o$ or $F_o = (d_o/d_i)^2 F_i$. By making $d_o \gg d_i$, we can get huge factors of force multiplication, as is typical for hydraulic presses, jacks, and earth-moving equipment. (The shiny input piston rods are often visible on front loaders and backhoes.) Inversely, we can get a force reduction by making $d_i > d_o$, as in Follow-up Exercise 7.5.

However, don't think that you are getting something for nothing with large force multiplications: Energy is still a factor, and it can never be multiplied by a machine. (Why not?) Looking at the work involved and assuming that the work output is equal to the work input, $W_o = W_i$ (an ideal condition—why?), we have, from Eq. 5.1,

$$F_o x_o = F_i x_i$$

or

$$F_o = \left(\frac{x_i}{x_o}\right) F_i$$

where x_o and x_i are the output and input distances moved by the respective pistons.

Thus, the output force can be much greater than the input force only if the input distance is much greater than the output distance. For example, if $F_o = 10F_i$, then $x_i = 10x_o$, and the input piston must travel 10 times the distance of the output piston. We say that *force is multiplied at the expense of distance.*

Pressure Measurement

Pressure can be measured by mechanical devices that are often spring loaded (e.g., a tire gauge). Another type of instrument, called a manometer, uses a liquid—usually mercury—to measure pressure. An *open-tube manometer* is illustrated in ▼Fig. 7.10a. One end of the U-shaped tube is open to the atmosphere, and the other is connected to the container of gas whose pressure is to be measured. The

▼ **FIGURE 7.10 Pressure measurement** **(a)** For an open-tube manometer, the pressure of the gas in the container is balanced by the pressure of the liquid column and atmospheric pressure acting on the open surface of the liquid. The absolute pressure of the gas equals the sum of the atmospheric pressure (p_a) and ρgh, the gauge pressure. **(b)** A tire gauge measures gauge pressure, the difference between the pressure in the tire and atmospheric pressure: $p_{gauge} = p - p_a$. Thus, if a tire gauge reads 200 kPa (30 lb/in^2), the actual pressure within the tire is 1 atm higher, or 300 kPa. **(c)** A barometer is a closed-tube manometer that is exposed to the atmosphere and thus reads only atmospheric pressure.

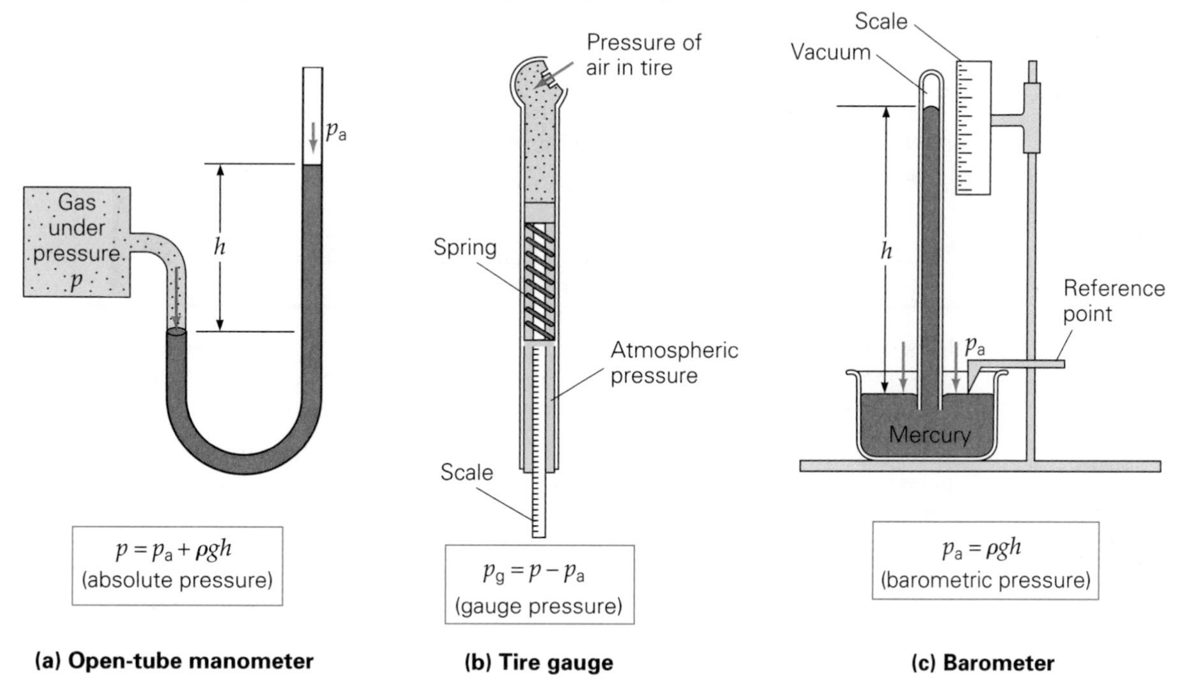

liquid in the U-tube acts as a reservoir through which pressure is transmitted according to Pascal's principle.

The pressure of the gas (p) is balanced by the weight of the column of liquid (of height h, the difference in the heights of the columns) and the atmospheric pressure (p_a) on the open liquid surface:

$$p = p_a + \rho g h \tag{7.12}$$

The pressure p is called the **absolute pressure**.

You may have measured pressure using pressure gauges; a tire gauge used to measure air pressure in automobile tires is a common example (Fig. 7.10b). Such gauges, quite appropriately, measure **gauge pressure**: A pressure gauge registers only the pressure *above* atmospheric pressure. Hence, to get the absolute pressure (p), you have to add the atmospheric pressure (p_a) to the gauge pressure (p_g):

$$p = p_a + p_g$$

For example, suppose your tire gauge reads a pressure of 200 kPa ($\approx$ 30 lb/in^2). The absolute pressure within the tire is then $p = p_a + p_g$ = 101 kPa + 200 kPa = 301 kPa, where normal atmospheric pressure is about 101 kPa (14.7 lb/in^2), as will be shown shortly.

The gauge pressure of a tire keeps the tire rigid or operational. In terms of the more familiar pounds per square inch (psi, or lb/in^2), a tire with a gauge pressure of 30 psi has an absolute pressure of about 45 psi (30 + 15, with atmospheric pressure $\approx$15 psi). Hence, the pressure on the inside of the tire is 45 psi, and that on the outside is 15 psi. The Δp of 30 psi keeps the tire inflated. If you open the valve or get a puncture, the internal and external pressures equalize and you have a flat!

Atmospheric pressure itself can be measured with a *barometer*. The principle of a mercury barometer is illustrated in Fig. 7.10c. The device was invented by Evangelista Torricelli (1608–1647), Galileo's successor as professor of mathematics at the academy in Florence. A simple barometer consists of a tube filled with mercury that is inverted into a reservoir. Some mercury runs from the tube into the reservoir, but a column supported by the air pressure on the surface of the reservoir remains in the tube. This device can be considered to be a *closed-tube manometer*, and the pressure it measures is just the atmospheric pressure, since the gauge pressure (the pressure *above* atmospheric pressure) is zero.

The atmospheric pressure is then equal to the pressure due to the weight of the column of mercury, or

$$p_a = \rho g h \tag{7.13}$$

A *standard atmosphere* is defined as the pressure supporting a column of mercury exactly 76 cm in height at sea level and at 0°C. (For a common biological atmospheric effect, see the Insight on page 233.)

Example 7.6 ■ Standard Atmospheric Pressure: Converting to Pascals

If a standard atmosphere supports a column height of exactly 76 cm of mercury (chemical symbol Hg), what is the standard atmospheric pressure in pascals? (The density of mercury is 13.5951×10^3 kg/m^3 at 0°C, and g = 9.806 65 m/s^2.)

Thinking It Through. This is a direct application of Eq. 7.13 to find standard atmospheric pressure in metric units (pascals, or newtons per square meter). Note that the height of the column is given in centimeters.

Solution.

Given: h = 76 cm = 0.76 m (exact)
$\rho_{Hg} = 13.5951 \times 10^3$ kg/m^3
g = 9.806 65 m/s^2

Find: p_a (atmospheric pressure)

INSIGHT

An Atmospheric Effect: Possible Earaches

Variations in atmospheric pressure can have a common physiological effect: changes in pressure in the ears with a change in altitude. This "plugging up and popping" of the ears is frequently experienced in ascents and descents on mountain roads or on airplanes. The eardrum, so important to your hearing, is a membrane that separates the middle ear from the outer ear. [See Fig. 2 in the Chapter 9 (Sound) Insight on Speech and Hearing, on p. 295, to view the anatomy of the ear.] The middle ear is connected to the throat by the Eustachian tube, the end of which is normally closed. The tube opens during swallowing or yawning to permit air to escape, so the internal and external pressures are equalized.

However, when you climb relatively quickly in a car in a hilly or mountainous region, the air pressure on the outside of the ear may be less than that in the middle ear. This difference in pressure would force the eardrum outward. If the outward pressure were not relieved, you might soon have an earache. But the pressure is relieved by a "pushing" of air through the Eustachian tube into the throat, which produces a "popping" sound. We often swallow or yawn to assist this process. Similarly, when we descend a hill or mountain, the higher outside pressure at lower altitudes needs to be equalized with the lower pressure in the middle ear.

Nature takes care of us, but it is important to understand what is going on. Suppose you have a throat infection. Then there may be a swelling of the opening of the Eustachian tube to the throat, partially blocking the tube. You may be tempted to hold your nose and blow with your mouth closed in order to clear your ears. Don't do it! You may blow infectious mucus into the inner ear and cause a painful inner-ear infection. Instead, swallow hard several times and give some big yawns to help open the Eustachian tube and equalize the pressure.

Using Eq. 7.13, we have

$$\begin{aligned} p_a &= \rho_{Hg} g h = (13.5951 \times 10^3\ \text{kg/m}^3)(9.80665\ \text{m/s}^2)(0.760000\ \text{m}) \\ &= 101325\ \text{N/m}^2 = 1.01325 \times 10^5\ \text{Pa} \quad (\text{or } 101.325\ \text{kPa}) \end{aligned}$$

Follow-up Exercise. What would be the height of a barometer column for 1 standard atmosphere if water were used instead of mercury?

Changes in atmospheric pressure can be observed as changes in the height of a column of mercury. These changes are due primarily to high- and low-pressure) air masses that travel across the country. Atmospheric pressure is commonly reported in terms of the height of the barometer column, and weather forecasters say that the barometer is rising or falling. That is,

$$\begin{aligned} 1\ \text{atm} &= 76\ \text{cm Hg} = 760\ \text{mm Hg} \\ &= 29.92\ \text{in. Hg (about 30 in. Hg)} \end{aligned}$$

In honor of Torricelli, a pressure supporting 1 mm of mercury is given the name *torr*:

$$1\ \text{mm Hg} \equiv 1\ \text{torr}$$

and

$$1\ \text{atm} = 760\ \text{torr}$$

Because mercury is highly toxic, it is sealed inside a barometer. A safer and less expensive device that is widely used to measure atmospheric pressure is the *aneroid* ("without fluid") *barometer*. In an aneroid barometer, a sensitive metal diaphragm on an evacuated container (something like a drumhead) responds to pressure changes, which are indicated on a dial. This is the kind of barometer you frequently find in homes in decorative wall mountings.

Note: Another unit sometimes used in weather reports is the millibar (mb). By definition, 1 atm = 1.01325 × 10^5 N/m^2 = 1.01325 bar = 1013.25 mb. Normal atmospheric pressures are around 1000 mb.

Since air is compressible, the atmospheric density and pressure are greatest at the Earth's surface and decrease with altitude. We live at the bottom of the atmosphere, but don't notice its pressure very much in our daily activities. Remember that our bodies are composed largely of fluids, which exert a matching

INSIGHT

Blood Pressure and Its Measurement

Basically, a pump is a machine that transfers mechanical energy to a fluid, thereby increasing the pressure and causing the fluid to flow. There is a wide variety of pumps, but one which is of interest to everyone is the heart, a muscular pump that drives blood through the body's circulatory network of arteries, capillaries, and veins. With each pumping cycle, the human heart's interior chambers enlarge and fill with freshly oxygenated blood from the lungs (Fig. 1).

When the chambers called ventricles contract, blood is forced out through the arteries. Smaller and smaller arteries branch off from the main ones, until the very small capillaries are reached. There, food and oxygen being carried by the blood are exchanged with the surrounding tissues, and wastes are picked up. The blood then flows into the veins to complete the circuit back to the heart.

The arterial blood pressure rises and falls in response to the cardiac cycle. That is, when the ventricles contract, forcing blood into the arterial system, the pressure in the arteries increases sharply. The maximum pressure achieved during the ventricular contraction is called the *systolic pressure*. When the ventricles relax, the arterial pressure drops, and the lowest pressure before the next contraction, called *diastolic pressure*, is reached. (These pressures are named after two parts of the pumping cycle, the *systole* and the *diastole*.)

The walls of the arteries have considerable elasticity and expand and contract with each pumping cycle. This alternate expansion and contraction can be felt as a *pulse* in an artery near the surface of the body. For example, the radial artery near the surface of the wrist is commonly used to measure a person's pulse. The pulse rate is equal to the ventricle contraction rate, and hence the pulse rate indicates the heart rate.

Taking a person's blood pressure involves measuring the pressure of the blood on the arterial walls. This is done with a *sphygmomanometer*. (The Greek word *sphygmo* means "pulse.") An inflatable cuff is used to shut off the blood

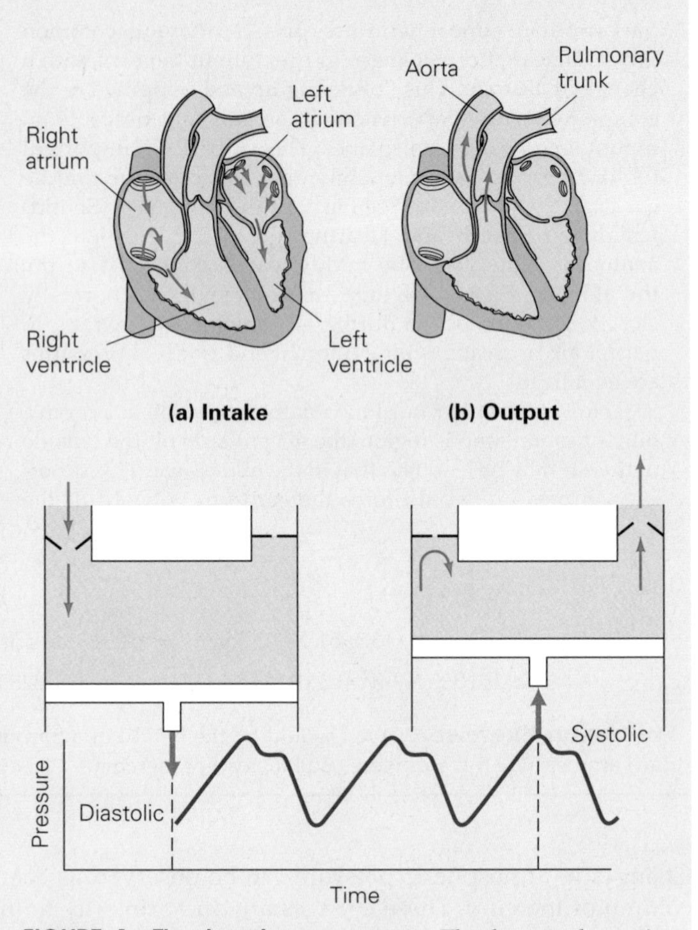

FIGURE 1 The heart as a pump The human heart is analogous to a mechanical force pump. Its pumping action, consisting of **(a)** intake and **(b)** output, gives rise to variations in blood pressure.

outward pressure. Indeed, the external pressure of the atmosphere is so important to our normal functioning that we take it with us wherever we can. The pressurized suits worn by astronauts in space or on the Moon are needed not only to supply oxygen, but also to provide an external pressure similar to that on the Earth's surface.

A very important gauge pressure reading is discussed in the Insight on blood pressure. Read it before going on to Example 7.7.

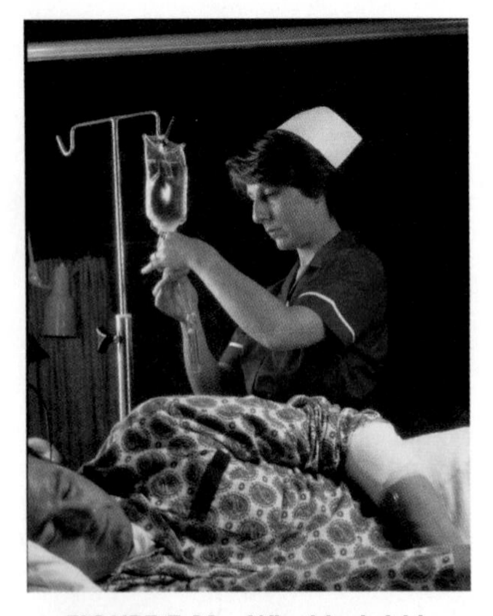

▲ **FIGURE 7.11 What height is needed?** See Example 7.7.

Example 7.7 ■ An IV: A Gravity Assist

Consider a hospital patient who receives an IV under gravity flow, as seen in ◀Fig. 7.11. If the blood gauge pressure in the vein is 20.0 mm Hg, above what height should the bottle be placed for the IV to function properly?

Thinking It Through. The fluid gauge pressure at the bottom of the IV tube must be greater than the pressure in the vein and can be computed from Eq. 7.9. (The liquid is assumed to be incompressible.)

INSIGHT

flow temporarily. The cuff pressure is slowly released, and the artery is monitored with a stethoscope (Fig. 2). A point is reached where blood is just forced through the constricted artery. This flow is turbulent and gives rise to a specific sound with each heartbeat. When the sound is first heard, the (systolic) pressure is noted on the gauge, which is normally about 120 mm Hg. (The gauge in Fig. 2 is an aneroid type; older types of sphygmomanometers used a mercury column to measure blood pressure.) When the turbulent beats disappear because of smooth blood flow, the diastolic reading is taken. The pressure at this point is normally about 80 mm Hg. Blood pressure is commonly reported by giving the systolic and diastolic pressures, separated by a slash—for example, 120/80 (read as "120 over 80"). Normal systolic blood pressure ranges between 100 and 140, normal diastolic between 70 and 90. (Blood pressure is a gauge pressure. Why?)

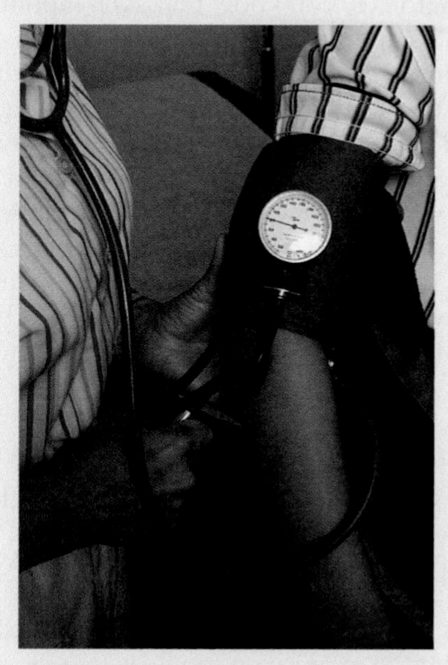

FIGURE 2 Measuring blood pressure The pressure is indicated on the gauge in millimeters Hg, or torr.

Away from the heart, blood vessels branch to smaller and smaller diameters. The pressure in the blood vessels decreases as their diameter decreases. In small arteries, such as those in the arm, the blood pressure is on the order of 10 to 20 mm Hg, and there is no systolic–diastolic variation.

High blood pressure is a common health problem. The elastic walls of the arteries expand under the hydraulic force of the blood pumped from the heart. Their elasticity may diminish with age, however. Fatty deposits (of cholesterols) can narrow and roughen the arterial passageways, impeding the blood flow and giving rise to a form of arteriosclerosis, or hardening of the arteries. Because of these defects, the driving pressure must increase to maintain a normal blood flow. The heart must work harder, which places a greater demand on its muscles. A relatively slight decrease in the effective cross-sectional area of a blood vessel has a rather large effect (an increase) on the flow rate, as will be shown in Section 7.4.

Related Exercises: 28, 79, and 89.

Solution.

Given: $p_v = 20.0$ mm Hg (vein gauge pressure)
$\rho = 1.05 \times 10^3\ \text{kg/m}^3$ (whole blood from Table 7.2)

Find: h (height for $p_v > 20$ mm Hg)

First, we need to change the common medical unit of mm Hg (or torr) to the SI unit of pascal (Pa, or N/m²):

$$p_v = (20.0\ \text{mm Hg})[133\ \text{Pa/(mm Hg)}] = 2.66 \times 10^3\ \text{Pa}$$

Then, for $p > p_v$,

$$p = \rho g h > p_v$$

or

$$h > \frac{p_v}{\rho g} = \frac{2.66 \times 10^3\ \text{Pa}}{(1.05 \times 10^3\ \text{kg/m}^3)(9.80\ \text{m/s}^2)} = 0.259\ \text{m}\ (\approx 26\ \text{cm})$$

The IV bottle needs to be at least 26 cm above the injection site.

Follow-up Exercise. The normal (gauge) blood pressure range is commonly reported as 120/80 (in millimeters Hg). Why is the blood pressure of 20 mm Hg in this Example so low?

7.3 Buoyancy and Archimedes' Principle

OBJECTIVES: To (a) relate the buoyant force to Archimedes' principle and (b) tell whether an object will float in a fluid, on the basis of relative densities.

When placed in a fluid, an object will either sink or float. This is most commonly observed with liquids; for example, objects float or sink in water. But the same effect occurs in gases: A falling object sinks in the atmosphere, and other bodies float (▸Fig. 7.12).

Things float because they are buoyant, or are buoyed up. For example, if you immerse a cork in water and release it, the cork will be buoyed up to the surface and float there. From your knowledge of forces, you know that such motion requires an upward net force on the object. That is, there must be an upward force acting on the object that is greater than the downward force of its weight. The forces are equal when the object floats in equilibrium. The upward force resulting from an object being wholly or partially immersed in a fluid is called the **buoyant force**.

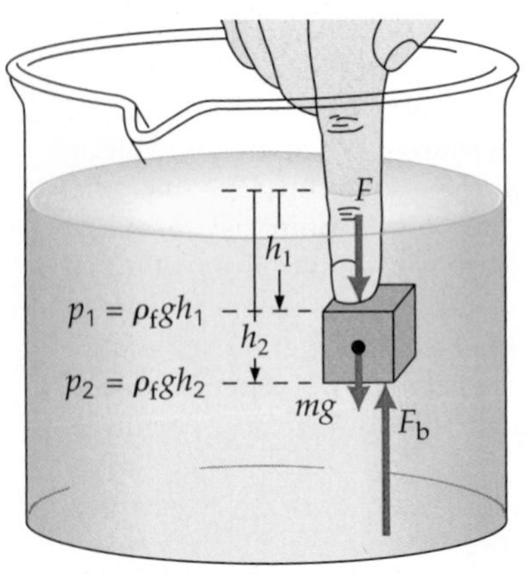

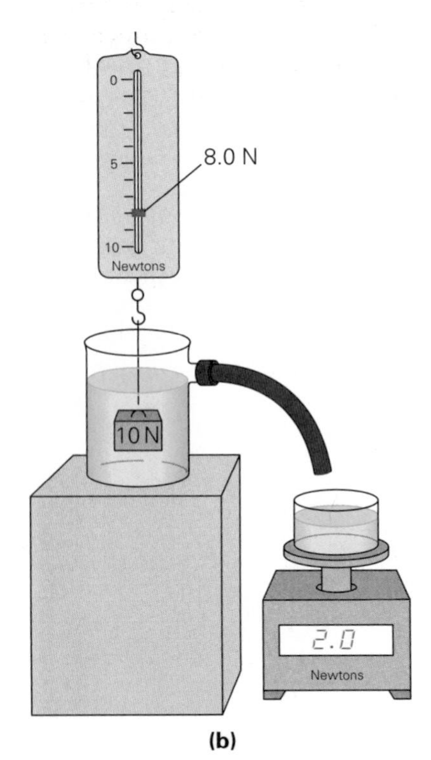

▲ **FIGURE 7.13 Buoyancy and Archimedes' principle** **(a)** A buoyant force arises from the difference in pressure at different depths. The pressure on the bottom of the submerged block (p_2) is greater than that on the top (p_1), so there is a (buoyant) force directed upward. (It is shifted for clarity.) **(b)** Archimedes' principle: The buoyant force on the object is equal to the weight of the volume of fluid displaced. (The scale is set to read zero when the container is empty.)

How the buoyant force comes about can be seen by considering a buoyant object being held under the surface of a fluid (◂Fig. 7.13a). The pressures on the upper and lower surfaces of the block are $p_1 = \rho_f g h_1$ and $p_2 = \rho_f g h_2$, respectively, where ρ_f is the density of the fluid. Thus, there is a pressure difference $\Delta p = p_2 - p_1 = \rho_f g\,(h_2 - h_1)$ between the top and bottom of the block, which gives an upward force (the buoyant force) F_b. This force is balanced by the applied force and the weight of the block.

It is not difficult to derive an expression for the magnitude of the buoyant force. We know that pressure is force per unit area. Thus, if both the top and bottom areas of the block are A, the magnitude of the net buoyant force in terms of the pressure difference is

$$F_b = p_2 A - p_1 A = (\Delta p)A = \rho_f g(h_2 - h_1)A$$

Since $(h_2 - h_1)A$ is the volume of the block, and hence the volume of fluid displaced by the block, V_f, we can write the expression for F_b as

$$F_b = \rho_f g V_f$$

But $\rho_f V_f$ is simply the mass of the fluid displaced by the block, m_f. Thus, we can write the expression for the buoyant force as $F_b = m_f g$: The magnitude of the buoyant force is equal to the weight of the fluid displaced by the block (Fig. 7.13b). This general result is known as **Archimedes' principle**:

> A body immersed wholly or partially in a fluid experiences a buoyant force equal in magnitude to the weight of the *volume of fluid* that is displaced:

$$F_b = m_f g = \rho_f g V_f \qquad (7.14)$$

Archimedes (287 B.C.–212 B.C.) was given the task of determining whether a crown made for a certain king was pure gold or contained some other, cheaper metal. Legend has it that the solution to the problem came to him when he was bathing, perhaps from seeing the water level rise when he got into the tub and experiencing the buoyant force on his limbs. In any case, it is said that he was so excited that he ran through the streets of the city shouting "Eureka!" (Greek for "I have found it".) Although Archimedes' solution to the problem involved density and volume (see Exercises 57 and 61), it presumably got him thinking about buoyancy.

Example 7.8 ■ Lighter Than Air: Buoyant Force

What is the buoyant force in air on a spherical helium balloon with a radius of 30 cm if $\rho_{air} = 1.29\ \text{kg/m}^3$? (Neglect the weight of the balloon.)

Thinking It Through. Helium is termed "lighter" (less dense) than air. Since the balloon displaces air, there is a buoyant force F_b on the balloon. This force is equal to the weight of the volume of air that the balloon displaces. To find that weight, we first find the balloon's volume and then use the density of air to find the air's mass and weight.

Solution.

Given: $r = 30\text{ cm} = 0.30\text{ m}$ *Find:* F_b (buoyant force)
$\rho_{air} = 1.29\text{ kg/m}^3$

The volume of the air in the balloon, assuming that the balloon is a sphere, is

$$V = \tfrac{4}{3}\pi r^3 = \tfrac{4}{3}\pi(0.30\text{ m})^3 = 0.11\text{ m}^3$$

Then, by Eq. 7.14, the weight of the air displaced by the balloon's volume, or the magnitude of the upward buoyant force, is

$$F_b = m_{air}g = (\rho_{air}V)g = (1.29\text{ kg/m}^3)(0.11\text{ m}^3)(9.8\text{ m/s}^2) = 1.4\text{ N}$$

Note that the buoyant force depends on the *density of the fluid* and *the volume of the body*. Shape makes no difference.

Follow-up Exercise. Would the buoyant force on the balloon be greater or lesser if the balloon were submerged in water, and by what factor? (Assume the same volume.)

▲ **FIGURE 7.12 Fluid buoyancy** The air is a fluid in which objects such as these dirigibles float. The helium inside the blimps is lighter or less dense than the surrounding air. The blimps are supported by the resulting buoyant forces.

Integrated Example 7.9 ■ Weight and Buoyant Force: Archimedes' Principle

A container of water with an overflow tube, similar to that shown in Fig. 7.13b, sits on a scale that reads 40 N. The water level is just below the exit tube in the side of the container. (a) An 8.0-N cube of wood is placed in the container. The water displaced by the floating cube runs out the exit tube into another container that is not on the scale. Will the scale reading then be (1) exactly 48 N, (2) between 40 N and 48 N, (3) exactly 40 N, or (4) less than 40 N? (b) Suppose you pushed down on the cube with your finger such that the top surface of the cube was even with the water level. How much force would have to be applied if the wooden cube measured 10 cm on a side?

(a) Conceptual Reasoning. By Archimedes' principle, the block is buoyed upward with a force equal in magnitude to the weight of the water displaced. Since the block floats, the upward buoyant force must balance the weight of the cube and so has a magnitude of 8.0 N. Thus, a volume of water weighing 8.0 N is displaced from the container as 8.0 N of weight is added to the container. The scale still reads 40 N, so the answer is (3).

Note that the upward buoyant force and the block's weight act *on the block*. The reaction force (pressure) of the block *on the water* is transmitted to the bottom of the container (Pascal's principle) and is registered on the scale.

(b) Thinking It Through. Here there are three forces acting on the stationary cube: the buoyant force upward and the weight and the force applied by the finger downward. The weight of the cube is known, so to find the applied finger force, we need to determine the buoyant force on the cube.

Given: $\ell = 10\text{ cm} = 0.10\text{ m}$ (side length of cube)
$w = 8.0\text{ N}$ (weight of cube)

Find: downward applied force necessary to put cube even with water level

The summation of the forces acting on the cube is $\Sigma F_i = +F_b - w - F_f = 0$, where F_b is the upward buoyant force and F_f is the downward force applied by the finger. Hence, $F_f = F_b - w$. As we know, the magnitude of the buoyant force is equal to the weight of the water the cube displaces, which is given by $F_b = \rho_f g V_f$ (Eq. 7.14). The density of the fluid is that of water, which is known ($1.0 \times 10^3\text{ kg/m}^3$, Table 7.2), so

$$F_b = \rho_f g V_f = (1.0 \times 10^3\text{ kg/m}^3)(9.8\text{ m/s}^2)(0.10\text{ m})^3 = 9.8\text{ N}$$

Thus,

$$F_f = F_b - w = 9.8\text{ N} - 8.0\text{ N} = 1.8\text{ N}$$

Follow-up Exercise. In part (a), would the scale still read 40 N if the object had a density greater than that of water? In part (b), what would the scale read?

Buoyancy and Density

We commonly say that helium and hot-air balloons float because they are lighter than air. To be technically correct, we should say they are *less dense than air*. An object's density will tell you whether it will sink or float in a fluid, as long as you also know the density of the fluid. Consider a solid uniform object that is totally immersed in a fluid. The weight of the object is

$$w_o = m_o g = \rho_o V_o g$$

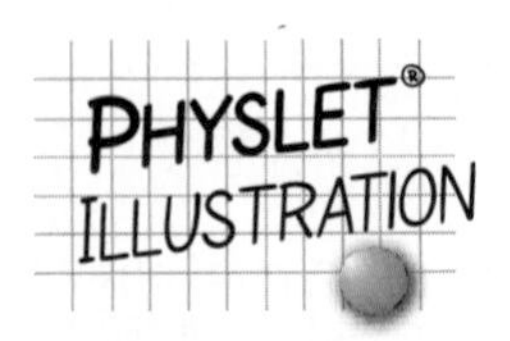

Archimedes' Principle

The weight of the volume of fluid displaced, or the magnitude of the buoyant force, is

$$F_b = w_f = m_f g = \rho_f V_f g$$

If the object is *completely submerged*, $V_f = V_o$. Dividing the second equation by the first gives

$$\frac{F_b}{w_o} = \frac{\rho_f}{\rho_o} \quad \text{or} \quad F_b = \left(\frac{\rho_f}{\rho_o}\right) w_o \quad \textit{(completely submerged)} \qquad (7.15)$$

Thus, if ρ_o is less than ρ_f, then F_b will be greater than w_o, and the object will be buoyed to the surface and float. If ρ_o is greater than ρ_f, then F_b will be less than w_o, and the object will sink. If ρ_o equals ρ_f, then F_b will be equal to w_o, and the object will remain in equilibrium at any submerged depth (as long as the density of the fluid is constant). If the object is not uniform, so that its density varies over its volume, then the density of the object in Eq. 7.15 means average density.

Expressed in words, these three conditions are as follows:

Float or sink? Depends on densities of object and fluid

An object will float in a fluid if the average density of the object is less than the density of the fluid ($\rho_o < \rho_f$).

An object will sink in a fluid if the average density of the object is greater than the density of the fluid ($\rho_o > \rho_f$).

An object will be in equilibrium at any submerged depth in a fluid if the average density of the object and the density of the fluid are equal ($\rho_o = \rho_f$).

See ◂Fig. 7.14 for an example of the last condition.

▲ **FIGURE 7.14 Equal densities and buoyancy** This soft drink contains colored gelatin beads that remain suspended for months with no change. What is the density of the beads compared to the density of the drink?

A quick look at Table 7.2 will tell you whether an object will float in a fluid, regardless of the shape or volume of the object. The three conditions just stated also apply to a fluid in a fluid, provided that the two are immiscible (do not mix). For example, you might think that cream is "heavier" than skim milk, but that's not so: Since cream floats on milk, it is less dense than milk.

In general, the densities of objects or fluids will be assumed to be uniform and constant in this book. (The density of the atmosphere does vary with altitude, but is relatively constant near the surface of the Earth.) In any event, in practical applications it is the *average* density of an object that often matters with regard to floating and sinking. For example, an ocean liner is, on average, less dense than water, even though it is made of steel. Most of its volume is occupied by air, so the liner's average density is less than that of water. Similarly, the human body has air-filled spaces, so most of us float in water. The surface depth at which a person floats depends on his or her density. (Why?)

In some instances, the overall density of an object is purposefully varied. For example, a submarine submerges by flooding its tanks with seawater (called "taking on ballast"), which increases its average density. When the sub is to surface, the water is pumped out of the tanks, so the average density of the sub becomes less than that of the surrounding seawater.

Example 7.10 ■ Float or Sink? Comparison of Densities

A uniform solid cube of material 10 cm on each side has a mass of 700 g. (a) Will the cube float in water? (b) If so, how much of its volume will be submerged?

Thinking It Through. (a) The question is whether the density of the material the cube is made of greater or less than that of water, so we compute the cube's density. (b) If the cube floats, then the buoyant force and the cube's weight are equal. Both of these forces are related to the cube's volume, so we can write them in terms of that volume and equate them.

Solution.

Given: $m = 700\text{ g} = 0.700\text{ kg}$
$L = 10\text{ cm}$
$\rho_{H_2O} = 1.00 \times 10^3\text{ kg/m}^3 = 1.00\text{ g/cm}^3$ (Table 7.2)

Find: (a) Whether the cube will float in water
(b) The percentage of the volume submerged if the cube does float

It is sometimes convenient to work in cgs units in comparing quantities, particularly when one is working with ratios. For densities in g/cm^3, drop the "$\times 10^3$" from the values given in Table 7.2 for solids and liquids, and add "$\times 10^{-3}$" for gases.

(a) The density of the cube is

$$\rho_c = \frac{m}{V_c} = \frac{m}{L^3} = \frac{700\text{ g}}{(10\text{ cm})^3} = 0.70\text{ g/cm}^3 < \rho_{H_2O} = 1.00\text{ g/cm}^3$$

Since ρ_c is less than ρ_{H_2O} the cube will float.

(b) The weight of the cube is $w_c = \rho_c g V_c$. When the cube is floating, it is in equilibrium, which means that its weight is balanced by the buoyant force. That is, $F_b = \rho_{H_2O} g V_{H_2O}$, where V_{H_2O} is the volume of water the submerged part of the cube displaces. Equating the expressions for weight and buoyant force gives

$$\rho_{H_2O} g V_{H_2O} = \rho_c g V_c$$

or

$$\frac{V_{H_2O}}{V_c} = \frac{\rho_c}{\rho_{H_2O}} = \frac{0.70\text{ g/cm}^3}{1.00\text{ g/cm}^3} = 0.70$$

Thus, $V_{H_2O} = 0.70 V_c$, and 70% of the cube is submerged.

Follow-up Exercise. Most of an iceberg floating in the ocean (▶Fig. 7.15) is submerged. What is seen is the proverbial "tip of the iceberg." What percentage of an iceberg's volume is seen above the surface? [Note: Icebergs are frozen *fresh* water floating in cold (salty) water.]

▲ **FIGURE 7.15 The tip of the iceberg** The vast majority of an iceberg's bulk is underneath the water. (Does the submerged ice have to be directly below the exposed tip of the iceberg?)

A quantity called specific gravity is related to density. It is commonly used for liquids, but also applies to solids. The **specific gravity** (*sp. gr.*) of a substance is equal to the ratio of the density of the substance (ρ_s) to the density of water (ρ_{H_2O}) at 4°C, the temperature for maximum density:

$$sp.\,gr. = \frac{\rho_s}{\rho_{H_2O}}$$

Because it is a ratio of densities, specific gravity has no units. In cgs units, $\rho_{H_2O} = 1.00\text{ g/cm}^3$, so

$$sp.\,gr. = \frac{\rho_s}{1.00} = \rho_s$$

That is, the specific gravity of a substance is equal to the numerical value of its density *in cgs units*. For example, if a liquid has a density of 1.5 g/cm^3, its specific gravity is 1.5, which tells you that it is 1.5 times denser than water. To get density values in grams per cubic centimeter, divide the value in Table 7.2 by 10^3. The

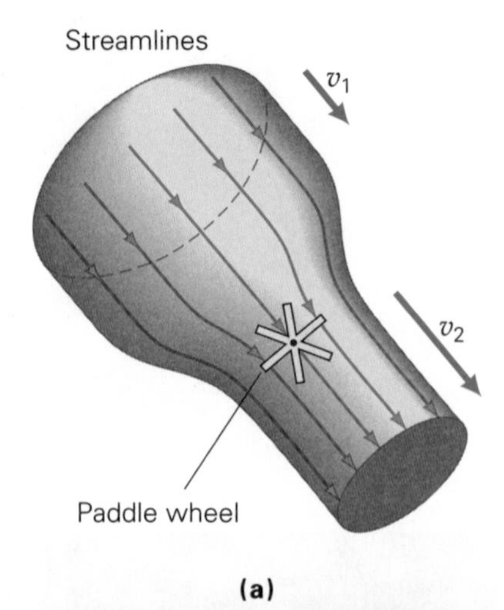

▲ **FIGURE 7.16 Streamline flow** **(a)** Streamlines never cross and are closer together in regions of greater fluid velocity. The stationary paddle wheel indicates that the flow is irrotational, or without whirlpools and eddy currents. **(b)** The smoke from an extinguished candle begins to rise in nearly streamline flow, but quickly becomes rotational and turbulent.

specific gravities of automobile coolant and battery electrolyte (both water solutions) are measured so as to determine their relative concentrations of antifreeze and sulfuric acid, respectively.

7.4 Fluid Dynamics and Bernoulli's Equation

OBJECTIVES: **To (a) identify the simplifications used in describing ideal fluid flow and (b) use the continuity equation and Bernoulli's equation to explain common effects of ideal fluid flow.**

In general, fluid motion is difficult to analyze. For example, think of trying to describe the motion of a particle (a molecule, as an approximation) of water in a rushing stream. The overall motion of the stream may be apparent, but a mathematical description of the motion of any one particle of it may be virtually impossible because of eddy currents (small whirlpool motions), the gushing of water over rocks, frictional drag on the stream bottom, and so on. A basic description of fluid flow is conveniently obtained by ignoring such complications and considering an ideal fluid. Actual fluid flow can then be approximated with reference to this simpler theoretical model.

In this simplified approach to fluid dynamics, it is customary to consider four characteristics of an **ideal fluid**. In such a fluid, flow is (1) *steady*, (2) *irrotational*, (3) *nonviscous*, and (4) *incompressible*.

Condition 1: *Steady flow* means that all the particles of a fluid have the same velocity as they pass a given point.

Steady flow might be called smooth or regular flow. The path of steady flow can be depicted in the form of **streamlines** (◂Fig. 7.16). Every particle that passes a particular point moves along a streamline. That is, every particle moves along the same path (streamline) as particles that passed by earlier. Streamlines never cross; if they did, a particle would have alternative paths and abrupt changes in its velocity, in which case the flow would not be steady.

Steady flow requires low velocities. For example, steady flow is approximated by the flow relative to a canoe that is gliding slowly through still water. When the flow velocity is high, eddies tend to appear, especially near boundaries, and the flow becomes turbulent.

Streamlines also indicate the relative magnitude of the velocity of a fluid. The velocity is greater where the streamlines are closer together. Notice this effect in Fig. 7.16a. The reason for it will be explained shortly.

Condition 2: *Irrotational flow* means that a fluid element (a small volume of the fluid) has no net angular velocity, which eliminates the possibility of whirlpools and eddy currents. (The flow is nonturbulent.)

Consider the small paddle wheel in Fig. 7.16a. With a zero net torque, the wheel does not rotate. Thus, the flow is irrotational.

Condition 3: *Nonviscous flow* means that viscosity is negligible.

Viscosity refers to a fluid's internal friction, or resistance to flow. (For example, honey has a much greater viscosity than water.) A truly nonviscous fluid would flow freely with no energy lost within it. Also, there would be no frictional drag between the fluid and the walls containing it. In reality, when a liquid flows through a pipe, the speed is lower near the walls because of frictional drag and is higher toward the center of the pipe. (Viscosity is discussed in more detail in Section 7.5.)

Condition 4: *Incompressible flow* means that the fluid's density is constant.

Liquids can usually be considered incompressible. Gases, by contrast, are quite compressible. Sometimes, however, gases approximate incompressible flow—for example, air flowing relative to the wings of an airplane traveling at low speeds.

Theoretical or ideal fluid flow is not characteristic of most real situations, but the analysis of ideal flow provides results that approximate, or generally describe, a variety of applications. Usually, this analysis is derived, not from Newton's laws, but instead from two basic principles: conservation of mass and conservation of energy.

Equation of Continuity

If there are no losses of fluid within a uniform tube, the mass of fluid flowing into the tube in a given time must be equal to the mass flowing out of the tube in the same time (by the conservation of mass). For example, in ▼Fig. 7.17a, the mass (Δm_1) entering the tube during a short time (Δt) is

$$\Delta m_1 = \rho_1 \Delta V_1 = \rho_1(A_1 \Delta x_1) = \rho_1(A_1 v_1 \Delta t)$$

where A_1 is the cross-sectional area of the tube at the entrance and, in a time Δt, a fluid particle moves a distance equal to $v_1 \Delta t$. Similarly, the mass leaving the tube in the same interval is (Fig. 7.17b)

$$\Delta m_2 = \rho_2 \Delta V_2 = \rho_2(A_2 \Delta x_2) = \rho_2(A_2 v_2 \Delta t)$$

Since the mass is conserved, $\Delta m_1 = \Delta m_2$, and it follows that

$$\rho_1 A_1 v_1 = \rho_2 A_2 v_2 \quad \text{or} \quad \rho A v = \text{constant} \tag{7.16}$$

This general result is called the **equation of continuity**.

Equation of continuity or flow rate equation

For an incompressible fluid, the density ρ is constant, so

$$A_1 v_1 = A_2 v_2 \quad \text{or} \quad Av = \text{constant} \quad (\textit{for an incompressible fluid}) \tag{7.17}$$

This is sometimes called the **flow rate equation**, since Av has the SI units of cubic meters per second (m^3/s, or volume/time). (In the British system, the

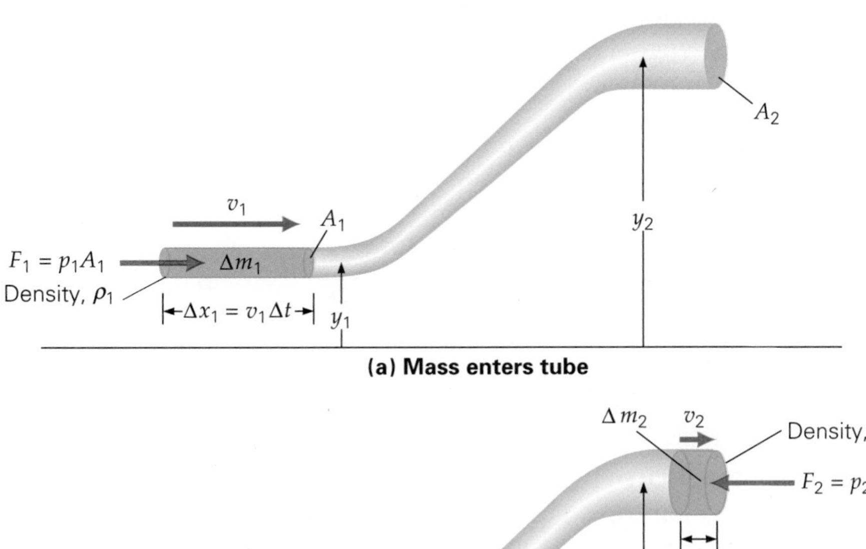

◀ **FIGURE 7.17 Flow continuity** Ideal fluid flow can be described in terms of the conservation of mass by the equation of continuity.

▲ **FIGURE 7.18 Flow rate** By the flow rate equation, the speed of a fluid is greater when the cross-sectional area of the tube through which the fluid is flowing is smaller. Think of a hose that is equipped with a nozzle such that the cross-sectional area of the hose is made smaller.

unit gallons per minute is often used.) Note that the flow rate equation shows that the fluid velocity is greater where the cross-sectional area of the tube is smaller. That is,

$$v_2 = \left(\frac{A_1}{A_2}\right)v_1$$

and v_2 is greater than v_1 if A_2 is less than A_1. This effect is evident in the common experience that the speed of water is greater from a hose fitted with a nozzle than from the same hose without a nozzle (◂Fig. 7.18).

The flow rate equation can be applied to the flow of blood in your body. Blood flows from the heart into the aorta. It then makes a circuit through the circulatory system, passing through arteries, arterioles (small arteries), capillaries, and venules (small veins) and back to the heart through veins. The speed is lowest in the capillaries. Is this a contradiction? No: The *total* area of the capillaries is much larger than that of the arteries or veins, so the flow rate equation holds.

Example 7.11 ■ Blood Flow: Cholesterol and Plaque

High cholesterol in the blood can cause fatty deposits called plaques to form on the walls of blood vessels. Suppose a plaque reduces the effective radius of an artery by 25%. How does this partial blockage affect the speed of blood through the artery?

Thinking It Through. The flow rate equation (Eq. 7.17) applies, but note that no values of area or speed are given. This indicates that we should use ratios.

Solution. Taking the unclogged artery to have a radius r_1, we can say that the plaque then reduces the effective radius to r_2.

Given: $r_2 = 0.75r_1$ (for a 25% reduction) ***Find:*** v_2

Writing the flow rate equation in terms of the radii, we have

$$A_1v_1 = A_2v_2$$
$$(\pi r_1^2)v_1 = (\pi r_2^2)v_2$$

Rearranging and canceling, we get

$$v_2 = \left(\frac{r_1}{r_2}\right)^2 v_1$$

From the given information, $r_1/r_2 = 1/0.75$, so

$$v_2 = (1/0.75)^2\, v_1 = 1.8\, v_1$$

Hence, the speed through the clogged artery increases by 80%.

Follow-up Exercise. By how much would the effective radius of an artery have to be reduced to have a 50% increase in the speed of the blood flowing through it?

Bernoulli's Equation

The conservation of energy or the general work–energy theorem leads to another relationship that has great generality for fluid flow. This relationship was first derived in 1738 by the Swiss mathematician Daniel Bernoulli (1700–1782) and is named for him.

Let's look again at the ideal fluid flowing in the tube in Fig. 7.17. Work is done by the external forces at the ends of the tube; F_1 does positive work (in the same direction as the fluid's motion) and F_2 does negative work (opposite to the fluid motion). The net work done on the system by these forces is then

$$W_{net} = F_1\Delta x_1 - F_2\Delta x_2 = (p_1A_1)(v_1\Delta t) - (p_2A_2)(v_2\Delta t)$$

The flow rate equation (Eq. 7.17) requires that $A_1v_1 = A_2v_2$, so we may write the work equation as

$$W_{net} = A_1v_1\Delta t(p_1 - p_2)$$

Recall from the preceding derivation of the equation of continuity that $\Delta m_1 = \rho_1\Delta V_1 = \rho_1(A_1v_1\Delta t)$ and $\Delta m_1 = \Delta m_2$, so we may write, in general,

$$W_{net} = \frac{\Delta m}{\rho}(p_1 - p_2)$$

The net work done on the system by the external forces (nonconservative work) must be equal to the change in total mechanical energy. That is, $W_{net} = \Delta E = \Delta K + \Delta U$. Looking at the change in kinetic energy of an element of mass Δm, we have

$$\Delta K = \tfrac{1}{2}\Delta m(v_2^2 - v_1^2)$$

The corresponding change in gravitational potential energy is

$$\Delta U = \Delta mg(y_2 - y_1)$$

Thus,

$$W_{net} = \Delta K + \Delta U$$

$$\frac{\Delta m}{\rho}(p_1 - p_2) = \tfrac{1}{2}\Delta m(v_2^2 - v_1^2) + \Delta mg(y_2 - y_1)$$

Canceling each Δm and rearranging gives the common form of **Bernoulli's equation**:

Bernoulli's equation

$$p_1 + \tfrac{1}{2}\rho v_1^2 + \rho g y_1 = p_2 + \tfrac{1}{2}\rho v_2^2 + \rho g y_2 \quad (7.18)$$

or

$$p + \tfrac{1}{2}\rho v^2 + \rho g y = \text{constant}$$

Note that in working with a fluid, the terms in Bernoulli's equation are work or energy per unit volume (J/m^3). That is, $W = F\,\Delta x = p(A\,\Delta x) = p\,\Delta V$ and therefore $p = W/\Delta V$ (work/volume). Similarly, with $\rho = m/V$, we have $\frac{1}{2}\rho v^2 = \frac{1}{2}mv^2/V$ (energy/volume) and $\rho g y = mgy/V$ (energy/volume).

Note: Compare the derivation of Eq. 5.10 in Section 5.5.

Bernoulli's equation, or principle, can be applied to many situations. If there is horizontal flow ($y_1 = y_2$), then $p + \frac{1}{2}\rho v^2 = $ constant, which indicates that the pressure decreases if the speed of the fluid increases (and vice versa). This effect is illustrated in ▼Fig. 7.19, where the difference in flow heights through the pipe is considered negligible (so the $\rho g y$ term drops out).

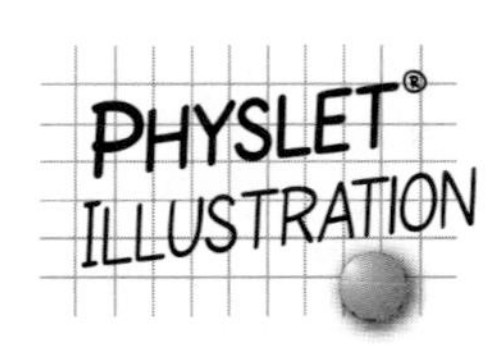

Blood Flow in Arteries

▼ **FIGURE 7.19 Flow rate and pressure** Taking the horizontal difference in flow heights to be negligible in a constricted pipe, we obtain, for Bernoulli's equation, $p + \frac{1}{2}\rho v^2 = $ constant. In a region of smaller cross-sectional area, the flow speed is greater (see flow rate equation); from Bernoulli's equation, the pressure in that region is lower than in other regions.

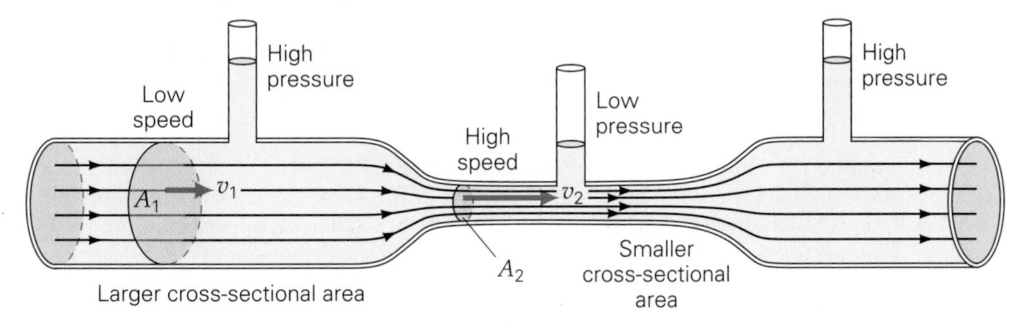

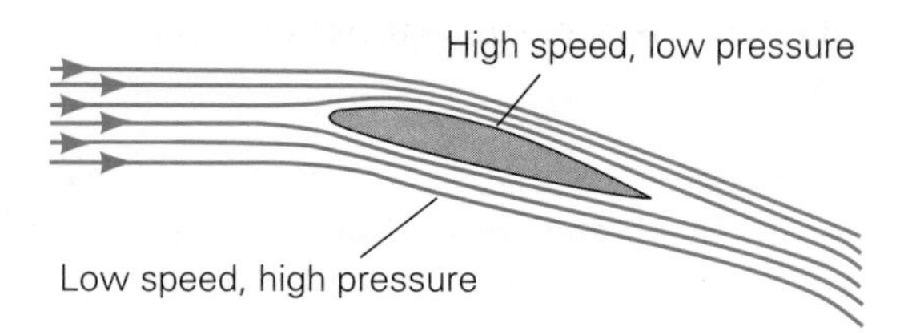

▶ **FIGURE 7.20 Airplane lift—Bernoulli's principle in action** Because of the shape and orientation of an airfoil or airplane wing, the air streamlines are closer together, and the air speed is greater above the wing than below it. By Bernoulli's principle, the resulting pressure difference supplies an upward force, or lift.

Chimneys and smokestacks are tall in order to take advantage of the more consistent and higher wind speeds at greater heights. The faster the wind blows over the top of a chimney, the lower is the pressure, and the greater is the pressure difference between the bottom and top of the chimney. Thus, the chimney draws exhaust out better. Bernoulli's equation and the continuity equation ($Av = \text{constant}$) also tell you that if the cross-sectional area of a pipe is reduced, so that the velocity of the fluid passing through it is increased, then the pressure is reduced.

The Bernoulli effect (as it is sometimes called) is also partially responsible for the lift of an airplane. Ideal airflow over an airfoil or wing is shown in ▲Fig. 7.20. (Turbulence is neglected.) The wing is curved on the top side and is angled relative to the incident streamlines. As a result, the streamlines above the wing are closer together than those below, which causes a higher air speed and lower pressure above the wing. With a higher pressure on the bottom of the wing, there is a net upward force, or *lift*. Note in the figure that the streamlines leaving the wing curve downward. This curving reflects the fact that, since the wing is acquiring upward momentum, the air molecules must acquire an equal downward component of momentum.

Suppose a fluid is at rest ($v_2 = v_1 = 0$). Bernoulli's equation then becomes

$$p_2 - p_1 = \rho g(y_1 - y_2)$$

This is the pressure–depth relationship derived earlier (Eq. 7.10).

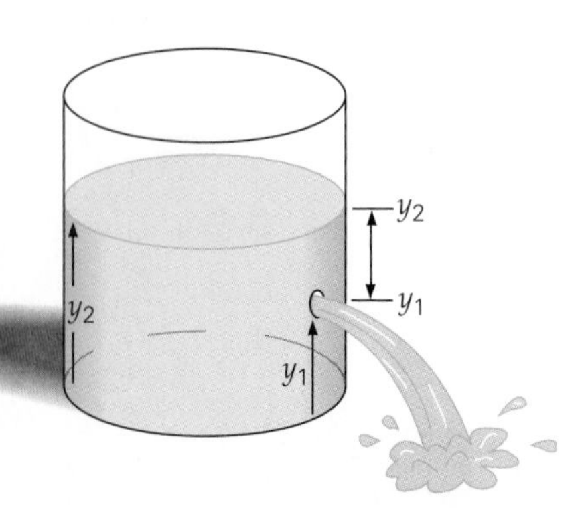

▲ **FIGURE 7.21 Fluid flow from a tank** The flow rate is given by Bernoulli's equation. See Example 7.12.

Example 7.12 ■ Flow Rate from a Tank: Bernoulli's Equation

A cylindrical tank containing water has a small hole punched in its side below the water level, and water runs out (◀Fig. 7.21). What is the approximate initial flow rate of water out of the tank?

Thinking It Through. Equation 7.17 ($A_1v_1 = A_2v_2$) is the flow rate equation, where Av has units of m^3/s, or volume/time. The v terms can be related by Bernoulli's equation, which also contains y, which can be used to find differences in height. The areas are not given, so relating the v terms might require some sort of approximation, as will be seen. (Note that the *approximate* initial flow rate is wanted.)

Solution.

Given: No specific values are given, so symbol variables will be used.

Find: An expression for the approximate initial water flow rate from the hole.

Bernoulli's equation,

$$p_1 + \tfrac{1}{2}\rho v_1^2 + \rho g y_1 = p_2 + \tfrac{1}{2}\rho v_2^2 + \rho g y_2$$

can be used to write $y_2 - y_1$, which is the height of the surface of the liquid above the hole. The atmospheric pressures acting on the open surface and at the hole, p_1 and p_2, respectively, are essentially equal and cancel from the equation, as does the density, so

$$v_1^2 - v_2^2 = 2g(y_2 - y_1)$$

By the equation of continuity (the flow rate equation, Eq. 7.17), $A_1v_1 = A_2v_2$, where A_2 is the cross-sectional area of the tank and A_1 is that of the hole. Since A_2 is much greater than A_1, v_1 is much greater than v_2 (initially, $v_2 \approx 0$). So, to a good approximation,

$$v_1^2 = 2g(y_2 - y_1) \quad \text{or} \quad v_1 = \sqrt{2g(y_2 - y_1)}$$

The flow rate (volume/time) is then

$$\text{flow rate} = A_1 v_1 = A_1 \sqrt{2g(y_2 - y_1)}$$

Given the area of the hole and the height of the liquid above it, you can find the initial speed of the water coming from the hole and the flow rate. (What happens as the water level falls?)

Follow-up Exercise. What would be the percentage change in the initial flow rate from the tank in this Example if the diameter of the small circular hole were increased by 30.0%?

Another example of the Bernoulli effect is given in the Insight on p. 246.

Conceptual Example 7.13 ■ A Stream of Water: Smaller and Smaller

You have probably observed that a steady stream of water flowing out of a faucet gets smaller the farther the water gets from the faucet. Why does that happen?

Reasoning and Answer. This effect can be explained by Bernoulli's principle. As the water falls, it accelerates and its speed increases. Then, by Bernoulli's principle, the internal liquid pressure inside the stream decreases. (See Fig. 7.19.) A pressure difference between that inside stream and the atmospheric pressure on the outside is thus created. As a result, there is an increasing inward force as the stream falls, so it becomes smaller. Eventually, the stream may get so thin that it breaks up into individual droplets.

Follow-up Exercise. The equation of continuity can also be used to explain this stream effect. Give this explanation.

*7.5 Surface Tension, Viscosity, and Poiseuille's Law

OBJECTIVES: To (a) describe the source of surface tension and its effects and (b) discuss fluid viscosity.

Surface Tension

The molecules of a liquid exert small attractive forces on each other. Even though molecules are electrically neutral overall, there is often some slight asymmetry of charge that gives rise to attractive forces between them (called *van der Waals forces*). Within a liquid, any molecule is completely surrounded by other molecules, and the net force is zero (▸ Fig. 7.22a). However, for molecules at the surface of the liquid, there is no attractive force acting from above the surface. (The effect of air molecules is small and considered negligible.) As a result, net forces act upon the molecules of the surface layer, due to the attraction of neighboring molecules just below the surface. This inward pull on the surface molecules causes the surface of the liquid to contract and to resist being stretched or broken, a property called **surface tension**.

If a sewing needle is carefully placed on the surface of a bowl of water, the surface acts like an elastic membrane under tension. There is a slight depression in the surface, and molecular forces along the depression act at an angle to the surface (Fig. 7.22b). The vertical components of these forces balance the weight (mg) of the needle, and the needle "floats" on the surface. Similarly, surface tension supports the weight of a water strider (Fig. 7.22c).

INSIGHT

Throwing a Curveball

In baseball, a pitcher can cause the ball to curve as it moves toward home plate by giving it an appropriate spin. Why a curveball curves can be understood in terms of Bernoulli's equation and the viscous properties of air.

If air were an ideal fluid, the spin of a pitched ball would have no effect in changing the direction of the ball's motion. (In Fig. 1a, the streamlines are those which would be seen by an observer moving with the ball.) However, because air is viscous, friction between it and the ball causes a thin (boundary) layer of air to be dragged around by the spinning ball. This effect is illustrated in Fig. 1b for a relatively slow airstream in which the flow is generally smooth. The speed of the ball relative to the air is thus greater on one side than on the other, because the velocities of the ball and of the air are in the same direction on one side (top in Fig. 1b) and in opposite directions on the other. By Bernoulli's equation, the low-velocity side (v') has a greater pressure than the high-velocity side (v''). Thus, there is a net force on the ball toward the low-pressure side, and the ball is deflected. (Its path curves.)

However, baseballs are usually pitched very fast, and another effect applies. With a high airflow speed, the rotation of the ball causes the boundary layer to separate at different points on either side of the ball. This separation gives rise to a turbulent wake that is deflected in the direction of the ball's spin (Fig. 2). A pressure difference results, and the ball is deflected or curves the opposite way. This is called the Magnus effect (after Gustav Magnus, who observed the effect in 1852). In terms of Newton's third law, the turbulent wake is deflected in one direction and the reaction force deflects the ball in the opposite direction.

Note that the ball in Fig. 2 is rotating counterclockwise and is deflected to the left (toward the top, in this overhead view). To have the ball curve to the right requires a clockwise rotation. In general, the curve is in the direction that the front part of the ball is rotating. With the spin axis in the horizontal plane, the deflecting force may be up or down, which can cause the ball not to drop as much under the influence of gravity or to "sink" even faster. The spin axis can be oriented in any direction to produce a variety of effects with the deflecting force and gravity.

Incidentally, golf balls are dimpled to create turbulence, which is usually a bad thing in trying to get distance in a resistive medium (air). A swimmer, for example, wants as little turbulence (and resistance) as possible. However, with golf balls, localized turbulence can reduce drag. This involves the Magnus effect and is a bit complicated, but it gives golf balls a greater range.

Related Exercise: 75.

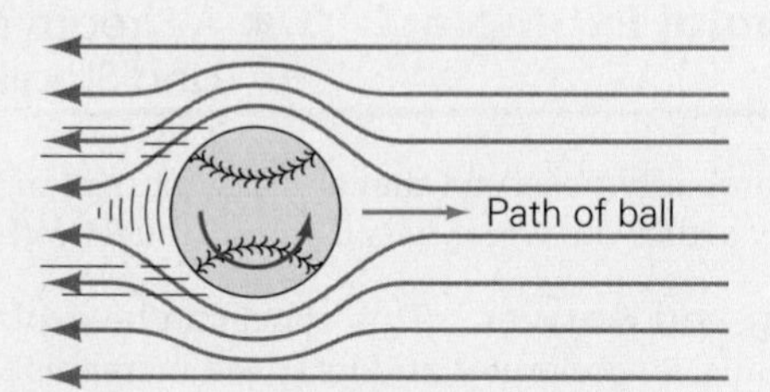

(a) No viscosity: same airflow on both sides

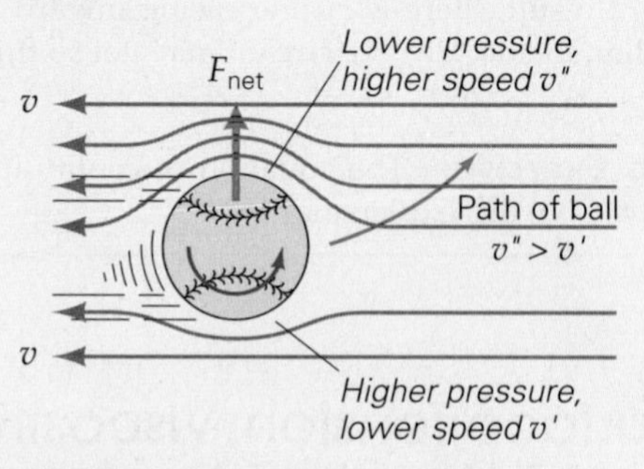

(b) With viscosity: faster airflow on one side of the ball creates a pressure difference

FIGURE 1 Bernoulli effect **(a)** If air were an ideal fluid (without viscosity) and spin were applied, the airflow would be the same on both sides of the ball. **(b)** Because air has viscosity, some air is dragged around with the ball, so the speed of the ball with respect to the air is greater on one side (top view shown). Pressure on that side is lower, resulting in a net force in that direction.

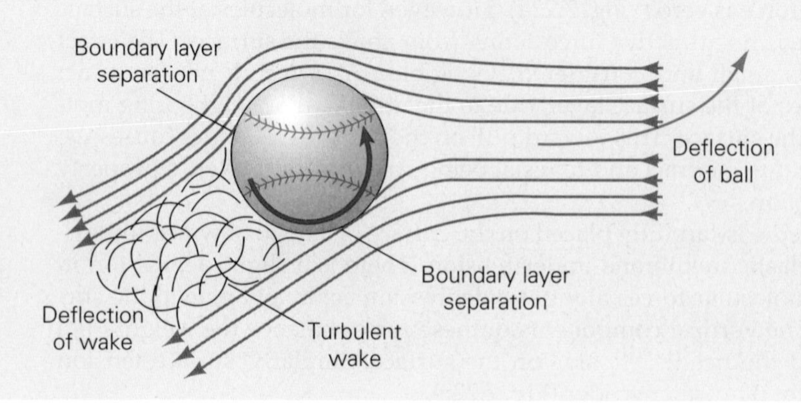

FIGURE 2 Magnus effect The turbulent wake of a fast-moving ball causes the ball to curve. In terms of Newton's third law, the wake is deflected in one direction, and the ball is deflected in the opposite direction by the reaction force.

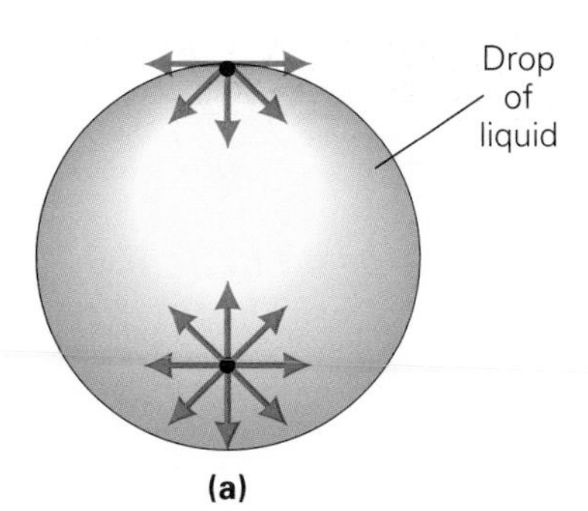

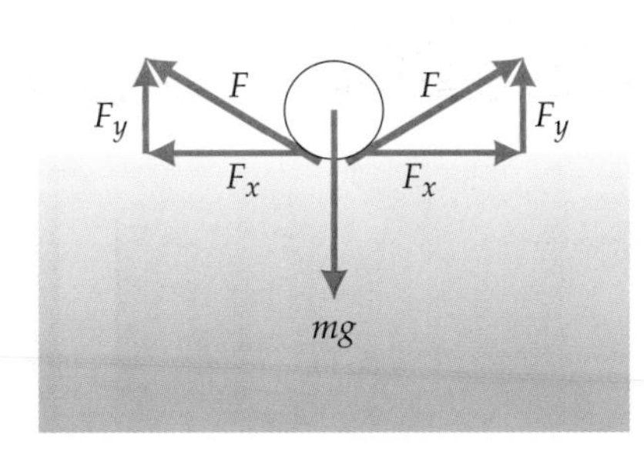

(b)

▲ **FIGURE 7.22 Surface tension** **(a)** The net force on a molecule in the interior of a liquid is zero, because the molecule is surrounded by other molecules. However, a nonzero net force acts on a molecule at the surface, due to the attractive forces of the neighboring molecules just below the surface. **(b)** For an object such as a needle to form a depression on the surface, work must be done, since more interior molecules must be brought to the surface to increase its area. As a result, the surface area acts like a stretched elastic membrane, and the weight of the object is supported by the upward components of the surface tension. Insects such as this water strider can walk on water because of the upward components of the surface tension, much as you might walk on a large trampoline. Note the depressions in the surface of the liquid where the legs touch it.

The net effect of surface tension is to make the surface area of a liquid as small as possible. That is, a given volume of liquid tends to assume the shape that has the least surface area. As a result, drops of water and soap bubbles have spherical shapes, because a sphere has the smallest surface area for a given volume (▼Fig. 7.23). In forming a drop or bubble, surface tension pulls the molecules together to minimize the surface area.

Viscosity

All real fluids have an internal resistance to flow, or **viscosity**, which can be considered to be friction between the molecules of a fluid. In liquids, viscosity is caused by short-range cohesive forces, and in gases, it is caused by collisions between molecules. (See the discussion of air resistance in Section 4.6.) The viscous drag for both liquids and gases depends on their velocity and may be directly proportional to it in some cases. However, the relationship varies with the conditions; for example, the drag is approximately proportional to v^2 or v^3 in turbulent flow.

Internal friction causes the layers of a fluid to move relative to each other in response to a shear stress. This layered motion, called *laminar flow*, is characteristic

▼ **FIGURE 7.23 Surface tension at work** Because of surface tension, **(a)** water droplets and **(b)** soap bubbles tend to assume the shape that minimizes their surface area—that of a sphere.

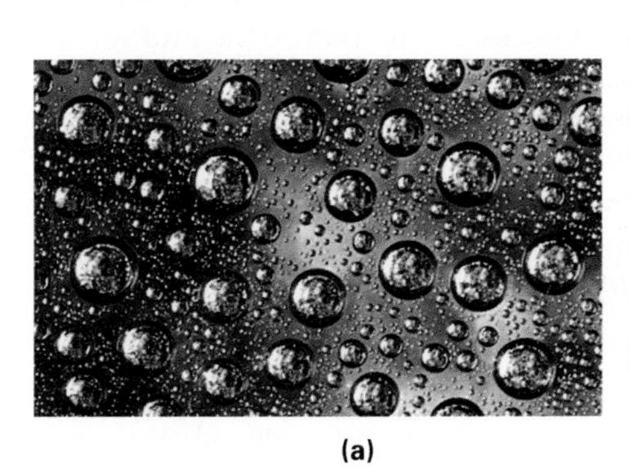

(a)

(b)

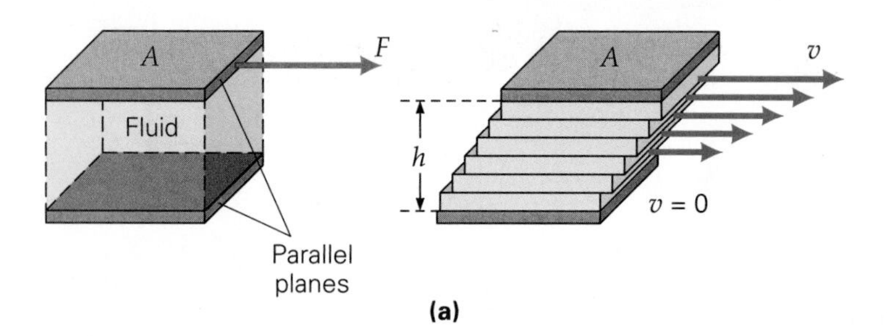

FIGURE 7.24 Laminar flow **(a)** A shear stress causes layers of a fluid to move over each other in laminar flow. The shear force and the flow rate depend on the viscosity of the fluid. **(b)** For laminar flow through a pipe, the speed of the fluid is less near the walls of the pipe than near the center because of frictional drag between the walls and the fluid.

of steady flow for viscous liquids at low velocities (▲Fig. 7.24a). At higher velocities, the flow becomes rotational, or *turbulent*, and difficult to analyze.

Viscosity: resistance to flow

Since there are shear stresses and shear strains (deformation) in laminar flow, the viscous property of a fluid can be described by a coefficient, like the elastic moduli discussed in Section 7.1. Viscosity is characterized by a *coefficient of viscosity*, η (the Greek letter eta), commonly referred to as simply the viscosity.

The coefficient of viscosity is, in effect, the ratio of the shear stress to the rate of change of the shear strain (since motion is involved). Unit analysis shows that the SI unit of viscosity is the pascal-second (Pa · s). This combined unit is called the *poiseuille* (Pl), in honor of the French scientist Jean Poiseuille (1799–1869), who studied the flow of liquids, particularly blood. (Poiseuille's law on flow rate will be presented shortly.) The cgs unit of viscosity is the *poise* (P). A smaller multiple, the *centipoise* (cP), is widely used because of its convenient size; 1 Pl = 10^2 cP.

The viscosities of some fluids are listed in Table 7.3. The greater the viscosity of a liquid, which is easier to visualize than that of a gas, the greater is the shear stress required to get the layers of the liquid to slide along each other. Note, for example, the large viscosity of glycerin compared to that of water.*

As you might expect, viscosity, and thus fluid flow, varies with temperature, which is evident from the old saying, "slow as molasses in January." A familiar application is the viscosity grading of motor oil used in automobiles. In winter, a low-viscosity, or relatively thin, oil should be used (such as SAE grade 10W or 20W), because it will flow more readily, particularly when the engine is cold at start-up. In summer, a higher viscosity, or thicker, oil is used (SAE 30, 40, or even 50). Seasonal changes in the grade of motor oil are not necessary if you use the multigrade year-round oils. These oils contain additives called viscosity improvers, which are polymers whose molecules are long, coiled chains. An increase in temperature causes the molecules to uncoil and intertwine. Thus, the normal decrease in viscosity is counteracted. The action is reversed on cooling, and the oil maintains a relatively small viscosity range over a large temperature range. Such motor oils are graded, for example, as SAE 10W–30 (or 10W–30, for short).

Note: *SAE* stands for *Society of Automotive Engineers*, an organization that designates the grades of motor oils based on their viscosity.

*If you want to think about a very large viscosity, consider that of glass. It has been said that the glass in the stained-glass windows of medieval churches has "flowed" over time, such that the panes are now thicker at the bottom than at the top. A recent analysis indicates that window glass may even flow over incredibly long periods that exceed the limits of human history. On human time scales, such a flow would not be evident. [See E. D. Zanotto, *Am. J. Phys.* **66** (May, 1998), 392–395.]

TABLE 7.3 Viscosities of Various Fluids*

Fluid	Viscosity (η) Poiseuille (Pl)
Liquids	
Alcohol, ethyl	1.2×10^{-3}
Blood, whole (37°C)	1.7×10^{-3}
Blood plasma (37°C)	2.5×10^{-3}
Glycerin 1.5	1.5×10^{3}
Mercury	1.55×10^{-3}
Oil, light machine	1.1
Water	1.00×10^{-3}
Gases	
Air	1.9×10^{-5}
Oxygen	2.2×10^{-5}

*At 20°C unless otherwise indicated.

Poiseuille's Law Viscosity makes analyzing fluid flow difficult. For example, when a fluid flows through a pipe, there is frictional drag between the liquid and the walls, and the fluid velocity is greater toward the center of the pipe (Fig. 7.24b). In practice, this effect makes a difference in a fluid's *average flow rate* $Q = A\bar{v} = \Delta V/\Delta t$ (see Eq. 7.17), which describes the volume (ΔV) of fluid flowing past a given point during a time Δt. The SI unit of flow rate is cubic meters per second (m^3/s). The flow rate depends on the properties of the fluid and the dimensions of the pipe, as well as on the pressure difference (Δp) between the ends of the pipe.

Jean Poiseuille studied flow in pipes and tubes, assuming a constant viscosity and steady or laminar flow. He derived the following relationship, known as **Poiseuille's law**, for the flow rate:

Poiseuille's law

$$Q = \frac{\Delta V}{\Delta t} = \frac{\pi r^4 \Delta p}{8 \eta L} \qquad (7.19)$$

Here, r is the radius of the pipe and L is its length.

As expected, the flow rate is inversely proportional to the viscosity (η) and the length of the pipe. Also as expected, the flow rate is directly proportional to the pressure difference Δp between the ends of the pipe. Somewhat surprisingly, however, the flow rate is proportional to r^4, which makes it more highly dependent on the radius of the tube than we might have thought.

An application of fluid flow in a medical IV was examined in Example 7.7. However, Poiseuille's law, which incorporates the flow rate, affords more reality to this application, as the next Example shows.

Example 7.14 ■ Poiseuille's Law: A Blood Transfusion

A hospital patient needs a blood transfusion, which will be administered through a vein in the arm via a gravity IV. The physician wishes to have 500 cc of whole blood delivered over a period of 10 min by an 18-gauge needle with a length of 50 mm and an inner diameter of 1.0 mm. At what height above the arm should the bag of blood be hung? (Assume a venous blood pressure of 15 mm Hg.)

Thinking It Through. This is an application of Poiseuille's law (Eq. 7.19) to find the pressure needed at the inlet of the needle that will provide the required flow rate (Q). Note that $\Delta p = p_{in} - p_{out}$ (inlet pressure minus outlet pressure). Knowing the inlet pressure, we can find the required height of the bag as in Example 7.7. (*Caution*: There are a lot of nonstandard units here, and some quantities are assumed to be known from tables.)

Solution. First we write the given (and known) quantities, converting to standard SI units as we go:

Given: $\Delta V = 500 \text{ cc} = 500 \text{ cm}^3 (1 \text{ m}^3/10^6 \text{ cm}^3) = 5.00 \times 10^{-4} \text{ m}^3$
$\Delta t = 10 \text{ min} = 600 \text{ s} = 6.00 \times 10^2 \text{ s}$
$L = 50 \text{ mm} = 5.0 \times 10^{-2} \text{ m}$
$d = 1.0 \text{ mm}, \text{ or } r = 0.50 \text{ mm} = 5.0 \times 10^{-4} \text{ m}$
$p_{out} = 15 \text{ mm Hg} = 15 \text{ torr } (133 \text{ Pa/torr}) = 2.0 \times 10^3 \text{ Pa}$
$\eta = 1.7 \times 10^{-3}$ Pl (whole blood, from Table 7.3)

Find: h (height of bag)

The flow rate is

$$Q = \frac{\Delta V}{\Delta t} = \frac{5.00 \times 10^{-4} \text{ m}^3}{6.00 \times 10^2 \text{ s}} = 8.33 \times 10^{-7} \text{ m}^3/\text{s}$$

We insert this number into Eq. 7.19 and solve for Δp:

$$\Delta p = \frac{8\eta LQ}{\pi r^4} = \frac{8(1.7 \times 10^{-3} \text{ Pl})(5.0 \times 10^{-2} \text{ m})(8.33 \times 10^{-7} \text{ m}^3/\text{s})}{\pi(5.0 \times 10^{-4} \text{ m})^4} = 2.9 \times 10^3 \text{ Pa}$$

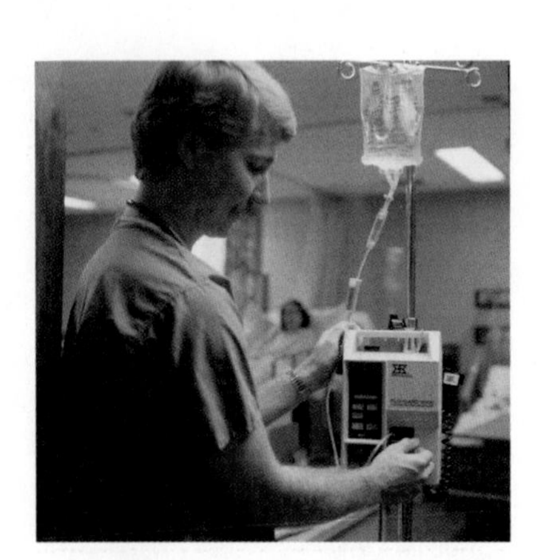

▲ **FIGURE 7.25 IV technology** The mechanism of intravenous injection is still a gravity assist, but IV flow rates are now commonly controlled and monitored by machines.

With $\Delta p = p_{in} - p_{out}$, we have

$$p_{in} = \Delta p + p_{out} = (2.9 \times 10^3 \text{ Pa}) + (2.0 \times 10^3 \text{ Pa}) = 4.9 \times 10^3 \text{ Pa}$$

Then, to find the height of the bag that will deliver this amount of pressure, we use $p_{in} = \rho g h$ (where $\rho_{\text{whole blood}} = 1.05 \times 10^3 \text{ kg/m}^3$, from Table 7.2). Thus,

$$h = \frac{p_{in}}{\rho g} = \frac{4.9 \times 10^3 \text{ Pa}}{(1.05 \times 10^3 \text{ kg/m}^3)(9.80 \text{ m/s}^2)} = 0.48 \text{ m}$$

Hence, for the prescribed flow rate, the bag of blood should be hung about 48 cm above the needle in the arm.

Follow-up Exercise. Suppose the physician wants to follow up the blood transfusion with 500 cc of saline solution at the same rate of flow. At what height should the saline bag be placed? (The *isotonic* saline solution administered by IV is a 0.85% aqueous salt solution, which has the same salt concentration as do body cells. To a good approximation, saline has the same density as water.)

Gravity-flow IVs are still used, but with modern technology, the flow rates of IVs are now often controlled and monitored by machines (◂Fig. 7.25).

Chapter Review

Important Concepts and Equations

- In the deformation of elastic solids, **stress** is a measure of the force causing the deformation:

$$\text{stress} = \frac{F}{A} \tag{7.1}$$

  strain is a relative measure of the deformation a stress causes:

$$\text{strain} = \frac{\text{change in length}}{\text{original length}} = \frac{|\Delta L|}{L_o} = \frac{|L - L_o|}{L_o} \tag{7.2}$$

- An **elastic modulus** is the ratio of stress to strain.

Young's Modulus:

$$Y = \frac{F/A}{\Delta L/L_o} \tag{7.4}$$

Shear Modulus:

$$S = \frac{F/A}{x/h} \approx \frac{F/A}{\phi} \tag{7.5}$$

Bulk Modulus:

$$B = \frac{F/A}{-\Delta V/V_o} = -\frac{\Delta p}{\Delta V/V_o} \tag{7.6}$$

- Pressure is the force per unit area.

$$p = \frac{F}{A} \qquad (7.8a)$$

- **Pascal's principle**. Pressure applied to an enclosed fluid is transmitted undiminished to every point in the fluid and to the walls of the container.

  Pressure–Depth Equation (for an incompressible fluid at constant density):

$$p = p_o + \rho g h \qquad (7.10)$$

- **Archimedes' principle**. A body immersed wholly or partially in a fluid is buoyed up by a force equal in magnitude to the weight of the volume of fluid displaced.

  Buoyant force:

$$F_b = m_f g = \rho_f g V_f \qquad (7.14)$$

- An object will float in a fluid if the average density of the object is less than the density of the fluid. If the average density of the object is greater than the density of the fluid, the object will sink.
- For an ideal fluid, the flow is (1) steady, (2) irrotational, (3) nonviscous, and (4) incompressible. The following equations describe such a flow:

Equation of Continuity:

$$\rho_1 A_1 v_1 = \rho_2 A_2 v_2 \quad \text{or} \quad \rho A v = \text{constant} \qquad (7.16)$$

Flow Rate Equation (for an incompressible fluid):

$$A_1 v_1 = A_2 v_2 \quad \text{or} \quad Av = \text{constant} \qquad (7.17)$$

Bernoulli's Equation (for an incompressible fluid):

$$p_1 + \tfrac{1}{2}\rho v_1^2 + \rho g y_1 = p_2 + \tfrac{1}{2}\rho v_2^2 + \rho g y_2$$

or

$$p + \tfrac{1}{2}\rho v^2 + \rho g y = \text{constant} \qquad (7.18)$$

- Bernoulli's equation is a statement of the conservation of energy for a fluid.
- **Viscosity** is a fluid's internal resistance to flow. All real fluids have a nonzero viscosity.

  **Poiseuille's Law* (flow rate in pipes and tubes for fluids with constant viscosity and steady or laminar flow):

$$Q = \frac{\pi r^4 \Delta p}{8 \eta L} \qquad (7.19)$$

Exercises

7.1 Solids and Elastic Moduli

(Use as many significant figures as you need to show small changes.)

1. The pressure on an elastic body is described by (a) a modulus, (b) work, (c) stress, or (d) strain.

2. Shear moduli are not zero for (a) solids, (b) liquids, (c) gases, or (d) all of these.

3. CQ Which has a greater Young's modulus, a steel wire or a rubber band? Explain.

4. CQ Why are scissors sometimes called shears? Is this a descriptive name in the physical sense?

5. ■ Write the general form of Hooke's law, and find the units of the "spring constant" for elastic deformation.

6. ■ Suppose you use the tip of one finger to support a 5.0-kg object. If your finger has a diameter of 2.0 cm, what is the stress on your finger?

7. ■ A 5.0-m-long rod is stretched 0.10 m by a force. What is the strain in the rod?

8. ■ A 250-N force is applied at a 37° angle to the surface of the end of a square bar. The surface is 4.0 cm on a side. What are (a) the compressional stress and (b) the shear stress on the bar?

9. ■■ A metal wire 1.0 mm in diameter and 2.0 m long hangs vertically with a 6.0-kg object suspended from it. If the wire stretches 1.4 mm under the tension, what is the value of Young's modulus for the metal?

10. ■■ A 5.0-kg object is supported by an aluminum wire of length 2.0 m and diameter 2.0 mm. How much will the wire stretch?

11. ■■ A copper wire has a length of 5.0 m and a diameter of 3.0 mm. Under what load will its length increase by 0.3 mm?

12. IE ■■ When railroad tracks are installed, gaps are left between the rails. (a) Should a greater gap be used if the rails are installed on (1) a cold day or (2) a hot day? Or (3) Does it make any difference? Why? (b) Each steel rail is 8.0 m long and has a cross-sectional area of 0.0025 m^2. On a hot day, each rail thermally expands as much as 3.0×10^{-3} m. If there were no gaps between the rails, what would be the force on the ends of each rail?

13. ■■ A rectangular steel column (20.0 cm × 15.0 cm) supports a load of 12.0 metric tons. If the column is 2.00 m in length before being stressed, what is the decrease in length?

14. IE ■■ A bimetallic rod as illustrated in ▼Fig 7.26 is composed of brass and copper. (a) If the rod is subjected to a compressive force, will the rod bend toward the brass or the copper? Why? (b) Justify your answer mathematically if the compressive force is 5.00×10^4 N.

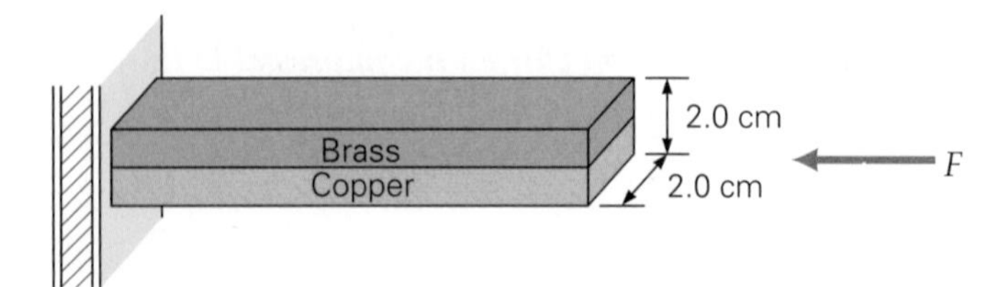

▲ **FIGURE 7.26 Bimetallic rod and mechanical stress** See Exercise 14.

15. ■■ A 500-N shear force is applied to one face of a cube of aluminum measuring 10 cm on each side. What is the displacement of that face relative to the opposite face?

16. IE ■■ Two same-size metal posts, one aluminum and one copper, are subjected to equal shear stresses. (a) Which post will show the larger deformation angle, (1) the copper post or (2) the aluminum post? Or (3) Is the angle the same for both? Why? (b) By what factor is the deformation angle of one post greater than the other?

17. ■■ A rectangular block of gelatin of length, width, and height 10 cm, 8.0 cm, and 4.0 cm, respectively, is subjected to a 0.40-N shear force on its upper surface. If the top surface is displaced 0.30 mm relative to the bottom surface, what is the shear modulus of the gelatin?

18. ■■ Two metal plates are held together by two steel rivets, each of diameter 0.20 cm and length 1.0 cm. How much force must be applied parallel to the plates to shear off both rivets?

19. IE ■■ (a) Which of the liquids in Table 7.1 has the greatest compressibility? Why? (b) For equal volumes of ethyl alcohol and water, which would require more pressure to be compressed by 0.10%, and how many times more?

20. ■■■ A brass cube 6.0 cm on each side is placed in a pressure chamber and subjected to a pressure of 1.2×10^7 N/m^2 on all of its surfaces. By how much will each side be compressed under this pressure?

21. ■■■ A 45-kg traffic light is suspended from two steel cables of equal length and radii 0.50 cm. If each cable makes a 15° angle with the horizontal, what is the fractional increase in their length due to the weight of the light?

7.2 Fluids: Pressure and Pascal's Principle

22. ▶Figure 7.27 shows a famous magician's "trick." The magician lies on a bed of thousands of nails, and a sledgehammer is used to crack a concrete block on his chest. The nails will not pierce the magician's skin. Explain why.

▲ **FIGURE 7.27 The nail mattress** See Exercise 22.

23. For the pressure–depth relationship for a fluid ($p = \rho g h$), it is assumed that (a) the pressure decreases with depth, (b) a pressure difference depends on the reference point, (c) the fluid density is constant, or (d) the relationship applies only to liquids.

24. CQ Two dams form artificial lakes of equal depth. However, one lake backs up 15 km behind the dam, and the other backs up 50 km behind. What effect does the difference in length have on the pressures on the dams?

25. CQ A water dispenser for pets has an inverted plastic bottle, as shown in ▼Fig. 7.28. (The water is dyed blue for contrast.) When a certain amount of water is drunk from the bowl, more water flows automatically from the bottle into the bowl. The bowl never overflows. Explain the operation of the dispenser. Does the height of the water in the bottle depend on the surface area of the water in the bowl?

◀ **FIGURE 7.28 Pet barometer** See Exercise 25.

26. CQ (a) Liquid storage cans, such as gasoline cans, generally have capped vents. What is the purpose of the vents, and what happens if you forget to remove the cap before you pour the liquid? (b) Explain how a medicine

dropper works. (c) Explain how we breathe (inhalation and exhalation).

27. CQ Automobile tires are inflated to about 30 lb/in^2, whereas thin bicycle tires are inflated to 90 to 115 lb/in^2—at least three times higher pressure! Why?

28. CQ Blood pressure is usually measured at the arm. However, suppose the pressure reading were taken on the calf of the leg of a standing person. Would there be a difference, in principle? Explain.

29. CQ Atmospheric pressure can be tremendous. Why is it that our bodies are not crushed under this enormous pressure?

30. CQ Explain in terms of fluid pressure how you are able to use a straw to drink soda from a bottle.

31. IE ■ In his original barometer, Pascal used water instead of mercury. (a) Water is less dense than mercury, so the water barometer would have (1) a higher height than, (2) a lower height than, or (3) the same height as the mercury barometer. Why? (b) How high would the water column have been?

32. ■ If you dive to 15 m below the surface of a lake, (a) what is the pressure due to the water alone? (b) What is the total or absolute pressure at that depth?

33. IE ■ In an open U-tube, the pressure of a water column on one side is balanced by the pressure of a column of gasoline on the other side. (a) Compared to the height of the water column, the gasoline column will have (1) a higher, (2) a lower, or (3) the same height. Why? (b) If the height of the water column is 15 cm, what is the height of the gasoline column?

34. ■ A 75-kg athlete does a single-hand handstand. If the area of the hand in contact with the floor is 125 cm^2, what pressure is exerted on the floor?

35. ■ The gauge pressure in both tires of a bicycle is 690 kPa. If the bicycle and the rider have a combined mass of 90.0 kg, what is the area of contact of *each* tire with the ground? (Assume that each tire supports half the total weight of the bicycle.)

36. ■■ In a sample of seawater taken from an oil spill, an oil layer 4.0 cm thick floats on 55 cm of water. If the density of the oil is 0.75×10^3 kg/m^3, what is the absolute pressure on the bottom of the container?

37. IE ■■ In a lecture demonstration, an empty can is used to demonstrate the force exerted by air pressure (▸Fig. 7.29). A small quantity of water is poured into the can, and the water is brought to a boil. Then, the can is sealed with a rubber stopper. As you watch, the can is slowly crushed with sounds of metal bending. (Why is a rubber stopper used as a safety precaution?) (a) This is because of (1) thermal expansion and contraction, (2) a higher steam pressure inside the can, or (3) a lower pressure inside the can as steam condenses. Why? (b) Assuming the dimensions of the can are $0.24 \text{ m} \times 0.16 \text{ m} \times 0.10 \text{ m}$ and the inside of the can is in a perfect vacuum, what is the total force exerted on the can by the air pressure?

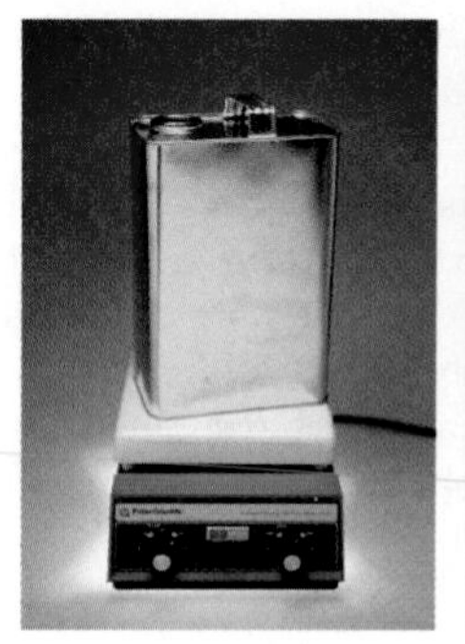

▲ **FIGURE 7.29 Air pressure** See Exercise 37.

38. ■■ What is the fractional decrease in pressure when a barometer is raised 35 m to the top of a building? (Assume that the density of air is constant over that distance.)

39. ■■ A student decides to compute the standard barometric reading on top of Mt. Everest (29 028 ft) by assuming that the density of air has the same constant density as at sea level. Try this yourself. What does the result tell you?

40. ■■ Here is a demonstration Pascal used to show the importance of a fluid's pressure on the fluid's depth (▾Fig. 7.30): An oak barrel with a lid of area 0.20 m^2 is filled with water. A long, thin tube of cross-sectional area 5.0×10^{-5} m^2 is inserted into a hole at the center of the lid, and water is poured into the tube. When the water reaches 12 m high, the barrel bursts. (a) What was the weight of the water in the tube? (b) What was the pressure

▲ **FIGURE 7.30 Pascal and the bursting barrel** See Exercise 40.

of the water on the lid of the barrel? (c) What was the net force on the lid due to the water pressure?

41. ■■ The door and the seals on an aircraft are subject to a tremendous amount of force during flight. At an altitude of 10 000 m (about 33 000 ft), the air pressure outside the airplane is only $2.7 \times 10^4 \text{ N/m}^2$, while the inside is still at normal atmospheric pressure, due to pressurization of the cabin. Calculate the net force due to the air pressures on a door of area 3.0 m^2.

42. ■■ The pressure exerted by a person's lungs can be measured by having the person blow as hard as possible into one side of a manometer. If a person blowing into one side of an open-tube manometer produces an 80-cm difference between the heights of the columns of water in the manometer arms, what is the gauge pressure of the lungs?

43. ■■ In 1960, the U.S. Navy's bathyscaphe *Trieste* (a submersible) descended to a depth of 10 912 m (about 35 000 ft) into the Marianas Trench in the Pacific Ocean. (a) What was the pressure at that depth? (Assume that seawater is incompressible.) (b) What was the force on a circular observation window with a diameter of 15 cm?

44. ■■ The output piston of a hydraulic press has a cross-sectional area of 0.20 m^2. (a) How much pressure on the input piston is required for the press to generate a force of 1.5×10^6 N? (b) What force is applied to the input piston if it has a diameter of 5.0 cm?

45. ■■ A hydraulic lift in a garage has two pistons: a small one of cross-sectional area 4.00 cm^2 and a large one of cross-sectional area 250 cm^2. If this lift is designed to raise a 3000-kg car, what minimum force must be applied to the small piston? If the force is applied through compressed air, what must be the minimum air pressure applied to the small piston?

46. ■■■ A hypodermic syringe has a plunger of area 2.5 cm^2 and a $5.0 \times 10^{-3}\text{-cm}^2$ needle. (a) If a 1.0-N force is applied to the plunger, what is the gauge pressure in the syringe's chamber? (b) If a small obstruction is at the end of the needle, what force does the fluid exert on it? (c) If the blood pressure in a vein is 50 mm Hg, what force must be applied on the plunger so that fluid can be injected into the vein?

47. ■■■ A hydraulic balance used to detect small changes in mass is shown in ▸Fig. 7.31. If a mass m of 0.25 g is placed on the balance platform, by how much will the height of the water in the smaller, 1.0-cm-diameter cylinder have changed when the balance comes to equilibrium?

7.3 Buoyancy and Archimedes' Principle

48. A wood block floats in a swimming pool. The buoyant force exerted on the block by water depends on (a) the volume of water in the pool, (b) the volume of the wood block, (c) the volume of the wood block under water, or (d) all of the above.

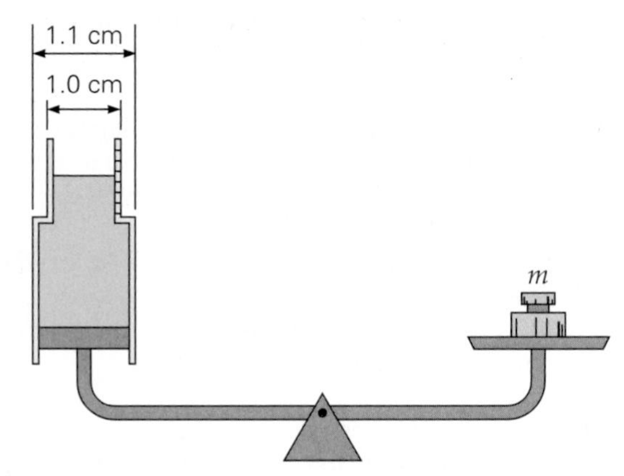

▲ **FIGURE 7.31 A hydraulic balance** See Exercise 47.

49. If a submerged object displaces an amount of liquid of greater weight than its own and is then released, the object will (a) rise to the surface and float, (b) sink, or (c) remain in equilibrium at its submerged position.

50. CQ (a) What is the most important factor in constructing a life jacket that will keep a person afloat? (b) Why is it so easy to float in Utah's Great Salt Lake?

51. CQ An ice cube floats in a glass of water. As the ice melts, how does the level of the water in the glass change? Would it make any difference if the ice cube were hollow? Explain.

52. CQ Oceangoing ships in port are loaded to the so-called *Plimsoll mark*, which is a line indicating the maximum safe loading depth. However, in New Orleans, located at the mouth of the Mississippi River, where the water is brackish (partly salty and partly fresh), ships are loaded until the Plimsoll mark is somewhat below the water line. Why?

53. CQ Two blocks of equal volume, one iron and one aluminum, are dropped into a body of water. Which block will experience the greater buoyant force? Why?

54. CQ How do you think balloonists control the altitude of a hot-air balloon?

55. CQ A bucket of water is sitting on a flat scale. Will the reading of the scale change if you dip a finger in the water without touching the bucket? Explain.

56. IE ■ (a) If the density of an object is exactly equal to the density of a fluid, the object will (1) float, (2) sink, or (3) stay at any height in the fluid, as long as it is totally immersed. Why? (b) A cube 8.5 cm on each side has a mass of 0.65 kg. Will the cube float or sink in water? Prove your answer.

57. ■ Suppose that Archimedes found that the king's crown had a mass of 0.750 kg and a volume of 3.980×10^{-5} m^3. (a) What simple approach did Archimedes use to determine the crown's volume? (b) Was the crown pure gold?

58. ■ A rectangular boat, as illustrated in ▼Fig. 7.32, is overloaded such that the water level is just 1.0 cm below the top of the boat. What is the combined mass of the people and the boat?

▲ **FIGURE 7.32 An overloaded boat** (Not drawn to scale.) See Exercise 58.

59. ■ An aluminum cube 0.15 m on each side is completely submerged in water. What is the buoyant force on it? How does the answer change if the cube is made of steel?

60. ■■ An object has a weight of 8.0 N in air. However, it apparently weighs only 4.0 N when it is completely submerged in water. What is the density of the object?

61. ■■ When a 0.80-kg crown is submerged in water, its apparent weight is measured to be 7.3 N. Is the crown pure gold?

62. IE ■■ (a) Given a piece of metal with a light string attached, a scale, and a container of water in which the piece of metal can be submersed, how could you find the volume of the piece without using the variation in the water level? (b) An object has a weight of 0.882 N. It is suspended from a scale, which reads 0.735 N when the piece is submerged in water. What are the volume and density of the piece of metal?

63. ■■ A flat-bottomed rectangular boat is 4.0 m long and 1.5 m wide. If the load is 2000 kg (including the mass of the boat), how much of the boat will be submerged when it floats in a lake?

64. ■■ A block of iron quickly sinks in water, but ships constructed of iron float. A solid cube of iron 1.0 m on each side is made into sheets. To make these sheets into a hollow cube that will not sink, what should be the minimum length of the sides of the sheets?

65. ■■ Plans are being made to bring back the zeppelin, a lighter-than-air airship like the Goodyear blimp that carries passengers and cargo, but is filled with helium, not flammable hydrogen (as was used in the ill-fated *Hindenburg*). One design calls for the ship to be 110 m long and to have a total mass (without helium) of 30.0 metric tons. Assuming the ship's "envelope" to be cylindrical, what would its diameter have to be so as to lift the total weight of the ship and the helium?

66. ■■■ A girl floats in a lake with 97% of her body beneath the water. What are (a) her mass density and (b) her weight density?

67. ■■■ A block of wood made of oak is held under the water's surface in a swimming pool. At the instant the block is released, what is its acceleration?

7.4 Fluid Dynamics and Bernoulli's Equation

68. If the speed at some point in a fluid changes with time, the fluid flow is *not* (a) steady, (b) irrotational, (c) incompressible, (d) nonviscous.

69. CQ The speed of blood flow is greater in arteries than in capillaries. However, the flow rate equation ($Av =$ constant) seems to predict that the speed should be greater in the smaller capillaries. Can you resolve this apparent inconsistency?

70. CQ Explain why water shoots out farther from a hose if you put your finger over the tip of the hose.

71. According to Bernoulli's equation, if the pressure on the liquid in Fig. 7.19 is increased, (a) the flow speed always increases, (b) the height of the liquid always increases, (c) both the flow speed and the height of the liquid may increase, or (d) none of these.

72. CQ When you suddenly turn on a water faucet in a shower, the shower curtain moves inward. Why?

73. CQ If an Indy car had a flat bottom, it would be highly unstable (like an airplane wing) due to the lift it gets when it moves at a high speed. To increase friction and stability of the car, the bottom has a concave section called the *Venturi tunnel* (▼Fig. 7.33). In terms of Bernoulli's

▲ **FIGURE 7.33 Venturi tunnel** See Exercise 73.

equation, explain how this concavity supplies extra downward force to the car in addition to that supplied by the front and rear wings (Exercise 4.79).

74. CQ Here are two common demonstrations of Bernoulli effects: (a) If you hold a narrow strip of paper in front of your mouth and blow over the top surface, the strip will rise (▼Fig. 7.34a). (Try it.) Why? (b) A plastic egg is supported vertically by a stream of air from a tube (Fig. 7.34b). The egg will not move away from the midstream position. Why not?

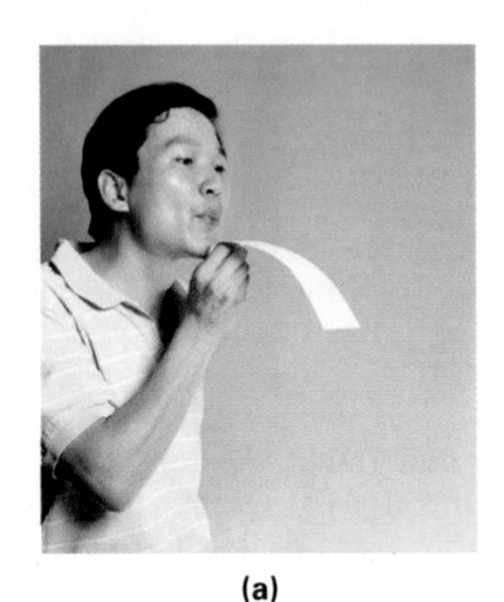

(a)

(b)

▲ **FIGURE 7.34 Bernoulli effects** See Exercise 74.

75. CQ A "split-finger" fastball sinks faster than a regular fastball. How should the ball be spinning for this to happen? Explain.

76. ■ An ideal fluid is moving at 3.0 m/s in a section of a pipe of radius 0.20 m. If the radius in another section is 0.35 m, what is the flow speed there?

77. IE ■ (a) If the radius of a pipe narrows to half of its original size, will the flow speed in the narrow section (1) increase by a factor of 2, (2) increase by a factor of 4, (3) decrease by a factor of 2, or (4) decrease by a factor of 4? Why? (b) If the radius widens to three times its original size, what is the ratio of the flow speed in the wider section to that in the narrow section?

78. ■■ Show that the static pressure–depth equation can be derived from Bernoulli's equation.

79. ■■ The speed of blood in a major artery of diameter 1.0 cm is 4.5 cm/s. (a) What is the flow rate in the artery? (b) If the capillary system has a total cross-sectional area of 2500 cm^2, the average speed of blood through the capillaries is what percentage of that through the major artery? (c) Why must blood flow at low speed through the capillaries?

80. ■■ A room measures 3.0 m by 4.5 m by 6.0 m. If the heating and air-conditioning ducts to and from the room are circular with diameter 0.30 m and all the air in the room is to be exchanged every 12 min, (a) what is the average flow rate? (b) What is the necessary flow speed in the duct? (Assume that the density of the air is constant.)

81. ■■ The spout heights in the container in ▼Fig. 7.35 are 10 cm, 20 cm, 30 cm, and 40 cm. The water level is maintained at a 45-cm height by an outside supply. (a) What is the speed of the water out of each hole? (b) Which water stream has the greatest range relative to the base of the container? Justify your answer.

▲ **FIGURE 7.35 Streams as projectiles** See Exercise 81.

82. ■■■ In an industrial cooling process, water is circulated through a system. If the water is pumped with a speed of 0.45 m/s under a pressure of 400 torr from the first floor through a 6.0-cm diameter pipe, what will be the pressure on the next floor 4.0 m above in a pipe with a diameter of 2.0 cm?

83. ■■■ Water flows at a rate of 25 L/min through a horizontal 7.0-cm-diameter pipe under a pressure of 6.0 Pa. At one point, calcium deposits reduce the cross-sectional area of the pipe to 30 cm^2. What is the pressure at this point? (Consider the water to be an ideal fluid.)

84. ■■■ A Venturi meter can be used to measure the flow speed of a liquid. A simple such device is shown in ▼Fig. 7.36. Show that the flow speed of an ideal fluid is given by $v_1 = \sqrt{\dfrac{2g\Delta h}{(A_1^2/A_2^2) - 1}}$.

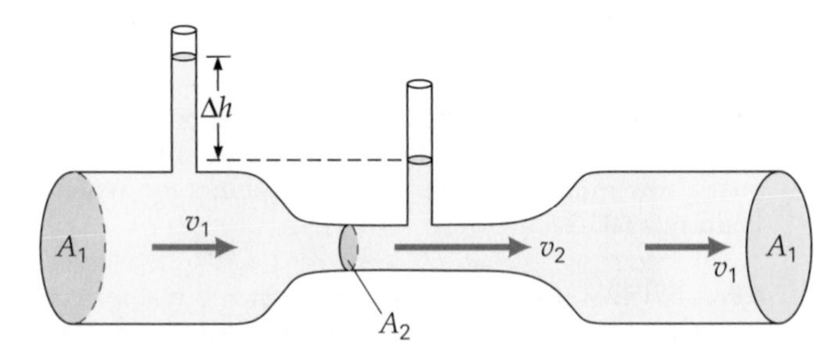

▲ **FIGURE 7.36 A flow speed meter** See Exercise 84.

*7.5 Surface Tension, Viscosity, and Poiseuille's Law

85. Water droplets and soap bubbles tend to assume the shape of a sphere. This effect is due to (a) viscosity,

(b) surface tension, (c) laminar flow, or (d) none of the above.

86. Some insects can walk on water because (a) the density of water is greater than that of the insect, (b) water is viscous, (c) water has surface tension, or (d) none of the above.

87. The viscosity of a fluid is due to (a) forces causing friction between the molecules, (b) surface tension, (c) density, or (d) none of the above.

88. CQ A motor oil is labeled 10W–40. What do the numbers 10 and 40 measure? How about the "W"?

89. ■■ The pulmonary artery, which connects the heart to the lungs, is about 8.0 cm long and has an inside diameter of 5.0 mm. If the flow rate in it is to be 25 mL/s, what is the required pressure difference over its length?

90. ■■ A hospital patient receives a quick 500-cc blood transfusion through a needle with a length of 5.0 cm and an inner diameter of 1.0 mm. If the blood bag is suspended 0.85 m above the needle, how long does the transfusion take? (Neglect the viscosity of the blood flowing in the plastic tube between the bag and the needle.)

Additional Exercises

91. A copper wire 100.00 cm long is stretched to 100.02 cm when it supports a certain load. If an aluminum wire of the same diameter is used to support the same load, what should its initial length be if its stretched length is to be 100.02 cm also?

92. A steel cube 0.25 m on each side is suspended from a scale and immersed in water. What will the scale read?

93. A wood cube 0.30 m on each side has a density of 700 kg/m^3 and floats levelly in water. (a) What is the distance from the top of the wood to the water surface? (b) What mass has to be placed on top of the wood so that its top is just at the water level?

94. A 60-kg woman balances herself on the heel of one of her high-heeled shoes. If the heel is a square of sides 1.5 cm, what is the pressure exerted on the floor? (Express your answer in Pa, lb/in^2, and atm.)

95. What is the total inward force the atmosphere exerts on a surface area of 1.30 m^2 of a person's body? (Express your answer in both newtons and pounds.)

96. A scuba diver dives to a depth of 12 m in a lake. If the circular glass plate on the diver's face mask has a diameter of 18 cm, what is the force on it due to the water only?

97. Oil is poured into the open side of an open-tube manometer containing mercury. What is the density of the oil if a column of mercury 5.0 cm high supports a column of oil 80 cm high?

98. If the atmosphere had a constant density equal to its density at the Earth's surface, how high would it extend? What does this tell you?

99. A cylinder has a diameter of 15 cm (▼Fig. 7.37). The water level in the cylinder is maintained at a constant height of 0.45 m. If the diameter of the spout pipe is 0.50 cm, how high is h, the vertical stream of water? (Assume the water to be an ideal fluid.)

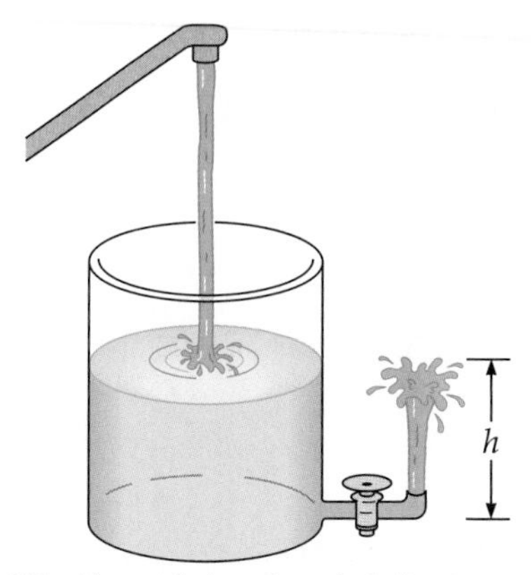

▲ **FIGURE 7.37 How high a fountain?** See Exercise 99.

100. A vertical steel beam with a rectangular cross-sectional area of 24 cm^2 is used to support a sagging floor in a building. If the beam supports a load of 10 000 N, by what percentage is the beam compressed?

101. A container 100 cm deep is filled with water. If a small hole is punched in its side 25 cm from the top, at what initial speed will the water flow from the hole?

102. Show that specific gravity is equivalent to a ratio of densities, given that its strict definition is the ratio of the weight of a given volume of a substance to the weight of an equal volume of water.

103. The flow rate of water through a garden hose is 66 cm^3/s, and the hose and nozzle have cross-sectional areas of 6.0 cm^2 and 1.0 cm^2, respectively. (a) If the nozzle is held 10 cm above the spigot, what are the flow speeds through the spigot and the nozzle? (b) What is the pressure difference between these points? (Consider the water to be an ideal fluid.)

104. CQ Ancient stonemasons sometimes split huge blocks of rock by inserting wooden pegs into holes drilled in the rock and then pouring water on the pegs. Can you explain the physics that underlies this technique? [*Hint*: Think about sponges and paper towels.]

105. A crane lifts a rectangular iron bar from the bottom of a lake. The dimensions of the bar are 0.25 m × 0.20 m × 10 m. What is the minimum upward force the crane must

supply when the bar is (a) in the water and (b) out of the water?

106. A submarine has a mass of 10 000 metric tons. What weight of water must be displaced for the sub to be in equilibrium just below the ocean surface?

107. ▸Figure 7.38 shows a simple laboratory experiment. Calculate (a) the volume and (b) the density of the suspended sphere. (Assume that the density of the sphere is uniform and that the liquid in the beaker is water.) (c) Would you be able to make the same determinations if the liquid in the beaker were mercury? (See Table 7.2.) Explain.

▲ **FIGURE 7.38 Dunking a sphere** See Exercise 107.

Temperature and Kinetic Theory

Like sailboats, hot-air balloons are low-tech devices in a high-tech world. You can equip a balloon with the latest satellite-linked, computerized navigational system and attempt to fly across the Pacific, but the basic principles that keep you aloft were known and understood centuries ago.

But why must the air in a hot-air balloon be hot? More fundamentally, what do we mean by "hot"? How does hot air differ from cool air? Temperature and heat are frequent subjects of conversation, but if you had to state what the words really mean, you might find yourself at a loss. We use thermometers of all sorts to record temperatures, which provide an objective equivalent for our sensory experience of hot and cold. Also, we know that a temperature change generally results from the application or removal of heat. Temperature, therefore, is related to heat. But what is heat? In this chapter, you'll find that the answers to such questions lead to an understanding of some far-reaching physical principles.

An early theory of heat considered it to be a fluidlike substance called caloric (from the Latin word *calor*, meaning "heat") that could be made to flow into and out of a body. Even though this theory has been abandoned, we still speak of heat as flowing from one object to another. Heat is now known to be energy in transit, and temperature and thermal properties are explained by considering the atomic and molecular behavior of substances. This and the next two chapters examine the nature of temperature and heat in terms of microscopic (molecular) theory and macroscopic observations. Here, you'll explore the nature of heat and the ways in which we measure temperature. You'll also encounter the gas laws, which explain not only the behavior of hot-air balloons, but also more important phenomena, such as how our lungs supply us with the oxygen we need to live.

8.1 Temperature and Heat

OBJECTIVE: **To distinguish between temperature and heat.**

A good way to begin studying thermal physics is with definitions of temperature and heat. **Temperature** is a relative measure, or indication, of hotness or coldness. A hot stove is said to have a high temperature and an ice cube to have a low temperature. An object that has a higher temperature than another object is said to be hotter. Note that *hot* and *cold* are relative terms, like *tall* and *short*. We can perceive temperature by touch. However, this temperature sense is somewhat unreliable, and its range is too limited to be useful for scientific purposes.

Heat is related to temperature and describes the process of energy transfer from one object to another. That is, **heat** is *the net energy transferred from one object to another because of a temperature difference*. Thus, heat is energy in transit, so to speak. Once transferred, the energy becomes part of the total energy of the molecules of the object or system, its **internal energy**. So heat (energy) transfers between objects can result in internal energy changes.

On a microscopic level, temperature is associated with molecular motion. We will show that in kinetic theory (Section 8.5), which treats gas molecules as point particles, temperature is a measure of the average random *translational* kinetic energy of the molecules. However, diatomic molecules and other real substances, besides having such translational "temperature" energy, also may have kinetic energy due to linear vibration and rotation, as well as potential energy due to the attractive forces between molecules. These energies do not contribute to the temperature of the gas, but are definitely part of its internal energy, which is the sum of all such energies (▸Fig. 8.1).

Note that a higher temperature does not necessarily mean that one system has a greater internal energy than another. For example, in a classroom on a cold day, the air temperature is relatively high compared to that of the outdoor air. But all that cold air outside the classroom has far more internal energy than does the warm air inside, simply because there is so much *more* of it. If this were not the case, heat pumps would not be practical. In other words, the internal energy of a system also depends on its mass, or the number of molecules in the system.

When heat is transferred between two objects, regardless of whether they are touching, the objects are said to be in *thermal contact*. When there is no longer a net heat transfer between objects in thermal contact, they have come to the same temperature and are said to be in *thermal equilibrium*.

8.2 The Celsius and Fahrenheit Temperature Scales

OBJECTIVES: **To (a) explain how a temperature scale is constructed and (b) convert temperatures from one scale to another.**

A measure of temperature is obtained by using a **thermometer**, a device constructed to make use of some property of a substance that changes with temperature. Fortunately, many physical properties of materials change sufficiently with temperature to be used as the bases for thermometers. By far the most obvious and commonly used property is **thermal expansion** (Section 8.4), a change in the dimensions or volume of a substance that occurs when the temperature changes.

Almost all substances expand with increasing temperature, but they do so to different extents. Most substances also contract with decreasing temperature. (Thermal expansion refers to both expansion and contraction; contraction is considered to be a negative expansion.) Because some metals expand more than oth-

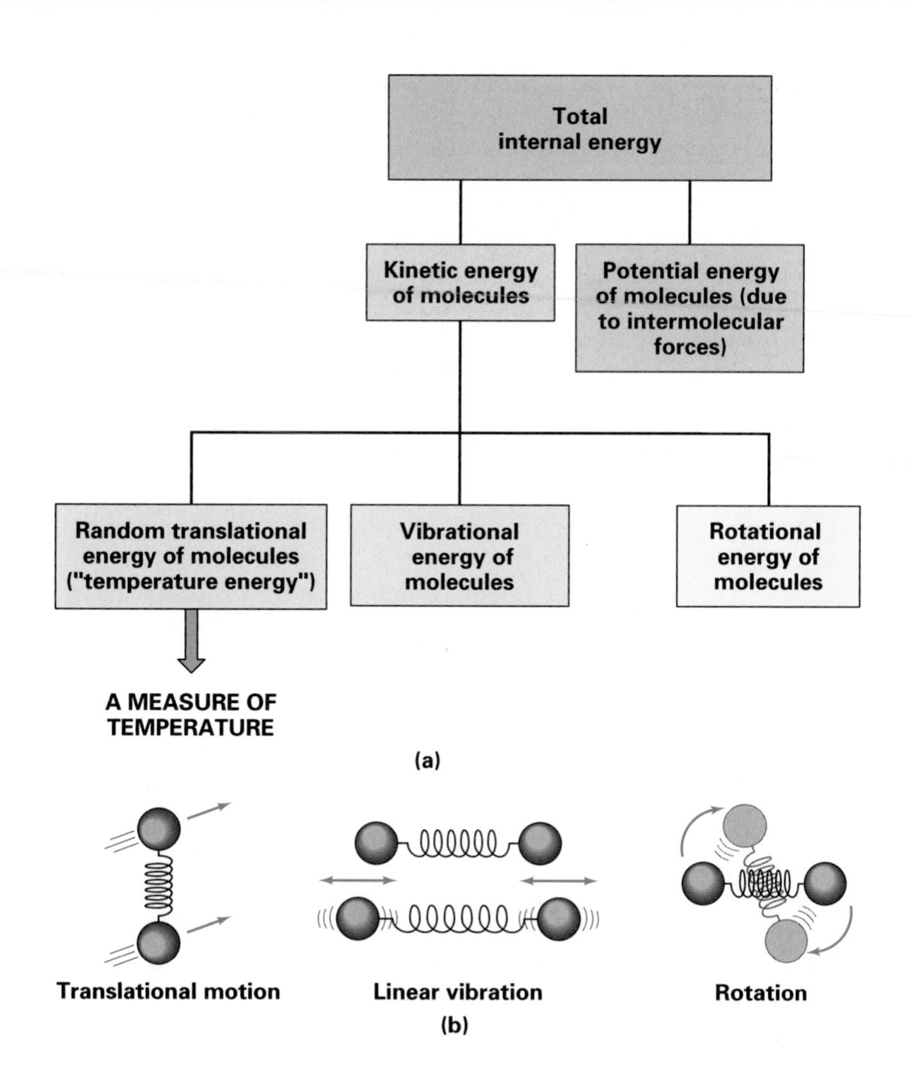

◀ **FIGURE 8.1 Molecular motions** **(a)** Temperature is associated with random translational motion; the internal energy of a system is its total energy. **(b)** A molecule may move as a whole in translational motion or may have vibrational or rotational motions (or any combination of the three kinds of motion).

ers, a bimetallic strip (a strip made of two different metals bonded together) can be used to measure temperature changes. As heat is added, the composite strip will bend away from the side made of the metal that expands more (▼Fig. 8.2). Coils formed from such strips are used in dial thermometers and in common household thermostats (▶Fig. 8.3).

A common thermometer is the liquid-in-glass type, which is based on the thermal expansion of a liquid. A liquid in a glass bulb expands into a glass

▼ **FIGURE 8.2 Thermal expansion** **(a)** A bimetallic strip is made of two strips of different metals bonded together. **(b)** When such a strip is heated, it bends because of unequal expansions of the two metals. Here, brass expands more than iron, so the deflection is toward the iron. The deflection of the end of a strip could be used to measure temperature.

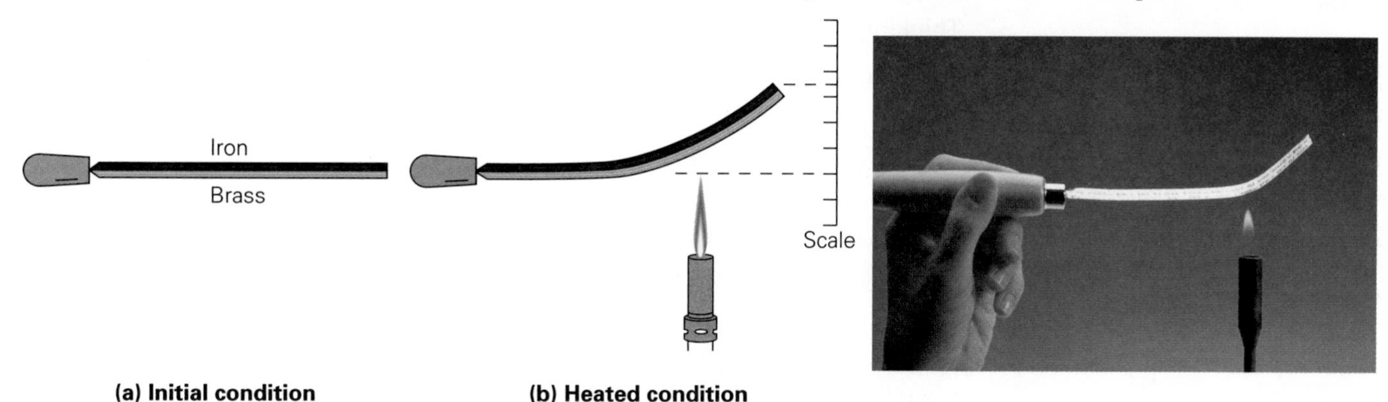

(a)

(b)

▲ **FIGURE 8.3 Bimetallic coil** Bimetallic coils are used in **(a)** dial thermometers (the coil is in the center) and **(b)** household thermostats (the coil is to the right). Thermostats are used to regulate a heating or cooling system, turning off and on as the temperature of the room changes. The expansion and contraction of the coil causes the tilting of a glass vial containing mercury, which makes and breaks electrical contact.

stem, rising in a capillary bore (a thin tube). Mercury and alcohol (usually dyed red to make it more visible) are the liquids used in most liquid-in-glass thermometers. These substances are chosen because of their relatively large thermal expansion and because they remain liquids over normal temperature ranges.

Thermometers are calibrated so that a numerical value can be assigned to a given temperature. For the definition of any standard scale or unit, two fixed reference points are needed. The ice point and the steam point of water at standard atmospheric pressure are two convenient fixed points. More commonly known as the freezing and boiling points, these are the temperatures at which pure water freezes and boils, respectively, under a pressure of 1 atm (standard pressure).

The two most familiar temperature scales are the **Fahrenheit temperature scale** (used in the United States) and the **Celsius temperature scale** (used in the rest of the world). As shown in ▸Fig. 8.4, the ice and steam points have values of 32°F and 212°F, respectively, on the Fahrenheit scale and 0°C and 100°C, respectively, on the Celsius scale. On the Fahrenheit scale, there are 180 equal intervals, or degrees (F°), between the two reference points; on the Celsius scale, there are 100 degrees (C°). Therefore, since $180/100 = 9/5 = 1.8$, a Celsius degree is almost twice as large as a Fahrenheit degree. (See margin note for difference between °C and C°.)

A relationship for converting between the two scales can be obtained from a graph of Fahrenheit temperature (T_F) versus Celsius temperature (T_C), such as the one in ▸Fig. 8.5. The equation of the straight line (in slope–intercept form, $y = mx + b$) is $T_F = (180/100)T_C + 32$, and

$$T_F = \tfrac{9}{5}T_C + 32 \quad \text{or} \quad T_F = 1.8T_C + 32 \qquad \textit{Celsius-to-Fahrenheit conversion} \tag{8.1}$$

where $\frac{9}{5}$ or 1.8 is the slope of the line and 32 is the intercept on the vertical axis. Thus, to change from a Celsius temperature (T_C) to its equivalent Fahrenheit temperature (T_F), you simply multiply the Celsius reading by $\frac{9}{5}$ and add 32.

The equation can be solved for T_C to convert from Fahrenheit to Celsius:

$$T_C = \tfrac{5}{9}(T_F - 32) \qquad \textit{Fahrenheit-to-Celsius conversion} \tag{8.2}$$

Note: For distinction, a particular temperature measurement, such as $T = 20°C$, is written with °C (pronounced 20 degrees Celsius), whereas a temperature interval, such as $\Delta T = 80°C - 60°C = 20$ C°, is written with C° (pronounced 20 Celsius degrees).

Example 8.1 ■ Converting Temperature Scale Readings: Fahrenheit and Celsius

What are (a) the typical room temperature of 20°C and a cold temperature of −18°C on the Fahrenheit scale; and (b) another cold temperature of −10°F and normal body temperature, 98.6°F, on the Celsius scale?

Thinking It Through. This is a direct application of Eqs. 8.1 and 8.2.

Solution. We wish to make the following conversions:

Given: (a) $T_C = 20°C$ and $T_C = -18°C$
(b) $T_F = -10°F$ and $T_F = 98.6°F$

Find: for each temperature,
(a) T_F
(b) T_C

(a) Equation 8.1 is for changing Celsius readings to Fahrenheit:

20°C: $T_F = \frac{9}{5}T_C + 32 = \frac{9}{5}(20) + 32 = 68°F$

−18°C: $T_F = \frac{9}{5}T_C + 32 = \frac{9}{5}(-18) + 32 = 0°F$

(This typical room temperature of 20°C is a good one to remember.)

(b) Equation 8.2 changes Fahrenheit to Celsius:

$$-10°\text{F}: \quad T_C = \tfrac{5}{9}(T_F - 32) = \tfrac{5}{9}(-10 - 32) = 23°\text{C}$$

$$98.6°\text{F}: \quad T_C = \tfrac{5}{9}(T_F - 32) = \tfrac{5}{9}(98.6 - 32) = 37.0°\text{C}$$

From the last calculation, we see that normal body temperature has a whole-number value on the Celsius scale. Keep in mind that a Celsius degree is 1.8 times (almost twice) as large as a Fahrenheit degree, so a temperature elevation of several degrees on the Celsius scale makes a big difference. For example, a temperature of 40.0°C represents an elevation of 3.0 C° over normal body temperature. However, on the Fahrenheit scale, this is an increase of $3.0 \times 1.8 = 5.4$ F°, or a temperature of $98.6 + 5.4 = 104.0$°F. (For more on "normal" body temperature, see the Insight on p. 264.)

Follow-up Exercise. Convert the following temperatures: (a) −40°F to Celsius and (b) −40°C to Fahrenheit. *(Answers to all Follow-up Exercises are at the back of the text.)*

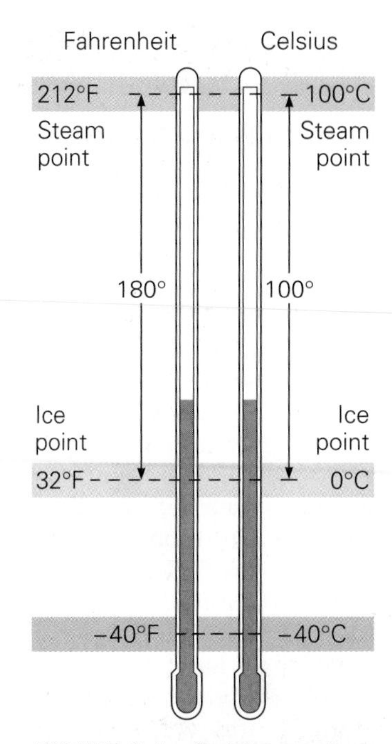

▲ **FIGURE 8.4 Celsius and Fahrenheit temperature scales** Between the ice and steam fixed points, there are 100 degrees on the Celsius scale and 180 degrees on the Fahrenheit scale. Thus, a Celsius degree is 1.8 times larger than a Fahrenheit degree.

Problem-Solving Hint

Because Eqs. 8.1 and 8.2 are so similar, it is easy to miswrite them. Since they are equivalent, you need to know only one of them—say, Celsius to Fahrenheit (Eq. 8.1, $T_F = \frac{9}{5}T_C + 32$). Solving this equation for T_C algebraically gives Eq. 8.2. A good way to make sure that you have written the conversion equation correctly is to test it with a known temperature, such as the boiling point of water. For example, $T_C = 100°$, so

$$T_F = \tfrac{9}{5}T_C + 32 = \tfrac{9}{5}(100) + 32 = 212°\text{F}$$

Thus, we know the equation is correct.

Liquid-in-glass thermometers are adequate for many temperature measurements, but problems arise when highly accurate determinations are needed. A material may not expand uniformly over a wide temperature range. When calibrated to the ice and steam points, an alcohol thermometer and a mercury thermometer have the same readings at those points, but because alcohol and mercury have different expansion properties, the thermometers will not have exactly the same reading at an intermediate temperature, such as room temperature. For very sensitive temperature measurements and to define intermediate temperatures precisely, some other type of thermometer must be used. One such thermometer, a *gas thermometer*, is discussed next.

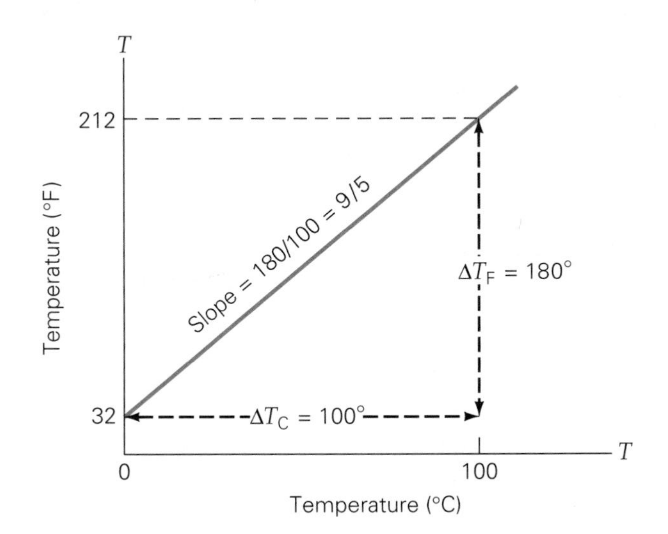

◀ **FIGURE 8.5 Fahrenheit versus Celsius** A plot of Fahrenheit temperature versus Celsius temperature gives a straight line of the general form $y = mx + b$, where $T_F = \frac{9}{5}T_C + 32$.

INSIGHT

Human Body Temperature

We commonly take "normal" human body temperature to be 98.6°F (or 37.0°C). The source of this value is a study of human temperature readings done in 1868—more than 130 years ago! A more recent study, conducted in 1992, notes that the 1868 study used thermometers that were not as accurate as modern electronic thermometers. The new study has some interesting results.

The "normal" human body temperature from oral measurements varies among individuals over a range of about 96°F to 101°F, with an average temperature of 98.2°F. After strenuous exercise, the oral temperature can rise as high as 103°F. When the body is exposed to cold, oral temperatures can fall below 96°F. A rapid drop in temperature of 2 to 3 F° produces uncontrollable shivering. There is a contraction not only of the skeletal muscles, but also of the tiny muscles attached to the hair follicles. The result is "goose bumps."

Your body temperature is typically lower in the morning, after you have slept and your digestive processes are at a low point. "Normal" body temperature generally rises during the day to a peak and then recedes. The 1992 study also indicated that women have a slightly higher average body temperature than do men (98.4°F versus 98.1°F).

What about the extremes? A fever temperature is typically between 102°F and 104°F. A body temperature above 106°F is extremely dangerous. At such temperatures, the enzymes that take part in certain chemical reactions in the body begin to be inactivated, and a total breakdown of body chemistry can result.

On the cold side, decreasing the body temperature results in memory lapse and slurred speech, muscular rigidity, erratic heartbeats, and loss of consciousness. Below 78°F, death occurs due to heart failure. However, mild hypothermia (lower-than-normal body temperature) can be beneficial. A decrease in body temperature slows down the body's chemical reactions, and cells use less oxygen than they normally do. This effect is applied in some surgeries (Fig. 1). A patient's body temperature may be lowered significantly to avoid damage to the heart, which must be stopped during such procedures, and to the brain.

Related Exercise: 10

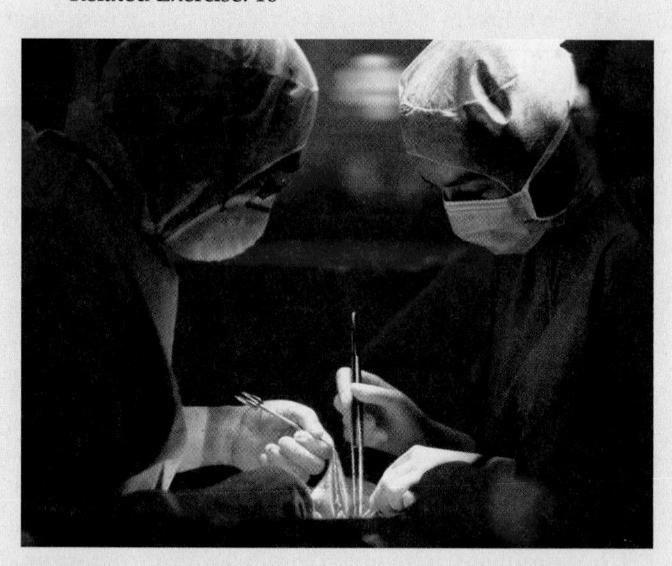

FIGURE 1 Lower than normal During some surgeries, the patient's body temperature is lowered to slow down the body's chemical reactions and to reduce the need for blood to supply oxygen to the tissues.

8.3 Gas Laws and Absolute Temperature

OBJECTIVES: **To (a) describe the ideal gas law, (b) explain how it is used to determine absolute zero, and (c) understand the Kelvin temperature scale.**

Whereas different liquid-in-glass thermometers show slightly different readings for temperatures other than fixed points because of the liquids' different expansion properties, a thermometer that uses a gas gives the same readings regardless of the gas used. The reason is that at very low densities all gases exhibit the same expansion behavior.

The variables that describe the behavior of a given quantity (mass) of gas are pressure, volume, and temperature (p, V, and T). When temperature is held constant, the pressure and volume of a quantity of gas are related as follows:

$$pV = \text{constant} \quad \text{or} \quad p_1V_1 = p_2V_2 \quad (\textit{at constant temperature}) \tag{8.3}$$

That is, the product of pressure and volume is a constant. This relationship is known as *Boyle's law*, after Robert Boyle (1627–1691), the English chemist who discovered it.

When the pressure is held constant, the volume of a quantity of gas is related to the *absolute* temperature (to be defined shortly):

$$\frac{V}{T} = \text{constant} \quad \text{or} \quad \frac{V_1}{T_1} = \frac{V_2}{T_2} \quad \textit{(at constant pressure)} \tag{8.4}$$

That is, the ratio of the volume to the temperature is a constant. This relationship is known as *Charles's law*, named for the French scientist Jacques Charles (1747–1823), who made early hot-air balloon flights and was therefore quite interested in the relationship between the volume and temperature of a gas. A popular demonstration of Charles's law is shown in ▸Fig. 8.6.

Low-density gases obey these laws, which may be combined into a single relationship. Since pV = constant and V/T = constant for a given quantity of gas, pV/T must also equal a constant. This relationship is the **ideal gas law**:

$$\frac{pV}{T} = \text{constant} \quad \text{or} \quad \frac{p_1V_1}{T_1} = \frac{p_2V_2}{T_2} \quad \begin{array}{l}\textit{ideal gas law}\\ \textit{(ratio form)}\end{array} \tag{8.5}$$

That is, the ratio pV/T at one time (t_1) is the same as at another time (t_2), or at any other time, as long as the quantity (or mass) of gas does not change.

This relationship can be written in a more general form that applies not just to a given quantity of a single gas, but to any quantity of any low-pressure, dilute gas. With a quantity of gas determined by the number of molecules (N) in the gas (i.e., $pV/T \propto N$), it follows that

$$\frac{pV}{T} = Nk_B \quad \text{or} \quad pV = Nk_BT \quad \textit{ideal gas law} \tag{8.6}$$

where k_B is a constant of proportionality known as *Boltzmann's constant*: $k_B = 1.38 \times 10^{-23}$ J/K. The K stands for temperature on the Kelvin scale, discussed shortly. (Can you show that the units are correct?) Note that the mass of the sample does not appear explicitly in Eq. 8.6. However, the number of molecules N in a sample of a gas is proportional to the total mass of the gas. The ideal gas law, sometimes called the *perfect gas law*, applies to gases with low pressures and densities and describes the behavior of most gases fairly accurately at normal densities.

▲ **FIGURE 8.6 Charles's law in action** Demonstrations of the relationship between the volume and the temperature of a quantity of gas. A weighted balloon, initially at room temperature, is placed in a beaker of water. **(a)** When ice is placed in the beaker and the temperature falls, the balloon's volume is reduced. **(b)** When the water is heated and the temperature rises, the balloon's volume increases.

Ludwig Boltzmann was a 19th-century Austrian physicist who used stastical mechanics to investigate atomic phenomena.

Macroscopic Form of the Ideal Gas Law

Equation 8.6 is a "microscopic" (*micro* means small) form of the ideal gas law in that it refers specifically to the number of molecules, N. However, the law can be rewritten in a "macroscopic" (*macro* means large) form, which involves quantities that can be measured with everyday laboratory equipment. In this form, we have

$$pV = nRT \quad \textit{ideal gas law} \tag{8.7}$$

Note: The temperature T in the ideal gas law is absolute (Kelvin) temperature.

using nR rather than Nk_B for convenience. Here, n is the number of moles (mol) of the gas, a quantity defined next, and R is called the *universal gas constant*:

$$R = 8.31 \text{ J/(mol} \cdot \text{K)}$$

In chemistry, a **mole** (abbreviated mol) of a substance is defined as the quantity that contains **Avogadro's number** (N_A) of molecules:

$$N_A = 6.02 \times 10^{23} \text{ molecules/mol}$$

Note: N is the total number of molecules; N_A is Avogadro's number; $n = N/N_A$ is the number of moles.

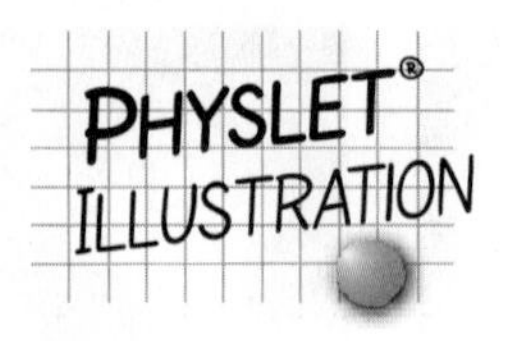

The Ideal Gas Law

Thus, n and N in the two forms of the ideal gas law are related by $N = nN_A$. From Eq. 8.7, it can be shown that 1 mol of *any* gas occupies 22.4 L at 0°C and 1 atm. These conditions are known as *standard temperature and pressure* (*STP*).

It is important to note what these equations for the macroscopic (Eq. 8.7) and microscopic (Eq. 8.6) forms of the ideal gas law represent. For the macroscopic form of the ideal gas law, the constant $R = pV/(nT)$ has units of $J/(mol \cdot K)$. For the microscopic form of the law, $k_B = pV/(NT)$, with units of $J/(molecule \cdot K)$. Note the difference between the macroscopic and microscopic forms of the ideal gas law is moles versus molecules, and we can measure moles.

Equation 8.7 is a practical form of the ideal gas law, because we generally work with measured (macroscopic or laboratory) quantities or moles (n) of gases rather than the number of molecules (N). To use Eq. 8.7, we need to know the number of moles of a gas. The mass of 1 mol of any substance is its *formula mass*, expressed in grams. The formula mass is determined from the chemical formula and the atomic masses of the atoms. (The latter are listed in Appendix IV and are commonly rounded to the nearest one-half.) For example, water, H_2O, with two hydrogen atoms and one oxygen atom, has a formula mass of $2m_H + 1m_O = 2(1.0) + 1(16.0) = 18.0$, because the atomic mass of each hydrogen atom is 1.0 g and that of an oxygen atom is 16.0 g. Thus, 1 mol of water has a formula mass of 18.0 g. Similarly, the oxygen we breathe, O_2, has a formula mass of $2 \times 16.0 = 32.0$. Hence, a mole of oxygen, with a mass of 32 g, would occupy 22.4 L at STP.

It is interesting to note that Avogadro's number allows you to compute the mass of a particular type of molecule. For example, suppose you want to know the mass of a water molecule (H_2O). As we have just seen, the formula mass of 1 mol of water is 18.0 g, or 18.0 g/mol. The *molecular mass* (m) is then given by

$$m = \frac{\text{formula mass (in kilograms)}}{N_A}$$

and, converting grams to kilograms, we have

$$m_{H_2O} = \frac{(18.0\text{ g/mol})(10^{-3}\text{ kg/g})}{6.02 \times 10^{23}\text{ molecules/mol}} = 2.99 \times 10^{-26}\text{ kg/molecule}$$

Thus, the *formula mass* (in kilograms) is also equivalent to the mass of 1 mol (in kilograms).

Absolute Zero and the Kelvin Temperature Scale

The product of the pressure and the volume of a sample of ideal gas is directly proportional to the temperature of the gas: $pV \propto T$. This relationship allows a gas to be used to measure temperature in a *constant-volume gas thermometer*. Holding the volume of the gas constant, which can be done easily in a rigid container (▸Fig. 8.7), means that $p \propto T$. Thus, using a constant-volume gas thermometer, one reads the temperature in terms of pressure. A plot of pressure versus temperature gives a straight line in this case (▸ Fig. 8.8a).

As can be seen in Fig. 8.8b, measurements of real gases (plotted data points) deviate from the values predicted by the ideal gas law at very low temperatures. This is because the gases liquefy at such temperatures. However, the relationship is linear over a large temperature range, and it looks as though the pressure might reach zero with decreasing temperature if the gas were to continue to be gaseous (ideal or perfect).

The absolute minimum temperature for an ideal gas is therefore inferred by extrapolating, or extending the straight line to the axis, as in Fig. 8.8b. This temperature is found to be −273.15°C and is designated as **absolute zero**. Absolute zero is believed to be the lower limit of temperature, but it has never been attained. In fact, there is a law of thermodynamics that says it never can be. There is no known

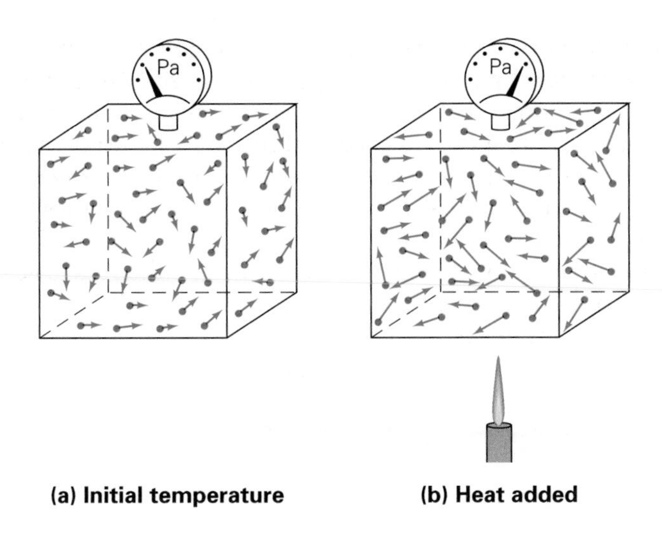

◀ **FIGURE 8.7 Constant-volume gas thermometer** Such a thermometer indicates temperature as a function of pressure, since, for a low-density gas, $p \propto T$. **(a)** At some initial temperature, the pressure reading has a certain value. **(b)** When the gas thermometer is heated, the pressure (and temperature) reading is higher, because, on average, the gas molecules are moving faster.

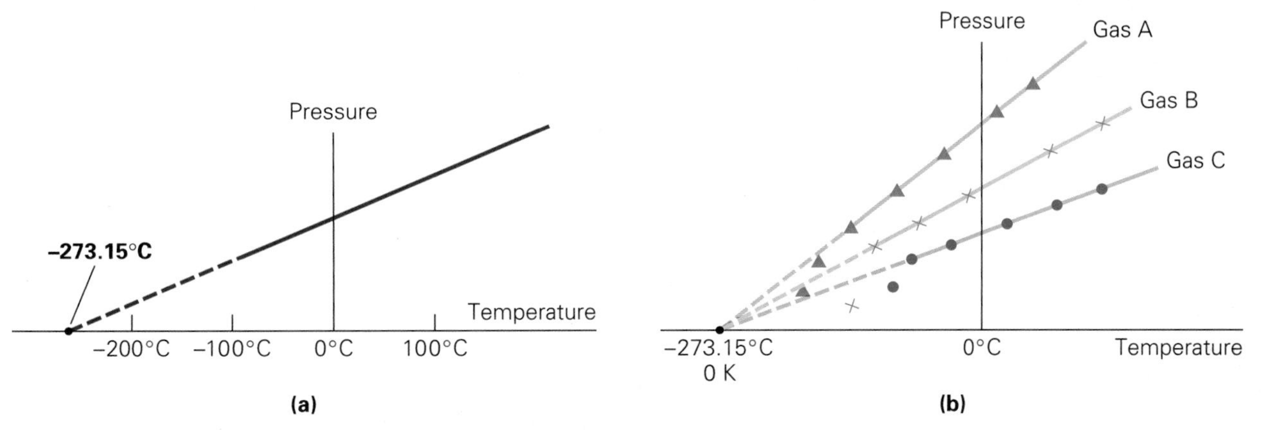

▲ **FIGURE 8.8 Pressure versus temperature** **(a)** A low-density gas kept at a constant volume gives a straight line on a graph of p versus T, that is, $p = (Nk_B/V)T$. When the line is extended to the zero pressure value, a temperature of −273.15°C is obtained, which is taken to be absolute zero. **(b)** Extrapolation of lines for all low-density gases indicates the same absolute zero temperature. The actual behavior of gases deviates from this straight-line relationship at low temperatures because the gases start to liquefy.

upper limit to temperature. For example, the temperatures at the centers of some stars are estimated to be greater than 100 million degrees.

Absolute zero is the foundation of the **Kelvin temperature scale**, named after the British scientist Lord Kelvin.* On this scale, −273.15°C is taken as the zero point—that is, as 0 K (▶Fig. 8.9). The size of a single unit of Kelvin temperature is the same as that of the Celsius degree, so temperatures on these scales are related by

$$T_K = T_C + 273.15 \quad \textit{Celsius-to-Kelvin conversion} \quad (8.8)$$

where T_K is the temperature in **kelvins** (*not* degrees Kelvin; for example, 300 kelvins). The kelvin is abbreviated as K (*not* °K). For general calculations, it is common to round the 273.15 in the Eq. 8.8 to 273, that is,

$$T_K = T_C + 273 \quad (\textit{for general calculations}) \quad (8.8a)$$

*Lord Kelvin, born William Thomson (1824–1907), developed devices to improve telegraphy and the compass and was involved in the laying of the first transatlantic cable. When he received his title, it is said that he considered choosing Lord Cable or Lord Compass as the title, but decided on Lord Kelvin, after a river that runs near the University of Glasgow in Scotland, where he was a professor of physics for 50 years.

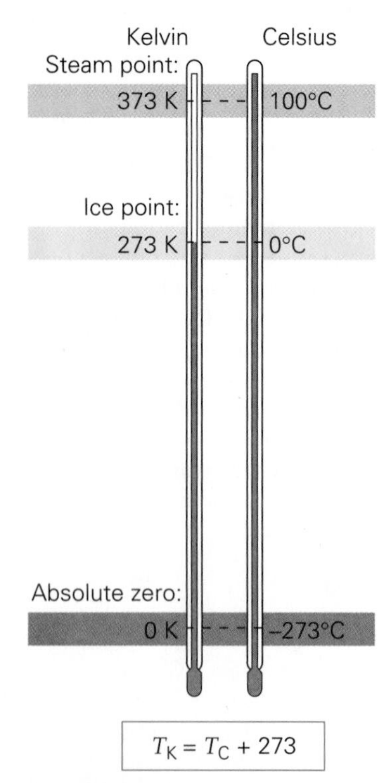

▲ **FIGURE 8.9 The Kelvin temperature scale** The lowest temperature on the Kelvin scale (corresponding to −273.15°C) is absolute zero. A unit interval on the Kelvin scale, called a kelvin and abbreviated K, is equivalent to a temperature change of 1 C°; thus, $T_K = T_C + 273.15$. (The constant is usually rounded to 273 for convenience.) For example, a temperature of 0°C is equal to 273 kelvins.

The absolute Kelvin scale is the official SI temperature scale; however, the Celsius scale is used in most parts of the world for everyday temperature readings. The absolute temperature in kelvins is used primarily in scientific applications.

Hint: Keep in mind that Kelvin temperatures *must* be used with the ideal gas law. It is a common mistake to use Celsius or Fahrenheit temperatures in that equation. Suppose you used a Celsius temperature of $T = 0°C$ in the gas law. You would have $pV = 0$, which makes no sense.

Note that there can be no negative temperatures on the Kelvin scale if absolute zero is the lowest possible temperature. That is, the Kelvin scale doesn't have an arbitrary zero temperature somewhere within the scale—zero K is absolute zero, period.

Example 8.2 ■ Deepest Freeze: Absolute Zero on the Fahrenheit Scale

What is absolute zero on the Fahrenheit scale?

Thinking It Through. We need to convert 0 K to the Fahrenheit scale. Let's make the first conversion to the Celsius scale. (Why?)

Solution.

Given: $T_K = 0\text{ K}$ *Find:* T_F

Temperatures on the Kelvin scale are related directly to Celsius temperatures by $T_K = T_C + 273.15$ (Eq. 8.8), so first we convert 0 K to a Celsius value:

$$T_C = T_K - 273.15 = 0 - 273.15 = -273.15°\text{C}$$

(We use −273.15°C for absolute zero to give a more accurate value of absolute zero on the Fahrenheit scale.) Then, converting to Fahrenheit (Eq. 8.1) gives

$$T_F = \tfrac{9}{5}T_C + 32 = \tfrac{9}{5}(-273.15) + 32 = -459.67°\text{F}$$

Thus, absolute zero is about −460°F.

Follow-up Exercise. There is an absolute temperature scale associated with the Fahrenheit temperature scale called the Rankine scale. A Rankine degree is the same size as a Fahrenheit degree, and absolute zero is taken as 0°R (zero degrees Rankine). Write the conversion equations between (a) the Rankine and the Fahrenheit scales, (b) the Rankine and the Celsius scales, and (c) the Rankine and the Kelvin scales.

Initially, gas thermometers were calibrated by using the ice and steam points. The Kelvin scale uses absolute zero, and a second fixed point adopted in 1954 by the International Committee on Weights and Measures. This second fixed point is the **triple point of water**, at which water coexists simultaneously in equilibrium as a solid (ice), liquid (water), and gas (water vapor). The triple point occurs at a unique set of values for temperature and pressure—a temperature of 0.01°C and a pressure of 4.58 mm of Hg—and provides a reproducible reference temperature for the Kelvin scale. The temperature of the triple point on the Kelvin scale was assigned a value of 273.16 K. The SI kelvin unit is then defined as 1/273.16 of the temperature at the triple point of water.*

Now let's use the ideal gas law, which requires absolute temperatures.

Example 8.3 ■ The Ideal Gas Law: Using Absolute Temperatures

A quantity of low-density gas in a rigid container is initially at room temperature (20°C) and a particular pressure (p_1). If the gas is heated to a temperature of 60°C, by what factor does the pressure change?

*The 273.16 value given here for the triple point temperature and the −273.15 value determined in Fig. 8.8 indicate different things. The −273.15°C is taken as 0 K. The 273.16 K (or 0.01°C) is a different reading on a different temperature scale.

Thinking It Through. A "factor" of change implies a ratio (p_2/p_1), so Eq. 8.5 should apply. Note that the container is rigid, which means that $V_1 = V_2$.

Solution.

Given: $T_1 = 20°C$ *Find:* p_2/p_1 (pressure ratio or factor)
$T_2 = 60°C$
$V_1 = V_2$

Since we want the factor by which the pressure changes, we write p_2/p_1 as a ratio. For example, if $p_2/p_1 = 2$, then $p_2 = 2p_1$, or the pressure would change (increase) by a factor of 2. The ratio also indicates that we should use the ideal gas law in ratio form. The law requires *absolute* temperatures, so we first change the Celsius temperatures to kelvins:

$$T_1 = 20°C + 273 = 293 \text{ K}$$
$$T_2 = 60°C + 273 = 333 \text{ K}$$

Observe that a rounded value of 273 was used in Eq. 8.8 for convenience. Then, using the ideal gas law (Eq. 8.5) in the form $p_2V_2/T_2 = p_1V_1/T_1$, we have, since $V_1 = V_2$,

$$p_2 = \left(\frac{T_2}{T_1}\right)p_1 = \left(\frac{333 \text{ K}}{293 \text{ K}}\right)p_1 = 1.14\,p_1$$

Thus, p_2 is 1.14 times p_1; that is, the pressure increases by a factor of 1.14, or 14 percent. (What would the factor be if the Celsius temperatures were *incorrectly* used? It would be much larger: $60°C/20°C = 3$, or $p_2 = 3p_1$.)

Follow-up Exercise. If the gas in this Example is heated at room temperature, so that the pressure increases by a factor of 1.26, what is the final Celsius temperature?

Note: *Always* use Kelvin (absolute) temperatures with the ideal gas law.

Because of its absolute nature, the Kelvin temperature scale has special significance. As we shall see in Section 8.5, the absolute temperature is directly proportional to the internal energy of an ideal gas and so can be used as an indication of that energy. There are no negative values on the absolute scale. Negative absolute temperatures would imply negative internal energy for the gas, a meaningless concept.

Suppose you were asked to double the temperatures of, say, −10°C and 0°C. What would you do? The following Integrated Example should help.

Integrated Example 8.4 ■ Some Like It Hot: Doubling the Temperature

The evening weather report gives the day's high temperature as 10°C and predicts the next day's high to be 20°C. (a) A father tells his son that this means it will be twice as warm tomorrow, but the son says it does not. With whom do you agree? (b) What is the factor increase for the temperatures on the Kelvin scale, and what does it indicate?

(a) Conceptual Reasoning. Keep in mind that temperature gives a relative *indication* of hotness or coldness. Certainly, 20°C would be warmer than 10°C. But just because the numerical value of the higher temperature is twice as great (or greater by a factor of 2, because $20°C/10°C = 2$) does not necessarily mean it is twice as warm, but only that the air temperature is 10 degrees higher and therefore relatively warmer. So the son wins.

(b) Thinking It Through. The Kelvin temperatures can be computed directly from Eq. 8.8, and a ratio of these temperatures will give the factor of increase. As noted, the absolute temperature is directly proportional to the internal energy of an ideal gas. If we consider a volume of air to be an ideal gas at these absolute temperatures, a ratio of the temperatures would give the factor of increase in internal energy.

Given: $T_{C_1} = 10°C$ *Find:* T_{K_2}/T_{K_1}
$T_{C_2} = 20°C$

The equivalent absolute temperatures are

$$T_{K_1} = T_{C_1} + 273 = 10°C + 273 = 283 \text{ K}$$
$$T_{K_2} = T_{C_2} + 273 = 20°C + 273 = 293 \text{ K}$$

and

$$\frac{T_{K_3}}{T_{K_1}} = \frac{293 \text{ K}}{283 \text{ K}} = 1.04$$

So there is an increase of 0.04, or 4%, in the internal energy of an ideal gas in going from 10°C to 20°C, and it would not be twice as warm.

Follow-up Exercise. The weather report gives the day's high temperature as 0°C. If the next day's temperature were double that, what would the temperature be in degrees Celsius? Would this be environmentally possible?

8.4 Thermal Expansion

OBJECTIVE: **To understand and be able to calculate the thermal expansions of solids and liquids.**

Changes in the dimensions and volumes of materials are common thermal effects. As you learned earlier, thermal expansion provides a means of measuring temperature. The thermal expansion of gases is generally described by the ideal gas law and is very obvious. Less dramatic, but by no means less important, is the thermal expansion of solids and liquids.

Note: Solids are discussed in Section 7.1.

Thermal expansion results from a change in the average distance separating the atoms of a substance. The atoms are held together by bonding forces, which can be simplistically represented as springs in a simple model of a solid. (See Fig. 7.1.) The atoms vibrate back and forth; with increased temperature (i.e., more internal energy), they become increasingly active and vibrate over greater distances. With wider vibrations in all dimensions, the solid expands as a whole.

The change in one dimension of a solid (length, width, or thickness) is called *linear* expansion. For small temperature changes, linear expansion is approximately proportional to ΔT, or $T - T_o$ (▼Fig. 8.10a). The *fractional* change* in length is

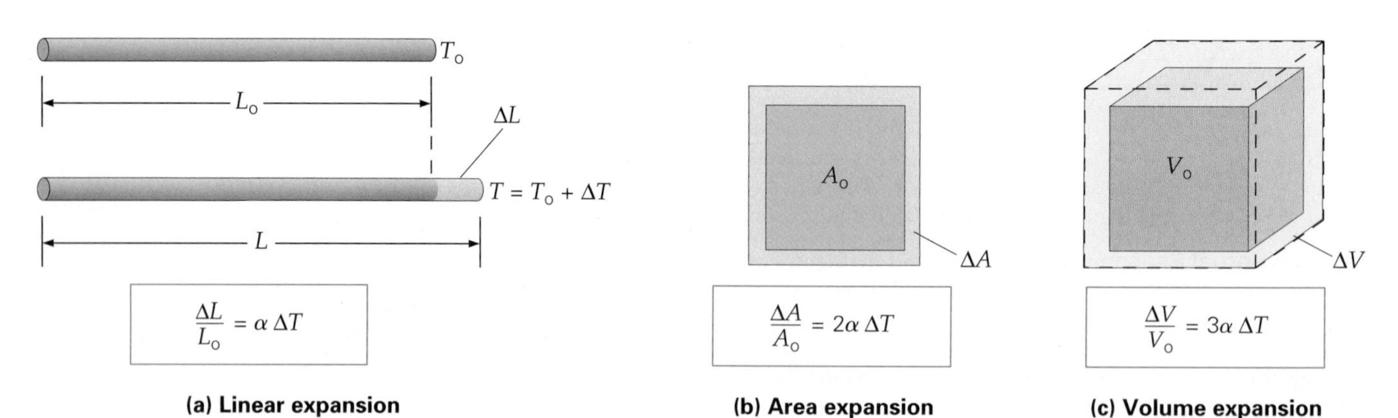

▲ **FIGURE 8.10 Thermal expansion (a)** Linear expansion is proportional to the temperature change; that is, the change in length ΔL is proportional to ΔT, and $\Delta L/L_o = \alpha\Delta T$, where α is the thermal coefficient of linear expansion. **(b)** For isotropic expansion, the thermal coefficient of area expansion is approximately 2α. **(c)** The thermal coefficient of volume expansion for solids is about 3α.

*A fractional change may also be expressed as a percent. For example, by analogy, if you invested \$100 (\$$_o$) and made \$10 (Δ\$), then the fractional change would be Δ\$/\$$_o$ = 10/100 = 0.10, or an increase of 10%.

$(L - L_o)/L_o$, or $\Delta L/L_o$, where L_o is the original length of the solid at the initial temperature. This ratio is related to the change in temperature by

$$\frac{\Delta L}{L_o} = \alpha \Delta T \quad \text{or} \quad \Delta L = \alpha L_o \Delta T \tag{8.9}$$

where α is the **thermal coefficient of linear expansion**. Note that the unit of α is inverse temperature: inverse Celsius degrees ($1/\text{C}°$, or $\text{C}°^{-1}$). Values of α for some materials are given in Table 8.1.

A solid may have different coefficients of linear expansion for different directions, but for simplicity, this book will assume that the same coefficient applies to all directions (in other words, that solids show *isotropic* expansion). Also, the coefficient of expansion may vary slightly for different temperature ranges. Since this variation is negligible for most common applications, α will be considered to be constant and independent of temperature.

Equation 8.9 can be rewritten to give the final length (L) after a change in temperature:

$$\begin{aligned} \Delta L &= \alpha L_o \Delta T \\ L - L_o &= \alpha L_o \Delta T \\ L &= L_o + \alpha L_o \Delta T \end{aligned}$$

or

$$L = L_o(1 + \alpha \Delta T) \tag{8.10}$$

We can then use Eq. 8.10 to compute the thermal expansion of *areas* of flat objects. Since area (A) is length squared (L^2) for a square, we get

$$A = L^2 = L_o^2(1 + \alpha \Delta T)^2 = A_o(1 + 2\alpha \Delta T + \alpha^2 \Delta T^2)$$

where A_o is the original area. Because the values of α for solids are much less than 1 ($\sim 10^{-5}$, as shown in Table 8.1), the second-order term (containing $\alpha^2 \simeq (10^{-5})^2 = 10^{-10} \ll 10^{-5}$) can be dropped with negligible error. As a first-order approximation, then, and with the understanding that the change in area, $\Delta A = A - A_o$, we have

$$A = A_o(1 + 2\alpha \Delta T) \quad \text{or} \quad \frac{\Delta A}{A_o} = 2\alpha \Delta T \tag{8.11}$$

Thus, the **thermal coefficient of area expansion** (Fig. 8.10b) is twice as large as the coefficient of linear expansion. (That is, it is equal to 2α.) This relationship is valid for all flat shapes. (See the Learn by Drawing feature.)

Learn by Drawing

Thermal Area Expansion

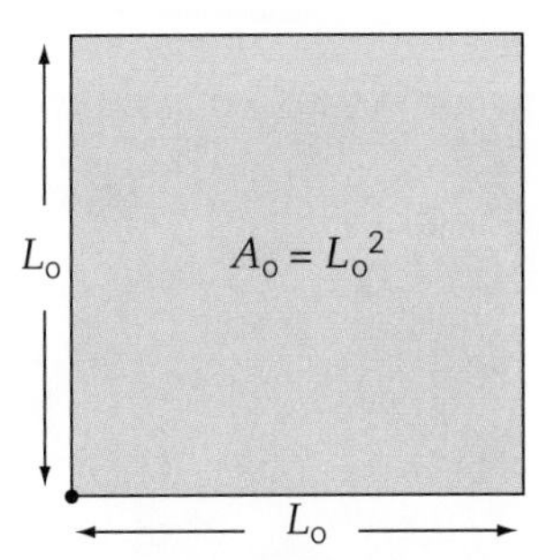

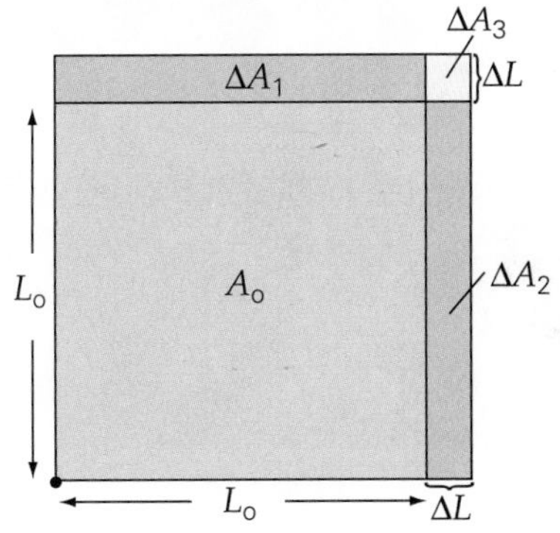

$\Delta A = \Delta A_1 + \Delta A_2 + \Delta A_3$
$\Delta A_1 = \Delta A_2 = L_o \Delta L$
$= L_o(\alpha L_o \Delta T) = \alpha A_o \Delta T$
Since ΔA_3 is very small compared to ΔA_1 and ΔA_2,
$\Delta A \approx 2\alpha A_o \Delta T$

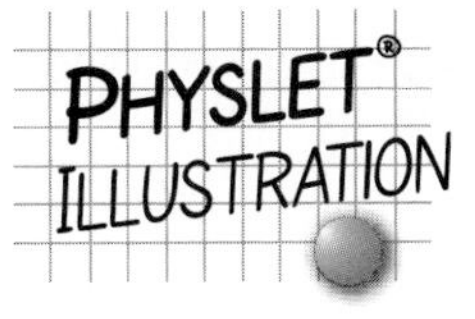

Thermal Expansion

TABLE 8.1 Values of Thermal Expansion Coefficients (in $\text{C}°^{-1}$) for Some Materials at 20°C

Material	*Coefficient of linear expansion* (α)	*Material*	*Coefficient of volume expansion* (β)
Aluminum	24×10^{-6}	Alcohol, ethyl	1.1×10^{-4}
Brass	19×10^{-6}	Gasoline	9.5×10^{-4}
Brick or concrete	12×10^{-6}	Glycerin	4.9×10^{-4}
Copper	17×10^{-6}	Mercury	1.8×10^{-4}
Glass, window	9.0×10^{-6}	Water	2.1×10^{-4}
Glass, Pyrex	3.3×10^{-6}		
Gold	14×10^{-6}	Air (and most other gases at 1 atm)	3.5×10^{-3}
Ice	52×10^{-6}		
Iron and steel	12×10^{-6}		

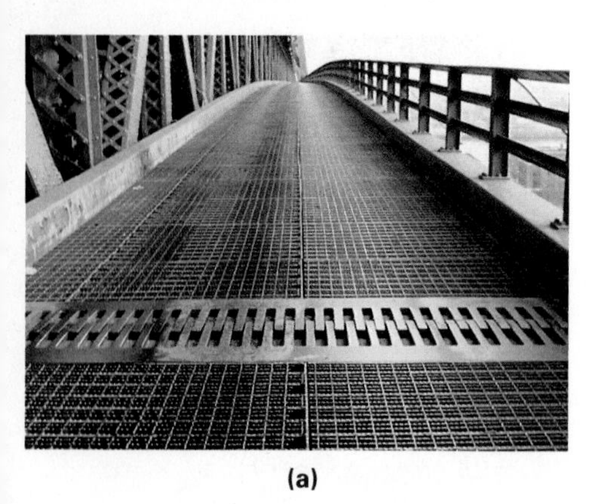

(a)

(b)

▲ **FIGURE 8.11 Expansion gaps** **(a)** Expansion gaps are built into bridge roadways to prevent contact stresses produced by thermal expansion. **(b)** These loops in oil pipelines serve a similar purpose. As hot oil passes through them, the pipes expand, and the loops take up the extra length. The loops also accommodate expansions resulting from day–night temperature variations.

Similarly, a first-order expression for thermal *volume* expansion is

$$V = V_o(1 + 3\alpha\,\Delta T) \quad \text{or} \quad \frac{\Delta V}{V_o} = 3\alpha\,\Delta T \tag{8.12}$$

The **thermal coefficient of volume expansion** (Fig. 8.10c) is equal to 3α (for isotropic solids and liquids).

The equations for thermal expansions are approximations. (Why?) Even though an equation is a description of a physical relationship, always keep in mind that it may be only an approximation of physical reality or may apply only in certain situations.

The thermal expansion of materials is an important consideration in construction. Seams are put in concrete highways and sidewalks to allow room for expansion and to prevent cracking. Expansion gaps in large bridges and between railroad rails are necessary to prevent damage. Similarly, expansion loops are found in oil pipelines (◂Fig. 8.11). The thermal expansion of steel beams and girders can produce tremendous pressures, as the following Example shows.

Example 8.5 ■ Temperature Rising: Thermal Expansion and Stress

A steel beam is 5.0 m long at a temperature of 20°C (68°F). On a hot day, the temperature rises to 40°C (104°F). (a) What is the change in the beam's length due to thermal expansion? (b) Suppose that the ends of the beam are initially in contact with rigid vertical supports. How much force will the expanded beam exert on the supports if the beam has a cross-sectional area of 60 cm^2?

Thinking It Through. (a) This is a direct application of Eq. 8.9. (b) As the constricted beam expands, it applies a stress, and hence a force, to the supports. For linear expansion, Young's modulus (Section 7.1) should come into play.

Solution.

Given:
$L_o = 5.0\text{ m}$
$T_o = 20°\text{C}$
$T = 40°\text{C}$
$\alpha = 12 \times 10^{-6}\,\text{C}°^{-1}$ (from Table 8.1)

$$A = 60\text{ cm}^2\left(\frac{1\text{ m}}{100\text{ cm}}\right)^2 = 6.0 \times 10^{-3}\text{ m}^2$$

Find: (a) ΔL (change in length)
(b) F (force)

(a) Using Eq. 8.9 to find the change in length with $\Delta T = T - T_o = 40°\text{C} - 20°\text{C} = 20\text{ C}°$, we get

$$\Delta L = \alpha L_o \Delta T = (12 \times 10^{-6}\,\text{C}°^{-1})(5.0\text{ m})(20\text{ C}°) = 1.2 \times 10^{-3}\text{ m} = 1.2\text{ mm}$$

This may not seem like much of an expansion, but it can give rise to a great deal of force if the beam is constrained and kept from expanding, as part (b) will show.

(b) By Newton's third law, if the beam is kept from expanding, the force the beam exerts on its constraint supports is equal to the force exerted by the supports to prevent the beam from expanding by a length ΔL. This is the same as the force that would be required to compress the beam by that length. Using the Young's modulus form of Hooke's law (Chapter 7) with $Y = 20 \times 10^{10}\text{ N/m}^2$ (Table 7.1), we calculate the stress on the beam as

$$\frac{F}{A} = \frac{Y\Delta L}{L_o} = \frac{(20 \times 10^{10}\text{ N/m}^2)(1.2 \times 10^{-3}\text{ m})}{5.0\text{ m}} = 4.8 \times 10^7\text{ N/m}^2$$

The force is then

$$F = (4.8 \times 10^7\text{ N/m}^2)A = (4.8 \times 10^7\text{ N/m}^2)(6.0 \times 10^{-3}\text{ m}^2)$$
$$= 2.9 \times 10^5\text{ N (about 65 000 lb, or 32.5 tons!)}$$

Follow-up Exercise. Expansion gaps between identical steel beams laid end to end are specified to be 0.060% of the length of a beam at the installation temperature. With this specification, what is the temperature range for noncontact expansion?

Conceptual Example 8.6 ■ Larger or Smaller? Area Expansion

A circular piece is cut from a flat metal sheet (▸Fig. 8.12a). If the sheet is then heated in an oven, the size of the hole will (a) become larger, (b) become smaller, (c) remain unchanged.

Reasoning and Answer. It is a common misconception to think that the area of the hole will shrink because the metal expands inwardly around it. To counter this misconception, think of the piece of metal removed from the hole rather than of the hole itself. This piece would expand with increasing temperature. The metal in the heated sheet reacts as if the piece that is removed were still part of it. (Think of putting the piece of metal back into the hole after heating, as in Fig. 8.12b, or consider drawing a circle on an uncut metal sheet and heating it.) So the answer is (a).

Follow-up Exercise. A circular ring of iron has a tight-fitting metal bar inside it, across its diameter. If the ring is heated in an oven to a high temperature, would it be distorted or bent out of shape, or would it remain circular?

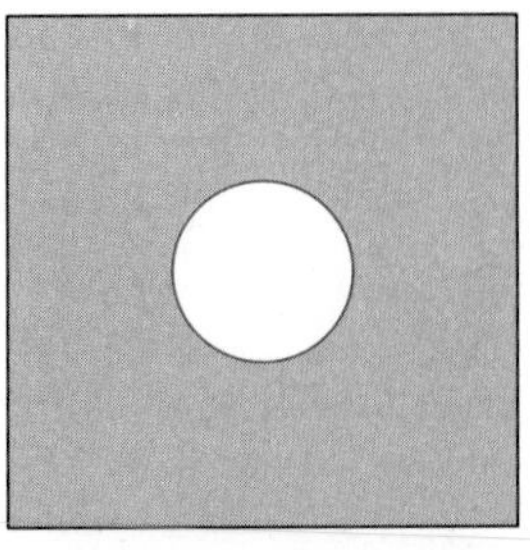

(a) Metal plate with hole

(b) Metal plate without hole

▲ **FIGURE 8.12 A larger or smaller hole?** See Conceptual Example 8.6.

Fluids (liquids and gases), like solids, normally expand with increasing temperature. Because fluids have no definite shape, only volume expansion (and not linear or area expansion) is meaningful. The expression is

$$\frac{\Delta V}{V_o} = \beta \Delta T \quad \textit{fluid volume expansion} \qquad (8.13)$$

where β is the coefficient of volume expansion for fluids. Note in Table 8.1 that the values of β for fluids are typically larger than the values of 3α for solids.

Unlike most liquids, water exhibits an anomalous expansion in volume near its freezing point. The volume of a given amount of water decreases as it is cooled from room temperature, until its temperature reaches 4°C (▾Fig. 8.13a). Below 4°C, the volume increases, and therefore the density decreases (Fig. 8.13b). This means that water has its maximum density ($\rho = m/V$) at 4°C (actually, 3.98°C).

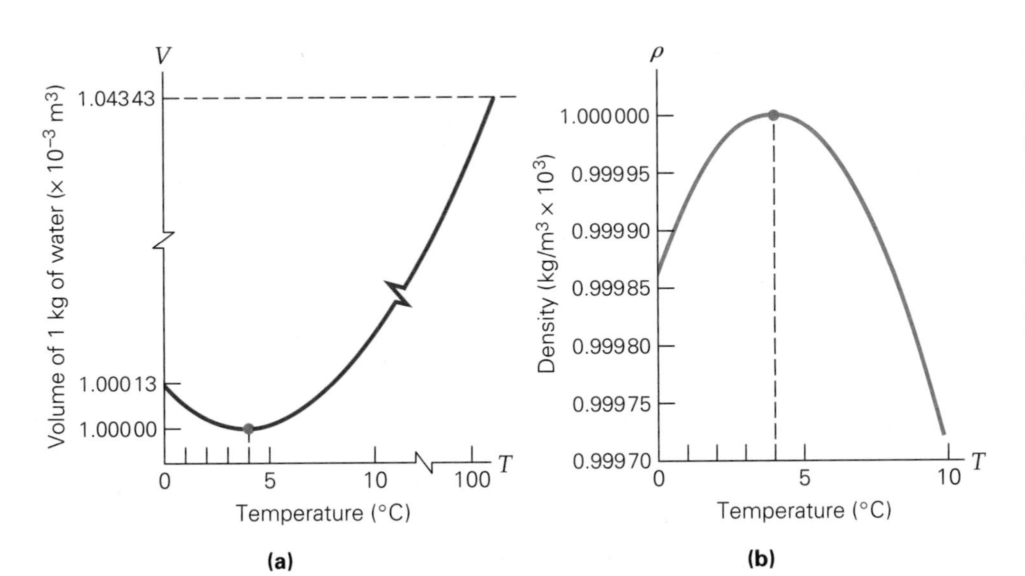

◂ **FIGURE 8.13 Thermal expansion of water** Water exhibits nonlinear expansion behavior near its freezing point. **(a)** Above 4°C (actually, 3.98°C), water expands with increasing temperature, but from 4°C down to 0°C, it expands with decreasing temperature. **(b)** As a result, water has its maximum density near 4°C.

When water freezes, its molecules form a hexagonal (six-sided) lattice pattern. (This is why snowflakes have hexagonal shapes.) It is the open structure of this lattice that gives water its almost unique property of expanding on freezing and being less dense as a solid than as a liquid. (This is why ice floats in water and frozen water pipes burst.) The variation in the density of water over the temperature range from 4°C to 0°C indicates that the open lattice structure is beginning to form at about 4°C rather than exactly at the freezing point.

This property has an important environmental effect: Bodies of water such as lakes and ponds freeze at the top first, and the ice that forms floats. As a lake cools toward 4°C, water near the surface loses energy to the atmosphere, becomes denser, and sinks. The warmer, less dense water near the bottom rises. However, once the colder water on top reaches temperatures below 4°C, it becomes less dense and remains at the surface, where it freezes. If water did not have this property, lakes and ponds would freeze from the bottom up, which would destroy much of their animal and plant life (and would make ice skating a lot less popular). There would also be no oceanic ice caps at the polar regions. Instead, there would be a thick layer of ice at the bottom of the ocean, covered by a layer of water.

Conceptual Example 8.7 ■ Quick Chill: Temperature and Density

Ice is put into a container of water at room temperature. For faster cooling, the ice should (a) be allowed to float naturally in the water or (b) be pushed to the bottom of the container with a stick and held there.

Reasoning and Answer. When the ice melts, the water in its vicinity is cooled and hence becomes denser (Fig. 8.13b). If the ice is permitted to float at the top, the denser water sinks and the warmer, less dense water rises. This mixing causes the water to cool quickly. If the ice were at the bottom of the container, however, the colder, denser water would remain there, and cooling of the top layer of warm water would be slowed, so the answer is (a).

Follow-up Exercise. Suppose that the density-versus-temperature curve for water (Fig. 8.13b) were inverted, so that it dipped downward. What would this imply for the situation in this Example and for the freezing of lakes? Explain.

8.5 The Kinetic Theory of Gases

OBJECTIVES: To (a) relate kinetic theory and temperature and (b) explain the process of diffusion.

If the molecules of a sample of gas are viewed as colliding particles, the laws of mechanics can be applied to each molecule of that gas. We should then be able to describe the gas's microscopic characteristics, such as pressure, internal energy, and so on, in terms of molecular motion. Because of the large number of particles involved, however, a statistical approach is employed for such a microscopic description.

One of the major accomplishments of theoretical physics was to do exactly that: derive the ideal gas law from mechanical principles. This derivation led to a new interpretation of temperature in terms of the translational kinetic energy of the gas molecules. As a theoretical starting point, the molecules of an ideal gas are viewed as point masses in random motion with relatively large distances separating them.

In this section, we will consider primarily the kinetic theory of *mon*atomic (single-atom) gases, such as He, and learn about the internal energy of such a gas. In the next section, the internal energy of *di*atomic (two-atom molecules) gases, such as O_2, will be considered. In either case, the vibrational and rotational motions can be ignored with regard to temperature and pressure, since these quantities depend only on *linear* motion.

According to the **kinetic theory of gases**, the molecules of a gas undergo perfectly elastic collisions with the walls of its container. (With the molecules taken to be point particles molecular collisions can be neglected.) From Newton's laws of motion, the force on the walls of the container can be calculated from the change in momentum of the gas molecules when they collide with the walls (▸ Fig. 8.14). If this force is expressed in terms of pressure (force/area), the following equation is obtained (see Appendix II for derivation):

Note: Elastic collisions are discussed in Section 6.4.

$$pV = \tfrac{1}{3} N m v_{rms}^2 \qquad (8.14)$$

Average molecular kinetic energy and temperature

Here, V is the volume of the container or gas, N is the number of gas molecules in the closed container, m is the mass of a gas molecule, and the speed v_{rms} is the average speed of the molecules, but a special kind of average. It is obtained by averaging the squares of the speeds and then taking the square root of the average—that is, $\sqrt{\overline{v^2}} = v_{rms}$. As a result, v_{rms} is called the *root-mean-square (rms)* speed.

Solving Eq. 8.6 for pV and equating the resulting expression with Eq. 8.14 shows how temperature came to be interpreted as a measure of translational kinetic energy:

$$pV = Nk_BT = \tfrac{1}{3} N m v_{rms}^2 \quad \text{or} \quad \tfrac{1}{2} m v_{rms}^2 = \tfrac{3}{2} k_B T \qquad (\textit{for all ideal gases}) \qquad (8.15)$$

Thus, the temperature of a gas (and that of the walls of the container or a thermometer bulb in thermal equilibrium with the gas) is directly proportional to its average random kinetic energy (per molecule), since $\overline{K} = \tfrac{1}{2} m v_{rms}^2 = \tfrac{3}{2} k_B T$. (Don't forget that T is the absolute temperature in kelvins.)

Example 8.8 ■ Molecular Speed: Relation to Absolute Temperature

What is the average (rms) speed of a helium atom (He) in a helium balloon at room temperature? (Take the mass of the helium atom to be 6.65×10^{-27} kg.)

Thinking It Through. All the data we need to solve for the average speed in Eq. 8.15 are known.

Solution.

Given: $m = 6.65 \times 10^{-27}$ kg
$T = 20°\text{C}$ (room temperature)
$k_B = 1.38 \times 10^{-23}$ J/K (known)

Find: v_{rms} (rms speed)

Eq. 8.15 will be used, so we list k_B among the given quantities.

The Celsius temperature must be changed to kelvins, and note that k_B has units of J/K, so

$$T_K = T_C + 273 = 20°\text{C} + 273 = 293\text{ K}$$

Rearranging Eq. 8.15, we have

$$v_{rms} = \sqrt{\frac{3k_BT}{m}} = \sqrt{\frac{3(1.38 \times 10^{-23}\text{ J/K})(293\text{ K})}{6.65 \times 10^{-27}\text{ kg}}} = 1.35 \times 10^3\text{ m/s} = 1.35\text{ km/s}$$

This is over 3000 mi/h—pretty fast!

Follow-up Exercise. In this Example, if the temperature of the gas were increased by 10C°, what would be the corresponding percentage increases in the average (rms) speed and in the average kinetic energy?

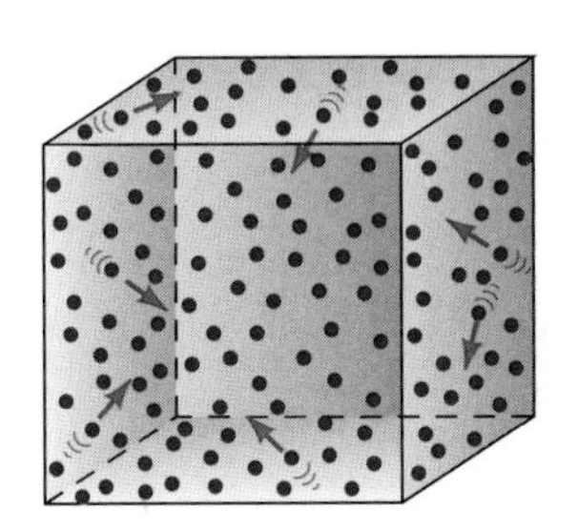

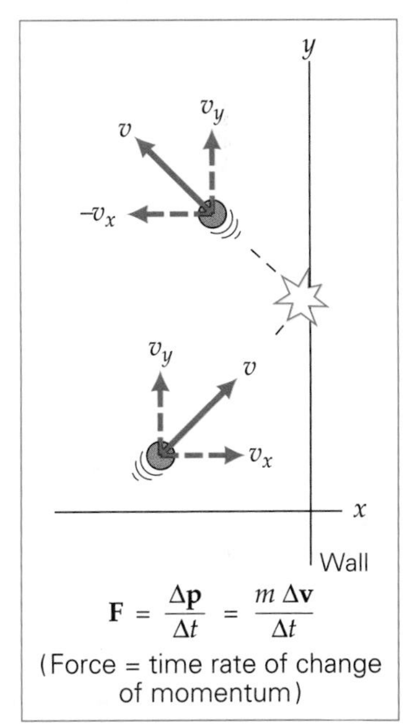

▲ **FIGURE 8.14 Kinetic theory of gases** The pressure a gas exerts on the walls of a container is due to the force resulting from the change in momentum of the gas molecules that collide with the wall. The force exerted by an individual molecule is equal to the time rate of change of momentum; that is, $\mathbf{F} = \Delta\mathbf{p}/\Delta t = m\Delta\mathbf{v}/\Delta t$, where $\mathbf{p} = m\mathbf{v}$. The sum of the instantaneous normal components of the collision forces gives rise to the average pressure on the wall.

Kinetic Theory

Interestingly, Eq. 8.15 predicts that at absolute zero ($T = 0$ K) all translational molecular motion of a gas would cease. According to classical theory, this would correspond to absolute zero energy. However, modern quantum theory says that there would still be some zero-point motion, and a corresponding minimum *zero-point energy*. Basically, absolute zero is the temperature at which all the energy that *can* be removed from an object has been removed.

Internal Energy of Monatomic Gases

Because the "particles" in an ideal monatomic gas do not vibrate or rotate, as explained previously, the total kinetic energy of all the molecules is equal to the total internal energy of the gas. That is, the gas's internal energy is all "temperature" energy (Section 8.1). With N molecules in a system, we can use Eq. 8.15, expressing the energy per molecule, to write an equation for the total internal energy U:

$$U = N(\tfrac{1}{2}mv_{\text{rms}}^2) = \tfrac{3}{2}Nk_{\text{B}}T = \tfrac{3}{2}nRT \quad \text{(for ideal monatomic gases only)} \qquad (8.16)$$

Thus, we see that the internal energy of an ideal monatomic gas is directly proportional to its absolute temperature. (In Section 8.6, we will see that this is true regardless of the molecular structure of the gas. However, the expression for U will be a bit different for gases that are not monatomic.) This means that if the absolute temperature of a gas is doubled (by heat transfer), for example, from 200 K to 400 K, then the internal energy of the gas is also doubled.

Diffusion

We depend on our sense of smell to detect odors, such as the smell of smoke from something burning. That you can smell something from a distance implies that molecules get from one place to another in the air—from the source to your nose. This process of random molecular mixing in which particular molecules move from a region where they are present in higher concentration to one where they are in lower concentration is called **diffusion**. Diffusion also occurs readily in liquids; think about what happens to a drop of ink in a glass of water (▼Fig. 8.15). It even occurs to some degree in solids.

The rate of diffusion for a particular gas depends on the rms speed of its molecules. Even though gas molecules have large average speeds (Example 8.8), their

▼ FIGURE 8.15 Diffusion in liquids Random molecular motion would eventually distribute the dye throughout the water. Here there is some distribution due to mixing, and the ink colors the water after a few minutes. The distribution would take more time by diffusion only.

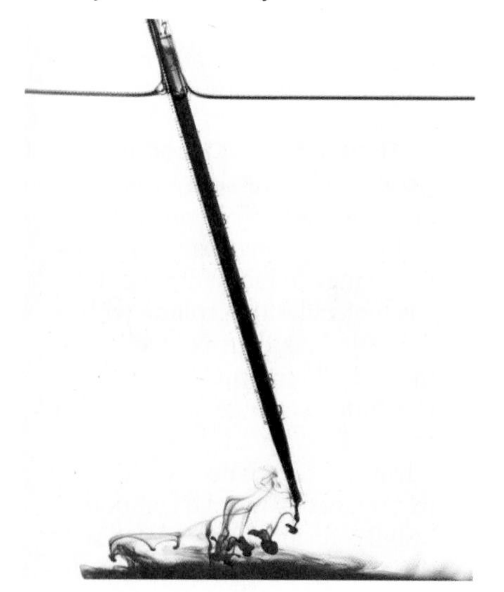

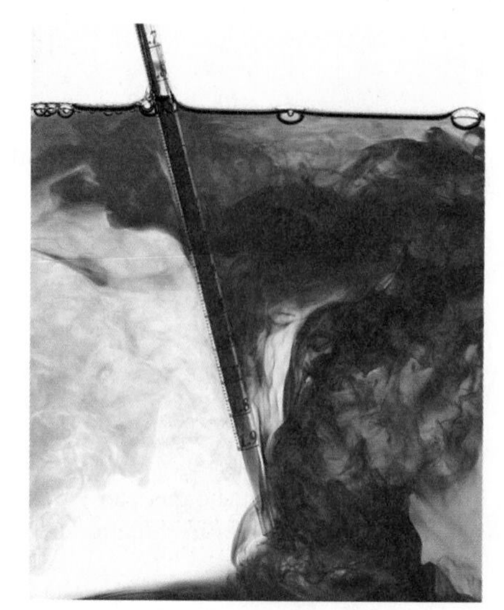

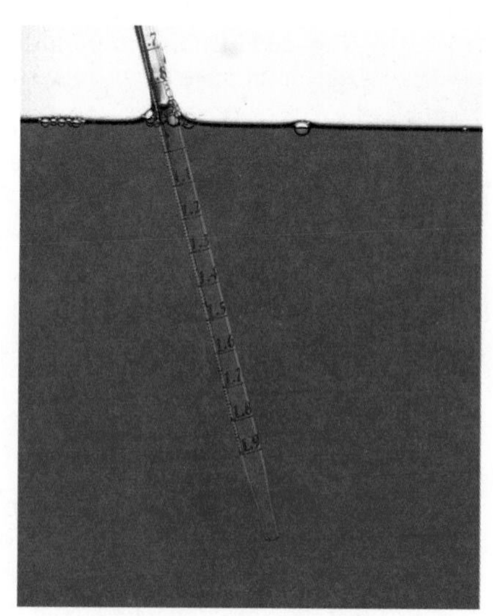

average positions change slowly, and the molecules do not fly from one side of a room to the other. Instead, there are frequent collisions, and as a result, the molecules "drift" rather slowly. For example, suppose someone opened a bottle of ammonia on the other side of a closed room. It would take some time for the ammonia to diffuse across the room until you could smell it. (Much of the movement that people commonly attribute to diffusion is actually due to air currents.)

Gases can also diffuse through porous materials or permeable membranes. (This process is sometimes referred to as *effusion*.) Energetic molecules enter the material through the pores (openings), and, colliding with the pore walls, they slowly meander through the material. Such gaseous diffusion can be used to physically separate the different gases making up a mixture.

The kinetic theory of gases says that the average translational kinetic energy (per molecule) of a gas is proportional to the absolute temperature of the gas: $\frac{1}{2}mv_{\text{rms}}^2 = \frac{3}{2}k_BT$. So, on the average, the molecules of different gases (having different masses) move at different speeds at a given temperature. As you might expect, because they move faster, lighter gas molecules diffuse through the tiny openings of a porous material faster than do heavier gas molecules.

For instance, at a particular temperature, molecules of oxygen (O_2) move faster on the average than do the more massive molecules of carbon dioxide (CO_2). Because of this difference in molecular speed, oxygen can diffuse through a barrier faster than carbon dioxide can. Suppose that a mixture of equal volumes of oxygen and carbon dioxide is contained on one side of a porous barrier (▼Fig. 8.16). After a while, some O_2 molecules and some CO_2 molecules will have diffused through the barrier, but more oxygen than carbon dioxide. Repeating the process on this diffused gas mixture would cause the oxygen concentration to become even greater on the far side of the barrier. Almost pure oxygen can be obtained by repeating the separation process many times. Separation by gaseous diffusion is a key process in obtaining enriched uranium, which was used in the first atomic bomb and in nuclear reactors that generate electricity.

Fluid diffusion is very important to organisms. In plant photosynthesis, carbon dioxide from the air diffuses into leaves, and oxygen and water vapor diffuse out. The diffusion of liquid water across a permeable membrane down a concentration gradient (a concentration difference) is called **osmosis**, a process that is vital in living cells. Osmotic diffusion is also important to kidney functioning: Tubules in the kidneys concentrate waste matter from the blood in much the same way that oxygen is removed from mixtures. (See the Insight on page 278 for other examples of diffusion.)

Osmosis is the tendency for the solvent of a solution, such as water, to diffuse across a semipermeable membrane from the side where the solvent is at higher concentration to the side where it is at lower concentration. When pressure is applied to the side with the lower concentration, the diffusion is reversed—a process called *reverse osmosis*. Reverse osmosis is used in desalination plants to provide freshwater from seawater in dry coastal regions.

Reverse osmosis is also used in water purification. You may have drunk such purified water. One of the popular bottled waters is purified "using state of the art treatment by reverse osmosis," according to the label.

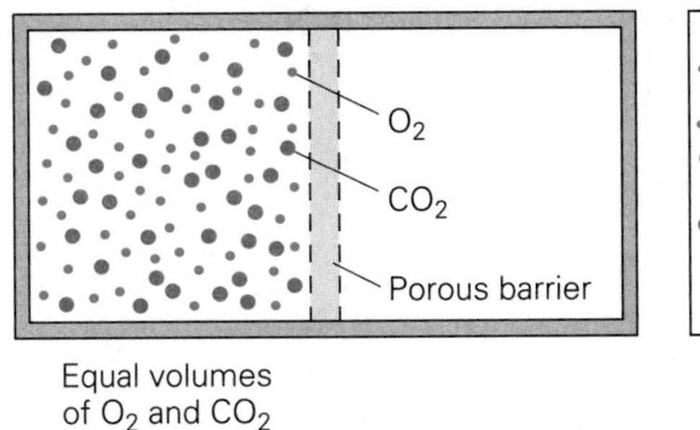

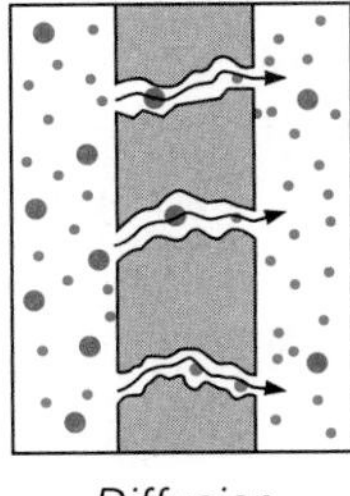

◀ **FIGURE 8.16 Separation by gaseous diffusion** The molecules of both gases diffuse (or effuse) through the porous barrier, but because oxygen molecules have the greater average speed, more of them pass through. Thus, over time, there is a greater concentration of oxygen molecules on the other side of the barrier.

INSIGHT

Physiological Diffusion in Life Processes

Diffusion plays a central role in many life processes. For example, consider a cell membrane in the lung. Such a membrane is permeable to a number of substances, any of which will diffuse through the membrane from a region where its concentration is high to a region where its concentration is low. Most importantly, the lung membrane is permeable to oxygen (O_2), and the transfer of O_2 across the membrane occurs because of a concentration gradient.

The blood carried to the lungs is low in O_2, having given up the oxygen during its circulation through the body to tissues requiring O_2 for metabolism. Conversely, the air in the lungs is high in O_2, because there is a continuous exchange of fresh air in the breathing process. As a result of this concentration difference, or gradient, O_2 diffuses from the lung volume into the blood that flows through the lung tissue, and the blood leaving the lungs is high in O_2.

Exchanges between the blood and the tissues occur across capillary walls, and diffusion again is a major factor. The chemical composition of arterial blood is regulated to maintain the proper concentrations of particular solutes (substances dissolved in the blood solution), so diffusion takes place in the appropriate directions across capillary walls. For example, as cells take up O_2 and glucose (blood sugar), the blood continuously brings in fresh supplies of the substances to maintain the concentration gradient needed for diffusion to the cells. The continuous production of carbon dioxide (CO_2) and metabolic wastes in the cells produces concentration gradients in the opposite direction for these substances. They therefore diffuse out of the cells into the blood, to be carried away from the tissues by the circulatory system.

During periods of physical exertion, cellular activity increases. More O_2 is used up and more CO_2 is produced, thereby increasing the concentration gradients and the diffusion rates. How do the lungs respond to satisfy an increased demand for O_2 to the blood? As you might expect, the rate of diffusion depends on the surface area and thickness of the lung membrane. Deeper breathing during exercise causes the alveoli (small air sacs in the lungs) to increase in volume. Such stretching increases the alveolar surface area and decreases the thickness of the membrane wall, allowing more rapid diffusion.

Also, the heart works harder during exercise, and the blood pressure is raised. The increased pressure forces open capillaries that are normally closed during rest or normal activity. As a result, the total exchange area between the blood and cells is increased. Each of these changes helps expedite the exchange of gases during exercise.

Now you can understand why people with emphysema (a disease involving the breakdown of alveoli walls) or pneumonia (a condition characterized by fluid accumulations within or around the lungs) have difficulty providing enough oxygen to their tissues.

*8.6 Kinetic Theory, Diatomic Gases, and the Equipartition Theorem

OBJECTIVES: To understand (a) the difference between monatomic and diatomic gases, (b) the meaning of the equipartition theorem, and (c) the expression for the internal energy of a diatomic gas.

In the real world, most of the gases we deal with are *not* monatomic gases. Recall from chemistry that monatomic gases are elements known as *noble* or *inert* gases, because they do not readily combine with other atoms. These elements are found on the far right side of the periodic chart: helium, neon, argon, krypton, xenon, and radon.

However, the mixture of gases we breathe (collectively known as "air") consists mainly of diatomic molecules of nitrogen (N_2, 78% by volume) and oxygen (O_2, 21% by volume). Each of these gases has two identical atoms chemically bonded together to form a single molecule. How do we deal with these realistic, more complicated molecules in terms of the kinetic theory of gases? [There are even more complicated gas molecules consisting of more than two atoms, such as carbon dioxide (CO_2). However, because of the complexity of such gas molecules, we will limit our discussion to diatomic molecules.]

The Equipartition Theorem

As we saw in Section 8.5, only the translational kinetic energy of a gas is determined by the gas's temperature. Thus, for any type of gas, regardless of how many atoms make up its molecules, it is *always true* that the average *translational* kinetic energy per molecule is still proportional to the temperature of the gas (Eq. 8.15): $\frac{1}{2}mv_{rms}^2 = \frac{3}{2}k_BT$ (for all gases).

Recall that for monatomic gases, the total internal energy U consists solely of translational kinetic energy. For diatomic molecules, this is not true, because a diatomic molecule is free to rotate and vibrate in addition to moving linearly. Therefore, these extra forms of energy must be taken into account. The expression given in Eq. 8.16 ($U = \frac{3}{2}Nk_BT$) for monatomic gases, which assumes that the total energy is due only to translational kinetic energy, therefore does *not* hold for diatomic gases.

Scientists wondered exactly how the expression for the internal energy of a diatomic gas might differ from that for a monatomic gas. In looking at the derivation of Eq. 8.16 from the kinetic theory, they realized that the factor of 3 in that equation was due to the fact that the gas molecules had three independent linear ways (dimensions) of moving. Thus, for each molecule, there were three independent ways of possessing kinetic energy: with x, y, and z linear motion. Each independent way a molecule has for possessing energy is called a **degree of freedom**.

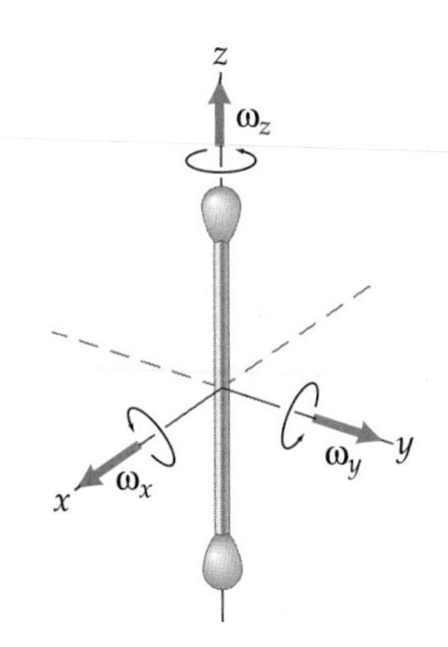

▲ **FIGURE 8.17 Model of a diatomic gas molecule** A dumbbell-like molecule can rotate about three axes. The moment of inertia, I, about the x- and y-axes is the same. The masses (molecules) on the ends of the rod are pointlike particles, so the moment of inertia about the z-axis is zero.

According to this scheme, a monatomic gas has only three degrees of freedom, since its molecules can move only linearly and can possess kinetic energy in three dimensions. Scientists reasoned that, quite possibly, a diatomic gas could vibrate (see Fig. 8.1), thus having vibrational kinetic and potential energies (two additional degrees of freedom). A diatomic molecule might also rotate.

Consider a symmetric diatomic molecule—for example, O_2. A classical model describes such a diatomic molecule as though the molecules were particles connected by a rigid rod (▸ Fig. 8.17). The rotational moment of inertia, I, has the same value about each of the axes (x and y) that pass perpendicularly through the center of the rod. The moment of inertia about the z-axis is essentially zero. (Why?) Thus, there are only two degrees of freedom associated with the kinetic energies of diatomic molecule rotation.

On the basis of the understanding of monatomic gases and their three degrees of freedom, the **equipartition theorem** was proposed. (As the name implies, the total energy of a gas or molecule is "partitioned," or divided, equally for each degree of freedom.) That is,

Definition of: Equipartition theorem

> On average, the total internal energy U of an ideal gas is divided equally among each degree of freedom its molecules possess. Furthermore, each degree of freedom contributes $\frac{1}{2}Nk_BT$ (or $\frac{1}{2}nRT$) to the total internal energy of the gas.

The equipartition theorem fits the special case of a monatomic gas, since the theorem predicts that $U = \frac{3}{2}Nk_BT$, which we know to be true. With three degrees of freedom, we have $U = 3(\frac{1}{2}Nk_BT)$, in agreement with the monatomic result given earlier (Eq. 8.16).

The Internal Energy of a Diatomic Gas

Exactly how does the equipartition theorem enable us to calculate the internal energy of a diatomic gas such as oxygen? To perform such a calculation, we must realize that U now includes all the available degrees of freedom. In addition to the translational degrees of freedom, what other motions are the molecules undergoing? The analysis is complicated and beyond the scope of this text, so we give only the general results. *Typically, for normal (room) temperatures, quantum theory predicts (and experiment verifies) that only the rotational motions are important in the degrees of freedom.*

So the total internal energy of a diatomic gas is composed of the internal energies due to the three linear degrees of freedom and the two rotational degrees of freedom, for a total of five degrees of freedom. Hence, we can write

$$\begin{aligned} U &= K_{\text{trans}} + K_{\text{rot}} = 3(\tfrac{1}{2}nRT) + 2(\tfrac{1}{2}nRT) \\ &= \tfrac{5}{2}nRT = \tfrac{5}{2}Nk_BT \end{aligned} \quad \textit{(for diatomic gases near room temperature)} \tag{8.17}$$

Thus, a monatomic sample of gas at normal room temperature has 40% less internal energy than a diatomic sample at the same temperature. Or, equivalently, the monatomic sample possesses only 60% of the internal energy of the diatomic sample.

Example 8.9 ■ Monatomic versus Diatomic: Are Two Atoms Better Than One?

More than 99% of the air we breathe consists of diatomic gases, mainly nitrogen (N_2, 78%) and oxygen (O_2, 21%). There are traces of other gases, one of which is radon (Ra), a monatomic gas arising from radioactive decay of uranium in the ground. [Radon itself is radioactive, which is irrelevant here, but this fact does make radon a possible health danger when concentrated inside a house.] (a) Calculate the total internal energy of 1.00-mol samples each of oxygen and radon at room temperature (20°C). (b) For each sample, calculate the amount of internal energy associated with molecular *translational* kinetic energy.

Thinking It Through. (a) We have to consider the number of degrees of freedom in a monatomic gas and a diatomic gas in computing the internal energy U. (b) Only three linear degrees of freedom contribute to the translational kinetic energy portion (U_{trans}) of the internal energy.

Solution. We list the data and convert to kelvins right away because we know that the internal energy is expressed in terms of absolute temperature:

Given: $n = 1.00$ mol
$T = 20°\text{C} + 273 = 293$ K

Find: (a) U for O_2 and Ra samples at room temperature
(b) U_{trans} for O_2 and Ra samples at room temperature

(a) Let's compute the total internal energy of the (monatomic) radon sample first, using Eq. 8.16:

$$U_{\text{Ra}} = \tfrac{3}{2}nRT = \tfrac{3}{2}(1.00\ \text{mol})[8.31\ \text{J/(mol}\cdot\text{K)}](293\ \text{K}) = 3.65 \times 10^3\ \text{J}$$

Since this sample is at room temperature, the (diatomic) oxygen will also include internal energy stored as two extra degrees of freedom, due to rotation. Thus, we have

$$U_{O_2} = \tfrac{5}{2}nRT = \tfrac{5}{2}(1.00\ \text{mol})[8.31\ \text{J/(mol}\cdot\text{K)}](293\ \text{K}) = 6.09 \times 10^3\ \text{J}$$

As we have seen, even though there is the same number of molecules in each sample and the temperature is the same, the oxygen sample has almost 70% more total internal energy.

(b) For (monatomic) radon, all the internal energy is in the form of translational kinetic energy; hence, the answer is the same as in (a):

$$U_{\text{trans}} = U_{\text{Ra}} = 3.65 \times 10^3\ \text{J}$$

For (diatomic) oxygen, only $\tfrac{3}{2}nRT$ of the total internal energy ($\tfrac{5}{2}nRT$) is in the form of translational kinetic energy, so the answer is the same as for radon; that is, $U_{\text{trans}} = 3.65 \times 10^3$ J for both gas samples.

Follow-up Exercise. (a) In this Example, how much energy is associated with the rotational motion of the oxygen molecules? (b) Which sample has the highest rms speed? (*Note*: The mass of one radon atom is about seven times the mass of an oxygen molecule.) Explain your reasoning.

Chapter Review

Important Concepts and Equations

Celsius-Fahrenheit conversion:

$$T_F = \tfrac{9}{5}T_C + 32 \quad \text{or} \quad T_F = 1.8T_C + 32 \qquad (8.1)$$

$$T_C = \tfrac{5}{9}(T_F - 32) \qquad (8.2)$$

- **Heat** is the net energy transferred from one object to another because of temperature differences. Once transferred, the energy becomes part of the internal energy of the object (or system).
- The **ideal (or perfect) gas law** relates the pressure, volume, and absolute temperature of an ideal or dilute gas.

Ideal (or perfect) gas law (always use absolute temperatures):

$$\frac{p_1V_1}{T_1} = \frac{p_2V_2}{T_2} \quad \text{or} \quad pV = Nk_BT \qquad (8.5, 8.6)$$

or

$$pV = nRT \qquad (8.7)$$

$$k_B = 1.38 \times 10^{-23}\ \text{J/K}$$

$$R = 8.31\ \text{J/(mol} \cdot \text{K)}$$

- **Absolute zero (0 K)** corresponds to $-273.15°C$.

Kelvin-Celsius conversion:

$$T_K = T_C + 273.15 \qquad (8.8)$$

$$T_K = T_C + 273 \quad (\textit{for general calculations}) \qquad (8.8a)$$

- **Thermal coefficients of expansion** relate the fractional change in dimension(s) to a change in temperature.

Thermal expansion of solids:

linear: $$\frac{\Delta L}{L_o} = \alpha\Delta T \quad \text{or} \quad L = L_o(1 + \alpha\Delta T) \qquad (8.9, 8.10)$$

area: $$\frac{\Delta A}{A_o} = 2\alpha\Delta T \quad \text{or} \quad A = A_o(1 + 2\alpha\Delta T) \qquad (8.11)$$

volume: $$\frac{\Delta V}{V_o} = 3\alpha\Delta T \quad \text{or} \quad V = V_o(1 + 3\alpha\Delta T) \qquad (8.12)$$

Thermal volume expansion of fluids:

$$\frac{\Delta V}{V_o} = \beta\Delta T \qquad (8.13)$$

- According to the **kinetic theory of gases**, the absolute temperature of a gas is directly proportional to the average random kinetic energy per molecule.

Results of kinetic theory of gases:

$$pV = \tfrac{1}{3}Nmv_{rms}^2 \qquad (8.14)$$

$$\tfrac{1}{2}mv_{rms}^2 = \tfrac{3}{2}k_BT \quad (\textit{all gases}) \qquad (8.15)$$

$$U = \tfrac{3}{2}Nk_BT = \tfrac{3}{2}nRT \quad (\textit{ideal monatomic gases only}) \qquad (8.16)$$

$$U = \tfrac{5}{2}Nk_BT = \tfrac{5}{2}nRT \quad (\textit{for diatomic gases near room temperature}) \qquad (8.17)$$

Exercises*

8.1 Temperature and Heat *and* 8.2 The Celsius and Fahrenheit Temperature Scales

1. Which one of the following is the closest to 15°C? (a) 8.3°F, (b) 27°F, (c) 40°F, or (d) 50°F

2. CQ Which temperature scale has the smaller degree interval, Celsius or Fahrenheit?

3. CQ Heat flows spontaneously from a body at a higher temperature to one at a lower temperature that is in thermal contact with it. Does heat always flow from a body with more internal energy to one with less internal energy? Explain.

4. CQ What is the hottest (highest temperature) item in a home? (*Hint:* Think about this one, and maybe a light will come on.)

*Assume all temperatures to be exact, and neglect significant figures for small changes in dimension.

5. CQ The tires of commercial jumbo jets are inflated with nitrogen, not air. Why?

6. CQ When temperature changes during the day, which scale, Celsius or Fahrenheit, will read a smaller change? Explain.

7. ■ Convert the following to Celsius readings: (a) 1000°F, (b) 0°F, (c) −20°F, and (d) −40°F.

8. ■ Convert the following to Fahrenheit readings: (a) 150°C, (b) 32°C, (c) −25°C, and (d) −273°C.

9. ■ The coldest inhabited village in the world is Oymyakon, a town located in eastern Siberia, where it gets as cold as −94°F. What is this temperature on the Celsius scale?

10. ■ A person running a fever has a body temperature of 39.4°C. What is this temperature on the Fahrenheit scale?

11. ■ The highest and lowest recorded air temperatures in the United States are, respectively, 134°F (Death Valley, California, 1913) and −80°F (Prospect Creek, Alaska, 1971). What are these temperatures on the Celsius scale?

12. ■ Which is the lower temperature? (a) 245°C or 245°F. (b) 200°C or 375°F.

13. ■ The highest and lowest recorded air temperatures in the world are, respectively, 58°C (Libya, 1922) and −89°C (Antarctica, 1983). What are these temperatures on the Fahrenheit scale?

14. IE ■■ There is one temperature at which the Celsius and Fahrenheit scales have the same reading. (a) To find that temperature, would you set (1) $5T_F = 9T_C$, (2) $9T_F = 5T_C$, or (3) $T_F = T_C$? Why? (b) Find the temperature.

15. ■■■ (a) The largest temperature drop recorded in the United States in one day occurred in Browning, Montana, in 1916, when the temperature went from 7°C to −49°C. What is the corresponding change on the Fahrenheit scale? (b) On the Moon, the average surface temperature is 127°C during the day and −183°C during the night. What is the corresponding change on the Fahrenheit scale?

16. IE ■■■ Fig. 8.5a is a plot of Fahrenheit temperature versus Celsius temperature. (a) Is the value of the y-intercept found by setting (1) $T_F = T_C$, (2) $T_C = 0$, or (3) $T_F = 0$? Why? (b) Compute the value of the y-intercept. (c) What would be the slope and y-intercept if the graph were plotted the opposite way (Celsius versus Fahrenheit)?

8.3 Gas Laws and Absolute Temperature

17. The temperature used in the ideal gas law must be expressed on which scale? (a) Celsius, (b) Fahrenheit, (c) Kelvin, or (d) any of the preceding.

18. When the temperature of a quantity of gas is increased, (a) the pressure must increase, (b) the volume must increase, (c) both the pressure and volume must increase, or (d) none of the preceding.

19. The temperature of a quantity of gas is decreased. How is the density affected (a) if the pressure is held constant? (b) if the volume is held constant?

20. CQ A type of constant-volume gas thermometer is shown in ▸Fig. 8.18. Describe how it operates.

21. CQ Describe how a constant-pressure gas thermometer might be constructed.

22. CQ In terms of the idea gas law, what would a temperature of absolute zero imply? How about a negative absolute temperature?

23. CQ Excited about a New Year's Eve party in Times Square, you pump up 10 balloons in your warm apartment and take them to the cold square. However, you are very disappointed with your decorations. Why?

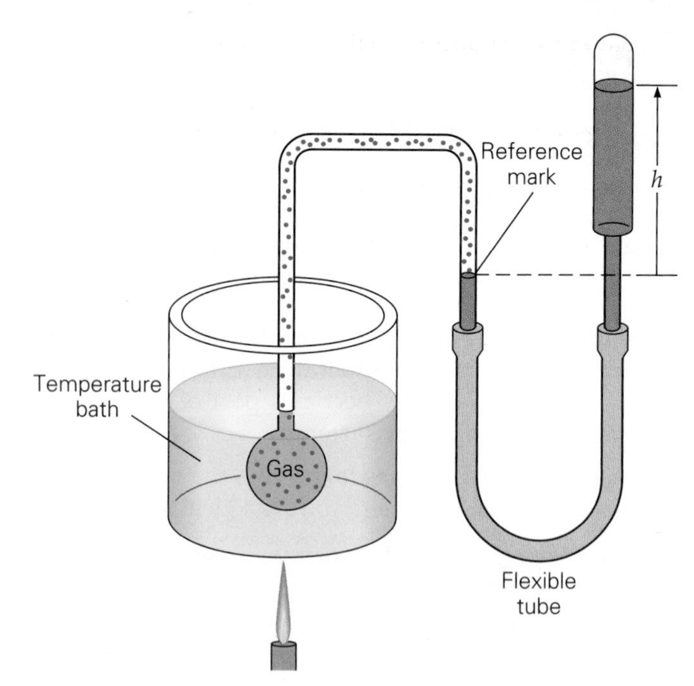

▲ **FIGURE 8.18 A type of constant-volume gas thermometer** See Exercise 20.

24. CQ Which has more molecules, 1 mole of oxygen or 1 mole of nitrogen? Explain.

25. CQ "Oxygen will start to flow even though the bag may not inflate." Heard that before? This is part of the safety instructions given by a flight crew before the plane takes off. Actually, the bag inflates fully at high altitude, but only slightly at lower altitude, when the cabin pressure is lost. Explain.

26. ■ Convert the following temperatures to absolute temperatures in kelvins: (a) 0°C, (b) 100°C, (c) 20°C, and (d) −35°C.

27. ■ Convert the following temperatures to degrees Celsius: (a) 0 K, (b) 250 K, (c) 273 K, and (d) 325 K.

28. ■ What are the absolute temperatures in kelvins for (a) −40°F and (b) −40°C?

29. ■ Which is the lower temperature, 300°F or 300 K?

30. ■ When lightning strikes, it can heat the air around it to more than 30 000 K, five times the surface temperature of the Sun. (a) What is this temperature on the Fahrenheit and Celsius scales? (b) The temperature is sometimes reported to be 30 000°C. Assuming that 30 000 K is correct, what is the percentage error of this Celsius value?

31. ■ How many moles are there in (a) 40 g of water, (b) 245 g of H_2SO_4 (sulfuric acid), (c) 138 g of NO_2 (nitrogen dioxide), and (d) 56 L of SO_2 (sulfur dioxide) at STP (stan-

dard temperature of exactly 0°C and pressure of exactly 1 atm)?

32. IE ■ (a) In a constant-volume gas thermometer, if the pressure of the gas decreases, will the temperature of the gas (a) increase, (2) decrease, or (3) remain the same? Why? (b) The initial absolute pressure of a gas is 1000 Pa at room temperature (20°C). If the pressure increases to 1500 Pa, what is the new Celsius temperature?

33. ■ The air in a balloon of volume 0.10 m^3 exerts a pressure of 1.4×10^5 Pa. If the volume of the balloon increases to 0.12 m^3 at constant temperature, what is the pressure?

34. ■ Show that 1.00 mol of ideal gas under STP occupies a volume of 0.0224 m^3 = 22.4 L.

35. ■ What is the volume occupied by 4.0 g of hydrogen under a pressure of 2.0 atm and a temperature of 300 K?

36. ■■ An athlete has a large lung capacity, 7.5 L. Assuming air to be an ideal gas, how many molecules of air are in the athlete's lung when the air temperature in the lungs is 37°C under normal atmospheric pressure?

37. IE ■■ (a) If the temperature of an ideal gas increases and its volume decreases, will the pressure of the gas (1) increase, (2) remain the same, or (3) decrease? Why? (b) The Kelvin temperature of an ideal gas is doubled and its volume is halved. How is the pressure affected?

38. ■■ On a warm day (92°F), an air-filled balloon occupies a volume of 0.20 m^3 and is under a pressure of 20.0 lb/in.^{2} If the balloon is cooled to 32°F in a refrigerator while its pressure is reduced to 14.7 lb/in.^{2}, what is the volume of the air in the container? (Assume that the air behaves as an ideal gas.)

39. ■■ A steel-belted radial automobile tire is inflated to a gauge pressure of 30.0 lb/in.^{2} when the temperature is 61°F. Later in the day, the temperature rises to 100°F. Assuming that the volume of the tire remains constant, what is the tire's pressure at the elevated temperature? (*Hint*: Remember that the ideal gas law uses absolute pressure.)

40. ■■ If 2.4 m^3 of a gas initially at STP is compressed to 1.6 m^3 and its temperature raised to 30°C, what is the final pressure?

41. IE ■■ The pressure on a low-density gas in a cylinder is kept constant as its temperature is increased. (a) Does the volume of the gas (1) increase, (2) decrease, or (3) remain the same? Why? (b) If the temperature is increased from 10°Cto 40°C, what is the percentage change in the volume of the gas?

42. ■■■ A diver releases an air bubble of volume 2.0 cm^3 from a depth of 15 m below the surface of a lake, where the temperature is 7.0°C. What is the volume of the bubble when it reaches just below the surface of the lake, where the temperature is 20°C?

8.4 Thermal Expansion

43. Are the units of the thermal coefficient of linear expansion (a) m/C°, (b) m^2/C°, (c) m·C°, or (d) 1/C°?

44. Is the thermal coefficient of volume expansion for a solid (a) α, (b) 2α, (c) 3α, or (d) α^3?

45. CQ A cube of ice sits on a bimetallic strip at room temperature (▼Fig. 8.19). What will happen if (a) the upper strip is aluminum and the lower strip brass, or (b) the upper strip is iron and the lower strip copper? (c) If the cube is made of a hot metal rather than ice and the two strips are brass and copper, should the brass or copper be on top to keep the cube from falling off?

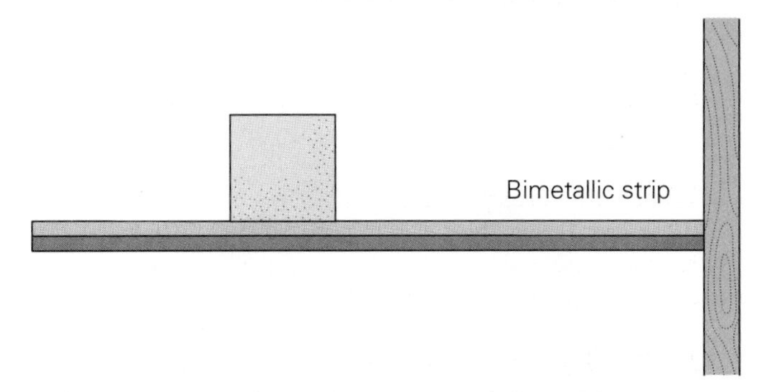

▲ **FIGURE 8.19 Which way will the cube go?** See Exercise 45.

46. CQ A demonstration of thermal expansion is shown in ▶Fig. 8.20. (a) Initially, the ball goes through the ring made of the same metal. When the ball is heated (b), it does not go through the ring (c). If both the ball and the ring are heated, the ball again goes through the ring. Explain what is being demonstrated.

47. CQ What happens to a volume of water if it is cooled from 4°Cto 2°C?

48. CQ A solid metal disk rotates freely, so the conservation of angular momentum applies. If the disk is heated while it is rotating, will there be any effect on the rate of rotation (the angular speed)?

49. CQ A circular ring of iron has a tight-fitting iron bar across its diameter, as illustrated in ▶Fig. 8.21. If the arrangement is heated in an oven to a high temperature, will the circular ring be distorted? What if the bar is made of aluminum?

50. CQ In terms of thermal expansion, which would be more accurate, a steel tape measure or an aluminum one? Explain.

51. CQ We often use hot water to loosen tightly sealed metal lids on glass jars. Explain why this works.

52. ■ A steel beam 10 m long is installed in a structure at 20°C. What are the beam's changes in length at the temperature extremes of −30°C to 45°C?

(a)

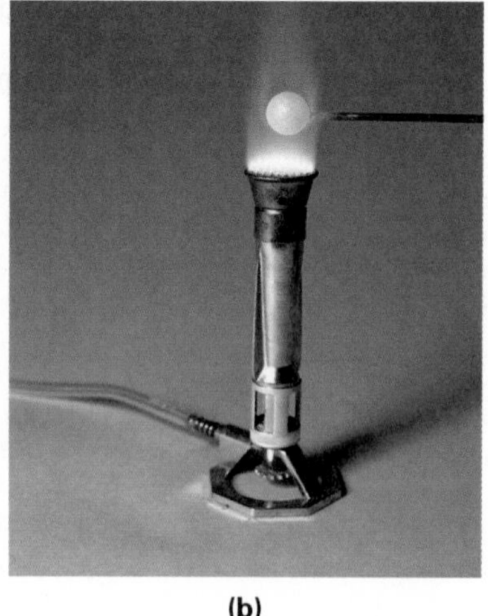

(b)

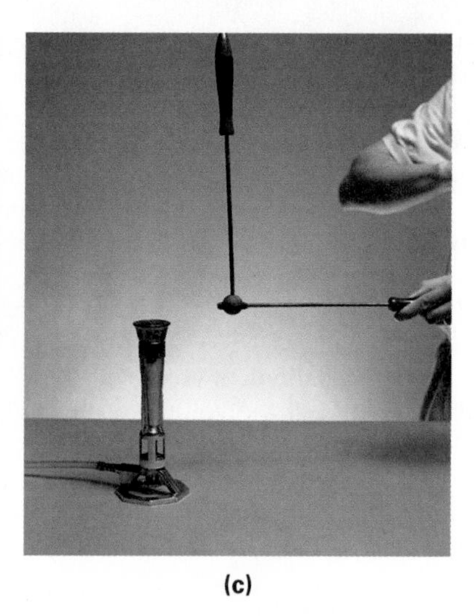

(c)

▲ **FIGURE 8.20 Ball-and-ring expansion** See Exercises 46 and 59.

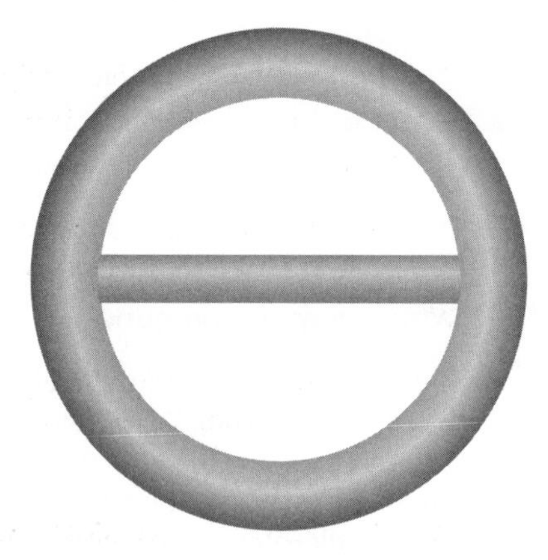

▲ **FIGURE 8.21 Stress out of shape?** See Exercise 49.

53. IE ■ An aluminum tape measure is accurate at 20°C. (a) If the tape measure is placed in a freezer, would it read (a) high, (2) low, or (3) the same? Why? (b) If the temperature of the freezer is −5.0°C, what would be the stick's percentage error because of thermal contraction?

54. ■ Concrete highway slabs are poured in lengths of 10.0 m. How wide should the expansion gaps between the slabs be at a temperature of 20°C to ensure that there will be no contact between adjacent slabs over a temperature range of −25°C to 45°C?

55. ■ A man's gold wedding ring has an inner diameter of 2.4 cm at 20°C. If the ring is dropped into boiling water, what will be the change in the inner diameter of the ring?

56. ■■ What temperature change would cause a 0.10% increase in the volume of a quantity of water that was initially at 20°C?

57. ■■ A piece of copper tubing used in plumbing has a length of 60.0 cm and an inner diameter of 1.50 cm at 20°C. When hot water at 85°C flows through the tube, what are (a) the tube's new length and (b) the change in its cross-sectional area? Does the latter affect the flow speed?

58. IE ■■ A circular piece is cut from an aluminum sheet at room temperature. (a) When the sheet is then placed in an oven, will the hole (1) get larger, (2) get smaller, or (3) remain the same? Why? (b) If the diameter of the hole is 8.00 cm at 20°C and the temperature of the oven is 150°C, what will be the new area of the hole?

59. IE ■■ In Fig 8.20, the steel ring of diameter 2.5 cm is 0.10 mm smaller in diameter than the steel ball at 20°C. (a) For the ball to go through the ring, should you heat (1) the ring, (2) the ball, or (3) both so that the ball will go through the ring? Why? (b) What is the minimum required temperature?

60. ■■ A circular steel plate of radius 0.10 m is cooled from 350°C to 20°C. By what percentage does the plate's area decrease?

61. IE ■■ One morning, an employee at a rental car company fills a car's steel gas tank to the top and then parks the car a short distance away. (a) That afternoon, when the temperature increases, will there be any gas spill or not? Why? (b) If the temperatures in the morning and afternoon are, respectively, 10°C and 30°C and the gas tank can hold 25 gal in the morning, how much gas will be lost? (Neglect the expansion of the tank.)

62. ■■ Show that the density of a solid substance varies with temperature as $\rho = \rho_o(1 - 3\alpha\,\Delta T)$.

63. ■■ The density of mercury is 13.6×10^3 kg/m^3 at 0°C. Calculate its density at 100°C.

64. ■■ A copper block has an internal spherical cavity with a 10-cm diameter (▸Fig. 8.22). The block is heated in an oven from 20°C to 500 K. (a) Does the cavity get larger or smaller? (b) What is the change in the cavity's volume?

65. ■■■ A brass rod has a circular cross section of radius 0.500 cm. The rod fits into a circular hole in a copper sheet with a clearance of 0.010 mm completely around it when

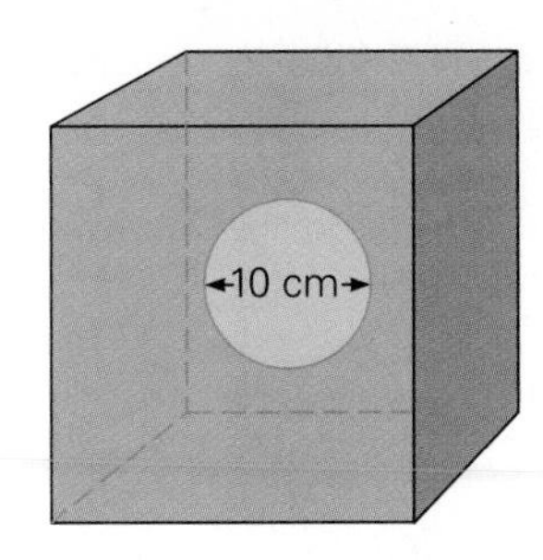

▲ **FIGURE 8.22 A hole in a block** See Exercise 64.

both it and the sheet are at 20°C. (a) At what temperature will the clearance be zero? (b) Would such a tight fit be possible if the sheet were brass and the rod were copper?

66. ■■■ A Pyrex beaker that has a capacity of 1000 cm^3 at 20°C contains 990 cm^3 of mercury at that temperature. Is there some temperature at which the mercury will completely fill the beaker? Justify your answer. (Assume that no mass is loss by vaporization.)

8.5 The Kinetic Theory of Gases

67. If the average kinetic energy of the molecules in an ideal gas initially at 20°C doubles, what is the final temperature of the gas? (a) 10°C, (b) 40°C, (c) 313°C, or (d) 586°C.

68. If the temperature of a quantity of ideal gas is raised from 100 K to 200 K, is the internal energy of the gas (a) doubled, (b) halved, (c) unchanged, or (d) none of the preceding?

69. CQ Equal volumes of helium gas (He) and neon gas (Ne) at the same temperature (and pressure) are on opposite sides of a porous membrane (▼Fig. 8.23). Describe what happens after a period of time, and why.

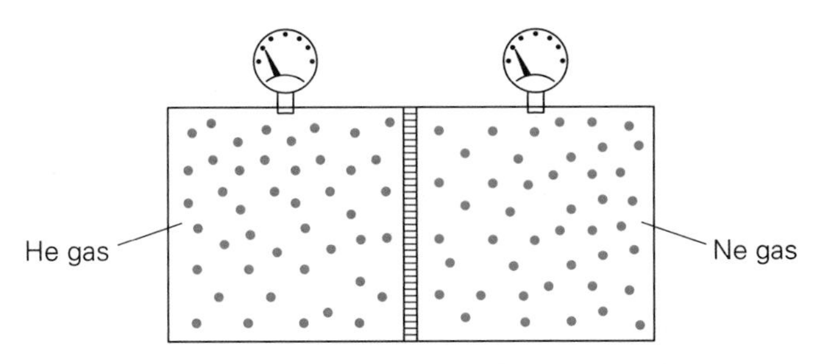

▲ **FIGURE 8.23 What happens as time passes?** See Exercise 69.

70. CQ Natural gas is odorless; to alert people to gas leaks, the gas company inserts an additive that has a distinctive scent. When there is a gas leak, the additive reaches your nose before the gas does. What can you conclude about the masses of the additive molecules and gas molecules?

71. ■ What is the average kinetic energy per molecule in an ideal gas at (a) 20°C and (b) 100°C?

72. IE ■ If the Celsius temperature of an ideal gas is doubled, (a) will the internal energy of the gas (1) double, (2) increase by less than a factor of 2, (3) be half as much, or (4) decrease by less than a factor of 2? Why? (b) If the temperature is raised from 20°C to 40°C, by how much will the internal energy of 2.0 mol of an ideal gas change?

73. ■ (a) What is the average kinetic energy per molecule of an ideal gas at a temperature of 27°C? (b) What is the average (rms) speed of the molecules if the gas is helium? (A helium molecule consists of a single atom of mass 6.65×10^{-27} kg.)

74. ■ What is the average speed of the molecules in low-density oxygen gas at 0°C? (The mass of an oxygen molecule, O_2, is 5.31×10^{-26} kg.)

75. ■■ If the temperature of an ideal gas increases from 300 K to 600 K, what happens to the rms speed of the gas molecules?

76. ■■ At a given temperature, which would be greater, the rms speed of oxygen (O_2) or of ozone (O_3), and how many times greater?

77. ■■ If the temperature of an ideal gas is raised from 25°C to 100°C, how many times faster is the new average (rms) speed of the gas molecules?

78. ■■ A quantity of an ideal gas is at 0°C. An equal quantity of another ideal gas is twice as hot. What is its temperature?

8.6 Kinetic Theory, Diatomic Gases, and the Equipartition Theorem

79. Is the temperature of a diatomic molecule like O_2 a measure of its (a) translational kinetic energy, (b) rotational kinetic energy, (c) vibrational kinetic energy, or (d) all of the above?

80. On the average, is the total internal energy of a gas divided equally among (a) each atom, (b) each degree of freedom, (c) linear motion, rotational motion, and vibrational motion, or (d) none of the above?

81. CQ Why does a sample of gas with diatomic molecules have more internal energy than a similar sample with monatomic molecules at the same temperature?

82. ■ If 1.0 mol of ideal monoatomic gas has a total internal energy of 5.0×10^3 J at a certain temperature, what is the total internal energy of 1.0 mol of a diatomic gas at the same temperature?

83. ■ What is the total internal energy of 1.0 mol of O_2 gas at 20°C?

84. ■■ For an average molecule of N_2 gas at 0°C, what are its (a) translational kinetic energy, (b) rotational kinetic energy, and (c) total energy?

Additional Exercises

85. In Exercise 61, if the expansion of the steel gas tank is *not* ignored, what is the volume of gas spilled?

86. To conserve energy, thermostats in an office building are set at 78°F in the summer and 65°F in the winter. What would the settings be if the thermostats had a Celsius scale?

87. A copper wire 0.500 m long is at 20°C. If the temperature is increased to 100°C, what is the change in the wire's length?

88. If 2.0 mol of oxygen gas is confined in a 10-L bottle under a pressure of 6.0 atm, what is the average kinetic energy of an oxygen molecule?

89. A mercury thermometer has a uniform capillary bore whose cross-sectional area is 0.012 mm^2. The volume of the mercury in the thermometer bulb at 10°C is 0.130 cm^3. If the temperature is increased to 50°C, how much will the height of the mercury column in the capillary bore change? (Neglect the expansion of the mercury in the bore and of the glass of the thermometer.)

90. If the rms speed of the molecules in an ideal gas at 20°C increases by a factor of two, what is the new temperature?

91. What temperature increase would produce a stress of $8.0 \times 10^7\ N/m^2$ on a rigidly held steel beam?

92. Using the ideal-gas law, express the coefficient of volume expansion in terms of temperature and pressure. (*Hint*: Use different temperatures and pressures.)

93. An ideal gas occupies a container of volume 0.75 L at STP. Find (a) the number of moles and (b) the number of molecules of the gas. (c) If the gas is carbon monoxide (CO), what is its mass?

94. An aluminum tape measure is used to measure a 1.0-m-long steel beam. At 0°C, the measurement is accurate. What will the instrument measure if the temperature increases to 40°C? (Ignore significant figures.)

95. (a) If the temperature drops by 10 C°, what is the corresponding temperature change on the Fahrenheit scale? (b) If the temperature rises by 10 F°, what is the corresponding change on the Celsius scale?

96. A new metal alloy is made into a 50-cm rod. (a) Determine the alloy's coefficient of linear expansion if after being heated from 20°Cto 250°C, the rod has elongated by 0.44 mm. (b) Is the new metal a potentially valuable alloy in terms of linear expansion? Explain.

97. Calculate the number of gas molecules in a container of volume 0.20 m^3 filled with gas under a partial vacuum of pressure 20 Pa at 20°C.

98. Is there a temperature that has the same numerical value on the Kelvin and Fahrenheit scales? Justify your answer.

99. Show that the coefficient of area expansion for flat, square solids is approximately equal to 2α.

100. In the troposphere (the lowest part of the atmosphere), the temperature decreases rather uniformly with altitude at a so-called "lapse" rate of about 6.5 C°/km. What are the temperatures (a) near the top of the troposphere (which has an average thickness of 11 km) and (b) outside a commercial aircraft flying at a cruising altitude of 34 000 ft? (Assume that the ground temperature is normal room temperature.)

101. A mercury thermometer has a bulb volume of 0.200 cm^3 and a capillary bore diameter of 0.065 mm. How far up the bore will the column of mercury move if the overall temperature of the thermometer is increased by 30 C°? (Neglect the expansion of the glass of the thermometer.)

102. On a hot, 40°C day, copper electric wires are used to connect a power box to a home 150 m away. Assuming the wire would break when the temperature dropped to 10°C, what should the minimum extra length of the wire be to avoid breaking?

103. A quantity of an ideal gas initially at atmospheric pressure is maintained at a constant temperature while it is compressed to half of its volume. What is the final pressure of the gas?

Sound

INSIGHTS

Good vibrations, clearly! We owe a lot to sound waves. Not only do they provide us with one of our main sources of enjoyment in the form of music, but they also bring us a wealth of vital information about our environment, from the chime of a doorbell to the warning shrill of a police siren to the song of a mockingbird. Indeed, sound waves are the basis for our major form of communication: speech. They can also constitute a highly irritating distraction (noise). But sound waves become music, speech, or noise only when our ears perceive them. Physically, sound is simply waves that propagate in solids, liquids, and gases. Without a medium, there can be no sound; in a vacuum such as outer space, there is utter silence.

This distinction between the sensory and physical meanings of sound gives you a way to answer the old philosophical question, If a tree falls in the forest where there is no one to hear it, does it make a sound? The answer depends on how sound is defined—it is no if we are thinking in terms of sensory hearing, but yes if we are considering only the physical waves. Since sound waves are all around us most of the time, we are exposed to many interesting sound phenomena. You'll explore some of the most important of these in this chapter.

9.1 Sound Waves

OBJECTIVES: **To (a) define sound and (b) explain the sound frequency spectrum.**

For sound waves to exist, there must be a disturbance or vibrations in some medium. This disturbance may be the clapping of hands or the skidding of tires as a car comes to a sudden stop. Under water, you can hear the click of rocks against one another. If you put your ear to a thin wall, you can hear sounds from the other side of the wall. **Sound waves** in gases and liquids (both are fluids) are primarily longitudinal waves. However, sound disturbances moving through solids can have both longitudinal and transverse components. The intermolecular interactions in solids are much stronger than in fluids and allow transverse components to propagate.

The characteristics of sound waves can be visualized by considering those produced by a tuning fork, essentially a metal bar bent into a U shape (▼Fig. 9.1). The prongs, or tines, vibrate when struck. The fork vibrates at its fundamental frequency (with an antinode at the end of each tine), so a single tone is heard. (A *tone* is sound with a definite frequency.) The vibrations disturb the air, producing alternating high-pressure regions called *condensations* and low-pressure regions called *rarefactions*. As the fork vibrates, these disturbances propagate outward, and a series of them can be described by a sinusoidal wave.

As the disturbances traveling through the air reach the ear, the eardrum (a thin membrane) is set into vibration by the pressure variations. On the other side of the eardrum, tiny bones (the hammer, anvil, and stirrup) carry the vibrations to the inner ear, where they are picked up by the auditory nerve. (See the Insight on p. 294.)

Characteristics of the ear limit the perception of sound. Only sound waves with frequencies between about 20 Hz and 20 kHz (kilohertz) initiate nerve impulses that are interpreted by the human brain as sound. This frequency range is called the **audible region** of the **sound frequency spectrum** (▶Fig. 9.2).

Frequencies lower than 20 Hz are in the **infrasonic region**. Waves in this region, which humans are unable to hear, are found in nature. Longitudinal waves generated by earthquakes have infrasonic frequencies, and we use these waves to study the Earth's interior. Infrasonic waves, or *infrasound*, are also generated by wind and weather patterns. Elephants and cattle have hearing response in the infrasonic region and may even give early warnings of earthquakes and weather disturbances. Aircraft, automobiles, and other rapidly moving objects also can produce infrasound.

Above 20 kHz is the **ultrasonic region**. Ultrasonic waves can be generated by high-frequency vibrations in crystals. Ultrasonic waves, or *ultrasound*, cannot be detected by humans, but can be by other animals. The audible region for dogs extends to about 45 kHz, so ultrasonic whistles can be used to call dogs without disturbing people. Cats and bats have even higher audible ranges, up to about 70 kHz and 100 kHz, respectively.

▼ **FIGURE 9.1 Vibrations make waves** **(a)** A vibrating tuning fork disturbs the air, producing alternating high-pressure regions (condensations) and low-pressure regions (rarefactions), which form sound waves. **(b)** After being picked up by a microphone, the pressure variations are converted to electrical signals. When these signals are displayed on an oscilloscope, the sinusoidal waveform is evident.

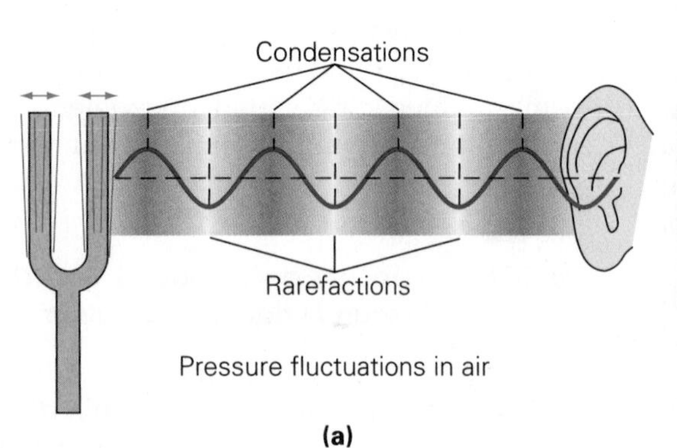

(a)

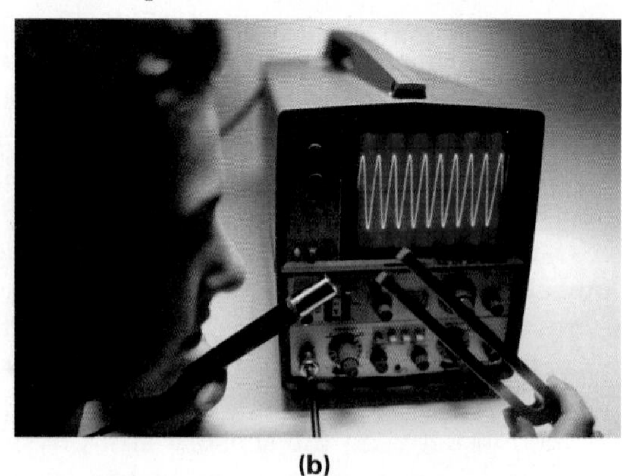

(b)

There are many practical applications of ultrasound. Since ultrasound can travel for kilometers in water, it is used in sonar, the ultrasound counterpart of radar, which employs radio waves for the detection and ranging of objects. Sound pulses generated by the sonar apparatus are reflected by underwater objects, and the resulting echoes are picked up by a detector. The time required for a sound pulse to make one round-trip, together with the speed of sound in water, gives the distance or range of the object. Sonar also is widely used by fishermen to detect schools of fish, and in a similar manner, ultrasound is used in autofocus cameras. Distance measurement allows focal adjustments to be made. An application of ultrasonic sonar from the natural world is given in the Insight on page 290.

In medicine, ultrasound is used to clean teeth (e.g., there are ultrasonic toothbrushes) and to examine internal tissues and organs that are nearly invisible to X rays. Perhaps the best-known medical application of ultrasound is its use to view a fetus without exposing it to the dangerous effects of X rays. Ultrasonic generators (transducers) made of quartz crystals produce high-frequency waves that are used to scan a designated region of the body from several angles. Reflections from the scanned areas are monitored, and a computer constructs an image from the reflected signals. Images are recorded several times each second. The series of images provides a "moving picture" of an internal structure, such as the heart of a fetus. A still shot, or echogram, is shown in ▾Fig. 9.3.

In industrial and home applications, ultrasonic baths are used to clean metal machine parts, dentures, and jewelry. The high-frequency (short wavelength) ultrasound vibrations loosen particles in otherwise inaccessible places.

Ultrasonic frequencies extend into the megahertz (MHz) range, but the sound frequency spectrum does not continue indefinitely. There is an upper limit of about 10^9 Hz, or 1 GHz (gigahertz), which is determined by the upper limit of the elasticity of the materials through which the sound propagates.

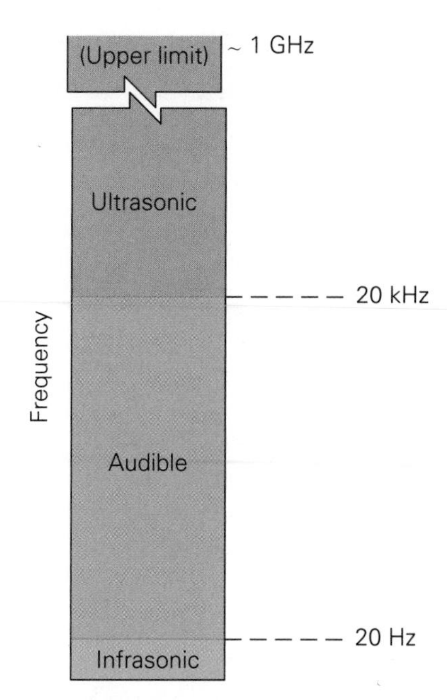

▲ **FIGURE 9.2 Sound frequency spectrum** The audible region of sound for humans lies between about 20 Hz and 20 kHz. Below this is the infrasonic region, and above it is the ultrasonic region. The upper limit is about 1 GHz, because of the elastic limitations of materials.

9.2 The Speed of Sound

OBJECTIVES: To (a) tell how the speed of sound differs in different media and (b) describe the temperature dependence of the speed of sound in air.

In general, the speed at which a disturbance moves through a medium depends on the elasticity and density of the medium. For example, the wave speed in a stretched string is given by $v = \sqrt{F_T/\mu}$, where F_T is the tension in the string and μ is the linear mass density of the string.

Similar expressions describe wave speeds in solids and liquids, for which the elasticity is expressed in terms of moduli (Chapter 7). In general, the speed

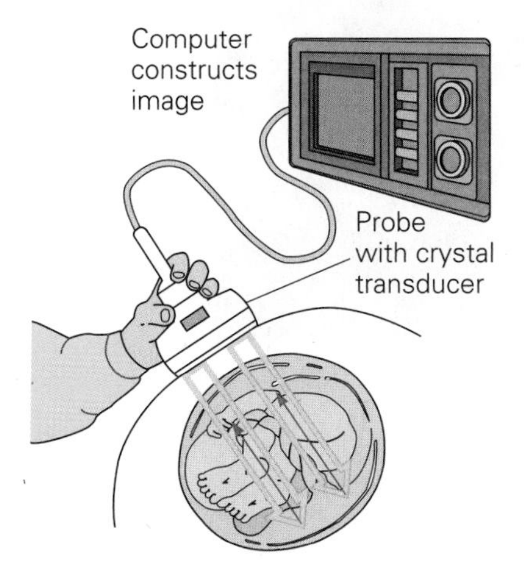

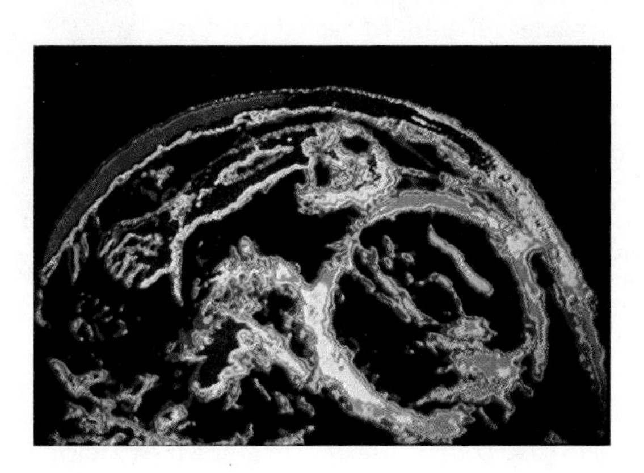

◀ **FIGURE 9.3 Ultrasound in use** Ultrasound generated by transducers, which convert electrical oscillations into mechanical vibrations and vice versa, is transmitted through tissue and is reflected from internal structures. The reflected waves are detected by the transducers, and the signals are used to construct an image, or echogram, shown here for a well-developed fetus.

INSIGHT

Audible and Ultrasonic: White Noise and Echolocation

White Noise

In an application of audible sound, one kind of noise is used to eliminate another. Noise is generally defined as unwanted sound, and you can probably think of occasions when you would have liked some distracting noise reduced or eliminated. If a radio or TV is too loud, the volume can be turned down. But what about people talking and ambient noises? It has been found that these noises can be reduced by countering them with *white noise*—sound that contains the complete range of audible frequencies. White noise is analogous to *white light*, which is light that contains all of the different colors or frequencies (Section 10.5). An electric fan produces a good approximation of white noise, as does the sound of cymbals and snare drums.

White noise can be used to mask other sounds. For example, if someone in another room is talking and distracting you from doing your homework, you might turn on a fan to mask the noise. What you are doing is "fooling" your brain so that it can get back to the homework. This effect is explained as follows: If two people nearby are talking simultaneously, the brain "selects" one of the voices, usually the loudest, and listens to it so as to understand what is being said. The same holds for three people talking at the same time. But suppose 1000 people were talking. The brain would not be able to pick out one voice. The talking from 1000 people sounds like white noise. So when you turn on a fan to create white noise, similar to that of the 1000 talking people, the voice distracting you from your homework makes it 1001, and the brain doesn't concentrate on it anymore.

Sound masking is available commercially for use in large offices where normal operations can produce distracting noise, such as several employees talking. As just described, the brain focuses on one voice and processes what is being said, which is distracting. Sound masking works by producing sound electronically, similar to that of soft blowing air, an approximation to the white noise produced by a fan. Speakers are located so as to put the masking sound in the appropriate areas.

There is also a musical application of white noise: Electronically synthesized white noise can be filtered (blocking some frequencies) so as to produce sounds with combinations of frequencies that are not heard from typical musical instruments. Maybe even music can be made with pure white noise? How would that sound?

Echolocaton

Sonar appeared in the animal kingdom long before it was developed by human engineers. On their nocturnal hunting flights, bats use a kind of natural sonar to navigate in and out of their caves and to locate and catch flying insects (Fig. 1). The bats emit pulses of ultrasound and track their prey by means of the reflected echoes. The technique is known as *echolocation*. Certain species of cave-dwelling birds have evolved the same ability.

The frequencies of bat cries vary with the species, in the range from 30 000 Hz to 80 000 Hz (30 to 80 kHz). The use of such high frequencies is essential to the bat's sonar system. To determine the nature of objects by means of reflected sounds, it is necessary that the wavelengths of the sounds be on the order of the dimensions of the object, and even shorter for finer details. When the bat's sound pulses strike a small object such as a flying insect, the reflected sound has only a small fraction of the original sound energy. Traveling to the bat through the air, the sound is further weakened. The auditory system and data-processing capabilities of bats are truly amazing. (Note the size of the bat's ears in Fig. 1.)

On the basis of the intensity of the echo, a bat can tell how big an insect is: The smaller the insect, the less intense is the echo. The direction of motion of an insect is sensed by the frequency of the echo. If an insect is moving away from the bat, the returning echo will have a lower frequency. If the insect is moving toward the bat, the echo will have a higher frequency. The change in frequency is known as the *Doppler effect*, which is presented in more detail in Section 9.5.

The bat, the only mammal to have evolved true flight, is a much maligned and feared creature. However, because they feed on tons of insects yearly, bats save the environment from a lot of insecticides. "Blind as a bat" is a common expression, yet bats have fairly good vision, which complements their use of echolocation. Finally, do you know why bats roost and hang upside down (Fig. 1)? That is their takeoff position. Unlike birds, bats can't launch themselves from the ground. Their wings don't produce enough lift to allow takeoff directly from the ground, and their legs are so small and underdeveloped that they can't run to build up takeoff speed. So, they use their claws to hang, and then fall into flight when they are ready to fly.

Related Exercises: 13, 23, 74

FIGURE 1 Echolocation results With the aid of their own natural sonar systems, bats hunt flying insects. The bats emit pulses of ultrasonic waves, which lie within their audible region, and use the echoes reflected from their prey to guide their attack. (Note the size of the ears.)

of sound in a solid and in a liquid is given by $v = \sqrt{Y/\rho}$ and $v = \sqrt{B/\rho}$, respectively, where Y is Young's modulus, B is the bulk modulus, and ρ is the density. The speed of sound in a gas is inversely proportional to the square root of the molecular mass, but the equation is more complicated and will not be presented here.

Solids are generally more elastic than liquids, which in turn are more elastic than gases. In a highly elastic material, the restoring forces between the atoms or molecules cause a disturbance to propagate faster. Thus, the speed of sound is generally about 2 to 4 times faster in solids than in liquids and about 10 to 15 times faster in solids than in gases such as air (Table 9.1).

Although not expressed explicitly in the preceding equations, the speed of sound generally depends on the temperature of the medium. In dry air, for example, the speed of sound is 331 m/s (about 740 mi/h) at 0°C. As the temperature increases, so does the speed of sound. For *normal environmental temperatures*, the speed of sound in air increases by about 0.6 m/s for each degree Celsius above 0°C. Thus, a good approximation of the speed of sound in air for a particular (environmental) temperature is given by

$$v = (331 + 0.6T_C)\ \text{m/s} \qquad \textit{speed of sound in dry air} \qquad (9.1)$$

where T_C is the air temperature in degrees Celsius.* Although not written explicitly, the units associated with the factor 0.6 are meters per second per Celsius degree $[\text{m}/(\text{s}\cdot\text{C}°)]$.

Let's take a comparative look at the speed of sound in different media.

TABLE 9.1 Speed of Sound in Various Media (typical values)

Medium	*Speed (m/s)*
Solids	
Aluminum	5100
Copper	3500
Iron	4500
Glass	5200
Polystyrene	1850
Zinc	3200
Liquids	
Alcohol, ethyl	1125
Mercury	1400
Water	1500
Gases	
Air (0°C)	331
Air (100°C)	387
Helium (0°C)	965
Hydrogen (0°C)	1284
Oxygen (0°C)	316

Example 9.1 ■ Solid, Liquid, Gas: Speed of Sound in Different Media

From their material properties, find the speed of sound in (a) a solid copper rod, (b) liquid water, and (c) air at room temperature (20°C).

Thinking It Through. We know that the speed of sound in a solid or a liquid depends on the elastic modulus and the density of the solid or liquid. These values are available in Tables 7.1 and 7.2. The speed of sound in air is given by Eq. 9.1.

Solution.

Given:
$Y_{Cu} = 11 \times 10^{10}\ \text{N/m}^2$
$B_{H_2O} = 2.2 \times 10^9\ \text{N/m}^2$
$\rho_{Cu} = 8.9 \times 10^3\ \text{kg/m}^3$
$\rho_{H_2O} = 1.0 \times 10^3\ \text{kg/m}^3$
(all values from Tables 7.1 and 7.2)
$T_C = 20°\text{C}$ (for air)

Find:
(a) v_{Cu} (speed in copper)
(b) v_{H_2O} (speed in water)
(c) v_{air} (speed in air)

(a) To find the speed of sound in a copper rod, we use the expression $v = \sqrt{Y/\rho}$:

$$v_{Cu} = \sqrt{\frac{Y}{\rho}} = \sqrt{\frac{11 \times 10^{10}\ \text{N/m}^2}{8.9 \times 10^3\ \text{kg/m}^3}} = 3.5 \times 10^3\ \text{m/s}$$

(b) For water, $v = \sqrt{B/\rho}$:

$$v_{H_2O} = \sqrt{\frac{B}{\rho}} = \sqrt{\frac{2.2 \times 10^9\ \text{N/m}^2}{1.0 \times 10^3\ \text{kg/m}^3}} = 1.5 \times 10^3\ \text{m/s}$$

*A better approximation of these and higher temperatures is given by the expression

$$v = \left(331\sqrt{1 + \frac{T_C}{273}}\right)\ \text{m/s}$$

In Table 9.1, see v for air at 100°C, which is outside the normal environmental temperature range.

(c) For air at 20°C, by Eq. 9.1, we have

$$v_{air} = (331 + 0.6T_C)\text{ m/s} = [331 + 0.6(20)]\text{ m/s} = 343\text{ m/s} = 3.43 \times 10^2\text{ m/s}$$

Follow-up Exercise. In this Example, how many times faster is the speed of sound in copper (a) than in water and (b) than in air (at room temperature)? Compare your results with the values given at the beginning of the section. *(Answers to all Follow-up Exercises are at the back of the text.)*

A generally useful value for the speed of sound in air is $\frac{1}{3}$ km/s (or $\frac{1}{5}$ mi/s). Using this value, you can, for example, estimate how far away lightning is by counting the number of seconds between the time you observe the flash and the time you hear the associated thunder. Because the speed of light is so fast, you see the lightning flash almost instantaneously. The sound waves of the thunder travel relatively slowly, at about $\frac{1}{3}$ km/s. For example, if the interval between the two events is measured to be 6 s (often by counting "one thousand one, one thousand two, . . . "), the lightning stroke was about 2 km away ($\frac{1}{3}$ km/s $\times$ 6 s).

You may also have noticed the delay in the arrival of sound relative to that of light at a baseball game. If you're sitting in the outfield stands, you see the batter hit the ball before you hear the crack of the bat.

Integrated Example 9.2 ■ Safe or Out? You Make the Call

On a cool October afternoon (air temperature = 15°C), from your seat in the centerfield stands 113 m from first base, you witness the play that will decide the World Series. You see the runner's foot touch the bag; half a second later, straining your ears, you hear the faint thud of the ball in the first baseman's glove. The umpire signals safe; half the fans boo loudly. (a) How could you determine whether the umpire was correct? (b) Did the ump blow it? Apply the physics from part (a) to find out.

(a) Conceptual Reasoning. This situation has to do with the delay in hearing the sound caused by an action; hence, it involves the speed of sound. You can see the action almost instantaneously, yet the sound takes an appreciable time to reach you, because the speed of light is much faster than that of sound. If the travel time of sound is less than $\frac{1}{2}$ s, then the runner had already touched the base when the first baseman caught the ball, and the runner is safe. If the travel time is greater than $\frac{1}{2}$ s, he's out.

(b) Thinking It Through. To see if the ump was wrong, we need to calculate the time it took for the sound to travel to you.

Given: $d = 113$ m *Find:* t (travel time of sound)
$T = 15°\text{C}$
$t = \frac{1}{2}$ s

From Eq. 9.1, with a temperature of 15°C, the speed of sound is

$$v = (331 + 0.6T_C)\text{ m/s} = [331 + 0.6(15°\text{C})]\text{ m/s} = 340\text{ m/s}$$

For a constant speed, the general distance–time relation is $d = vt$, so the time for the sound to travel the distance to your seat is

$$t = \frac{d}{v} = \frac{113\text{ m}}{340\text{ m/s}} = 0.332\text{ s}$$

or just under one-third of a second. The runner reached the base about $\frac{1}{2}$ s $-$ $\frac{1}{3}$ s $=$ $\frac{1}{6}$ s before the ball arrived. The ump was right!

To show why it is justified to say that the visual observation takes place almost instantaneously, let's see how long it takes for light to travel from first base to your seat. For practical purposes, the speed of light in air is the same as that in a vacuum,

$c = 3.00 \times 10^8$ m/s, which is on the order of 10^6 (a million) times greater than the speed of sound. The time for light to travel 113 m is then

$$t = \frac{d}{c} = \frac{113 \text{ m}}{3.00 \times 10^8 \text{ m/s}} = 3.77 \times 10^{-7} \text{ s}$$

or 0.377μs—not a very long time.

Follow-up Exercise. On a day when the air temperature is 20°C, a hiker shouts and hears the echo from the face of a vertical stone cliff 5.00 s later. (a) How far away is the cliff? (b) If the air temperature were 15°C, what would be the difference in the time it takes to hear the echoes?

The speed of sound in air depends on various factors. Temperature is the most important, but there are other considerations, such as the homogeneity and composition of the air. For example, the air composition may not be "normal" in a polluted area. These effects are relatively small and will not be considered, except conceptually in the next Example.

Conceptual Example 9.3 ■ Speed of Sound: Sound Traveling Far and Wide

Note that the speed of sound in *dry* air for a given temperature is given to a good approximation by Eq. 9.1. However, the moisture content of the air (humidity) varies, and this variation affects the speed of sound. At the same temperature, would sound travel faster in (a) dry air or (b) moist air?

Reasoning and Answer. According to an old folklore saying, "Sound traveling far and wide, a stormy day will betide." This saying implies that sound travels faster on a highly humid day, when a storm or precipitation is likely. But is the saying true?

Near the beginning of this section, we learned that the speed of sound in a gas is inversely proportional to the square root of the molecular mass of the gas. So, at constant pressure, is moist air more or less dense than dry air?

In a volume of moist air, a large number of water (H_2O) molecules occupy the space normally occupied by either nitrogen (N_2) or oxygen (O_2) molecules, which make up 98% of the air. Water molecules are less massive than both nitrogen and oxygen molecules. [From Section 8.3, the molecular (formula) masses are H_2O, 18 g; N_2, 28 g; and O_2, 32 g.] Thus, the average molecular mass of a volume of moist air is less than that of dry air, and the speed of sound is greater in moist air.

We can look at this situation another way: Since water molecules are less massive, they have less inertia and respond to the sound wave faster than nitrogen or oxygen molecules do. The water molecules therefore propagate the disturbance faster.

Follow-up Exercise. Considering only molecular masses, would you expect the speed of sound to be greatest in nitrogen, oxygen, or helium (at the same temperature and pressure)? Explain.

Note: Humidity was included here as an interesting consideration for the speed of sound in air. However, henceforth, in computing the speed of sound in air at a certain temperature, we will consider only dry air (Eq. 9.1) unless otherwise stated.

Always keep in mind that our discussion generally assumes ideal conditions for the propagation of sound. Actually, the speed of sound depends on many things, one of which is humidity, as the previous Conceptual Example shows. A variety of other properties affect the propagation of sound. As an example, let's ask the question, Why do ships' foghorns have such a low pitch or frequency? The answer is, Because low-frequency sound waves travel farther than high-frequency ones under identical conditions. This effect is explained by a couple of characteristics of sound waves. First, sound waves are attenuated (i.e., they lose energy) because of the

INSIGHT

Speech and Hearing

Sound is one of our most important means of interpersonal communication, and our most important source of sound is the human voice. Let's look at the anatomy and physics of the voice and the ear, the latter of which serves as our receiver of sound.

The Human Voice

The energy for sounds associated with the human voice originates in the muscle action of the diaphragm, which forces air up from the lungs. To produce variations in sound, this steady stream of air must be periodically disturbed, or "modulated." The fundamental modulating organ is the larynx (the "voice box"), across which are stretched membranelike folds called the vocal cords. The opening of the vocal cords modulates the airstream to produce sounds (Fig. 1).

As illustrated in the figure, there are two sets of vocal cords: (1) the *false vocal cords*, which do not produce sound, but help close the larynx during swallowing, and (2) the *true vocal cords*, which are elastic and are responsible for vocal sounds.

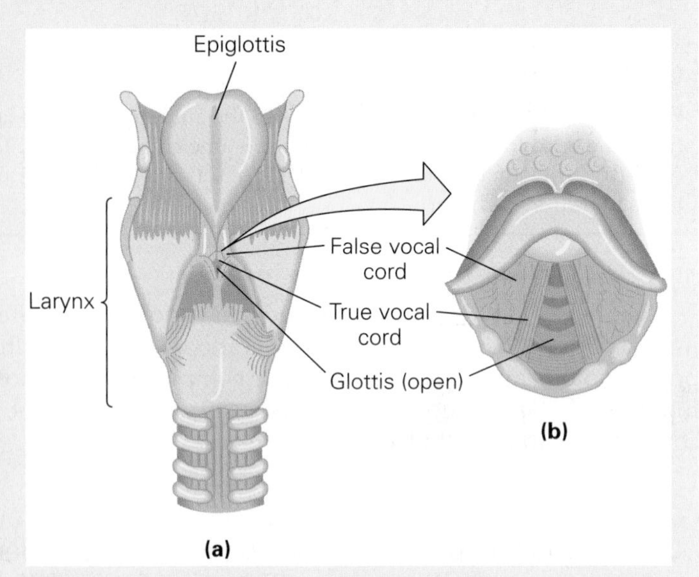

FIGURE 1 Anatomy of the voice box **(a)** A cross section of the larynx. **(b)** A down-the-throat view of the vocal cords.

Changing the tension of the vocal cords controls the pitch (perceived frequency) of the vocal sounds (as we shall see in Section 9.6). The loudness of the sound is related to the pressure of the air passing over the vocal cords. A strong blast of air results in a greater amplitude of the vibrations and hence a louder sound.

The waveforms of voice sounds are quite specific to individuals and provide a "voiceprint" that can be used for identification, just as fingerprints are. The validity of voiceprints for legal identification, however, is highly controversial.

Hearing

The anatomy of the human ear is illustrated in Fig. 2. Sound enters the outer ear and travels through the ear (or auditory)

viscosity of the air (Ch. 7.5). Second, sound waves tend to interact with oxygen and water molecules in the air. The combined result of these two properties is that the total attenuation of sound in air depends on the frequency of the sound: the higher the frequency, the more is the attenuation and the shorter is the distance traveled. For example, a 200-Hz sound will travel much farther than an 800-Hz sound. Thus, low-frequency foghorns are used. In accordance with this dependence on frequency, you might notice that when a storm's lightning is farther away, the thunder you generally hear is a low-frequency rumble. Sound is one of our major means of communicating. (For more on our speech and hearing, see the Insight above.)

9.3 Sound Intensity and Sound Intensity Level

OBJECTIVES: **To (a) define sound intensity and explain how it varies with distance from a point source and (b) calculate sound intensity levels on the decibel scale.**

Wave motion involves the propagation of energy. The rate of energy transfer is expressed in terms of **intensity**, which is the energy transported per unit time across a unit area. Since energy divided by time is power, intensity is power divided by area:

$$\text{intensity} = \frac{\text{energy/time}}{\text{area}} = \frac{\text{power}}{\text{area}} \qquad \left[I = \frac{E/t}{A} = \frac{P}{A} \right]$$

The standard units of intensity (power/area) are watts per square meter (W/m^2).

INSIGHT

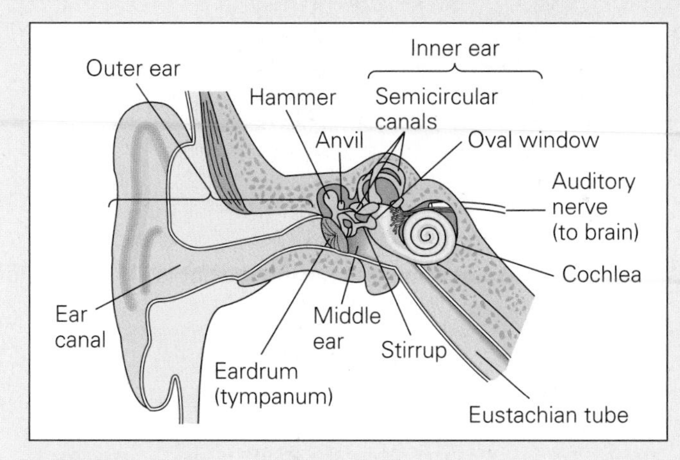

FIGURE 2 Anatomy of the human ear The ear converts pressure in the air into electrical nerve impulses that are interpreted as sounds by the brain.

canal to the *eardrum* (the tympanum), which separates the outer ear from the middle ear. The eardrum is a membrane that vibrates in response to the impinging sound waves. The vibrations are transmitted through the middle ear, which contains an intricate set of connected bones, commonly called the *hammer* (malleus), *anvil* (incus), and *stirrup* (stapes), because of their shapes.

The inner ear includes the semicircular canals, which are important in controlling balance, and the *cochlea*. It is in the cochlea that sound waves are translated into nerve impulses and that pitch or frequency discrimination is made. The cochlea consists of a series of liquid-filled tubes or ducts, coiled into a spiral shape that resembles a snail shell. The *basilar membrane* supports the cochlea and forms the floor of the cochlear ducts. Within the ducts are thousands of special receptor cells called *hair cells*.

The hair cells are specialized nerve receptors. When a region of the basilar membrane is set vibrating by sound of a particular frequency, hair cells in that region are stimulated and nerve impulses are sent to the brain, where they are interpreted as sound. The brain translates this positional information (impulses from particular fibers originating in specific regions of the basilar membrane) back into frequency information (the subjective physiological sensation of pitch).

Incidentally, the middle ear is connected to the throat by the Eustachian tube, the end of which is normally closed. It opens during swallowing and yawning to permit air to enter and leave, so that internal and external pressures are equalized. You have probably experienced a "stopping up" of your ears with a sudden change in atmospheric pressure (e.g., during rapid ascents or descents in elevators or airplanes). Swallowing opens the Eustachian tubes and relieves the excess pressure difference on the middle ear.

Related Exercises: 24, 31, 84

Consider a point source that sends out spherical sound waves, as shown in ▸Fig. 9.4. If there are no losses, the sound intensity at a distance R from the source is

$$I = \frac{P}{A} = \frac{P}{4\pi R^2} \tag{9.2}$$

where P is the power of the source and $4\pi R^2$ is the area of a sphere of radius R, through which the sound energy passes perpendicularly.

The intensity of a point source of sound is therefore *inversely proportional to the square of the distance from the source* (an inverse-square relationship). Two intensities at different distances from a source of constant power can be compared as a ratio:

$$\frac{I_2}{I_1} = \frac{P/(4\pi R_2^2)}{P/(4\pi R_1^2)} = \frac{R_1^2}{R_2^2}$$

or

$$\frac{I_2}{I_1} = \left(\frac{R_1}{R_2}\right)^2 \tag{9.3}$$

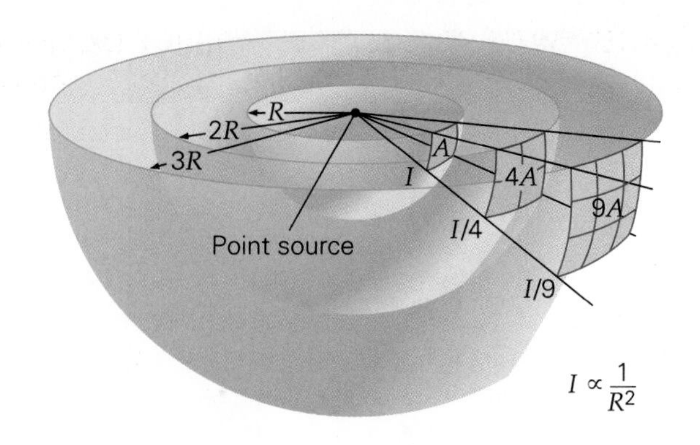

▶ **FIGURE 9.4 Intensity of a point source** The energy emitted from a point source spreads out equally in all directions. Since intensity is power divided by area, $I = P/A = P/(4\pi R^2)$, where the area is that of a spherical surface. The intensity then decreases with the distance from the source as $1/R^2$ (figure not to scale).

Suppose that the distance from a point source is doubled; that is, $R_2 = 2R_1$, or $R_1/R_2 = \frac{1}{2}$. Then

$$\frac{I_2}{I_1} = \left(\frac{R_1}{R_2}\right)^2 = \left(\frac{1}{2}\right)^2 = \frac{1}{4}$$

and

$$I_2 = \frac{I_1}{4}$$

Since the intensity decreases by a factor of $1/R^2$, doubling the distance decreases the intensity to a quarter of its original value.

A good way to understand this inverse-square relationship intuitively is to look at the geometry of the situation. As Fig. 9.4 shows, the greater the distance from the source, the larger the area over which a given amount of sound energy is spread, and thus the lower its intensity. (Imagine having to paint two walls of different areas. If you had the same amount of paint to use on each, you'd have to spread it more thinly over the larger wall.) Since this area increases as the square of the radius R, the intensity decreases accordingly—that is, as $1/R^2$.

Sound intensity is perceived by the ear as **loudness**. On the average, the human ear can detect sound waves (at 1 kHz) with an intensity as low as 10^{-12} W/m^2. This intensity (I_o) is referred to as the *threshold of hearing*. Thus, for us to hear a sound, it must not only have a frequency in the audible range, but also be of sufficient intensity. As the intensity is increased, the perceived sound becomes louder. At an intensity of 1.0 W/m^2, the sound is uncomfortably loud and may be painful to the ear. This intensity (I_p) is called the *threshold of pain*.

Note that the thresholds of pain and hearing differ by a factor of 10^{12}:

$$\frac{I_p}{I_o} = \frac{1.0\ \text{W/m}^2}{10^{-12}\ \text{W/m}^2} = 10^{12}$$

That is, the intensity at the threshold of pain is a *trillion* times greater than that at the threshold of hearing. Within this enormous range, the perceived loudness is not directly proportional to the intensity. Thus, if the intensity is doubled, the perceived loudness does not double. In fact, a doubling of perceived loudness corresponds approximately to an increase in intensity by a factor of 10. For example, a sound with an intensity of 10^{-5} W/m^2 would be perceived to be twice as loud as one with an intensity of 10^{-6} W/m^2. (The smaller the negative exponent, the larger is the number.)

Sound Intensity Level: The Bel and the Decibel

It is convenient to compress the large range of sound intensities by using a logarithmic scale (base 10) to express intensity levels. The intensity level of a sound must be referenced to a standard intensity, which is taken to be that of the threshold of hearing, $I_o = 10^{-12}\ \mathrm{W/m^2}$. Then, for any intensity I, the intensity level is the logarithm (or log) of the ratio of I to I_o, that is, $\log I/I_o$. For example, if a sound has an intensity of $I = 10^{-6}\ \mathrm{W/m^2}$,

$$\log \frac{I}{I_o} = \log \frac{10^{-6}\ \mathrm{W/m^2}}{10^{-12}\ \mathrm{W/m^2}} = \log 10^6 = 6\ \mathrm{B}$$

(Recall that $\log_{10} 10^x = x$.) The exponent of the power of 10 in the final log term is taken to have a unit called the **bel** (B). Thus, a sound with an intensity of $10^{-6}\ \mathrm{W/m^2}$ has an intensity level of 6 B on this scale. That way, the intensity range from $10^{-12}\ \mathrm{W/m^2}$ to $1.0\ \mathrm{W/m^2}$ is compressed into a scale of intensity levels ranging from 0 B to 12 B.

Note: The bel was named in honor of Alexander Graham Bell, the inventor of the telephone.

A finer intensity scale is obtained by using a smaller unit, the **decibel** (dB), which is a tenth of a bel. The range from 0 to 12 B corresponds to 0 to 120 dB. In this case, the equation for the relative **sound intensity level**, or **decibel level** (β), is

Sound intensity level in decibels

$$\beta = 10 \log \frac{I}{I_o} \qquad (\text{where } I_o = 10^{-12}\ \mathrm{W/m^2}) \tag{9.4}$$

Note that the sound intensity level (in decibels, which are dimensionless) is *not* the same as the sound intensity (in watts per square meter).

Threshold of hearing: $I_o = 10^{-12}\ \mathrm{W/m^2}$

Threshold of pain: $I_p = 1.0\ \mathrm{W/m^2}$

The decibel intensity scale and familiar sounds at some intensity levels are shown in ▼Fig. 9.5. Sound intensities can have detrimental effects on hearing, and because of this, the U.S. government has set occupational noise-exposure limits.

Example 9.4 ■ Sound Intensity Levels: Using Logarithms

What are the intensity levels of sounds with intensities of (a) $10^{-12}\ \mathrm{W/m^2}$ and (b) $5.0 \times 10^{-6}\ \mathrm{W/m^2}$?

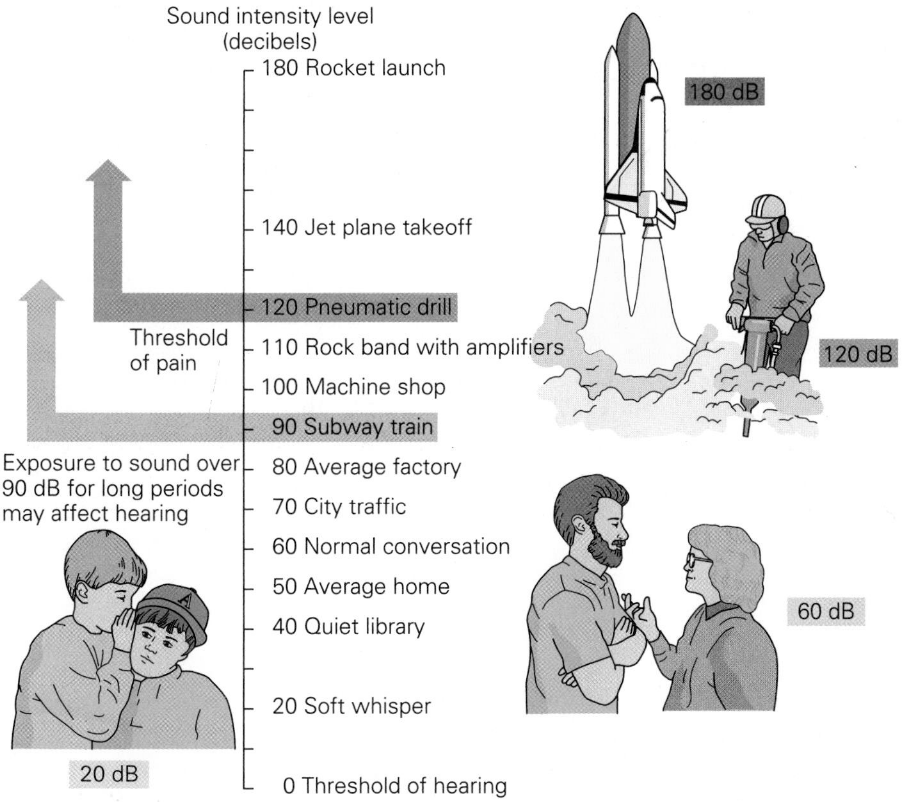

◀ **FIGURE 9.5 Sound intensity levels and the decibel scale** The intensity levels of some common sounds on the decibel (dB) scale.

Thinking It Through. The sound intensity levels can be found by using Eq. 9.4.

Solution.

Given: (a) $I = 10^{-12}\ \text{W/m}^2$ (b) $I = 5.0 \times 10^{-6}\ \text{W/m}^2$

Find: (a) β (sound intensity level) (b) β

(a) Using Eq. 9.4, we have

$$\beta = 10 \log \frac{I}{I_o} = 10 \log \left(\frac{10^{-12}\ \text{W/m}^2}{10^{-12}\ \text{W/m}^2}\right) = 10 \log 1 = 0\ \text{dB}$$

The intensity is the same as that at the threshold of hearing. (Recall that $\log 1 = 0$, since $1 = 10^0$ and $\log 10^0 = 0$.) Note that an intensity level of 0 dB does not mean that there is no sound.

(b) $$\beta = 10 \log \frac{I}{I_o} = 10 \log \left(\frac{5.0 \times 10^{-6}\ \text{W/m}^2}{10^{-12}\ \text{W/m}^2}\right)$$

$$= 10 \log (5.0 \times 10^6) = 10(\log 5.0 + \log 10^6) = 10(0.70 + 6.0) = 67\ \text{dB}$$

Follow-up Exercise. Note in this Example that the intensity of $5.0 \times 10^{-6}\ \text{W/m}^2$ is halfway between 10^{-6} and 10^{-5} (or 60 and 70 dB), yet this intensity does not correspond to a midway value of 65 dB. (a) Why? (b) What intensity *does* correspond to 65 dB? (Compute it to three significant figures.)

Example 9.5 ■ Intensity Level Differences: Using Ratios

(a) What is the difference in the intensity levels if the intensity of a sound is doubled? (b) By what factors does the intensity increase for intensity level *differences* of 10 dB and 20 dB?

Thinking It Through. (a) If the intensity is doubled, then $I_2 = 2I_1$, or $I_2/I_1 = 2$. We can then use Eq. 9.4 to find the intensity difference. Recall that $\log a - \log b = \log a/b$. (b) Here, it is important to note that these values are intensity level *differences*, $\Delta\beta = \beta_2 - \beta_1$, *not* intensity *levels*. The equation developed in (a) will work. (Why?)

Solution. Listing the data, we have.

Given: (a) $I_2 = 2I_1$ (b) $\Delta\beta = 10$ dB, $\Delta\beta = 20$ dB

Find: (a) $\Delta\beta$ (intensity level difference) (b) I_2/I_1 (factors of increase)

(a) Using Eq. 9.4 and the relationship $\log a - \log b = \log a/b$, we have, for difference $\Delta\beta = \beta_2 - \beta_1 = 10[\log(I_2/I_o) - \log(I_1/I_o)] = 10 \log[(I_2/I_o)/(I_1/I_o)] = 10 \log I_2/I_1$. Then,

$$\Delta\beta = 10 \log \frac{I_2}{I_1} = 10 \log 2 = 3\ \text{dB}$$

Thus, doubling the intensity increases the intensity level by 3 dB (e.g., an increase from 55 dB to 58 dB).

(b) For a 10-dB difference,

$$\Delta\beta = 10\ \text{dB} = 10 \log \frac{I_2}{I_1} \quad \text{and} \quad \log \frac{I_2}{I_1} = 1.0$$

Since $\log 10^1 = 1$, the intensity ratio is 10:1 because

$$\frac{I_2}{I_1} = 10^1 \quad \text{and} \quad I_2 = 10\, I_1$$

Similarly, for a 20-dB difference,

$$\Delta\beta = 20\text{ dB} = 10\log\frac{I_2}{I_1} \qquad \text{and} \qquad \log\frac{I_2}{I_1} = 2.0$$

Since $\log 10^2 = 2$,

$$\frac{I_2}{I_1} = 10^2 \qquad \text{and} \qquad I_2 = 100\, I_1$$

Thus, an intensity level difference of 10 dB corresponds to changing (increasing or decreasing) the intensity by a factor of 10. An intensity level difference of 20 dB corresponds to changing the intensity by a factor of 100.

You should be able to guess the factor that corresponds to an intensity level difference of 30 dB. In general, the factor of the intensity change is $10^{\Delta B}$, where ΔB is the difference in levels of bels. Since 30 dB = 3 B and $10^3 = 1000$, the intensity changes by a factor of 1000 for an intensity level difference of 30 dB.

Follow-up Exercise. A $\Delta\beta$ of 20 dB and a $\Delta\beta$ of 30 dB correspond to factors of 100 and 1000, respectively, in intensity changes. Does a $\Delta\beta$ of 25 dB correspond to an intensity change factor of 500? Explain.

Example 9.6 ■ Combined Sound Levels: Adding Intensities

Sitting at a sidewalk restaurant table, a friend talks to you in normal conversation (60 dB). At the same time, the intensity level of the street traffic reaching you is also 60 dB. What is the total intensity level of the combined sounds?

Thinking It Through. It is tempting simply to add the two sound intensity levels together and say that the total is 120 dB. But intensity levels in decibels are logarithmic, so you can't add them in the normal way. However, intensities (I) can be added arithmetically, since energy and power are scalar quantities. Then the combined intensity level can be found from the sum of the intensities.

Solution. We have the following information:

Given: $\beta_1 = 60\text{ dB}$ *Find:* Total β
$\beta_2 = 60\text{ dB}$

Let's find the intensities associated with the intensity levels:

$$\beta_1 = 60\text{ dB} = 10\log\frac{I_1}{I_o} = 10\log\left(\frac{I_1}{10^{-12}\text{ W/m}^2}\right)$$

By inspection, we have

$$I_1 = 10^{-6}\text{ W/m}^2$$

Similarly, $I_2 = 10^{-6}\text{ W/m}^2$, since both intensity levels are 60 dB. So the total intensity is

$$I_{\text{total}} = I_1 + I_2 = 1.0 \times 10^{-6}\text{ W/m}^2 + 1.0 \times 10^{-6}\text{ W/m}^2 = 2.0 \times 10^{-6}\text{ W/m}^2$$

Then, converting back to intensity level, we get

$$\beta = 10\log\frac{I_{\text{total}}}{I_o} = 10\log\left(\frac{2.0\times 10^{-6}\text{ W/m}^2}{10^{-12}\text{ W/m}^2}\right) = 10\log(2.0\times 10^6)$$
$$= 10(\log 2.0 + \log 10^6) = 10(0.30 + 6.0) = 63\text{ dB}$$

This value is a long way from 120 dB! Notice that the combined intensities doubled the intensity value, and the intensity level increased by 3 dB, in agreement with our finding in part (a) of Example 9.5.

Follow-up Exercise. In this Example, suppose the added noise gave a total that *tripled* the intensity level of the conversation. What would be the total combined intensity level in this case?

Protect Your Hearing

Hearing may be damaged by excessive noise, so our ears sometimes need protection from continuous loud sounds (▼Fig. 9.6). Hearing damage depends on the sound intensity level (decibel level) and the exposure time. The exact combinations vary for different people, but a general guide to noise levels is given in Table 9.2. Studies have shown that sound levels of 90 dB and above will damage

▶ **FIGURE 9.6 Protect your hearing** Continuous loud sounds can damage hearing, so our ears may need protection as shown here. Note in Table 9.2 that the intensity level of lawn mowers is on the order of 90 dB.

TABLE 9.2 Sound Levels and Ear Damage Exposure Times

	Decibels (dB)	*Examples*	*Damage Can Occur with Nonstop Exposure*
Faint	30	Quiet library, whispering	
Moderate	60	Normal conversation, sewing machine	
Very loud	80	Heavy traffic, noisy restaurant, screaming child	10 hours
	90	Lawn mower, motorcycle, loud party	Less than 8 hours
	100	Chain saw, subway train, snowmobile	Less than 2 hours
Extremely loud	110	Stereo headset at full blast, rock concert	30 minutes
	120	Dance clubs, car stereos, action movies, some musical toys	15 minutes
	130	Jackhammer, loud computer games, loud sporting events	Less than 15 minutes
Painful	140	Boom stereos, gunshot blast, firecrackers	Any length (for example, hearing loss can occur from a few shots of a high-powered gun if protection is not worn)

Courtesy of The EAR Foundation.

receptor nerves in the ear, resulting in a loss of hearing. At 90 dB, it takes 8 hours or less for damage to occur. In general, if the sound level is increased by 5 decibels, the safe exposure time is cut in half. For example, if a sound level of 95 dB (that of a loud lawn mower or motorcycle) takes 4 hours to damage your hearing, then a sound level of 105 dB takes only 1 hour to do damage.

9.4 Sound Phenomena

OBJECTIVES: **To (a) explain the reflection, refraction, and diffraction of sound and (b) distinguish between constructive and destructive interference.**

Reflection, Refraction, and Diffraction

An echo is a familiar example of the *reflection* of sound—sound "bouncing" off a surface. Sound *refraction* is less common than reflection, but you may have experienced it on a calm summer evening, when it is possible to hear distant voices or other sounds that ordinarily would not be audible. This effect is due to the refraction, or bending (change in direction), of the sound waves as they pass from one region into a region where the air density is different. The effect is similar to what would happen if the sound passed into another medium.

The required conditions for sound to be refracted are a layer of cooler air near the ground or water and a layer of warmer air above it. These conditions occur frequently over bodies of water, which cool after sunset (▼Fig. 9.7). As a result of the cooling, the waves are refracted in an arc that may allow a distant person to receive an increased intensity of sound.

Another bending phenomenon is *diffraction*. Sound may be diffracted, or bent, around corners or around an object. We usually think of waves as traveling in straight lines. However, you can hear someone you cannot see standing around a corner. This bending is different from that of refraction, in which no obstacle causes the bending.

Reflection, refraction, and diffraction are described in a general sense here for sound. These phenomena are important considerations for light waves as well and will be discussed more fully in Chapter 10.

▼ **FIGURE 9.7 Sound refraction** Sound travels more slowly in the cool air near the water surface than in the upper, warmer air. As a result, the waves are refracted, or bent. This bending increases the intensity of the sound at a distance where it otherwise might not be heard.

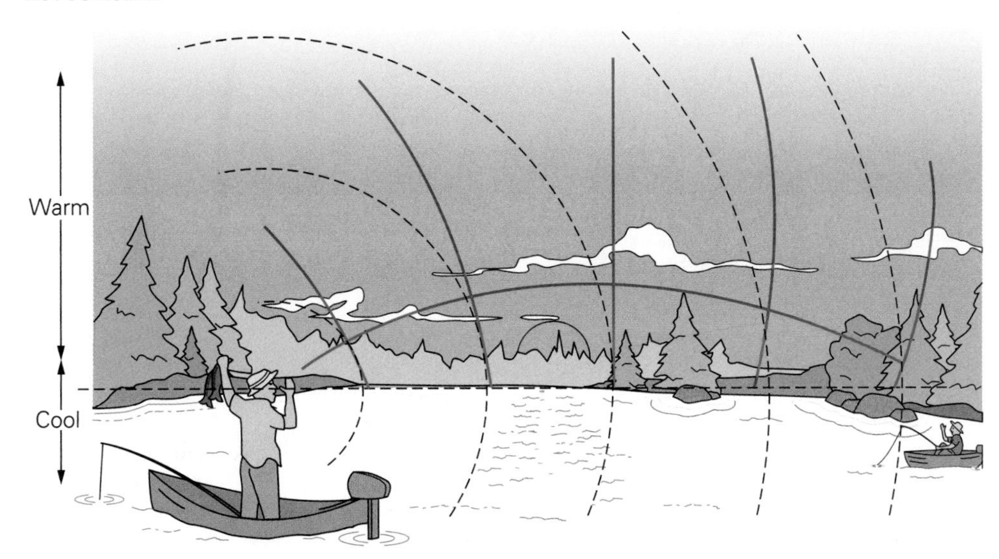

Interference

Like waves of any kind, sound waves *interfere* when they meet. Suppose that two loudspeakers separated by some distance emit sound waves in phase at the same frequency. If we consider the speakers to be point sources, then the waves will spread out spherically and interfere (▼Fig. 9.8a). The lines from a particular speaker represent wave crests (or condensations), and the troughs (or rarefactions) lie in the intervening white areas.

In particular regions of space, there will be constructive or destructive interference. For example, if two waves meet in a region where they are exactly in phase (two crests or two troughs coincide), there will be total **constructive interference** (Fig. 9.8b). Notice that the waves have the same motion at point C in the figure. If, instead, the waves meet such that the crest of one coincides with the trough of the other (at point D), the two waves will cancel each other out (Fig. 9.8c). The result will be total **destructive interference**.

It is convenient to describe the path lengths traveled by the waves in terms of wavelength (λ) to determine whether they arrive in phase. Consider the waves arriving at point C in Fig. 9.8b. The path lengths in this case are $L_{AC} = 4\lambda$ and $L_{BC} = 3\lambda$. The **phase difference** ($\Delta\theta$) is related to the **path-length difference** (ΔL) by the simple relationship

$$\Delta\theta = \frac{2\pi}{\lambda}(\Delta L) \qquad \textit{phase difference and path-length difference} \qquad (9.5)$$

Since 2π rad is equivalent, in angular terms, to a full wave cycle or wavelength, multiplying the path-length difference by $2\pi/\lambda$ gives the phase difference in radians. For the example illustrated in Fig. 9.8b, we have

$$\Delta\theta = \frac{2\pi}{\lambda}(L_{AC} - L_{BC}) = \frac{2\pi}{\lambda}(4\lambda - 3\lambda) = 2\pi \text{ rad}$$

When $\Delta\theta = 2\pi$ rad, the waves are shifted by one wavelength. This is the same as $\Delta\theta = 0°$, so the waves are actually back in phase. Thus, the waves interfere constructively in the region of point C, increasing the intensity, or loudness, of the sound detected there.

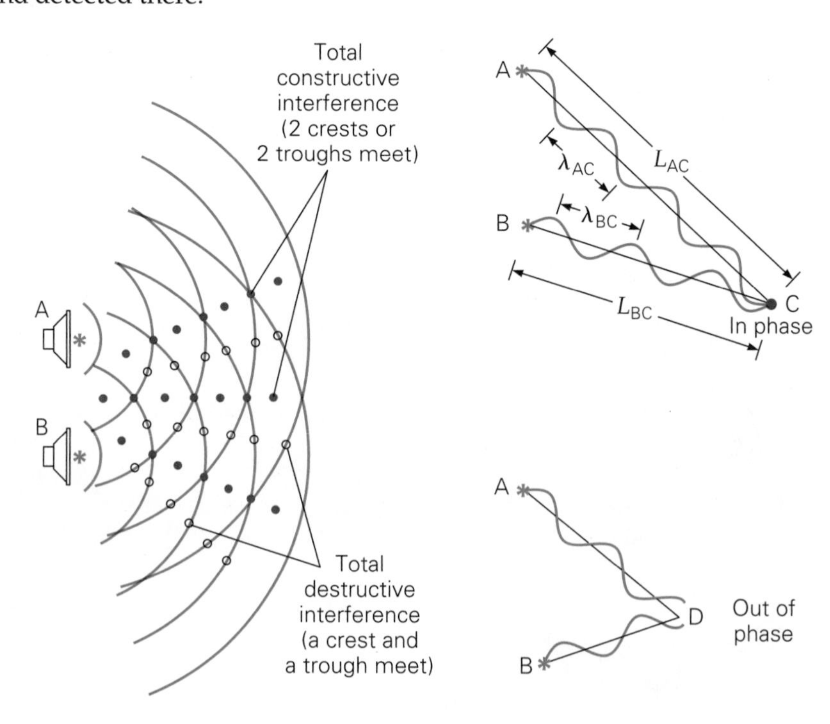

▶ **FIGURE 9.8 Interference** **(a)** Sound waves from two point sources spread out and interfere. **(b)** At points where the waves arrive in phase (with a zero phase difference), such as point C, constructive interference occurs. **(c)** At points where the waves arrive completely out of phase (with a phase difference of 180°), such as point D, destructive interference occurs. The phase difference at a particular point depends on the path lengths the waves travel to reach that point.

From Eq. 9.5, we see that the sound waves are in phase at any point where the path-length difference is zero or an integral multiple of the wavelength. That is,

$$\Delta L = n\lambda \qquad (n = 0, 1, 2, 3, \ldots) \qquad \textit{condition for constructive interference} \tag{9.6}$$

A similar analysis of the situation in Fig. 9.8c, where $L_{AD} = 2\frac{3}{4}\lambda$ and $L_{BD} = 2\frac{1}{4}\lambda$, gives

$$\Delta\theta = \frac{2\pi}{\lambda}(2\tfrac{3}{4}\lambda - 2\tfrac{1}{4}\lambda) = \pi \text{ rad}$$

or $\Delta\theta = 180°$. At point D, the waves are completely out of phase, and destructive interference occurs in this region.

Sound waves will be out of phase at any point where the path-length difference is an odd number of half-wavelengths ($\lambda/2$), or

$$\Delta L = m\left(\frac{\lambda}{2}\right) \qquad (m = 1, 3, 5, \ldots) \qquad \textit{condition for destructive interference} \tag{9.7}$$

At these points, a softer, or less intense, sound will be heard or detected. If the amplitudes of the waves are exactly equal, the destructive interference is total and no sound is heard.

An application of destructive interference in sound waves is to reduce loud noises. For example, engine noise in a helicopter can be distracting and cause hearing discomfort. Special headsets, with a microphone near the ear, pick up the loud noise and supply sound with a phase difference that cancels the original sound as much as possible. Ideally, the sound that is supplied is 180° out of phase with the undesirable noise.

Example 9.7 ■ Pump Up the Volume: Sound Interference

At an open-air concert on a hot day (with an air temperature of 25°C), you sit 7.00 m and 9.10 m, respectively, from a pair of speakers, one at each side of the stage. A musician, warming up, plays a single 494-Hz tone. What do you hear? (Consider the speakers to be point sources.)

Thinking It Through. The sound waves from the speakers interfere. Is the interference constructive, destructive, or something in between? It depends on the path-length difference, which we can compute from the given distances.

Solution.

Given: $d_1 = 7.00$ m and $d_2 = 9.10$ m, $f = 494$ Hz, $T = 25°C$

Find: ΔL (path-length difference in wavelength units)

The path-length difference (2.10 m) between the waves arriving at your location must be expressed in terms of the wavelength of the sound. To do this, we first need to know the wavelength. Given the frequency, we can find the wavelength from the relationship $\lambda = v/f$, provided that the speed of sound, v, at the given temperature is known. The speed v can be found by using Eq. 9.1:

$$v = 331 + 0.6T_C = 331 + 0.6(25) = 346 \text{ m/s}$$

The wavelength of the sound waves is then

$$\lambda = \frac{v}{f} = \frac{346 \text{ m/s}}{494 \text{ Hz}} = 0.700 \text{ m}$$

Thus, the distances in terms of wavelength are

$$d_1 = (7.00 \text{ m})\left(\frac{\lambda}{0.700 \text{ m}}\right) = 10.0\lambda \quad \text{and} \quad d_2 = (9.10 \text{ m})\left(\frac{\lambda}{0.700 \text{ m}}\right) = 13.0\lambda$$

The path-length difference in terms of wavelengths is

$$\Delta L = d_2 - d_1 = 13.0\lambda - 10.0\lambda = 3.0\lambda$$

This is an integral number of wavelengths ($n = 3$), so constructive interference occurs. The sounds of the two speakers reinforce each other, and you hear an intense tone at 494 Hz.

Follow-up Exercise. Suppose that in this Example the tone traveled to a person sitting 7.00 m and 8.75 m, respectively, from the two speakers. What would be the situation in that case?

Another interesting interference effect occurs when two tones of nearly the same frequency ($f_1 \approx f_2$) are sounded simultaneously. The ear senses pulsations in loudness known as **beats**. The human ear can detect as many as 7 beats per second before they sound "smooth" (continuous, without any pulsations).

Suppose that two sinusoidal waves with the same amplitude, but slightly different frequencies, interfere (▼Fig. 9.9a). Figure 9.9b represents the resulting sound wave. The amplitude of the combined wave varies sinusoidally, as shown by the black curves (known as *envelopes*) that outline the wave.

What does this variation in amplitude mean in terms of what the listener perceives? A listener will hear a pulsating sound (beats), as determined by the envelopes. The maximum amplitude is $2A$ (at the point where the maxima of the two original waves interfere constructively). Detailed mathematics shows that a listener will hear the beats at a frequency called the **beat frequency** (f_b), given by

$$f_b = |f_1 - f_2| \tag{9.8}$$

The absolute value is taken because the frequency f_b cannot be negative, even if $f_2 > f_1$. A negative beat frequency would be meaningless.

Beats can be produced when tuning forks of nearly the same frequency are vibrating at the same time. For example, using forks with frequencies of 516 Hz and

▼ **FIGURE 9.9 Beats** Two traveling waves of equal amplitude and slightly different frequencies interfere and give rise to pulsating tones called beats. The beat frequency is given by $f_b = |f_1 - f_2|$.

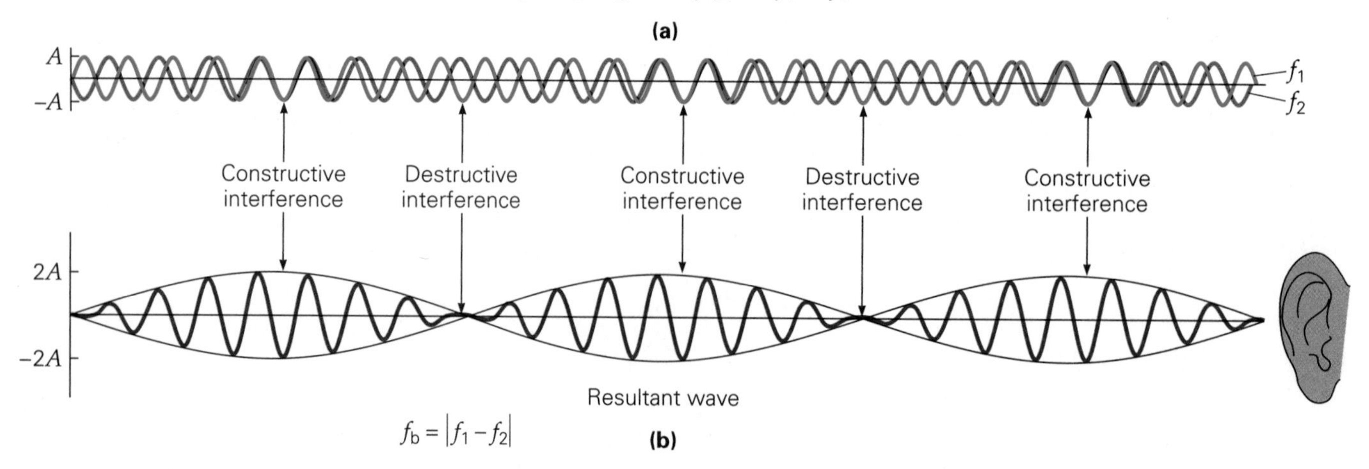

513 Hz, one can generate a beat frequency of $f_b = 516\text{ Hz} - 513\text{ Hz} = 3\text{ Hz}$, and three beats are heard each second. Musicians tune two stringed instruments to the same note by adjusting the tensions in the strings until the beats disappear ($f_1 = f_2$).

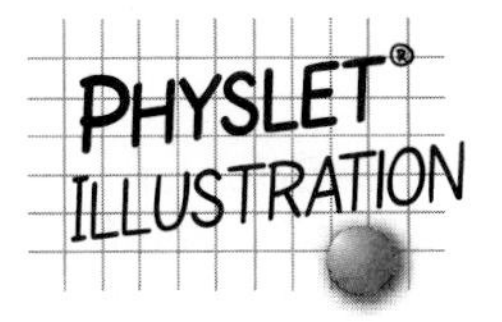

Beats

9.5 The Doppler Effect

OBJECTIVES: To (a) describe and explain the Doppler effect and (b) give some examples of its occurrences and applications.

If you stand along a highway and a car or truck approaches you with its horn blowing, the **pitch** (the perceived frequency) of the sound is higher as the vehicle approaches and lower as it recedes. You can also hear variations in the frequency of the motor noise when you watch a race car going around a track. A variation in the perceived sound frequency due to the motion of the source is an example of the **Doppler effect**.

The Austrian physicist Christian Doppler (1803–1853) first described what we now call the Doppler effect.

As ▼Fig. 9.10 shows, the sound waves emitted by a moving source tend to bunch up in front of the source and spread out in back. The Doppler shift in frequency can be found by assuming that the air is at rest in a reference frame such as that depicted in ▶Fig. 9.11. The speed of sound in air is v, and the speed of the moving source is v_s. The frequency of the sound produced by the source is f_s. In one period, $T = 1/f_s$, a wave crest moves a distance $d = vT = \lambda$. (The sound wave would travel this distance in still air in any case, regardless of whether the source is moving.) But in one period, the source travels a distance $d_s = v_sT$ before emitting another wave crest. The distance between the successive wave crests is thus shortened to a wavelength λ':

$$\lambda' = d - d_s = vT - v_sT = (v - v_s)T = \frac{v - v_s}{f_s}$$

▼ **FIGURE 9.10 The Doppler effect** The sound waves bunch up in front of a moving source—the whistle—giving a higher frequency there. They trail out behind the source, giving a lower frequency there. (The figure is not drawn to scale. Why?)

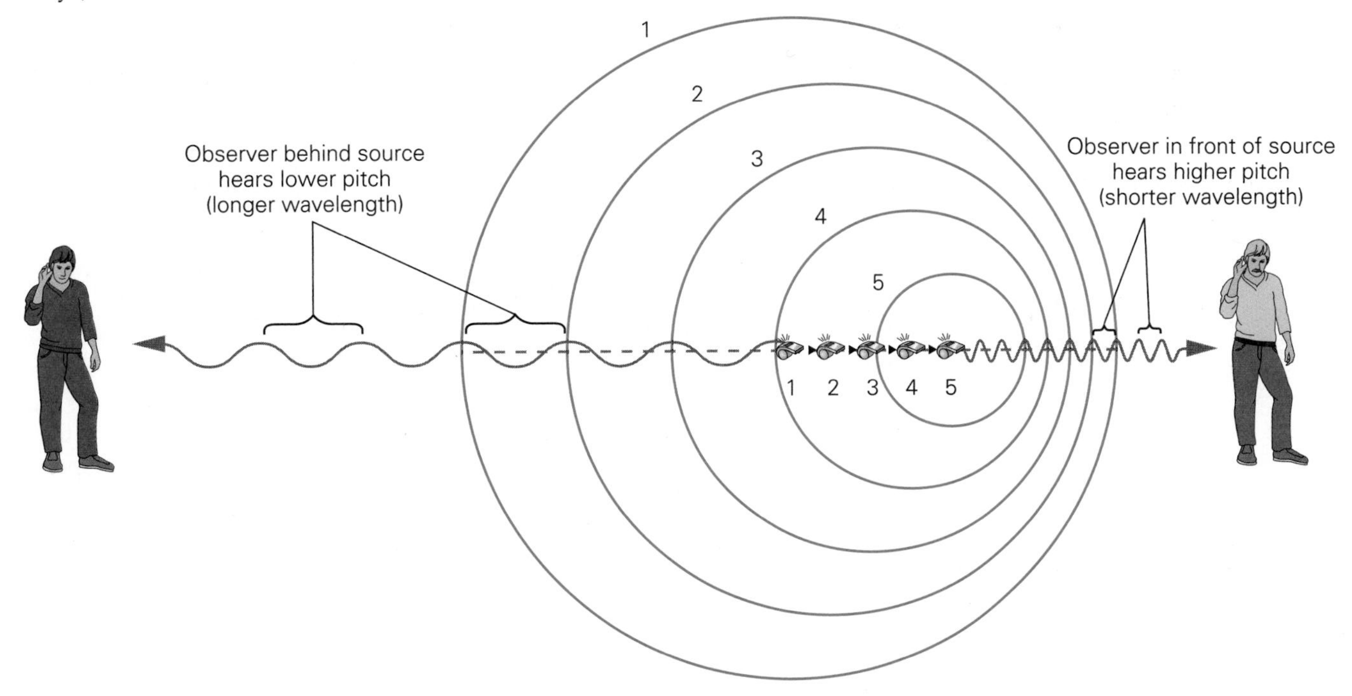

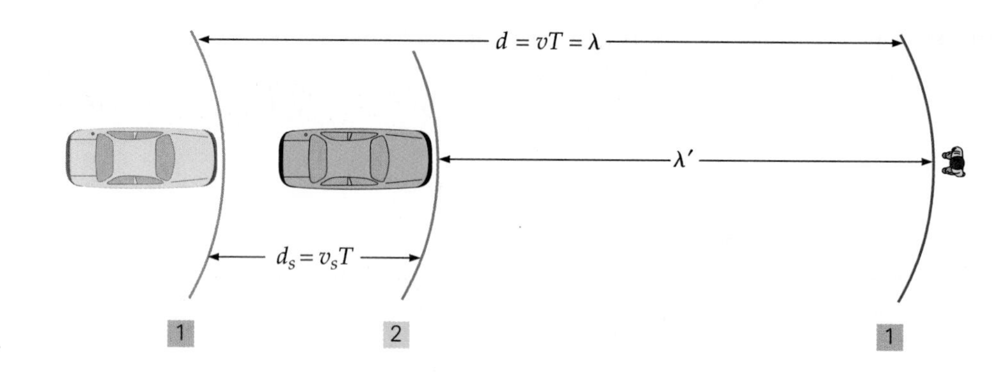

▶ FIGURE 9.11 The Doppler effect and wavelength Sound from a moving car's horn travels a distance d in a time T. During this time, the car (the source) travels a distance d_s before putting out a second pulse, thereby shortening the observed wavelength of the sound in the approaching direction.

The frequency heard by the observer (f_o) is related to the shortened wavelength by $f_o = v/\lambda'$, and substituting λ' gives

$$f_o = \frac{v}{\lambda'} = \left(\frac{v}{v - v_s}\right) f_s$$

or

$$f_o = \left(\frac{1}{1 - \dfrac{v_s}{v}}\right) f_s \quad \textit{(source moving toward a stationary observer)} \tag{9.9}$$

where v_s = *speed of source*
and v = *speed of sound*

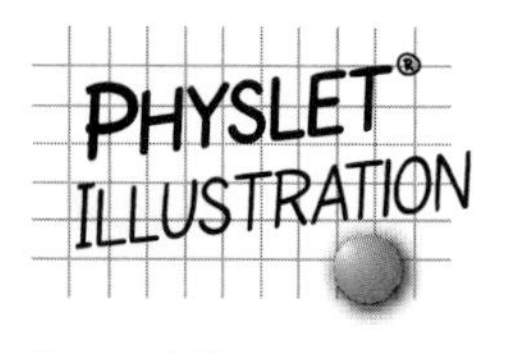

Doppler Effect

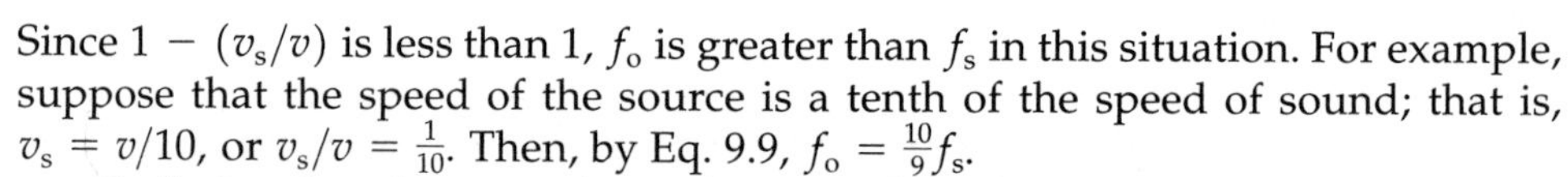

Since $1 - (v_s/v)$ is less than 1, f_o is greater than f_s in this situation. For example, suppose that the speed of the source is a tenth of the speed of sound; that is, $v_s = v/10$, or $v_s/v = \frac{1}{10}$. Then, by Eq. 9.9, $f_o = \frac{10}{9} f_s$.

Similarly, when the source is moving away from the observer ($\lambda' = d + d_s$), the observed frequency is given by

$$f_o = \left(\frac{v}{v + v_s}\right) f_s = \left(\frac{1}{1 + \dfrac{v_s}{v}}\right) f_s \quad \textit{(source moving away from a stationary observer)} \tag{9.10}$$

Here, f_o is less than f_s. (Why?)

Combining Eqs. 9.9 and 9.10 yields a general equation for the observed frequency with a moving source and a stationary observer:

$$f_o = \left(\frac{v}{v \pm v_s}\right) f_s = \left(\frac{1}{1 \pm \dfrac{v_s}{v}}\right) f_s \quad \begin{cases} - \textit{ for source moving toward stationary observer} \\ + \textit{ for source moving away from stationary observer} \end{cases} \tag{9.11}$$

As you might expect, the Doppler effect also occurs with a moving observer and a stationary source, although this situation is a bit different. As the observer moves toward the source, the distance between successive wave crests is the normal wavelength (or $\lambda = v/f_s$), but the measured wave speed is different. Relative to the approaching observer, the sound from the stationary source has a wave speed of $v' = v + v_o$, where v_o is the speed of the observer and v is the speed of sound in still air. (The observer moving toward the source is moving in a direction opposite that of the propagating waves and thus meets more wave crests in a given time.)

With $\lambda = v/f_s$, the observed frequency is then

$$f_o = \frac{v'}{\lambda} = \left(\frac{v + v_o}{v}\right) f_s$$

or

$$f_o = \left(1 + \frac{v_o}{v}\right) f_s \quad \textit{(observed moving toward a stationary source)} \tag{9.12}$$

where v_o = *speed of observer*
and v = *speed of sound*

Similarly, for an observer moving away from a stationary source, the perceived wave speed is $v' = v - v_o$, and

$$f_o = \frac{v'}{\lambda} = \left(\frac{v - v_o}{v}\right) f_s$$

or

$$f_o = \left(1 - \frac{v_o}{v}\right) f_s \quad \textit{(observer moving away from a stationary source)} \tag{9.13}$$

Equations 9.12 and 9.13 can be combined into a general equation for a moving observer and a stationary source:

$$f_o = \left(\frac{v \pm v_o}{v}\right) f_s = \left(1 \pm \frac{v_o}{v}\right) f_s \quad \begin{cases} + \textit{ for observer moving toward stationary source} \\ - \textit{ for observer moving away from stationary source} \end{cases} \tag{9.14}$$

Example 9.8 ■ On the Road Again: The Doppler Effect

As a truck traveling at 96 km/h approaches and passes a person standing along the highway, the driver sounds the horn. If the horn has a frequency of 400 Hz, what are the frequencies of the sound waves heard by the person (a) as the truck approaches and (b) after it has passed? (Assume that the speed of sound is 346 m/s.)

Thinking It Through. This situation is an application of the Doppler effect, Eq. 9.11, with a moving source and a stationary observer. In such problems, it is important to identify the data correctly.

Solution.

Given: $v_s = 96 \text{ km/h} = 27 \text{ m/s}$
$f_s = 400 \text{ Hz}$
$v = 346 \text{ m/s}$

Find: (a) f_o (observed frequency while truck is approaching)
(b) f_o (observed frequency while truck is moving away)

(a) From Eq. 9.11 with a minus sign (source approaching stationary observer),

$$f_o = \left(\frac{v}{v - v_s}\right) f_s = \left(\frac{346 \text{ m/s}}{346 \text{ m/s} - 27 \text{ m/s}}\right)(400 \text{ Hz}) = 434 \text{ Hz}$$

(b) A plus sign is used in Eq. 9.11 when the source is moving away:

$$f_o = \left(\frac{v}{v + v_s}\right) f_s = \left(\frac{346 \text{ m/s}}{346 \text{ m/s} + 27 \text{ m/s}}\right)(400 \text{ Hz}) = 371 \text{ Hz}$$

Follow-up Exercise. Suppose that the observer in this Example were initially moving toward and then past a stationary 400-Hz source at a speed of 96 km/h. What would be the observed frequencies? (Would they differ from those for the moving source?)

There are also cases in which both the source and the observer are moving, either toward or away from one another (see Exercise 102). We will not consider them mathematically here (but will do so conceptually in the next Example).

Conceptual Example 9.9 ■ It's All Relative: Moving Source and Moving Observer

Suppose a sound source and an observer are moving away from one another in opposite directions, each at half the speed of sound in air. Then the observer would (a) receive sound with a frequency higher than the source frequency, (b) receive sound with a frequency lower than the source frequency, (c) receive sound with the same frequency as the source frequency, or (d) receive no sound from the source.

Reasoning and Answer. As we know, when a source moves away from a stationary observer, the observed frequency is lower (Eq. 9.10). Similarly, when an observer moves away from a stationary source, the observed frequency is also lower (Eq. 9.13). With both source and observer moving away from each other in opposite directions, the combined effect would make the observed frequency even less, so neither (a) nor (c) is the answer.

It would appear that (b) is the correct answer, but we must logically eliminate (d) for completeness. Remember that the speed of sound relative to the air is constant. Therefore, (d) would be correct *only if the observer is moving faster than the speed of sound* relative to the air. Since the observer is moving at only half the speed of sound, (b) is the correct answer.

Think about it this way: Regardless of how fast the source is moving, the sound from the source is moving at the speed of sound through the air toward the observer. The observer is moving at only half the speed of sound through the air, so the sound from the source can easily reach and pass the observer. (For a mathematical expression for a moving source and a moving observer, see Exercise 102.)

Follow-up Exercise. What would be the situation if both the source and the observer were traveling in the same direction with the same subsonic speed? (*Subsonic*, as opposed to *supersonic*, refers to a speed that is less than the speed of sound in air.)

Problem-Solving Hint

You may find it difficult to remember whether a plus or minus sign is used in the general equations for the Doppler effect. Let your experience help you. For the common case of a stationary observer, the frequency of the sound increases when the source approaches, so the denominator in Eq. 9.11 must be smaller than the numerator. Accordingly, in this case you use the minus sign. When the source is receding, the frequency is lower. The denominator in Eq. 9.11 must then be larger than the numerator, and you use the plus sign. Similar reasoning will help you choose a plus or minus sign for the numerator in Eq. 9.14.

The Doppler effect also applies to light waves, although the equations describing the effect are different from those just given. When a distant light source such as a star moves away from us, the frequency of the light we receive from it is lowered. That is, the light is shifted toward the red (long wavelength) end of the spectrum, an effect known as a *Doppler red shift*. Similarly, the frequency of light from an object approaching us is increased—the light is shifted toward the blue (short wavelength) end of the spectrum, producing a *Doppler blue shift*. The magnitude of the shift is related to the speed of the source.

The Doppler shift of light from astronomical objects is very useful to astronomers. The rotation of a planet, a star, or some other body can be established by looking at the Doppler shifts of light from opposite sides of the object; because of the rotation, one side is receding (and hence is red shifted) and the other is approaching (and thus is blue shifted). Similarly, the Doppler shifts of light from stars in different regions of our galaxy, the Milky Way, indicate that the galaxy is rotating.

You have been subjected to a practical application of the Doppler effect if you have ever been caught speeding in your car by police radar, which uses reflected radio waves. (*Radar* stands for *ra*dio *d*etecting *a*nd *r*anging and is similar to underwater sonar, which uses ultrasound.) If radio waves are reflected from a parked car, the reflected waves return to the source with the same frequency. But for a car that is moving toward a patrol car, the reflected waves have a higher frequency, or are Doppler shifted. Actually, there is a double Doppler shift: In receiving the wave, the moving car acts like a moving observer (the first Doppler shift), and in reflecting the wave, the car acts like a moving source emitting a wave (the second Doppler shift). The magnitudes of the shifts depend on the speed of the car. A computer quickly calculates this speed and displays it for the police officer.

For other important applications of the Doppler effect, see the Insight on p. 310.

Sonic Booms

Consider a jet plane that can travel at supersonic speeds. As the speed of a moving source of sound approaches the speed of sound, the waves ahead of the source come close together (▼Fig. 9.12a). When a plane is traveling at the speed of sound,

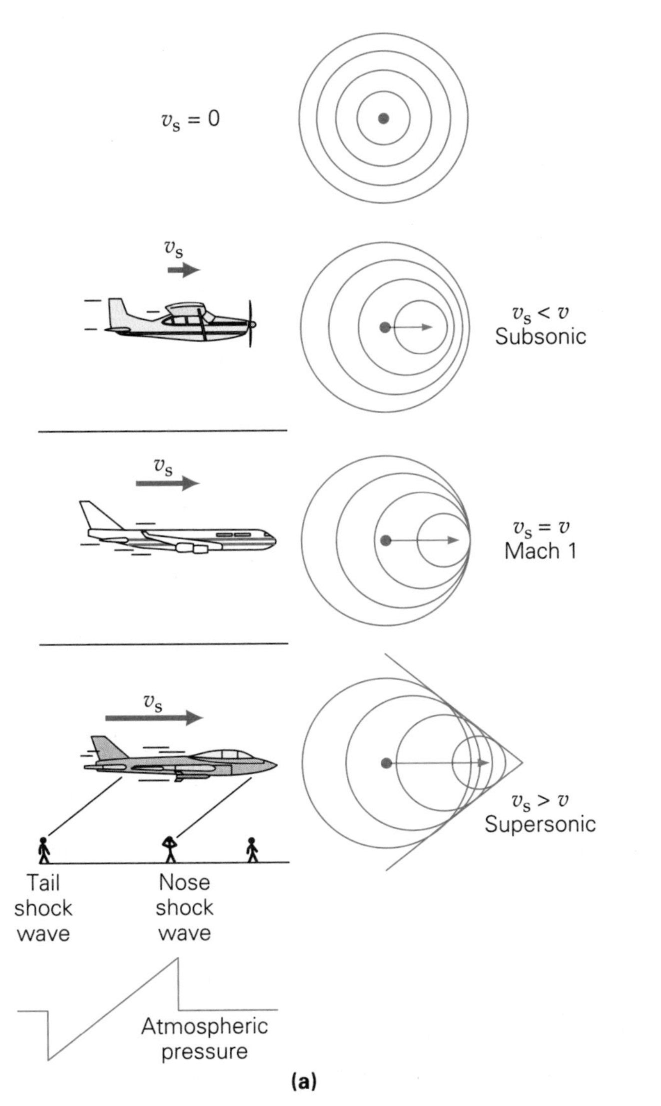

◀ **FIGURE 9.12 Bow waves and sonic booms** **(a)** When an aircraft exceeds the speed of sound in air, v_s, the sound waves form a pressure ridge, or shock wave. As the trailing shock wave passes over the ground, observers hear a sonic boom (actually, two booms, because shock waves are formed at the front and tail of the plane). **(b)** A bullet traveling at a speed of 500 m/s. Note the shock waves produced (and the turbulence behind the bullet). The image was made by using interferometry with polarized light and a pulsed laser, with an exposure time of 20 ns.

INSIGHT

Doppler Applications: Blood Cells and Raindrops

Blood cells Besides its well-known role of producing an image of a fetus (Fig. 9.3), ultrasound provides a variety of other uses in the medical field. Since the Doppler effect can detect and provide information on moving objects, it can be used to examine blood flow in the major arteries and veins in the arms and legs (Fig. 1). The reflectors here are red blood cells. The tests provide physicians information that helps them diagnose such things as blood clots, arterial occlusion (closing), and venous insufficiency. Ultrasound procedures offer a less invasive alternative to other diagnostic procedures, such as arteriography (X-ray pictures of an artery after the injection of a dye).

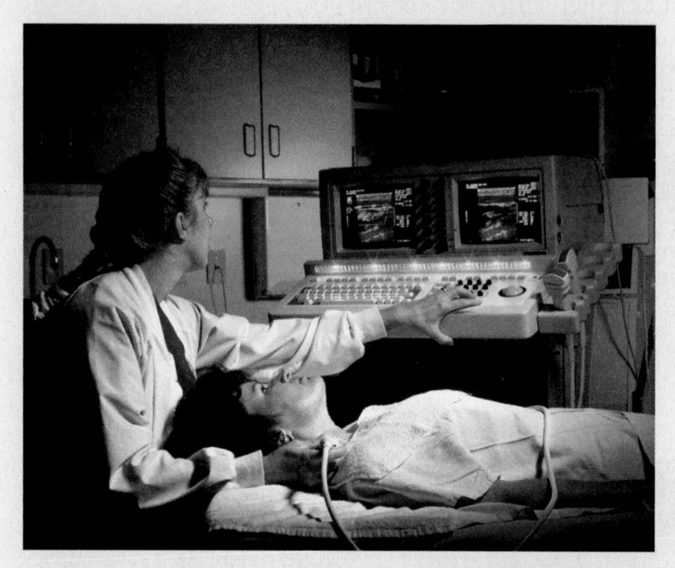

FIGURE 1 Medical application of the Doppler effect The Doppler effect is used to examine blood flow in major arteries and veins, here the carotid artery in the neck. Turbulence in the blood flow can be detected, which might reveal a narrowing of blood vessels, clots, or aneurysms (abnormal blood-filled dilatation of blook vessels).

Another medical use of ultrasound is the electrocardiogram, which is an examination of the heart. On a monitor, this ultrasonic procedure can display the beating movements of the heart, and the physician can see the heart's chambers, valves, and blood flow as it makes its way in and out of the organ.

While we are focusing on the body and sound, here is something for you to try: In a quiet room, put both thumbs in your ears firmly and listen. Do you hear a low pulsating sound? Why is this? Would you believe that you are hearing the sound, at about 25 Hz, made by the contracting and relaxing of the muscle fibers in your hands and arms? Although in the audible range, these sounds are not normally heard, because the human ear is relatively insensitive to low-frequency sounds.

Raindrops Radar has been used since the early 1940s to provide information about rainstorms and other forms of precipitation. This information is obtained from the intensity of the reflected signal. Such conventional radars can also detect the hooked (rotational) "signature" of a tornado, but only after the storm is well developed.

A major improvement in weather forecasting came about with the development of a radar system that could measure the Doppler frequency shift in addition to the magnitude of the echo signal reflected from precipitation (usually raindrops). The Doppler shift is related to the velocity of the precipitation blown by the wind.

A Doppler-based radar system (Fig. 2a) can penetrate a storm and monitor its wind speeds. The direction of a storm's

the waves can't outrun it, and they pile up in front. At supersonic speeds, the waves overlap. This overlapping of a large number of waves produces many points of constructive interference, forming a large pressure ridge, or *shock wave*. This kind of wave is sometimes called a *bow wave* because it is analogous to the wave produced by the bow of a boat moving through water at a speed greater than the speed of the water waves. Figure 9.12b shows the shock wave of a bullet traveling at 500 m/s.

From aircraft traveling at supersonic speed, the shock wave trails out to the sides and downward. When this pressure ridge passes over an observer on the ground, the large concentration of energy produces what is known as a **sonic boom**. There is really a double boom, because shock waves are formed at both ends of the aircraft. Under certain conditions, the shock waves can break windows and cause other damage to structures on the ground. (Sonic booms are no longer heard as frequently as in the past. Pilots are now instructed to fly supersonically only at high altitudes and away from populated areas.)

On a smaller scale, you have probably heard a "mini" sonic boom, the "crack" of a whip. This type of sonic boom is created by the transonic speed of the whip's tip; that is, the speed of the tip changes from subsonic to supersonic (and back).

A common misconception is that a sonic boom is heard only when a plane breaks the sound barrier. As an aircraft approaches the speed of sound, the pres-

INSIGHT

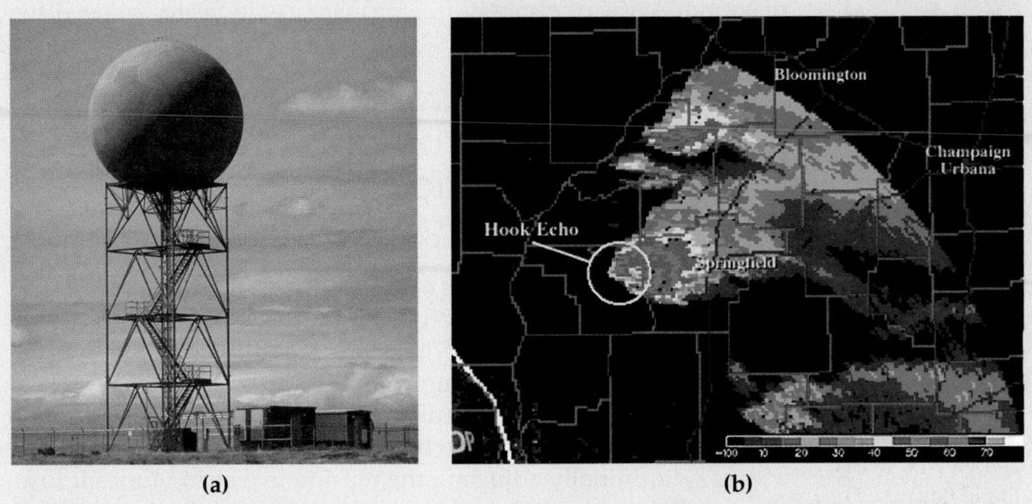

(a) (b)

FIGURE 2 Doppler radar **(a)** A Doppler radar installation. **(b)** Doppler radar depicts the precipitation inside a thunderstorm. A hook echo is a signature of a possible tornado.

wind-driven rain gives a wind "field" map of the affected region. Such maps provide strong clues of developing tornadoes, so meteorologists can detect them much earlier than was ever before possible (Fig. 2b). With Doppler radar, forecasters have been able to predict tornadoes as much as 20 min before they touch down, as compared with just over 2 min for conventional radar. Doppler radar has saved many lives with this increased warning time. The National Weather Service has a network of Doppler radars around the United States, and Doppler radar scans are now common on both TV weather forecasts and the Internet.

Doppler radars installed at major airports have another use. Several airplane crashes and near crashes have been attributed to downward wind bursts (also known as microbursts and downbursts). Such strong down drafts cause wind shears capable of forcing landing aircraft to crash.

Wind bursts generally result from high-speed downdrafts in the turbulence of thunderstorms, but they can also occur in clear air when rain evaporates high above ground. Since Doppler radar can detect the wind speed and the direction of raindrops in clouds, as well as dust and other objects floating in the air, it can provide an early warning against dangerous wind shear conditions. Two or three radar sites are needed to detect motions in two or three directions (dimensions), respectively.

Related Exercises: 58, 59

sure ridge in front of it is essentially a barrier that must be overcome with extra power. However, once supersonic speed is reached, the barrier is no longer there, and the shock waves, continuously created, trail behind the plane, producing booms along its ground path.

Ideally, the sound waves produced by a supersonic aircraft form a cone-shaped shock wave (▸Fig. 9.13). The waves travel outward with a speed v, and the speed of the source (plane) is v_s. Note from the figure that the angle between a line tangent to the spherical waves and the line along which the plane is moving is given by

$$\sin\theta = \frac{vt}{v_s t} = \frac{v}{v_s} = \frac{1}{M} \tag{9.15}$$

The inverse ratio of the speeds is called the **Mach number** (M), named after Ernst Mach (1838–1916), an Austrian physicist, who used it in studying supersonics, and is given by

$$M = \frac{v_s}{v} = \frac{1}{\sin\theta} \tag{9.16}$$

If v equals v_s, the plane is flying at the speed of sound, and the Mach number is 1 (i.e., $v_s/v = 1$). Therefore, a Mach number less than 1 indicates a subsonic speed, and a Mach number greater than 1 indicates a supersonic speed. In the latter case, the Mach number tells the speed of the aircraft in terms of a multiple of the speed of sound. A Mach number of 2, for instance, indicates a speed twice the speed of sound. Note that since $\sin\theta \leq 1$, no shock wave can exist unless $M \geq 1$.

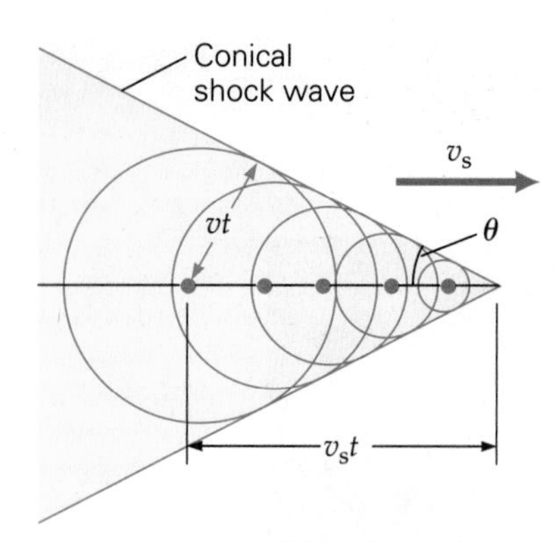

▲ **FIGURE 9.13 Shock wave cone and Mach number** When the speed of the source (v_s) is greater than the speed of sound in air (v), the interfering spherical sound waves form a conical shock wave that appears as a V-shaped pressure ridge when viewed in two dimensions. The angle θ is given by $\sin\theta = v/v_s$, and the inverse ratio v_s/v is called the Mach number.

9.6 Musical Instruments and Sound Characteristics

OBJECTIVE: **To explain some of the sound characteristics of musical instruments in physical terms.**

Musical instruments provide good examples of standing waves and boundary conditions. On some stringed instruments, different notes are produced by using finger pressure to vary the lengths of the strings (▾Fig. 9.14). The natural frequencies of a stretched string (fixed at each end, as is the case for the strings on an instrument) are $f_n = n(v/2L)$, where the speed of the wave in the string is given by $v = \sqrt{F_T/\mu}$. Initially adjusting the tension in a string tunes it to a particular (fundamental) frequency. Then the effective length of the string is varied by finger location and pressure.

Standing waves are also set up in wind instruments. For example, consider a pipe organ with fixed lengths of pipe, which may be open or closed (▸Fig. 9.15). An open pipe is open at both ends, and a closed pipe is closed at one end and open at the other (the end with the antinode). Analysis shows that the natural frequencies of the pipes are

$$f_n = \frac{v}{\lambda_n} = n\left(\frac{v}{2L}\right) = nf_1 \qquad n = 1, 2, 3, \ldots \qquad \textit{(natural frequencies for a pipe open on both ends)} \qquad (9.17)$$

and

$$f_m = \frac{v}{\lambda_m} = m\left(\frac{v}{4L}\right) = mf_1 \qquad m = 1, 3, 5, \ldots \qquad \textit{(natural frequencies for a pipe closed on both ends)} \qquad (9.18)$$

▲ **FIGURE 9.14 A shorter vibrating string, a higher frequency** Different notes are produced on stringed instruments such as guitars, violins, or cellos by placing a finger on a string to change its effective, or vibrating, length.

where v is the speed of sound in air. Note that the natural frequencies depend on the length of the pipe. This is an important consideration in a pipe organ (Fig. 9.15c), particularly in selecting the dominant or fundamental frequency. (The diameter of the pipe is also a factor, but is not considered in this simple analysis.)

The same physical principles apply to wind and brass instruments. In all of these, the human breath is used to create standing waves in an open tube. Most such instruments allow the player to vary the effective length of the tube and thus the pitch produced—either with the help of slides or valves that vary the actual length of tubing in which the air can resonate, as in most brasses, or by opening and closing holes in the tube, as in woodwinds (▸Fig. 9.16).

A musical note or tone is referenced to the fundamental vibrational frequency of an instrument. In musical terms, the first overtone is the second harmonic, the second overtone is the third harmonic, and so on. Note that for a closed organ pipe (Eq. 9.18), the even harmonics are missing.

Example 9.10 ■ Pipe Dreams: Fundamental Frequency

A particular open organ pipe has a length of 0.653 m. Taking the speed of sound in air to be 345 m/s, what is the fundamental frequency of this pipe?

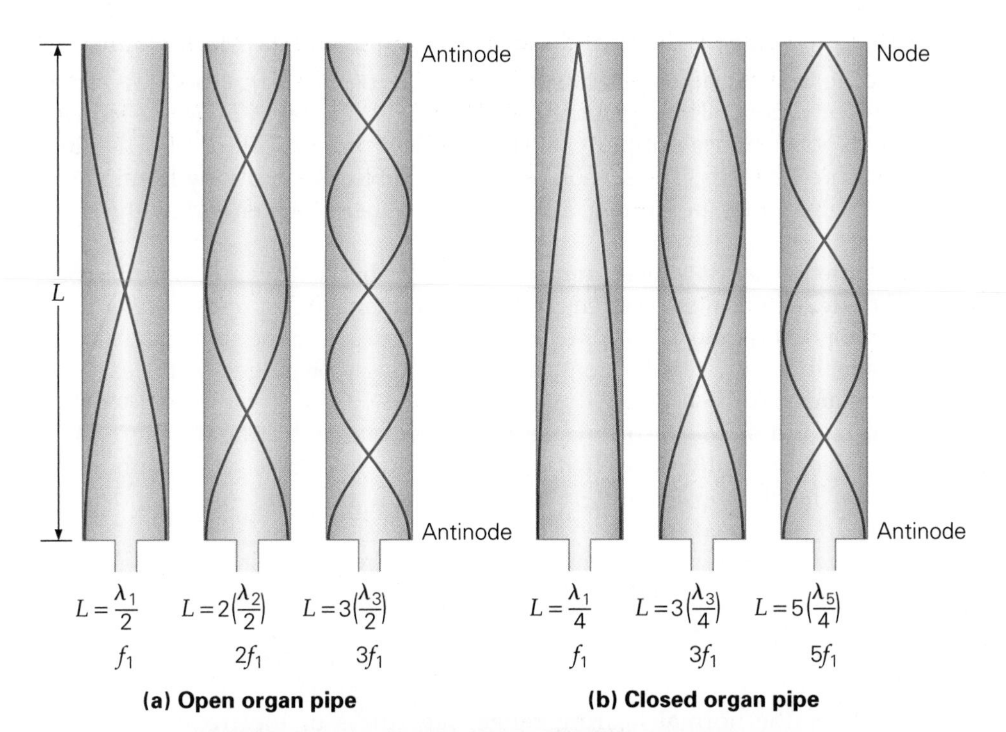

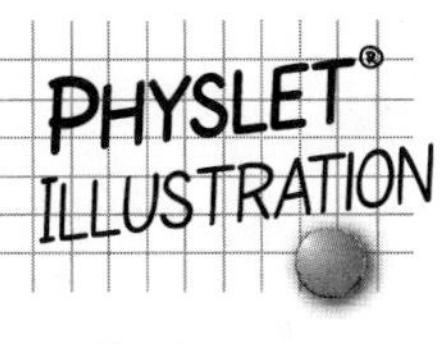

Standing Waves in a Pipe

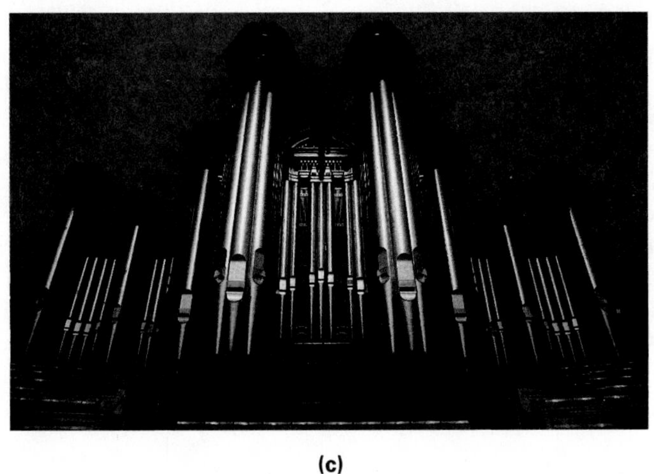

(c)

◀ **FIGURE 9.15 Organ pipes** Longitudinal standing waves (illustrated here as sinusoidal curves) are formed in vibrating air columns in pipes. **(a)** An open pipe has antinodes at both ends. **(b)** A closed pipe has a closed (node) end and an open (antinode) end. **(c)** A modern pipe organ. The pipes can be open or closed.

Thinking It Through. The fundamental frequency ($n = 1$) of an open pipe is given directly by Eq. 9.17. Physically, there is a half-wavelength ($\lambda/2$) in the length of the pipe, so $\lambda = 2L$.

Solution.

Given: $L = 0.653$ m
$v = 345$ m/s (speed of sound)

Find: f_1 (fundamental frequency)

With $n = 1$,

$$f_1 = \frac{v}{2L} = \frac{345 \text{ m/s}}{2(0.653 \text{ m})} = 264 \text{ Hz}$$

This frequency is middle C (C_4).

Follow-up Exercise. A closed organ pipe has a fundamental frequency of 256 Hz. What would be the frequency of its first overtone? Is this frequency audible?

Perceived sounds are described by terms whose meanings are similar to those used to describe the physical properties of sound waves. Physically, a wave is generally characterized by intensity, frequency, and waveform (harmonics). The corresponding terms used to describe the sensations of the ear are loudness, pitch, and quality (or timbre). These general correlations are shown in Table 9.3. However, the correspondence is not perfect. The physical properties are objective and can be measured directly. The sensory effects are subjective and vary from person to person. (Think of temperature as measured by a thermometer and by the sense of touch.)

Sound intensity and its measurement on the decibel scale were covered in Section 9.3. Loudness is related to intensity, but the human ear responds differently to sounds of different frequencies. For example, two tones with the same intensity (in watts per square meter), but different frequencies, might be judged by the ear to be different in loudness.

Frequency and *pitch* are often used synonymously, but again there is an objective–subjective difference: If the same low-frequency tone is sounded at two intensity levels, most people will say that the more intense sound has a lower pitch, or perceived frequency.

The curves in the graph of intensity level versus frequency shown in ▼Fig. 9.17 are called *equal-loudness contours* (or Fletcher–Munson curves, after the researchers who generated them). These contours join points representing intensity–frequency combinations that a person with average hearing judges to be equally loud. The top curve shows that the decibel level of the threshold of pain (120 dB) does not vary a great deal over the normal hearing range, regardless of the frequency of the sound. In contrast, the threshold of hearing, represented by the lowest contour, varies widely with frequency. For a tone with a frequency of 2000 Hz, the threshold of hearing is 0 dB, but a 20-Hz tone would have to have an intensity level of over 70 dB (the extrapolated y-intercept of the lowest curve) just to be heard.

It is interesting to note the dips (or minima) in the curves. These indicate that the ear is most sensitive to sounds with frequencies around 4000 Hz and 12 000 Hz. A tone with a frequency of 4000 Hz can be heard at intensity levels *below* 0 dB. The minima occur as a result of resonance in a closed cavity in the auditory canal (similar to a closed pipe). The length of the cavity is such that it has a fundamental resonance frequency of about 4000 Hz, resulting in extra sensitivity. As in a closed cavity, the next natural frequency is the third harmonic (see Eq. 9.18), which is three times the fundamental frequency, or about 12 000 Hz.

(a)

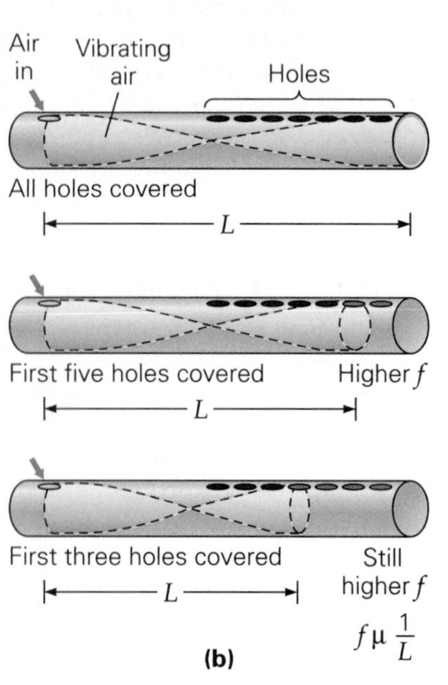

(b)

▲ **FIGURE 9.16 Wind instruments** **(a)** Wind instruments are essentially open tubes. (Here, Kenny G performs on a soprano saxophone at a Macy's Thanksgiving Day Parade.) **(b)** The effective length of the air column, and hence the pitch of the sound, is varied by opening and closing holes along the tube. The frequency f is inversely proportional to the effective length L of the air column.

▼ **FIGURE 9.17 Equal-loudness contours** The curves indicate tones that are judged to be equally loud, although they have different frequencies and intensity levels. For example, on the lowest contour, a 1000-Hz tone at 0 dB sounds as loud as a 50-Hz tone at 40 dB. Note that the frequency scale is logarithmic to compress the large frequency range.

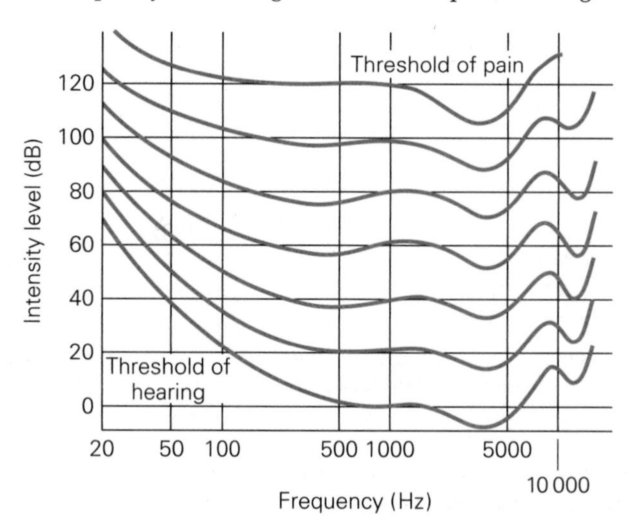

The **quality** of a tone is the characteristic that enables it to be distinguished from another tone of basically the same intensity and frequency. Tone quality depends on the waveform—specifically, the number of harmonics (overtones) present and their relative intensities (▼Fig. 9.18). The tone of a voice depends in large part on the vocal resonance cavities. One person can sing a tone with the same basic frequency and intensity as another, but different combinations of overtones give the two voices different qualities.

The notes of a musical scale correspond to certain frequencies; as we saw in Example 9.10, middle C (C_4) has a frequency of 264 Hz. When a note is played on an instrument, its assigned frequency is that of the first harmonic, which is the fundamental frequency. (The second harmonic is the first overtone, the third harmonic is the second overtone, and so on.) The fundamental frequency is dominant over the accompanying overtones that determine the sound quality of the instrument. The overtones which are produced depend on how an instrument is played. Whether a violin string is plucked or bowed, for example, can be discerned from the quality of identical notes.

TABLE 9.3 General Correlation between Perceptual and Physical Characteristics of Sound

Sensory Effect	*Physical Wave Property*
Loudness	Intensity
Pitch	Frequency
Quality (timbre)	Waveform (harmonics)

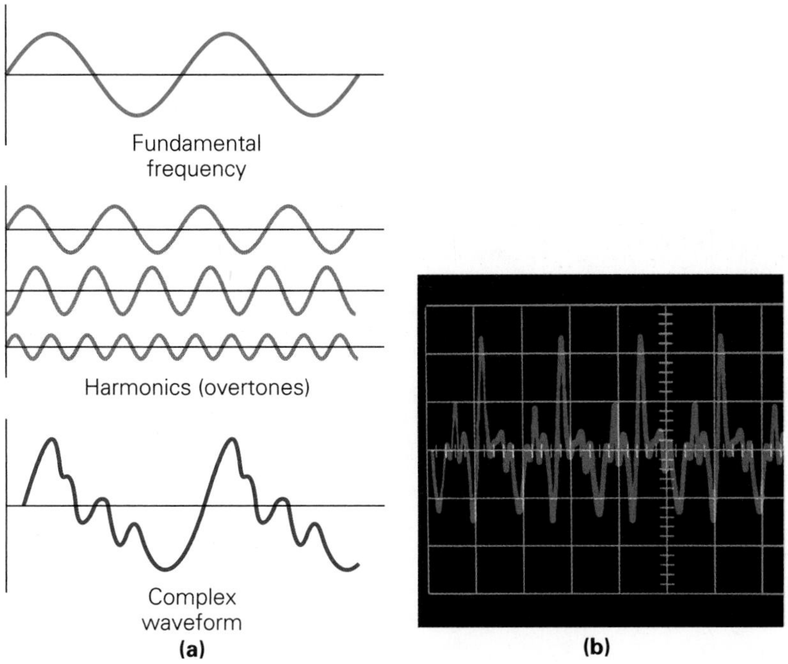

Fundamental frequency

Harmonics (overtones)

Complex waveform

(a)

(b)

◀ **FIGURE 9.18 Waveform and quality** **(a)** The superposition of sounds of different frequencies and amplitudes gives a complex waveform. The harmonics, or overtones, determine the quality of the sound. **(b)** The waveform of a violin tone is displayed on an oscilloscope.

Chapter Review

Important Concepts and Equations

- The sound frequency spectrum is divided into infrasonic ($f < 20$ Hz), audible ($20 \text{ Hz} < f < 20$ kHz), and ultrasonic ($f > 20$ kHz) frequency regions.
- The speed of sound in a medium depends on the elasticity of the medium and its density. In general, $v_{\text{solids}} > v_{\text{liquids}} > v_{\text{gases}}$.

Speed of sound in air (meters per second):

$$v = (331 + 0.6T_C) \text{ m/s} \quad (9.1)$$

- The intensity of a point source is inversely proportional to the square of the distance from the source.

Intensity of a point source:

$$I = \frac{P}{4\pi R^2} \quad \text{and} \quad \frac{I_2}{I_1} = \left(\frac{R_1}{R_2}\right)^2 \quad (9.2, 9.3)$$

- The sound intensity level is a logarithmic function of the sound intensity and is expressed in decibels (dB).

Intensity level (in decibels, dB):

$$\beta = 10 \log \frac{I}{I_o} \quad \text{where} \quad I_o = 10^{-12} \text{ W/m}^2 \quad (9.4)$$

- Sound wave interference of two point sources depends on phase difference as related to path-length difference. Sound waves that arrive at a point in phase reinforce each other (constructive interference); sound waves that arrive at a point out of phase cancel each other (destructive interference).

Phase difference (where ΔL is the path-length difference):

$$\Delta\theta = \frac{2\pi}{\lambda}(\Delta L) \tag{9.5}$$

Condition for constructive interference:

$$\Delta L = n\lambda \qquad (n = 0, 1, 2, 3, \dots) \tag{9.6}$$

Condition for destructive interference:

$$\Delta L = m\left(\frac{\lambda}{2}\right) \qquad (m = 1, 3, 5, \dots) \tag{9.7}$$

Beat frequency:

$$f_b = |f_1 - f_2| \tag{9.8}$$

- The Doppler effect depends on the velocities of the sound source and observer relative to still air. When the relative motion of the source and observer is toward each other, the observed pitch increases; when the relative motion of source and observer is away from each other, the observed pitch decreases.

Doppler effect:

$$f_o = \left(\frac{v}{v \pm v_s}\right)f_s = \left(\frac{1}{1 \pm \frac{v_s}{v}}\right)f_s \tag{9.11}$$

where v_s = *speed of source*
and v = *speed of sound*

$\begin{cases} - \text{for source moving toward stationary observer} \\ + \text{for source moving away from stationary observer} \end{cases}$

$$f_o = \left(\frac{v \pm v_o}{v}\right)f_s = \left(1 \pm \frac{v_o}{v}\right)f_s \tag{9.14}$$

where v_o = *speed of observer*
and v = *speed of sound*

$\begin{cases} + \text{for observer moving toward stationary source} \\ - \text{for observer moving away from stationary source} \end{cases}$

Angle for conical shock wave:

$$\sin\theta = \frac{vt}{v_s t} = \frac{v}{v_s} = \frac{1}{M} \tag{9.15}$$

Mach number:

$$M = \frac{v_s}{v} = \frac{1}{\sin\theta} \tag{9.16}$$

Natural frequencies of organ pipe open on both ends:

$$f_n = n\left(\frac{v}{2L}\right) = nf_1 \qquad (n = 1, 2, 3, \dots) \tag{9.17}$$

Natural frequencies of organ pipe closed on one end:

$$f_m = m\left(\frac{v}{4L}\right) = mf_1 \qquad (m = 1, 3, 5, \dots) \tag{9.18}$$

Exercises

9.1 Sound Waves *and* 9.2 The Speed of Sound

1. A sound wave with a frequency of 15 Hz is in what region of the sound spectrum? (a) audible, (b) infrasonic, (c) ultrasonic, or (d) supersonic.

2. A sound wave in air (a) is longitudinal, (b) is transverse, (c) has longitudinal and transverse components, or (d) travels faster than a sound wave through a liquid.

3. The speed of sound is generally greatest in (a) solids, (b) liquids, (c) gases, or (d) a vacuum.

4. The speed of sound in air (a) is about 1/3 km/s, (b) is about 1/5 mi/s, (c) depends on temperature, or (d) all of these.

5. CQ Suggest a possible explanation of why some flying insects produce buzzing sounds and some do not.

6. CQ Explain why sound travels faster in warmer than in colder air.

7. CQ Two sounds that differ in frequency are emitted from a single loudspeaker. Which sound will reach your ear first, the one with the lower or the higher frequency?

8. CQ The speed of sound in air depends on temperature. What effect, if any, should humidity have?

9. CQ When dogs sleep, they usually put their ear on the floor. Why do you suppose this is so? Is it related to people putting their ears on railroad tracks in Western movies?

10. ■ What is the speed of sound in air at (a) 10°C and (b) 20°C?

11. ■ The speed of sound in air on a summer day is 350 m/s. What is the air temperature?

12. ■ The thunder from a lightning flash is heard by an observer 3.0 s after she sees the flash. What is the approximate distance to the lightning strike in (a) kilometers and (b) miles?

13. ■ Sonar is used to map the ocean floor. If an ultrasonic signal is received 2.0 s after it is emitted, how deep is the ocean floor at that location?

14. ■ The wave speed in a liquid is given by $v = \sqrt{B/\rho}$, where B is the bulk modulus of the liquid and ρ is its density. Show that this equation is dimensionally correct. What about $v = \sqrt{Y/\rho}$ for a solid? (Y is Young's modulus.)

15. IE ■■ A tuning fork vibrates at a frequency of 256 Hz. (a) When the air temperature increases, the wavelength of the sound from the tuning fork (1) increases, (2) remains the same, or (3) decreases. Why? (b) If the temperature rises from 0°C to 20°C, what is the change in the wavelength?

16. ■■ Particles approximately 3.0×10^{-2} cm in diameter are to be scrubbed loose from machine parts in an aqueous ultrasonic cleaning bath. Above what frequency should the bath be operated to produce wavelengths of this size and smaller?

17. ■■ Medical ultrasound uses a frequency of around 20 MHz to diagnose human conditions and ailments. (a) If the speed of sound in tissue is 1500 m/s, what is the smallest detectable object? (b) If the penetration depth is about 200 wavelengths, how deep can this instrument penetrate?

18. ■■ Brass is an alloy of copper and zinc. Does the addition of zinc to copper cause an increase or a decrease in the speed of sound in brass rods compared to copper rods? Explain.

19. ■■ The speed of sound in steel is about 4.5 km/s. A steel rail is struck with a hammer, and an observer 0.30 km away has one ear to the rail. (a) How much time will elapse from the time the sound is heard through the rail until the time it is heard through the air? Assume that the air temperature is 20°C and that no wind is blowing. (b) How much time would elapse if the wind were blowing toward the observer at 36 km/h from where the rail was struck?

20. ■■ At a baseball game on a cool day (with an air temperature of 16°C), a fan hears the crack of the bat 0.25 s after observing the batter hit the ball. How far is the fan from home plate?

21. ■■ A 2000-Hz tone is sounded when the air temperature is 20°C and then again at 10°C. What is the percentage change in the wavelength of the sound between the higher and the lower temperature?

22. ■■ A person holds a rifle horizontally and fires at a target. The bullet has a muzzle speed of 200 m/s, and the person hears the bullet strike the target 1.00 s after firing it. The air temperature is 72°F. What is the distance to the target?

23. ■■ A freshwater dolphin sends ultrasonic sound to locate a prey. If the echo off the prey is received by the dolphin 0.12 second after being sent, how far is the prey from the dolphin?

24. ■■ The size of your eardrum (the tympanum; see Fig. 2 in the Insight on page 294) partially determines the upper frequency limit of your audible region, usually between 16 000 Hz and 20 000 Hz. If the wavelength is on the order of twice the diameter of the eardrum and the air temperature is 20°C, how wide is your eardrum? Is your answer reasonable?

25. IE ■■■ On hiking up a mountain that has several overhanging cliffs, a climber drops a stone at the first cliff to determine its height by measuring the time it takes to hear the stone hit the ground. (a) At a second cliff that is twice the height of the first, the measured time of the sound from the dropped stone is (1) less than double, (2) double, or (3) more than double that of the first. Why? (b) If the measured time is 4.8 s for the stone dropping from the first cliff, and the air temperature is 20°C, how high is the cliff? (c) If the height of a third cliff is three times that of the first one, what would be the measured time for a stone dropped there to reach the ground?

26. ■■■ Sound propagating through air at 30°C passes through a vertical cold front into air that is 4.0°C. If the sound has a frequency of 2400 Hz, by what percentage does its wavelength change in crossing the boundary?

9.3 Sound Intensity and Sound Intensity Level

27. If the air temperature increases, would the sound intensity from a constant-output point source (a) increase, (b) decrease, or (c) remain unchanged?

28. The decibel scale is referenced to a standard intensity of (a) 1.0 W/m^2, (b) 10^{-12} W/m^2, (c) normal conversation, or (d) the threshold of pain.

29. CQ The Richter scale, used to measure the intensity level of earthquakes, is a logarithmic scale, as is the decibel scale. Why are such scales used?

30. **CQ** Can there be negative decibel levels, such as −10 dB? If so, what would these mean?

31. ■ Assuming that the diameter of your eardrum is 1 cm (see Exercise 24), what is the sound power received by the eardrum at the threshold of (a) hearing and (b) pain?

32. ■ Calculate the intensity generated by a 1.0-W point source of sound at a location (a) 3.0 m and (b) 6.0 m from it.

33. **IE** ■ (a) If the distance from a point sound source triples, the sound intensity will be (1) 3, (2) 1/3, (3) 9, or (4) 1/9 times the original value. Why? (b) By how many times must the distance from a point source be increased to reduce the sound intensity by half?

34. ■ Calculate the intensity level for (a) the threshold of hearing and (b) the threshold of pain.

35. ■ Find the intensity levels in decibels for sounds with intensities of (a) 10^{-2} W/m^2, (b) 10^{-6} W/m^2, and (c) 10^{-15} W/m^2.

36. ■ If the intensity of one sound is 10^{-4} W/m^2 and the intensity of another is 10^{-2} W/m^2, what is the difference in their intensity levels?

37. **IE** ■■ (a) If the power of a sound source doubles, the intensity level at a certain distance from the source (1) increases, (2) exactly doubles, or (3) decreases. Why? (b) What are the intensity levels at a distance of 10 m from a 5.0-W and a 10-W source, respectively?

38. ■■ What is the intensity of a sound that has an intensity level of (a) 50 dB or (b) 90 dB? (a)

39. ■■ Noise levels for some common aircraft are given in Table 9.4. What are the lowest and highest intensities for (a) takeoff and (b) landing?

TABLE 9.4 Takeoff and Landing Noise Levels for Some Common Commercial Jet Aircraft*

Aircraft	*Takeoff noise (dB)*	*Landing noise (dB)*
737	85.7–97.7	99.8–105.3
747	89.5–110.0	103.8–107.8
DC-10	98.4–103.0	103.8–106.6
L-1011	95.9–99.3	101.4–102.8

*Noise level readings are taken from 198 m (650 ft). The range depends on the aircraft model and the type of engine used.

40. **IE** ■■ If the distance to a sound source is halved, (a) will the sound intensity level change by a factor of (1) 2, (2) 1/2, (3) 4, (4) 1/4, or (5) none of the above? Why? (b) What is the change in the sound intensity level?

41. ■■ What is the intensity level of a 23-dB sound after being amplified (a) 10 thousand times, (b) a million times, (c) a billion times?

42. ■■ A tape player has a signal-to-noise ratio of 53 dB. How many times larger is the intensity of the signal than that of the background noise?

43. ■■ The sound intensity levels for a machine shop and a quiet library are 90 dB and 40 dB, respectively. (a) What is each intensity? (b) How many times greater is the intensity of the sound in the machine shop than that in the library?

44. **IE** ■■ A dog's bark has a sound intensity level of 40 dB. (a) If two of the same dogs are barking, the intensity level is (1) less than 40 dB, (2) between 40 dB and 80 dB, or (3) 80 dB. (b) What would be the intensity level?

45. ■■ At a rock concert, the average sound intensity level for a person in a front-row seat is 110 dB for a single band. If all the bands scheduled to play produce sound of that same intensity, how many of them would have to play simultaneously for the sound level to be at or above the threshold of pain?

46. ■■ At a distance of 10.0 m from a point source, the intensity level is measured to be 70 dB. At what distance from the source will the intensity level be 40 dB?

47. ■■ At a 4th of July celebration, a firecracker explodes (▼Fig. 9.19). Considering the firecracker to be a point source, what are the intensities heard by observers at points B, C, and D, relative to that heard by the observer at A?

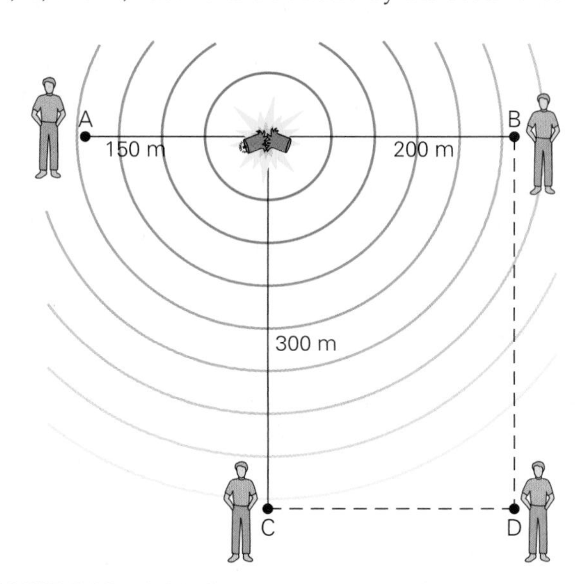

▲ **FIGURE 9.19 A big bang** See Exercise 47.

48. ■■ A person standing 4.0 m from a wall shouts such that the sound strikes the wall with an intensity of 2.5×10^{-4} W/m^2. Assuming that the wall absorbs 20% of the incident energy and reflects the rest, what is the sound intensity level just before and after the sound is reflected?

49. ■■ A gas-powered lawn mower is rated at 95 dB. (a) What is the sound intensity for this mower? (b) How

many times more intense is the sound of this mower than that of an electric-powered mower rated at 83 dB?

50. ■■■ A 1000-Hz tone from a loudspeaker has an intensity level of 100 dB at a distance of 2.5 m. If the speaker is assumed to be a point source, how far from the speaker will the sound have intensity levels (a) of 60 dB and (b) barely high enough to be heard?

51. ■■■ A bee produces a buzzing sound that is barely audible to a person 3.0 m away. How many bees would have to be buzzing at that distance to produce a sound with an intensity level of 50 dB?

9.4 Sound Phenomena *and* 9.5 The Doppler Effect

52. Beats are the direct result of (a) interference, (b) refraction, (c) diffraction, or (d) the Doppler effect.

53. Police radar makes use of (a) beats, (b) Doppler effect, (c) interference, or (d) sonic boom.

54. CQ Do interference beats have anything to do with the "beat" of music? Explain.

55. CQ (a) Is there a Doppler effect if a sound source and an observer are moving with the same velocity? (b) What would be the effect if a moving source accelerated toward a stationary observer?

56. CQ How fast would a "jet fish" have to swim to create an aquatic sonic boom?

57. CQ As a person walks *in between* a pair of loudspeakers that produce tones of the same amplitude and frequency, he hears a varying sound intensity. Explain.

58. CQ How can a Doppler radar used in weather forecasting measure both the location and motion of the clouds?

59. CQ Red light has a lower frequency than blue light. If an orange star appears red to us (this is the famous redshift in astronomy), what can you conclude about the motion of the star? Also, propose a method of measuring the velocity of the star.

60. ■ Two sound waves with the same wavelength, 0.50 m, arrive at a point after having traveled (a) 2.50 m and 3.75 m and (b) 3.25 m and 8.25 m, respectively. What type of interference occurs in each case?

61. ■ Two adjacent point sources, A and B, are directly in front of an observer and emit identical 1000-Hz tones. To what closest distance behind source B would source A have to be moved for the observer to hear no sound? (Assume that the air temperature is 20°C and ignore the falling off of intensity with distance.)

62. ■ A violinist and a pianist simultaneously sound notes with frequencies of 436 Hz and 440 Hz, respectively. What beat frequency will the musicians hear?

63. IE ■ A violinist tuning her instrument to a piano note of 264 Hz detects three beats per second. (a) The frequency of the violin could be (1) less than 264 Hz, (2) equal to 264 Hz, (3) greater than 264 Hz, or (4) both (1) and (3). Why? (b) What are the possible frequencies of the violin tone?

64. ■ What is the frequency heard by a person driving 50 km/h directly toward a factory whistle ($f = 800$ Hz) if the air temperature is 0°C?

65. IE ■ On a day with a temperature of 20°C and no wind blowing, the frequency heard by a moving person from a 500-Hz stationary siren is 520 Hz. (a) The person is (1) moving toward, (2) moving away from, or (3) stationary relative to the siren. Why? (b) What is the person's speed?

66. ■■ While standing near a railroad crossing, you hear a train horn. The frequency emitted by the horn is 400 Hz. If the train is traveling at 90.0 km/h and the air temperature is 25°C, what is the frequency you hear (a) when the train is approaching and (b) after it has passed?

67. ■■ Two identical strings on different cellos are tuned to the 440-Hz A note. The peg holding one of the strings slips, so its tension is decreased by 1.5%. What is the beat frequency heard when the strings are then played together?

68. ■■ How fast, in kilometers per hour, must a sound source be moving toward you to make the observed frequency 5.0% greater than the true frequency? (Assume that the speed of sound is 340 m/s.)

69. ■■ What is the half-angle of the shock wave of a jet aircraft just as it breaks the sound barrier?

70. IE ■■ On transatlantic flights, the supersonic transport (SST) Concorde flies at a speed of Mach 1.5. (a) If the Concorde were to fly faster than Mach 1.5, the half-angle of the conical shock wave would (1) increase, (2) remain the same, or (3) decrease. Why? (b) What is the half-angle of the conical shock wave formed by the Concorde at Mach 1.5?

71. ■■ The half-angle of the conical shock wave formed by a supersonic jet is 35°. What are (a) the Mach number of the aircraft and (b) the actual speed of the aircraft if the air temperature is −20°C?

72. ■■■ Two point-source loudspeakers are a certain distance apart, and a person stands 12.0 m in front of one of them on a line perpendicular to the baseline of the speakers. If the speakers emit identical 1000-Hz tones, what is their minimum nonzero separation so that the observer hears little or no sound? (Take the speed of sound to be exactly 340 m/s.)

73. ■■■ A bystander hears a siren vary in frequency from 476 Hz to 404 Hz as a fire truck approaches, passes by, and moves away on a straight street (▼Fig. 9.20). What is the speed of the truck? (Take the speed of sound in air to be 343 m/s.)

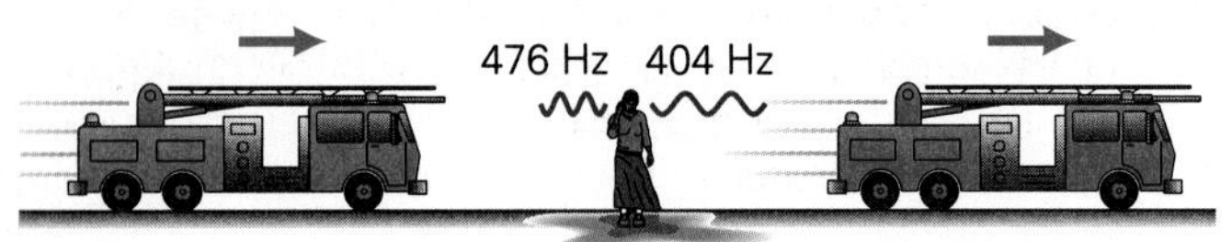

▲ **FIGURE 9.20 The siren's wail** See Exercise 73.

74. ■■■ Bats emit sounds of frequencies around 35.0 kHz and use echolocation to find their prey. If a bat is moving with a speed of 12.0 m/s toward an insect at an air temperature of 20.0°C, (a) what frequency is heard by the insect? (b) What frequency is heard by the bat from the reflected sound? (c) Would the speed of the bat affect the answers?

9.6 Musical Instruments and Sound Characteristics

75. The human ear can hear tones best at (a) 1000 Hz, (b) 4000 Hz, (c) 6000 Hz, or (d) all frequencies.

76. The quality of sound depends on its (a) waveform, (b) frequency, (c) speed, or (d) intensity.

77. CQ (a) After a snowfall, why does it seem particularly quiet? (b) Why do empty rooms sound hollow? (c) Why do people's voices sound fuller or richer when they sing in the shower?

78. CQ Why aren't the frets on a guitar evenly spaced?

79. CQ Is it possible for an open organ pipe and an organ pipe closed at one end, each of the same length, to produce notes of the same frequency? Justify your answer.

80. CQ When you blow across the top of a bottle with water in it, why does the frequency of the sound increase with increasing levels of water?

81. CQ Why are there no even harmonics in a pipe that is closed on one end?

82. ■ The first three natural frequencies of an organ pipe are 126 Hz, 378 Hz, and 630 Hz. (a) Is the pipe an open or a closed one? (b) (b) Taking the speed of sound in air to be 340 m/s, find the length of the pipe.

83. ■ A closed organ pipe has a fundamental frequency of 528 Hz (a C note) at 20°C. What is the fundamental frequency of the pipe when the temperature is 0°C?

84. ■ The human ear canal is about 2.5 cm long. It is open at one end and closed at the other. (See Fig. 2 in the Insight on p. 295.) (a) What is the fundamental frequency of the ear canal at 20°C? (b) To what frequency is the ear most sensitive? (c) If a person's ear canal is longer than 2.5 cm, is the fundamental frequency higher or lower than that in (a)? Explain.

85. ■■ An organ pipe that is closed at one end has a length of 0.90 m. At 20°C, what is the distance between a node and an adjacent antinode for (a) the second harmonic and (b) the third harmonic?

86. ■■ An open organ pipe and an organ pipe that is closed at one end both have lengths of 0.52 m at 20°C. What is the fundamental frequency of each pipe?

87. IE ■■ When all of its holes are closed, a flute is essentially a tube that is open at both ends, with the length being from the mouthpiece to the far end (as in Fig. 9.16b). If a hole is open, then the length of the tube is effectively from the mouthpiece to the hole. (a) Is the position at the mouthpiece (1) a node, (2) an antinode, or (c) neither a node nor an antinode? Why? (b) If the lowest fundamental frequency on a flute is 262 Hz, what is the minimum length of the flute at 20°C? (c) If a note of frequency 440 Hz is to be played, which hole should be open? Express your answer as a distance from the hole to the mouthpiece.

88. ■■ A tuning fork with a frequency of 440 Hz is held above a resonance tube that is partially filled with water. Assuming that the speed of sound in air is 342 m/s, for what three smallest heights of the air column will resonance occur? Draw the longitudinal standing waves in the air columns for each height. [*Hint*: For resonance to occur, the frequency of the tuning fork must match that of the tube.]

89. ■■■ An organ pipe that is closed at one end is filled with helium. The pipe has a fundamental frequency of 660 Hz in air at 0°C. What is the pipe's fundamental frequency with the helium in it?

Additional Exercises

90. Two identical sources producing 440-Hz tones are located 6.97 m and 8.90 m, respectively, from an observation point. If the air temperature that day is 15°C, how do the waves interfere at the point?

91. If a person standing 30.0 m from a 550-Hz point source moves 5.0 m closer to the source, by what factor does the sound intensity change?

92. An office in an e-commerce company has 50 computers, which generate a sound intensity level of 40 dB (from the keyboards). The office manager tries to cut the noise to half as loud by removing 25 computers. Does he achieve his goal? What is the intensity level generated by 25 computers?

93. How fast must an observer be moving toward a 500-Hz siren so that she hears double the frequency?

94. The intensity levels of two people holding a conversation are 60.0 dB and 65.0 dB, respectively. What is the intensity level of the combined sounds?

95. The intensity level of a sound is 90 dB at a certain distance from its source. How much energy falls on an eardrum with a diameter of 1.0 cm in 5.0 s?

96. A jet flies at a speed of Mach 2.0. What is the half-angle of the conical shock wave formed by the aircraft? Can you tell the speed of the shock wave?

97. The note A (440 Hz) is produced by a stringed musical instrument. The air temperature is 20°C. Approximately how many vibrations does the string make before the sound reaches a person 30 m away?

98. A person drops a stone into a deep well and hears it splash 3.16 s later. How deep is the well? (Assume the air temperature in the well to be 10°C.)

99. The frequency of an ambulance siren is 700 Hz. What are the frequencies heard by a stationary pedestrian as the ambulance approaches and passes her at a speed of 90.0 km/h? (Assume that the air temperature is 20°C).

100. One hunter sees another who is 300 km away fire his rifle. (Smoke comes out of the barrel.) If the air temperature is 5°C, how long will it be until the first hunter hears the shot? (Assume no wind.)

101. An open organ pipe has a length of 0.75 m. What would be the length of an organ pipe closed at one end whose third harmonic ($m = 3$) is the same as the fundamental frequency of the open pipe?

102. ■■ Show that the general equation of the Doppler effect for a moving source and a moving observer is given by

$$f_o = f_s\left(\frac{v \pm v_o}{v \mp v_s}\right)$$

using the sign convention of Eqs. 9.11 and 9.14.

103. ■■ A fire truck travels at a speed of 90 km/h with its siren emitting sound at a frequency of 500 Hz. What is the frequency heard by a passenger in a car traveling at 65 km/h in the oncoming lane to the fire truck (a) approaching it and (b) moving away from it? [*Hint*: See Exercise 102, and take the speed of sound to be 354 m/s. (It is a hot day.)]

CHAPTER 10 Reflection and Refraction of Light

We live in a visual world, surrounded by eye-catching images such as that shown in the photo. How these images are formed is something we take largely for granted—until we see something that we can't easily explain. Optics is the study of light and vision. Human vision requires light, specifically what we call visible light. The broad definition of *visible light* is "any radiation in or near the visible region of the electromagnetic spectrum." For our study, this definition includes infrared and ultraviolet radiation. Similar optical properties, such as reflection and refraction, are shared by all electromagnetic waves. Light acts like a wave in its propagation and as a particle when it interacts with matter.

In this chapter, we will investigate the basic optical phenomena of reflection, refraction, total internal reflection, and dispersion. The principles that govern reflection explain the behavior of mirrors, while those that govern refraction explain the properties of lenses. With the aid of these and other optical principles, we can understand many optical phenomena that we experience every day: why a glass prism spreads out light into a spectrum of colors, what causes mirages, how rainbows are formed, and why the legs of a person standing in a lake or swimming pool seem to shorten. We will also explore some less familiar territory, including the fascinating field of fiber optics.

A simple geometrical approach, involving straight lines and angles, can be used to investigate many aspects of the properties of light, especially how light propagates. For these purposes, we need not be concerned with the physical (wave) nature of electromagnetic waves.

10.1 Wave Fronts and Rays

OBJECTIVE: **To define and explain the concepts of wave fronts and rays.**

Waves, electromagnetic or otherwise, are conveniently described in terms of wave fronts. A **wave front** is the line or surface defined by adjacent portions of a wave that are in phase. If an arc is drawn along one of the crests of a circular water wave moving out from a point source, all the particles on the arc will be in phase (▸Fig. 10.1a). An arc along a wave trough would work equally well. For a three-dimensional spherical wave, such as a sound or light wave emitted from a point source, the wave front is a spherical surface rather than a circle.

Very far from the source, the curvature of a short segment of a circular or spherical wave front is extremely small. Such a segment may be approximated as a linear wave front (in two dimensions) or a **plane wave front** (in three dimensions), just as we take the surface of the Earth to be locally flat (Fig. 10.1b). A plane wave front can also be produced directly by a luminous flat surface. In a uniform medium, wave fronts propagate outward from the source at a speed characteristic of the medium. We saw this for sound waves in Chapter 9, and the same occurs for light, although at a much faster speed. The speed of light is greatest in a vacuum: $c = 3.00 \times 10^8$ m/s.

The geometrical description of a wave in terms of wave fronts tends to neglect the fact that the wave is actually oscillating. This simplification is carried a step further with the concept of a ray. As illustrated in Fig. 10.1, a line drawn perpendicular to a series of wave fronts and pointing in the direction of propagation is called a **ray**. Note that a ray points in the direction of the energy flow of a wave. A plane wave is assumed to travel in a straight line in a medium in the direction of its rays, perpendicular to its plane wave fronts. A beam of light can be represented by a group of rays or simply as a single ray (▾Fig. 10.2). The representation of light as rays is adequate and convenient for describing many optical phenomena.

The use of the geometrical representations of wave fronts and rays to explain phenomena such as the reflection and refraction of light is called **geometrical optics**. However, certain other phenomena, such as the interference of light, cannot be treated in this manner and must be explained in terms of actual wave characteristics.

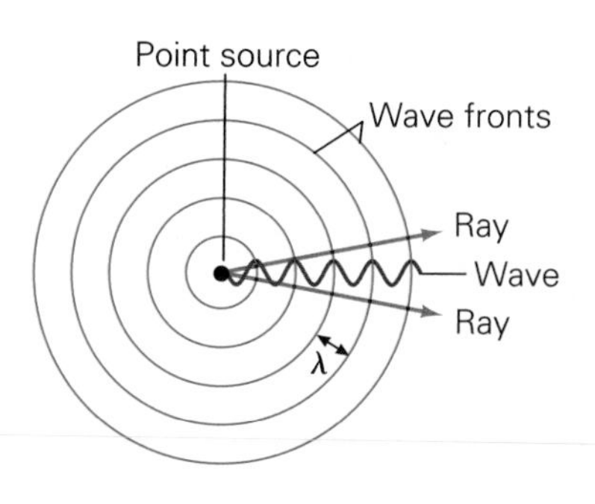

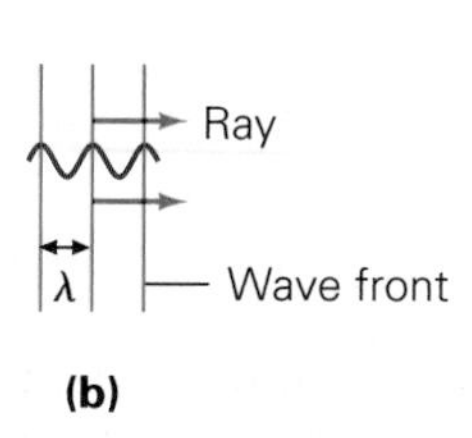

▲ **FIGURE 10.1 Wave fronts and rays** A wave front is defined by adjacent points on a wave that are in phase, such as those along wave crests or troughs. **(a)** Near a point source, the wave fronts are circular in two dimensions and spherical in three dimensions. **(b)** Very far from a point source, the wave fronts are approximately linear or planar. A line perpendicular to a wave front in the direction of the wave's propagation is called a ray.

10.2 Reflection

OBJECTIVES: **To (a) explain the law of reflection and (b) distinguish between regular (specular) and irregular (diffuse) reflection.**

The reflection of light is an optical phenomenon of enormous importance: If light were not reflected to our eyes by objects around us, we wouldn't see the objects at all. **Reflection** involves the absorption and reemission of light by means of complex electromagnetic vibrations in the atoms of the reflecting medium. However, the phenomenon is easily described by using rays.

A light ray incident on a surface is described by an **angle of incidence** (θ_i). This angle is measured relative to a *normal*—a line perpendicular to the reflecting surface (▸Fig. 10.3). Similarly, the reflected ray is described by an **angle of reflection** (θ_r), also measured from the normal. The relationship between these angles is given by the **law of reflection**:

The angle of incidence is equal to the angle of reflection, or

$$\theta_i = \theta_r \quad \textit{law of reflection} \tag{10.1}$$

Two other attributes of reflection are that the incident ray, the reflected ray, and the normal all lie in the same plane, which is sometimes called the plane of incidence, and that the incident and the reflected rays are on opposite sides of the normal.

When the reflecting surface is smooth, the reflected rays from parallel incident rays are also parallel (▸Fig. 10.4a). This type of reflection is called **regular**, or **specular, reflection** (Fig. 10.4b). The reflection from a flat mirror is specular or regular reflection. If the reflecting surface is rough, however, the reflected rays are not parallel, because of the irregular nature of the surface (▸Fig. 10.5). This type of reflection is termed **irregular**, or **diffuse, reflection**. The reflection of light from

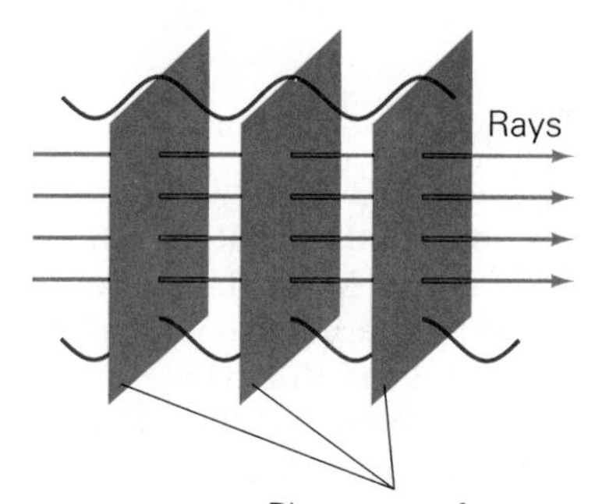

▲ **FIGURE 10.2 Light rays** A plane wave travels in a direction perpendicular to its wave fronts. A beam of light can be represented by a group of parallel rays (or by a single ray).

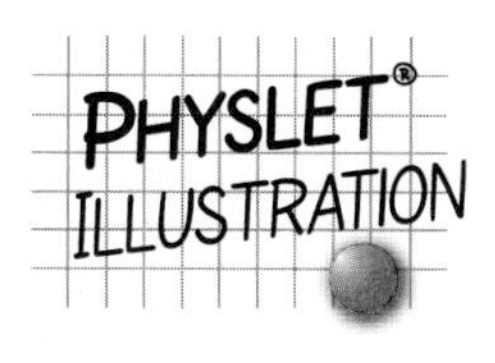

Law of Reflection

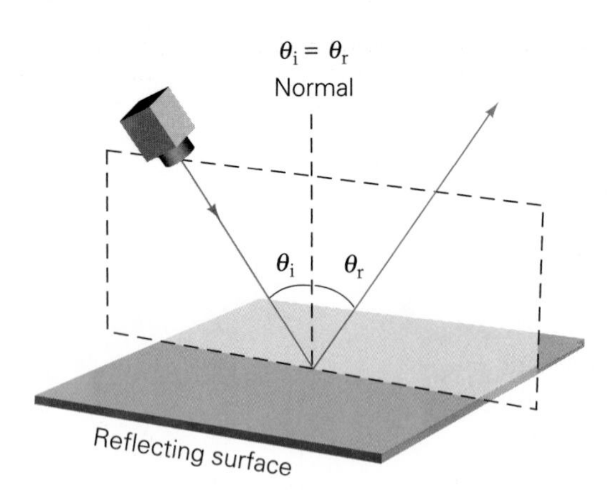

▲ **FIGURE 10.3 The law of reflection** According to the law of reflection, the angle of incidence (θ_i) is equal to the angle of reflection (θ_r). Note that the angles are measured relative to a normal (a line perpendicular to the reflecting surface). The normal and the incident and reflected rays always lie in the same plane.

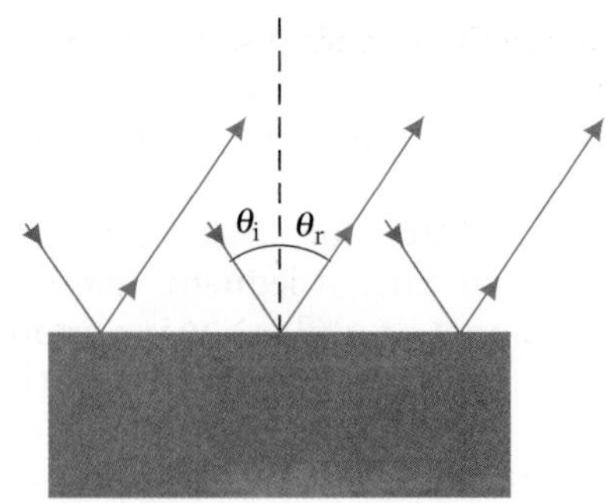

(a) Regular, or specular, reflection

(b)

▲ **FIGURE 10.4 Regular (specular) reflection** **(a)** When a light beam is reflected from a smooth surface and the reflected rays are parallel, the reflection is said to be regular or specular. **(b)** Regular, or specular, reflection from a smooth water surface produces an almost perfect mirror image of salt mounds at this Australian salt mine.

this page is an example of diffuse reflection. The Insight "Dark, Rainy Night," on p. 326, discusses more about the difference between specular and diffuse reflection in a real-life situation.

Note in Fig. 10.4a and Fig. 10.5 that the law of reflection still applies locally to both specular and diffuse reflection. However, the type of reflection involved determines whether we see images from a reflecting surface. In specular reflection, the reflected, parallel rays produce an image when they are viewed by an optical system such as an eye or a camera (Fig. 10.4b). Diffuse reflection does not produce an image, because the light is reflected in various directions.

Both experience with friction and direct investigations show that all surfaces are rough on a microscopic scale. What, then, determines whether reflection is specular or diffuse? In general, if the dimensions of the surface irregularities are greater than the wavelength of the light, the reflection is diffuse. Therefore, to make a good mirror, glass (with a metal coating) or metal must be polished at least until the surface irregularities are about the same size as the wavelength of light. The wavelength of visible light is on the order of 10^{-7} m. (You will learn more about reflection from a mirror in the Learn by Drawing exercise presented in Example 10.1.)

It is because of diffuse reflection that we are able to see illuminated objects, such as the Moon. If the Moon's spherical surface were smooth, only the reflected sunlight from a small region would come to an observer on the Earth, and only that small illuminated area would be seen. Also, you can see the beam of light from a flashlight or spotlight because of diffuse reflection from dust and particles in the air.

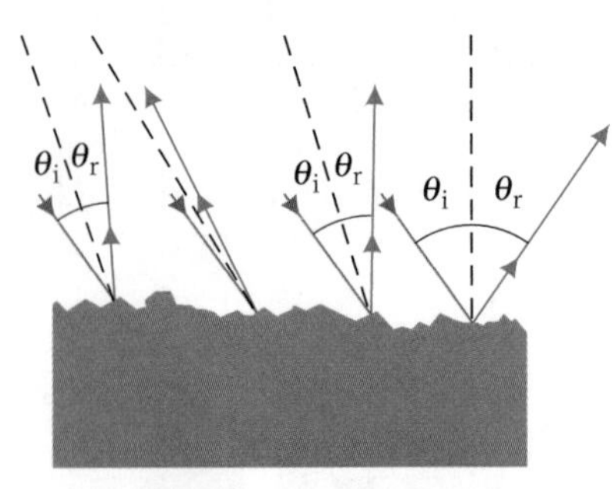

▲ **FIGURE 10.5 Irregular (diffuse) reflection** Reflected rays from a relatively rough surface, such as this page, are not parallel; the reflection is said to be irregular or diffuse. (Note that the law of reflection still applies locally to each individual ray.)

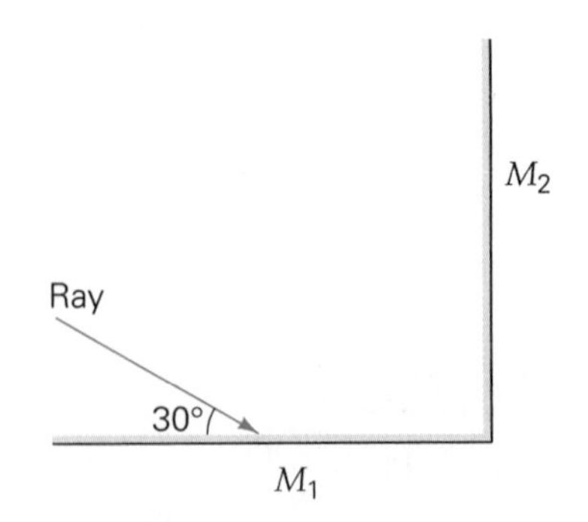

▲ **FIGURE 10.6 Trace the ray** See Example 10.1.

Example 10.1 ■ Learn by Drawing: Tracing the Reflecting Rays

Two mirrors, M_1 and M_2, are perpendicular to each other, and a light ray is incident on one of the mirrors as shown in ◂Fig. 10.6. (a) Sketch a diagram to trace the path of the light ray. (b) Find the direction of the ray after it is reflected by M_2.

Thinking It Through. The law of reflection can be used to determine the direction of the ray after it reaches both mirrors.

Note: Drawing diagrams like these is extremely important in the study of geometrical optics.

Solution.

Given: $\theta = 30°$ (angle relative to M_1) *Find:* (a) Sketch a diagram tracing the light ray
(b) θ_{r_2} (angle of reflection from M_2)

(a) and (b) follow steps 1–4 on the Learn by Drawing illustration:

(a) 1. Since the incident and reflected rays are all measured from the normal (a line perpendicular to the reflecting surface), we draw the normal to mirror M_1 at the point the incident ray hits M_1. From geometry, it can be seen that the angle of incidence on M_1 is $\theta_{i_1} = 60°$.

2. According to the law of reflection, the angle of reflection from M_1 is also $\theta_{r_1} = 60°$. Next, draw this reflected ray with an angle of reflection of 60°, and extend it until it hits M_2.

3. Draw another normal to M_2 at the point where the ray hits M_2. Also from geometry (focus on the triangle in the diagram), the angle of incidence on M_2 is $\theta_{i_2} = 30°$. (Why?)

(b) 4. The angle of reflection off of M_2 is $\theta_{r_2} = \theta_{i_2} = 30°$. This is the final ray reflected after reaching both mirrors.

What if the directions of the rays are reversed? In other words, if a ray is first incident on M_2, in the direction opposite that of the one we drew for (b), will all the rays reverse their directions? Draw another diagram to prove that this is indeed the case. Thus, light rays are reversible.

Follow-up Exercise. When following an 18-wheel truck, you may see a sign on the back stating, "If you can't see my mirror, I can't see you." What does this mean? *(Answers to all Follow-up Exercises are at the back of the text.)*

Learn by Drawing

Tracing the Reflecting Rays (see Example 10.1)

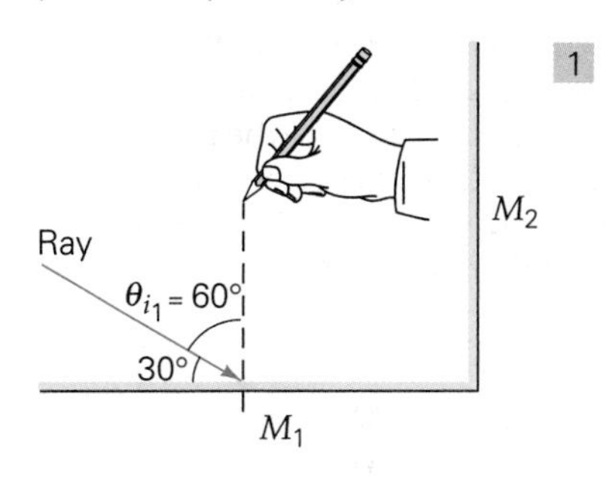

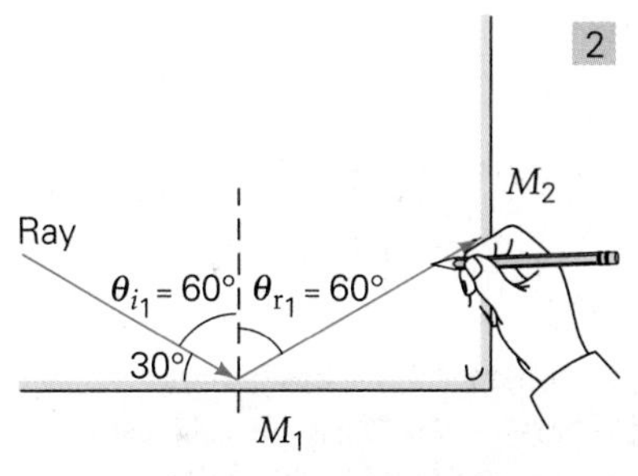

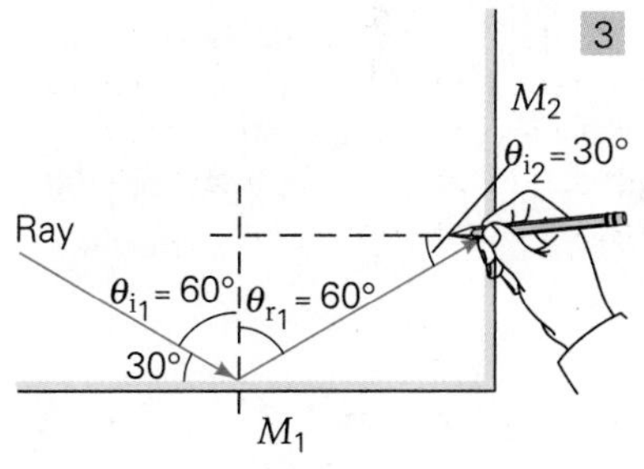

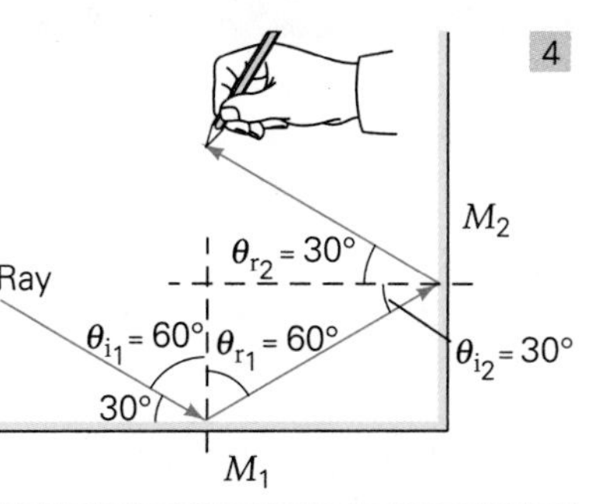

10.3 Refraction

OBJECTIVES: To (a) explain refraction in terms of Snell's law and the index of refraction and (b) give examples of refractive phenomena.

Refraction refers to the change in direction of a wave at a boundary where the wave passes from one transparent medium into another. In general, when a wave is incident on a boundary between media, some of the wave's energy is reflected and some is transmitted. For example, when light traveling in air is incident on a transparent material such as glass, it is partially reflected and partially transmitted (▶Fig. 10.7). But the direction of the transmitted light is different from the direction of the incident light, so the light is said to have been refracted; in other words, it has changed direction. This change in direction is caused by the fact that light travels with different speeds in different media. Intuitively, you might expect the passage of light to take longer through a medium with more atoms per volume, and the speed of light is, in fact, generally less in denser media. For example, the speed of light in water is about 75% of that in air or a vacuum. ▶Fig. 10.8a shows the refraction of light at an air–water boundary. You can read the Insight "Understanding Refraction: A Marching Analogy," on p. 328, to help you understand why a change in the speed of light from one medium to another results in a change in the direction of light propagation.

The change in the direction of wave propagation is described by the **angle of refraction**. In Fig. 10.8b, θ_1 is the angle of incidence and θ_2 is the angle of refraction. Willebord Snell (1591–1626), a Dutch physicist, discovered a relationship between the angles (θ) and the speeds (v) of light in two media, as shown in the figure:

$$\frac{\sin\theta_1}{\sin\theta_2} = \frac{v_1}{v_2} \quad \textit{Snell's law} \quad (10.2)$$

This expression is known as **Snell's law**. Note that θ_1 and θ_2 are always taken with respect to the normal.

INSIGHT

Dark, Rainy Night

When you drive on a dry night, you can see the road and the street signs ahead of you clearly. However, here is a familiar scene on a dark, rainy night: Even though you have your headlights on, you can hardly see the road ahead. When a car approaches, the situation becomes even worse. You see the reflections of the approaching car's headlights on the surface of the road, and they appear brighter than usual. You may be blinded and cannot see anything except the reflective glare of the oncoming headlights.

What causes these conditions and how can they be explained? When the road surface is dry, the reflection off of the road is irregular or diffuse because the surface is rough. Light from your headlights hitting the road in front of you reflects in all directions; some of it reflects back to you, and the road may be clearly seen (just as the page of this book can be read because the paper is microscopically rough). However, when the road surface is wet, water fills the crevices, turning the road into a relatively smooth reflecting surface (Fig. 1a). Light from your headlights then reflects ahead. The normally diffuse reflection is gone and is replaced by specular reflection. Images of lighted buildings and road lights form, confusing your view of the surface, and the specular reflection of oncoming cars' headlights may cause difficulty in seeing the road (Fig. 1b).

Besides wet, slippery surfaces, specular reflection is a major cause of accidents on rainy nights; thus, extra caution is advised under such conditions.

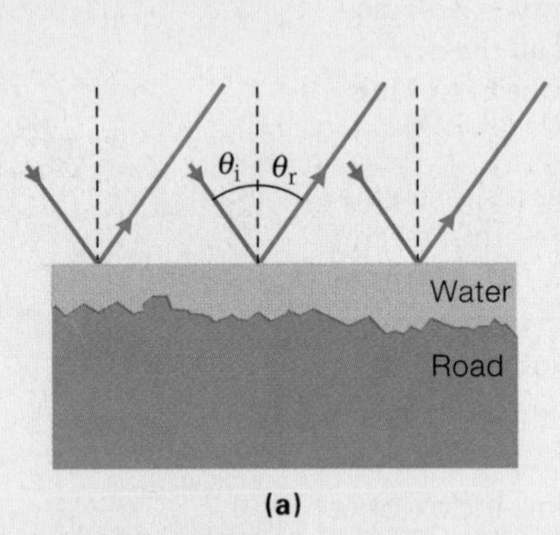

FIGURE 1 Diffuse to specular **(a)** Water on the road's surface turns the diffuse reflection from a dry road into specular reflection. **(b)** Thus, instead of seeing the road, a driver sees the reflected images of lights, buildings, etc.

▲ **FIGURE 10.7 Reflection and refraction** A beam of light is incident on a trapezoidal prism from the left. Part of the beam is reflected, and part is refracted. The refracted beam is partially reflected and partially refracted at the bottom glass–air surface. (What happens to the reflected portion?)

Thus, light is refracted when passing from one medium into another because the speed of light is different in the two media. The speed of light is greatest in a vacuum, and it is therefore convenient to compare the speed of light in other media with this constant value (c). We do so by defining a ratio called the **index of refraction** (n):

$$n = \frac{c}{v} = \frac{\text{speed of light in a vacuum}}{\text{speed of light in a medium}} \tag{10.3}$$

As a ratio of speeds, the index of refraction is a unitless quantity. The indices of refraction of several substances are given in Table 10.1. Note that these values are for a specific wavelength of light. The wavelength is specified because v, and consequently n, are slightly different for different wavelengths. (This is the cause of dispersion, to be discussed later in the chapter.). The values of n given in the table will be used in examples and exercises in this chapter for all wavelengths of light in the visible region, unless otherwise noted. Observe that n is always greater than 1, because the speed of light in a vacuum is greater than the speed of light in any material ($c > v$).

The frequency (f) of light does not change when the light enters another medium, but the wavelength of light in a material differs from the wavelength of that light in a vacuum, as can be easily shown:

$$n = \frac{c}{v} = \frac{\lambda f}{\lambda_m f}$$

(a)

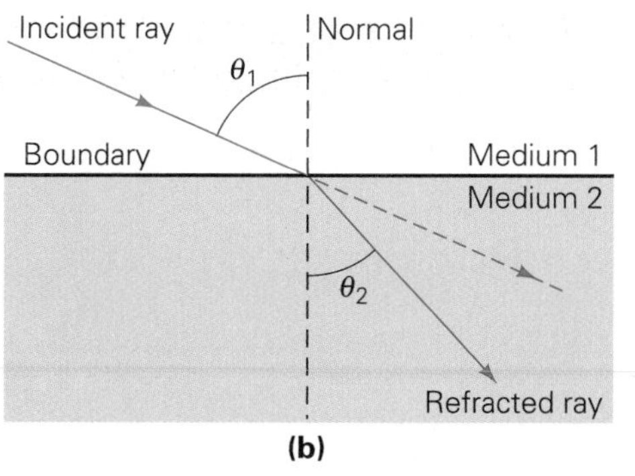

(b)

FIGURE 10.8 Refraction
(a) Light changes direction upon entering a different medium.
(b) The refracted ray is described by the angle of refraction, θ_2, measured from the normal.

or

$$n = \frac{\lambda}{\lambda_m} \tag{10.4}$$

Note: When light is refracted,
- its speed and wavelength are changed;
- its frequency remains unchanged.

The wavelength of light in the medium is then $\lambda_m = \lambda/n$. Since $n > 1$, it follows that $\lambda_m < \lambda$.

Example 10.2 ■ The Speed of Light in Water: Index of Refraction

Light from a laser with a wavelength of 632.8 nm travels from air into water. What are the speed and wavelength of the laser light in water?

Thinking It Through. If we know the index of refraction (n) of a medium, the speed and wavelength of light in the medium can be obtained from Eq. 10.3 and Eq. 10.4.

Solution.

Given: $n_{water} = 1.33$ (from Table 10.1)
$\lambda = 632.8$ nm
$c = 3.00 \times 10^8$ m/s (speed of light in air)

Find: v and λ_m (speed and wavelength of light in water)

Since $n = c/v$,

$$v = \frac{c}{n} = \frac{3.00 \times 10^8 \text{ m/s}}{1.33} = 2.26 \times 10^8 \text{ m/s}$$

Note that $1/n = v/c = 1/1.33 = 0.75$; therefore, v is 75% of the speed of light in a vacuum. Also, $n = \lambda/\lambda_m$, so

$$\lambda_m = \frac{\lambda}{n} = \frac{632.8 \text{ nm}}{1.33} = 475.8 \text{ nm}$$

Follow-up Exercise. The speed of light in a particular liquid is 2.40×10^8 m/s. What is the index of refraction of the liquid?

TABLE 10.1 Indices of Refraction (at $\lambda = 590$ nm)*

Substance	*n*
Air	1.000 29
Water	1.33
Human eye	1.336–1.406
Ethyl alcohol	1.36
Fused quartz	1.46
Glycerine	1.47
Polystyrene	1.49
Oil (typical value)	1.50
Glass (by type)†	1.45–1.70
crown	1.52
flint	1.66
Zircon	1.92
Diamond	2.42

*One nanometer (nm) is 10^{-9} m.
†Crown glass is a soda–lime silicate glass; flint glass is a lead–alkali silicate glass. Flint glass is more dispersive than crown glass (Section 10.5).

The index of refraction, n, is a measure of the speed of light in a transparent material, or technically, a measure of the *optical density* of the material. For example, the speed of light in water is less than that in air, so water is said to be optically denser than air. (Optical density in general correlates with mass density. However, in some instances, a material with a greater optical density than another can have a lower mass density.) Thus, the greater the index of refraction of a material, the greater is the material's optical density and the smaller is the speed of light in the material.

For practical purposes, the index of refraction is measured in air rather than in a vacuum, since the speed of light in air is very close to c, and

$$n_{air} = \frac{c}{v_{air}} \approx \frac{c}{c} = 1$$

INSIGHT

Understanding Refraction: A Marching Analogy

The refraction of light is not as easy to understand or visualize as its reflection. We say that the direction of the light changes when it enters a new medium because light has different speeds in different media. The transmission of light through a transparent medium involves complex atomic absorption and emission processes, but it makes sense to suppose that these processes would take longer in a denser medium, and that is indeed the case. What is difficult to visualize is why light changes direction because of a change in speed.

To afford some insight into this phenomenon, let's consider an analogy of a band marching across a field (Fig. 1). Part of the field is wet and muddy, and the marching column enters this region obliquely (at a nonzero angle of incidence). As the marchers enter the wet, slippery region, they keep marching with the same cadence (frequency). However, slipping in the mud, the stride (wavelength) of the marchers is shorter, so they are slowed down.

The band members in the far end of the same row are still on dry ground and continue on with their original stride. The effect of the change in speed is a change in direction when the band enters the second medium. We might think of the marching rows as wave fronts. As in refraction, the frequency (cadence) remains the same, but the wavelength, speed, and direction change (to keep a row aligned) as the band enters another medium.

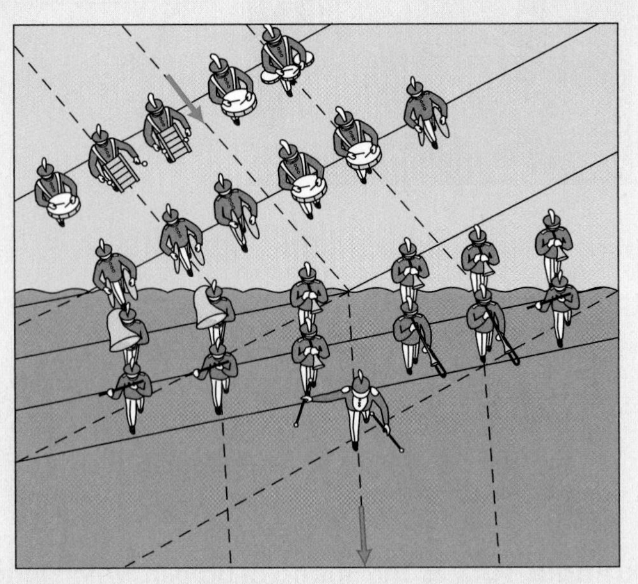

FIGURE 1 Marching analogy for refraction On obliquely entering a muddy field, a marching row changes direction slightly, analogous to the refraction of a wave front.

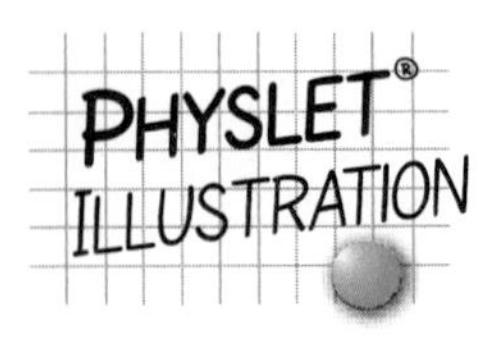

Law of Refraction

Note: The product of $n \sin\theta$ is a constant in any medium.

(From Table 10.1, $n_{\text{air}} = 1.00029$.)

A more practical form of Snell's law can be rewritten as

$$\frac{\sin\theta_1}{\sin\theta_2} = \frac{v_1}{v_2} = \frac{c/n_1}{c/n_2} = \frac{n_2}{n_1}$$

or

$$n_1 \sin\theta_1 = n_2 \sin\theta_2 \qquad \textit{Snell's law (another form)} \qquad (10.5)$$

where n_1 and n_2 are the indices of refraction for the first and second media, respectively.

Note that Eq. 10.5 can be used to measure the index of refraction. If the first medium is air, then $n_1 \approx 1$ and $n_2 \approx \sin\theta_1/\sin\theta_2$. Thus, only the angles of incidence and refraction need to be measured to determine the index of refraction of a material experimentally. On the other hand, if the index of refraction of a material is known, it can be used in Snell's law to find the angle of refraction for any angle of incidence.

Note also that the sine of the refraction angle is inversely proportional to the index of refraction: $\sin\theta_2 \approx \sin\theta_1/n_2$. Hence, for a given angle of incidence, the greater the index of refraction, the smaller is $\sin\theta_2$ and the smaller is the angle of refraction, θ_2.

More generally, the following relationships hold:

- If the second medium is more optically dense than the first medium ($n_2 > n_1$), the ray is refracted *toward* the normal ($\theta_2 < \theta_1$), as illustrated in ▸Fig. 10.9a.
- If the second medium is less optically dense than the first medium ($n_2 < n_1$), the ray is refracted *away from* the normal ($\theta_2 > \theta_1$), as illustrated in Fig. 10.9b.

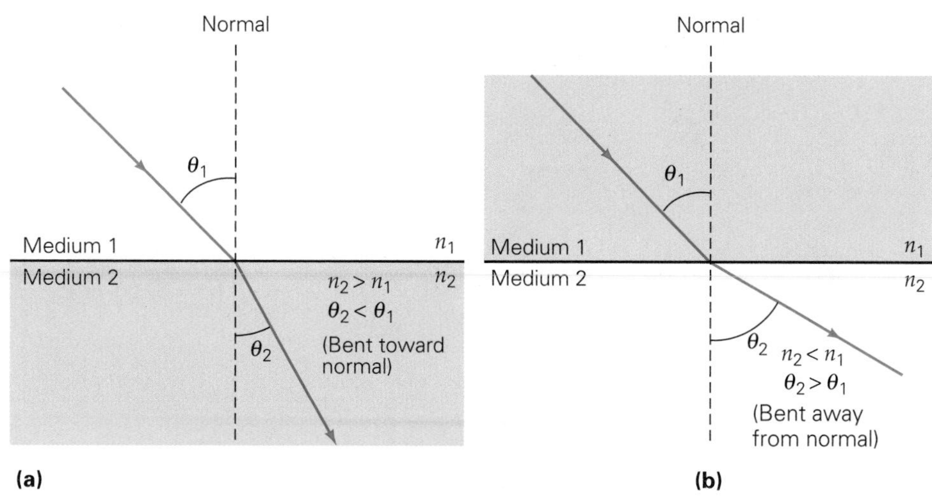

▲ **FIGURE 10.9 Index of refraction and ray deviation** **(a)** When the second medium is more optically dense than the first ($n_2 > n_1$), the ray is refracted toward the normal, as in the case of light entering water from air. **(b)** When the second medium is less optically dense than the first ($n_2 < n_1$), the ray is refracted away from the normal. [This is the case if the ray in part (a) is traced in reverse, going from medium 2 to medium 1.]

Integrated Example 10.3 ■ Angle of Refraction: Snell's Law

Light in air is incident on a piece of crown glass at an angle of 37.0° (relative to the normal). (a) Will the refracted ray bend (1) toward or (2) away from the normal? Use a diagram to illustrate. (b) What is the angle of refraction?

(a) Conceptual Reasoning. According to the alternative form of Snell's law (Eq. 10.5), $n_1 \sin \theta_1 = n_2 \sin \theta_2$, (1) is the correct answer. Since $n_2 > n_1$, the angle of refraction must be smaller than the angle of incidence ($\theta_2 < \theta_1$). Because both θ_1 and θ_2 are measured from the normal, the refracted ray will bend toward the normal. The ray diagram in this case is identical to Fig. 10.9a. (Remember the marching band analogy?)

(b) Thinking It Through. Again, the alternative form of Snell's law (Eq. 10.5) is most practical in this case. (Why?) Listing the given quantities, we have

Given: $\theta_1 = 37.0°$
$n_1 = 1.00$ (air)
$n_2 = 1.52$ (crown glass, from Table 10.1)

Find: (b) θ_2 (angle of refraction)

To find the angle of refraction, we use

$$\sin \theta_2 = \frac{n_1 \sin \theta_1}{n_2} = \frac{(1.00)(\sin 37.0°)}{1.52} = 0.396$$

and we obtain

$$\theta_2 = \sin^{-1}(0.396) = 23.3°$$

Follow-up Exercise. It is found experimentally that a beam of light entering a liquid from air at an angle of incidence of 37.0° exhibits an angle of refraction of 28.8° in the liquid. What is the speed of light in the liquid?

Example 10.4 ■ A Glass Tabletop: More about Refraction

A beam of light traveling in air strikes the glass top of a coffee table at an angle of incidence of 45° (▶Fig. 10.10). The glass has an index of refraction of 1.5. (a) What is the angle of refraction for the light transmitted into the glass? (b) Prove that the emergent beam is parallel to the incident beam—that is, that $\theta_4 = \theta_1$. (c) If the glass is 2.0 cm thick,

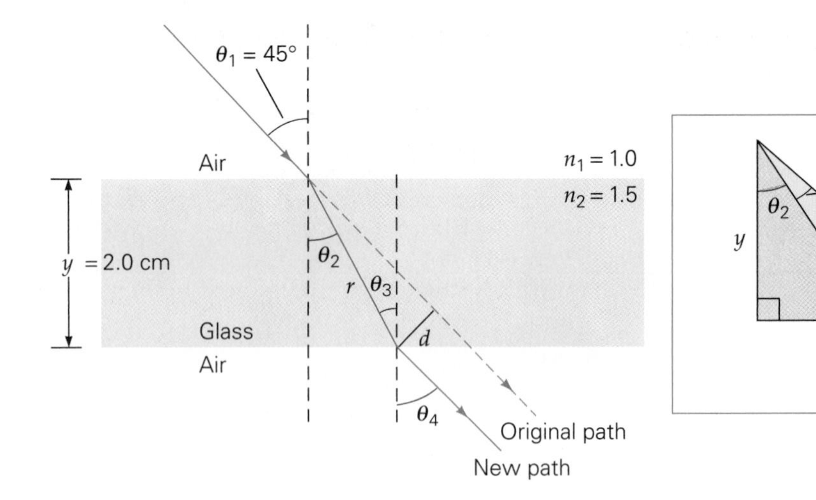

▶ **FIGURE 10.10 Two refractions** In the glass, the refracted ray is displaced laterally (sideways) a distance d from the incident ray, and the emergent ray is parallel to the original ray. (See Example 10.4.)

what is the lateral displacement between the ray entering and the ray emerging from the glass (the perpendicular distance between the two rays—d in the figure)?

Thinking It Through. Since there are two refractions involved in this example, we use Snell's law in (a), again in (b), and then some geometry and trigonometry in (c). [See Appendix I.]

Solution. Listing the data, we have the following:

Given: $\theta_1 = 45°$, $n_1 = 1.0$ (air), $n_2 = 1.5$, $y = 2.0$ cm

Find: (a) θ_2 (angle of refraction)
(b) Show that $\theta_4 = \theta_1$
(c) d (lateral displacement)

(a) Using the practical form of Snell's law, Eq. 10.5, with $n_1 = 1.0$ for air gives

$$\sin\theta_2 = \frac{\sin\theta_1}{n_2} = \frac{\sin 45°}{1.5} = \frac{0.707}{1.5} = 0.47$$

Thus,

$$\theta_2 = \sin^{-1}(0.47) = 28°$$

Note that the beam is refracted toward the normal.

(b) If $\theta_1 = \theta_4$, then the emergent ray is parallel to the incident ray. Applying Snell's law to the beam at both surfaces gives

$$n_1 \sin\theta_1 = n_2 \sin\theta_2$$

and

$$n_2 \sin\theta_3 = n_1 \sin\theta_4$$

From the figure, we see that $\theta_2 = \theta_3$. Therefore,

$$n_1 \sin\theta_1 = n_1 \sin\theta_4$$

or

$$\theta_1 = \theta_4$$

Thus, the emergent beam is parallel to the incident beam, but displaced laterally or perpendicularly at a distance d.

(c) It can be seen from the inset in Fig. 10.10 that, to find d, we need to first find r from the known information in the pink right triangle. We have

$$\frac{y}{r} = \cos\theta_2 \quad \text{or} \quad r = \frac{y}{\cos\theta_2}$$

In the yellow right triangle, $d = r \sin(\theta_1 - \theta_2)$. Substituting r from the previous step yields

$$d = \frac{y \sin(\theta_1 - \theta_2)}{\cos \theta_2} = \frac{(2.0 \text{ cm}) \sin(45^\circ - 28^\circ)}{\cos 28^\circ} = 0.66 \text{ cm}$$

Follow-up Exercise. If the glass in this Example had $n = 1.6$, would the lateral displacement be the same, larger, or smaller? Explain your answer conceptually, and then calculate the actual value to verify your reasoning.

Example 10.5 ■ The Human Eye: Refraction and Wavelength

A simplified representation of the crystalline lens in a human eye shows it to have a cortex (an outer layer) of $n_{\text{cortex}} = 1.386$ and a nucleus (core) of $n_{\text{nucleus}} = 1.406$. (Note that both refraction indices are within the range listed for the human eye in Table 10.1.) If a beam of monochromatic (single-frequency or wavelength) light of wavelength 590 nm is directed from air through the front of the eye and into the crystalline lens, qualitatively compare and list the frequency, speed, and wavelength of light in air, the nucleus, and the cortex. First do the comparison part without numbers, and then calculate the actual values to verify your reasoning.

Reasoning and Answer. First, we need the relative magnitudes of the indices of refraction, where $n_{\text{air}} < n_{\text{cortex}} < n_{\text{nucleus}}$.

As you learned earlier in this section, the frequency (f) of light is the same in all three media: air, the cortex, and the nucleus. Thus, the frequency can be calculated by using the speed and the wavelength of light in any of these materials, but it is easiest in air. (Why?) From the wave relationship $c = \lambda f$ we have

$$f = f_{\text{air}} = f_{\text{cortex}} = f_{\text{nucleus}} = \frac{c}{\lambda} = \frac{3.00 \times 10^8 \text{ m/s}}{590 \times 10^{-9} \text{ m}} = 5.08 \times 10^{14} \text{ Hz}$$

The speed of light in a medium depends on its index of refraction, since $v = c/n$. The smaller the index of refraction, the higher the speed. Therefore, the speed of light is the highest in air ($n = 1.00$ and $v = c = 3.00 \times 10^8$ m/s) and lowest in the nucleus ($n = 1.406$).

The speed of light in the cortex is

$$v_{\text{cortex}} = \frac{c}{n_{\text{cortex}}} = \frac{3.00 \times 10^8 \text{ m/s}}{1.386} = 2.16 \times 10^8 \text{ m/s}$$

and the speed of light in the nucleus is

$$v_{\text{nucleus}} = \frac{3.00 \times 10^8 \text{ m/s}}{1.406} = 2.13 \times 10^8 \text{ m/s}$$

We also know that the wavelength of light in a medium depends on the index of refraction of the medium ($\lambda_m = \lambda/n$.) The smaller the index of refraction, the longer is the wavelength. Therefore, the wavelength of light is the longest in air ($n = 1$ and $\lambda = 590$ nm) and shortest in the nucleus ($n = 1.406$).

The wavelength in the cortex can be calculated from Eq. 10.4:

$$\lambda_{\text{cortex}} = \frac{\lambda}{n_{\text{cortex}}} = \frac{590 \text{ nm}}{1.386} = 426 \text{ nm}$$

and the wavelength in the nucleus is

$$\lambda_{\text{nucleus}} = \frac{590 \text{ nm}}{1.406} = 420 \text{ nm}$$

Finally, we can construct a table to more easily compare the frequency, speed, and wavelength of light in the three media:

	Frequency (Hz)	*Speed (m/s)*	*Wavelength (nm)*
Air	5.08×10^{14}	3.00×10^{8}	590
Cortex	5.08×10^{14}	2.16×10^{8}	426
Nucleus	5.08×10^{14}	2.13×10^{8}	420

Follow-up Exercise. A light source of a single frequency is submerged in water in a special fish tank. The beam travels in the water, through double glass panes at the side of the tank (each glass pane has a different n), and into air. In general, what happens to (a) the frequency and (b) the wavelength of the light when it emerges into the outside air?

Refraction is common in everyday life and explains many things we observe. Let's look at refraction in action.

Mirage: A common example of this phenomenon sometimes occurs on a highway on a hot summer day. The refraction of light is caused by layers of air that are at different temperatures (the layer closer to the road is at a higher temperature, lower density, and lower index of refraction). This variation in indices of refraction gives rise to the observed "wet" spot and an inverted image of an object such as a car (▼Fig. 10.11a). The term *mirage* generally brings to mind a thirsty person in the desert "seeing" a pool of water that really isn't there. This optical illusion plays tricks on the mind, with the image usually seen as in a pool of water and our eye's past experience unconsciously leading us to conclude that there is water on the road.

In Fig. 10.11b, there are two ways to see the car. First, the horizontal rays come directly from the car to our eyes, so we see the car above the ground. Also, the rays from the car that travel toward the road surface will be refracted by the layered air. After hitting the surface, these rays will be refracted again and travel toward our eyes. (See the inset in the figure.) Cooler air has a higher density and so a higher index of refraction. A ray traveling toward the road surface will be gradually refracted with a larger angle of refraction until it hits the surface. It will then be refracted again with a smaller angle of refraction, going toward our eyes. As a consequence, we also see an inverted image of the car, below the road surface. In other words, the surface of the road acts almost like a mirror.

Not where it should be: You may have experienced a refractive effect while trying to reach for something underwater, such as a fish (▶Fig. 10.12a). We are used to

▼ **FIGURE 10.11 Refraction in action** **(a)** An inverted car on a "wet" road, a mirage. **(b)** The mirage is formed when light from the object is refracted by layers of air at different temperatures near the surface of the road.

(a)

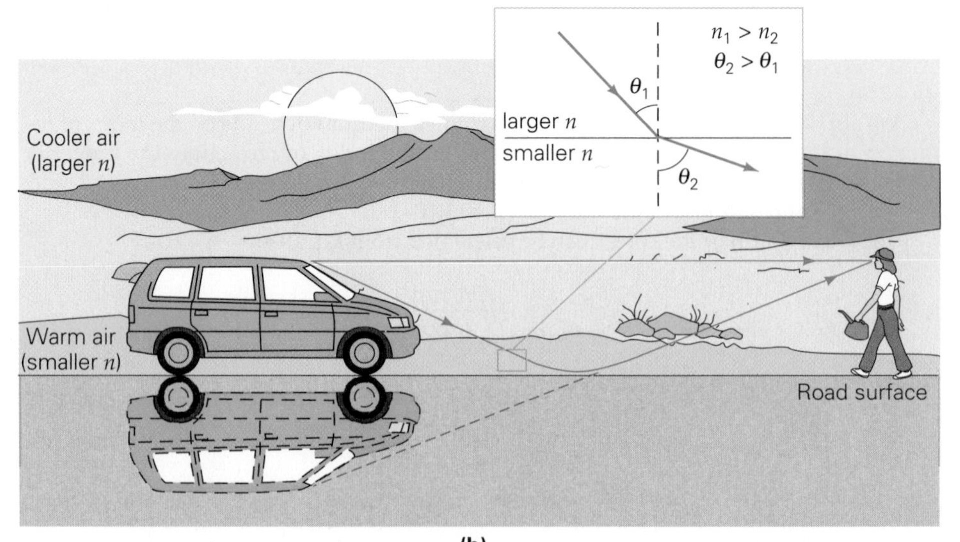

(b)

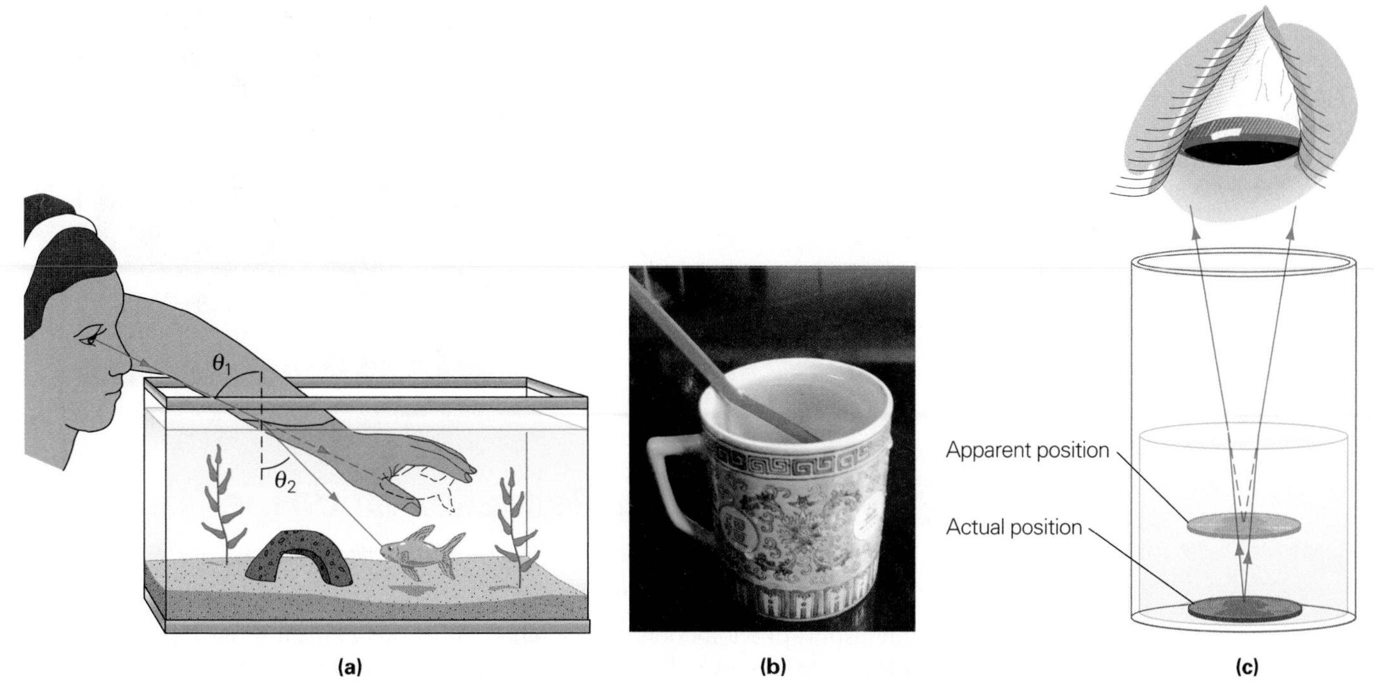

▲ **FIGURE 10.12 Refractive effects** **(a)** The light is refracted, and because we tend to think of light as traveling in straight lines, the fish is not where we think it is. **(b)** The chopstick appears bent at the air–water boundary. If the cup is transparent, we see another type of refraction. (See Exercise 27.) **(c)** Because of refraction, the coin appears to be closer than it actually is.

light traveling in straight lines from objects to our eyes, but the light reaching our eyes from a submerged object has a directional change at the air–water interface. (Note in the figure that the ray is refracted away from the normal.) As a result, the object appears to be closer to the surface than it actually is, and therefore we tend to miss the object when reaching for it. For the same reason, a chopstick in a cup appears bent (Fig. 10.12b), a coin in a glass of water will appear closer than it really is (Fig. 10.12c), and the legs of a person standing in water seem shorter than their actual length. The relationship between the true depth and the apparent depth can be calculated. (See Exercise 45.)

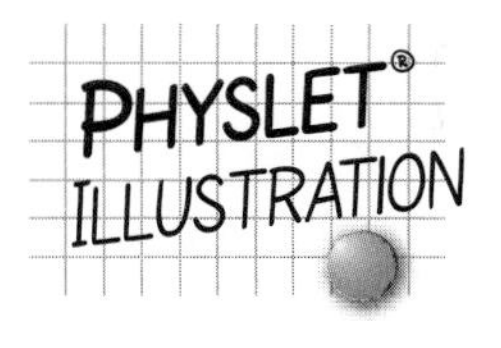

Apparent Depth

Atmospheric effects: The Sun on the horizon sometimes appears to be flattened, with its horizontal dimension greater than its vertical dimension (▾Fig. 10.13a). This effect is the result of temperature and density variations in the denser air along the horizon. These variations occur predominantly vertically, so light from the top and light from the bottom portions of the Sun are refracted differently as the two sets of beams pass through different atmospheric densities with different indices of refraction.

Atmospheric refraction lengthens the day, so to speak, by allowing us to see the Sun (or the Moon, for that matter) just before it actually rises above the horizon and just after it actually sets below the horizon (as much as 20 minutes on both ends). The denser air near the Earth refracts the light over the horizon toward us (Fig. 10.13b).

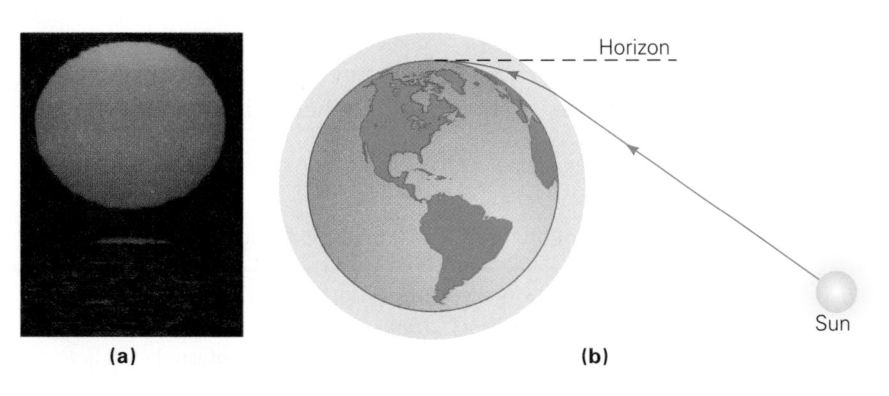

◀ **FIGURE 10.13 Atmospheric effects** **(a)** The Sun on the horizon commonly appears flattened as a result of atmospheric refraction. **(b)** Before rising and after setting, the Sun can be seen briefly also because of atmospheric refraction.

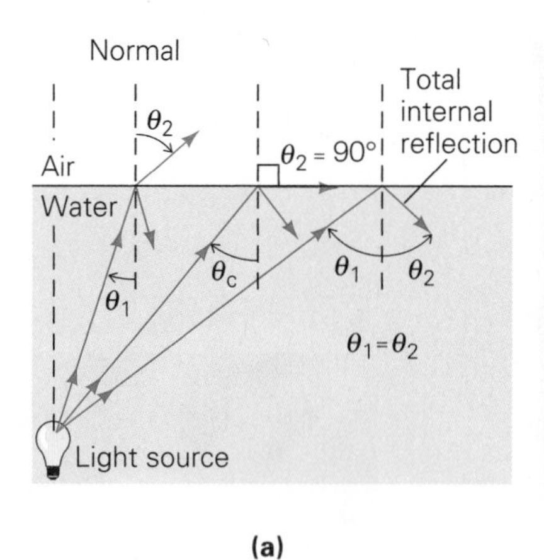

▶ **FIGURE 10.14 Internal reflection** **(a)** When light enters a less optically dense medium, it is refracted away from the normal. At a critical angle (θ_c), the light is refracted along the interface (common boundary) of the media. At an angle greater than the critical angle ($\theta_1 > \theta_c$), there is total internal reflection. **(b)** Can you estimate the critical angle in the photograph?

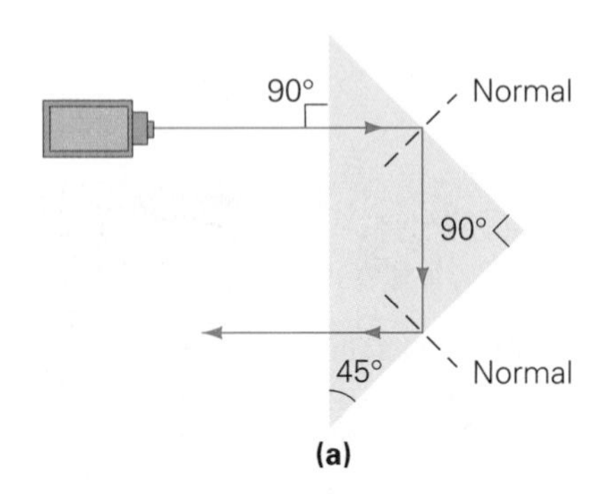

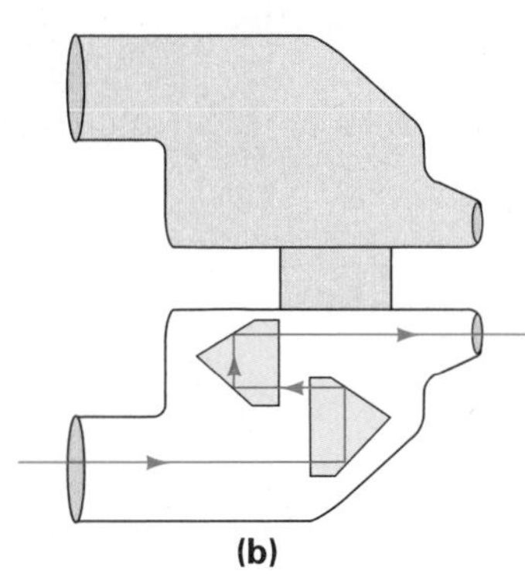

▲ **FIGURE 10.15 Internal reflection in a prism** **(a)** Because the critical angle of glass is less than 45°, prisms with 45° and 90° angles can be used to reflect light through 180°. **(b)** Internal reflection of light by prisms in binoculars makes this instrument much shorter than a telescope.

10.4 Total Internal Reflection and Fiber Optics

OBJECTIVES: To (a) describe total internal reflection and (b) understand fiber-optic applications.

An interesting phenomenon occurs when light travels from a more optically dense medium into a less optically dense one, such as when light goes *from* water *into* air. As you know, in such a case a ray will be refracted away from the normal. (The angle of refraction is larger than the angle of incidence.) Furthermore, Snell's law states that the greater the angle of incidence, the greater is the angle of refraction. That is, as the angle of incidence increases, the farther the refracted ray diverges from the normal.

However, there is a limit. For a certain angle of incidence called the **critical angle** (θ_c), the angle of refraction is 90°, and the refracted ray is directed along the boundary between the media. But what happens if the angle of incidence is even larger? If the angle of incidence is greater than the critical angle ($\theta_1 > \theta_c$), the light isn't refracted at all, but is internally reflected (▲Fig. 10.14). This condition is called **total internal reflection**. The reflection process is almost 100% efficient. (There is still some absorption of light in the materials.) Because of total internal reflection, glass prisms can be used as mirrors (◀Fig. 10.15). In summary, reflection and refraction occur at all angles for $\theta_1 \leq \theta_c$, but the refracted or transmitted ray disappears at $\theta_1 > \theta_c$.

An expression for the critical angle can be obtained from Snell's law. If $\theta_1 = \theta_c$ in the optically denser medium, $\theta_2 = 90°$, and it follows that

$$\frac{\sin\theta_1}{\sin\theta_2} = \frac{\sin\theta_c}{\sin 90°} = \frac{n_2}{n_1}$$

Since $\sin 90° = 1$,

$$\sin\theta_c = \frac{n_2}{n_1} \quad \textit{where } n_1 > n_2 \tag{10.6}$$

If the second medium is air, $n_2 \approx 1$, and the critical angle at the boundary from a medium into air is given by $\sin\theta_c = 1/n$, where n is the index of refraction of the medium.

Example 10.6 ■ A View from the Pool: Critical Angle

(a) What is the critical angle for light traveling in water and incident on a water–air boundary? (b) If a diver submerged in a pool looked up at the surface of the water at an angle of $\theta < \theta_c$, what would she see? (Neglect any thermal or motional effects.)

▶ **FIGURE 10.16 Panoramic and distorted** An underwater view of the surface of a swimming pool in Hawaii.

Thinking It Through. (a) The critical angle is given by Eq. 10.6. (b) As shown in Fig. 10.14a, θ_c forms a cone of vision for viewing from below the water.

Solution.

Given: $n_1 = 1.33$ (for water, from Table 10.1) $n_2 \approx 1$ (why?)

Find: (a) θ_c (critical angle) (b) View for $\theta < \theta_c$

(a) The critical angle is

$$\theta_c = \sin^{-1}\left(\frac{n_2}{n_1}\right) = \sin^{-1}\left(\frac{1}{1.33}\right) = 48.8°$$

(b) Using Fig. 10.14a, trace the rays in reverse for light coming from all angles outside the pool. Light coming from the above-water 180° panorama could be viewed only in a cone with a half-angle of 48.8°. As a result, objects above the surface would also appear distorted. An underwater panoramic view is seen in ▲Fig. 10.16. Now can you explain why wading birds like herons usually keep their locations low before trying to catch a fish?

Follow-up Exercise. What would the diver see when looking up at the water surface at an angle of $\theta > \theta_c$?

Internal reflections enhance the brilliance of cut diamonds. (Brilliance is a measure of the amount of light returning straight back to the viewer. Brilliance is reduced if light leaks out the back of a diamond—the reflection is not total.) The critical angle for a diamond–air surface is

$$\theta_c = \sin^{-1}\left(\frac{1}{n}\right) = \sin^{-1}\left(\frac{1}{2.42}\right) = 24.4°$$

A so-called brilliant-cut diamond has many facets, or faces (58 in all—33 on the upper face and 25 on the lower). Light entering the lower facets from the upper facets above the critical angle is internally reflected in the diamond. The light then emerges from the upper facets, giving rise to the diamond's brilliance (▶Fig. 10.17).

(a)

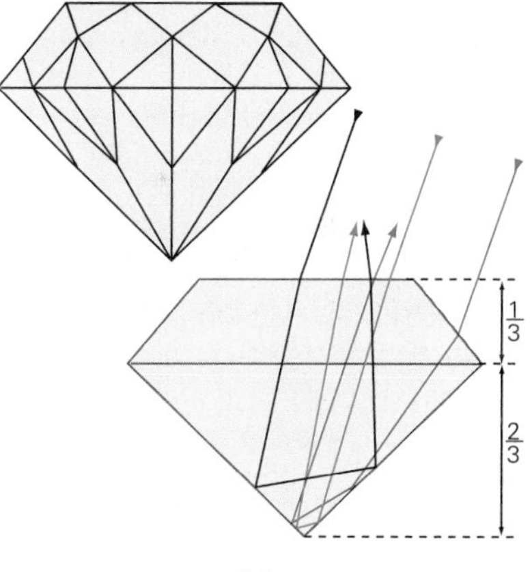

(b)

▲ **FIGURE 10.17 Diamond brilliance** **(a)** Internal reflection gives rise to a diamond's brilliance. **(b)** The "cut," or the depth proportions, of the facets is critical. If a stone is too shallow or too deep, light will be lost (refracted out) through the lower facets.

Fiber Optics

When a fountain is illuminated from below, the light is transmitted along the curved streams of water. This phenomenon was first demonstrated in 1870 by the British scientist John Tyndall (1820–1893), who showed that light was "conducted" along the curved path of a stream of water flowing from a hole in the side of a container. The phenomenon is observed because light undergoes total internal reflection along the stream.

Total internal reflection forms the basis of **fiber optics**, a fascinating field centered on the use of transparent fibers to transmit light. Multiple total internal reflections make it possible to "pipe" light along a transparent rod (just like streams of water), even if the rod is curved (▶Fig. 10.18). Note from the figure that the smaller the diameter of the light pipe, the more total internal reflections it has. In a small fiber, there can be as many as several hundred total internal reflections per centimeter.

Total internal reflection is an exceptionally efficient process. Optical fibers can be used to transmit light over very long distances with losses of only about 25% per kilometer. These losses are due primarily to impurities in the fiber, which scatter the light. Transparent materials have different degrees of transmission. Fibers are made of special plastics and glasses for maximum transmission efficiency. The greatest efficiency is achieved with infrared radiation, because there is less scattering.

The greater efficiency of multiple total internal reflections compared with multiple mirror reflections can be illustrated by a good reflecting plane mirror, which has at best a reflectivity of about 95%. After each reflection, the beam intensity is 95% of that of the incident beam from the preceding reflection ($I_1 = 0.95 I_o$; $I_2 = 0.95 I_1 = 0.95^2 I_o; \ldots$). Therefore, the intensity I of the reflected beam after n reflections is given by

$$I = 0.95^n I_o$$

where I_o is the initial intensity of the beam before the first reflection. Thus, after 14 reflections,

$$I = 0.95^{14} I_o = 0.49 I_o$$

In other words, after 14 reflections, the intensity is reduced to less than half (49%). For 100 reflections, $I = 0.006 I_o$, and the intensity is only 0.6% of the initial intensity! Compare this to about 75% of the initial intensity in optical fibers over a kilometer in length with *thousands and thousands* of reflections, and you can see the advantage of total internal reflection.

Fibers whose diameters are about 10 μm (10^{-5} m) are grouped together in flexible bundles that are 4 to 10 mm in diameter and up to several meters in length, depending on the application (▼Fig. 10.19). A fiber bundle with a cross-sectional area of 1 cm^2 can contain as many as 50 000 individual fibers. (A coating is needed to keep the fibers from touching.)

There are many important and interesting applications of fiber optics, ranging from communications and computer networking to medical applications. (See the

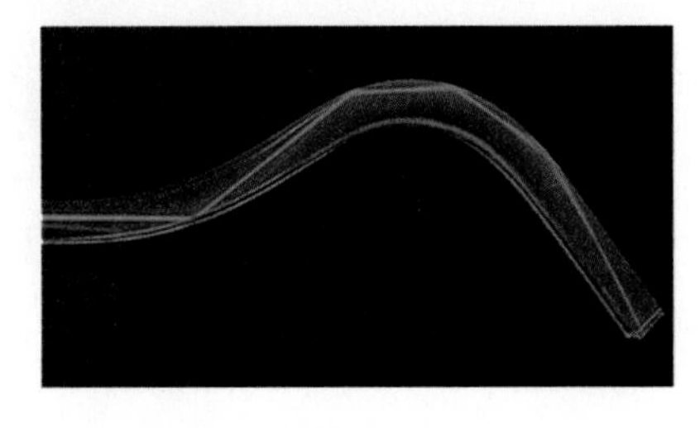

(a)

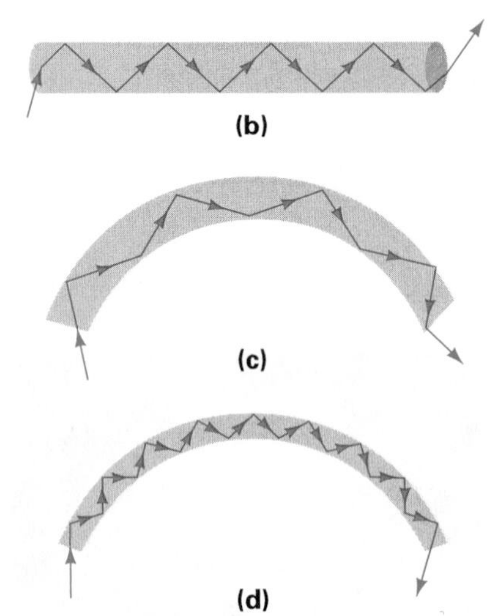

(b)

(c)

(d)

▲ **FIGURE 10.18 Light pipes**
(a) Total internal reflection in an optical fiber. **(b)** When light is incident on the end of a cylindrical form of transparent material such that the internal angle of incidence is greater than the critical angle of the material, the light undergoes total internal reflection down the length of the light pipe. **(c)** Light is also transmitted along curved light pipes by total internal reflection. **(d)** As the diameter of the rod or fiber becomes smaller, the number of reflections per unit length increases.

▼ **FIGURE 10.19 fiber-optic bundle** **(a)** Hundreds or even thousands of extremely thin fibers are grouped together **(b)** to make an optical fiber, colored blue by a laser.

(a)

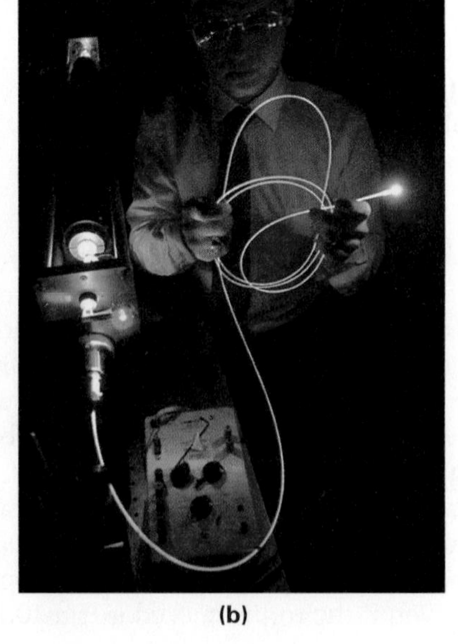

(b)

INSIGHT

Fiber Optics: Medical Applications

Before fiber optics, *endoscopes*—instruments used to view internal portions of the human body—consisted of lens systems in long, narrow tubes. Some contained a dozen or more lenses and produced relatively poor images. Also, because the lenses had to be aligned in certain ways, the tubes had to have rigid sections, which limited the endoscope's maneuverability. Such an endoscope could be inserted down the patient's throat into the stomach to observe the stomach lining. However, there would be blind spots due to the curvature of the stomach and the inflexibility of the instrument.

Fiber–optic bundles have eliminated these problems. Lenses placed at the end of the fiber bundles focus the light, and a prism is used to change the direction for its return. The incident light is usually transmitted by an outer layer of fiber bundles, and the image is returned through a central core of fibers. Mechanical linkages allow maneuverability. The end of a fiber endoscope can be equipped with devices to obtain specimens of the viewed tissues for biopsy (diagnostic examination) or even to perform surgical procedures (Fig. 1). For example, arthroscopic surgery is performed on the knees of injured athletes. The arthroscope that is now routinely used for inspecting *and* repairing damaged joints is simply a fiber endoscope fitted with appropriate surgical implements.

A fiber–optic *cardioscope* (for direct observation of heart valves) typically is a fiber bundle about 4 mm in diameter and 30 cm long. Such a cardioscope passes easily to the heart through the jugular vein in the neck, which is about 15 mm in diameter. To displace the blood and provide a clear field of view for observing and photographing, a transparent balloon at the tip of the cardioscope is inflated with saline (saltwater) solution.

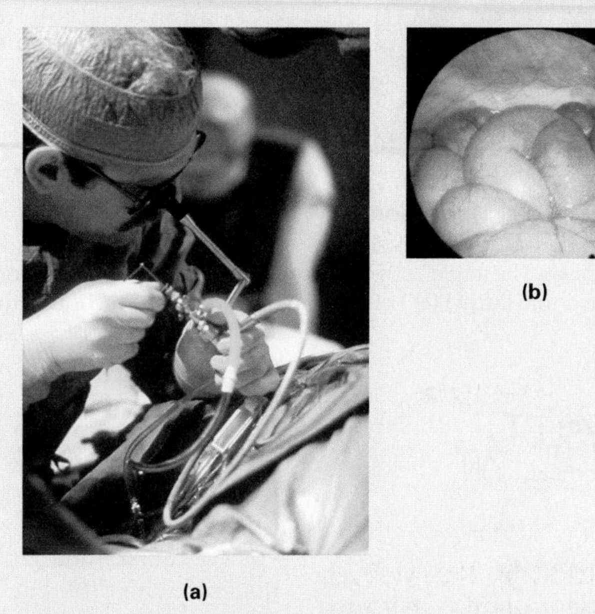

FIGURE 1 Endoscopy **(a)** Surgeons use a fiber–optic endoscope to perform surgery. **(b)** An endoscopic view of the intestines.

Insight on this page.) Light signals, converted from electrical signals, are transmitted through optical telephone lines and computer networks. At the other end, they are converted back to electrical signals. Optical fibers have lower energy losses than current-carrying wires, particularly at higher frequencies, and can carry far more data. Also, optical fibers are lighter than metal wires, have greater flexibility, and are not affected by electromagnetic disturbances (electric and magnetic fields), since they are made of materials that are electrical insulators.

10.5 Dispersion

OBJECTIVE: To explain dispersion and some of its effects.

Light of a single frequency, and consequently a single wavelength, is called *monochromatic light* (from the Greek *mono*, meaning "one," and *chroma*, meaning "color"). Visible light that contains all the component frequencies, or colors, at about the same intensities (e.g., sunlight) is termed *white light*. When a beam of white light passes through a glass prism, as shown in ▸Fig. 10.20a, it is spread out, or dispersed, into a spectrum of colors. This phenomenon led Newton to believe that sunlight is a mixture of colors. When the beam enters the prism, the component colors, corresponding to different wavelengths of light, are refracted at slightly different angles, so they spread out into a spectrum (Fig. 10.20b).

The emergence of a spectrum indicates that the index of refraction of glass is slightly different for different wavelengths, which is true of many transparent media (Fig. 10.20c). The reason has to do with the fact that in a dispersive

Note: You can remember the sequence of the colors of the visible spectrum (from the long-wavelength end to the short-wavelength end) by using the name ROY G. BIV, which is an acronym for *r*ed, *o*range, *y*ellow, *g*reen, *b*lue, *i*ndigo, and *v*iolet.

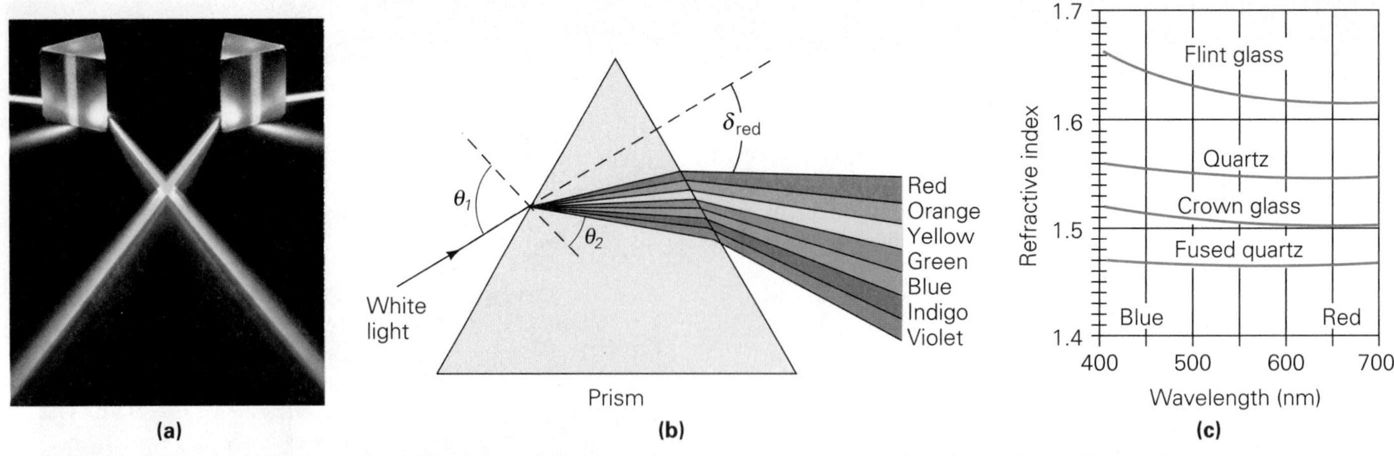

▲ **FIGURE 10.20 Dispersion** **(a)** White light is dispersed into a spectrum of colors by glass prisms. **(b)** In a dispersive medium, the index of refraction varies slightly with wavelength. Red light, longest in wavelength, has the smallest index of refraction and is refracted least. The angle between the incident beam and an emergent ray is the angle of deviation (δ) for that ray. (The angles are exaggerated for clarity.) **(c)** Variation in the index of refraction with wavelength for some common transparent media.

Dispersion in a Prism

medium the speed of light is slightly different for different wavelengths. Since the index of refraction n of a medium is a function of the speed of light in that medium ($n = c/v$), the index of refraction is different for different wavelengths. It follows from Snell's law that light of different wavelengths will be refracted at different angles.

We can summarize the preceding discussion by saying that in a transparent material with different indices of refraction for different wavelengths of light, refraction causes a separation of light according to wavelengths, and the material is said to exhibit **dispersion**. Dispersion varies with different media. Also, because the differences in the indices of refraction for different wavelengths are small, a representative value at some specified wavelength can be used for general purposes. (See Table 10.1.)

Example 10.7 ■ Forming a Spectrum: Dispersion

The index of refraction of a particular transparent material is 1.4503 for the red end ($\lambda_r = 700$ nm) of the visible spectrum and 1.4698 for the blue end ($\lambda_b = 400$ nm). If white light is incident on a prism of this material as in Fig. 10.20b at an angle of incidence of 45°, what is the angular separation of the visible spectrum inside the prism?

Thinking It Through. The angle of refraction is given by Snell's law, and we can compute the angle of refraction for the red and blue ends of the visible spectrum. The angular separation of the light inside the prism is the difference in these angles of refraction.

Solution.

Given: (red) $n_r = 1.4503$ for $\lambda_r = 700$ nm
(blue) $n_b = 1.4698$ for $\lambda_b = 400$ nm
$\theta_1 = 45°$

Find: $\Delta\theta_2$ (angular separation)

Using Eq. 10.5 with $n_1 = 1.00$ (air), we get

$$\sin\theta_{2_r} = \frac{\sin\theta_1}{n_{2_r}} = \frac{\sin 45°}{1.4503} = 0.48756 \quad \text{and} \quad \theta_{2_r} = 29.180°$$

Similarly,

$$\sin\theta_{2_b} = \frac{\sin\theta_1}{n_{2_b}} = \frac{\sin 45°}{1.4698} = 0.48109 \quad \text{and} \quad \theta_{2_b} = 28.757°$$

INSIGHT

The Rainbow

FIGURE 1 Rainbow Notice that the colors of the primary rainbow run vertically from red (top) to blue (bottom).

We have all been fascinated by the beautiful array of colors of a rainbow (Fig. 1). With the optical principles learned in this chapter, we are now in a position to understand the formation of this spectacular display.

A rainbow is formed by refraction, dispersion, and internal reflection of light within water droplets. When sunlight shines on millions of water droplets in the air during and after a rainstorm, we see a multicolored arc whose colors run from violet along the lower part of the spectrum (in order of wavelength) to red along the upper. Occasionally, more than one rainbow is seen: The main, or primary, rainbow is sometimes accompanied by a fainter and higher secondary rainbow (Fig. 1) or even a third rainbow. These higher order rainbows are caused by more than one total internal reflection within the water droplets.

The light that forms the primary rainbow is first refracted and dispersed in the water droplet, then reflected once inside each water droplet, and finally refracted and dispersed again upon exiting the water droplet, resulting in the light being spread out into a spectrum of colors (Fig. 2a). However, because of the conditions for refraction and total internal reflection in water, the angles between incoming and outgoing rays for violet to red light lie within a narrow range of 40°–42°. This means that you can see a rainbow only when the Sun is behind you, so that the dispersed light is reflected to you through these angles.

Red appears on the top of the rainbow because light of shorter wavelengths from those water droplets will pass over our eyes (Fig. 2b). Similarly, blue is at the bottom of the rainbow because light of longer wavelengths passes under our eyes.

We generally see rainbows only as arcs, because their formation by water droplets is cut off at the ground. If you were on a cliff or on an airplane, you might see a complete circular rainbow (Fig. 2b). Also, the higher the Sun is in the sky, the less of a rainbow you will be able to see from the ground. In fact, you won't see a primary rainbow if the Sun's angle above the horizon is greater than 42°. The primary rainbow can still be seen from a height, however. As an observer's elevation increases, more of the arc becomes visible. You may also have seen a circular rainbow in the spray from a garden hose.

So

$$\Delta\theta_2 = \theta_{2_r} - \theta_{2_b} = 29.180° - 28.757° = 0.423°$$

This is not much of a deviation, but as the light travels, it is refracted and dispersed again by the second boundary to spread out the colors further. Finally, the light emerges from the prism, and the dispersion becomes evident (Fig. 10.20a).

Follow-up Exercise. If the green light exhibits an angular separation of 0.156° from the red light, what is the index of refraction for green light in the hypothetical material of the example? Will the green light refract more or less than the red light? Explain.

A good example of a dispersive material is diamond, which is about five times more dispersive than glass. In addition to revealing the brilliance resulting from internal reflections off many facets, a cut diamond shows a display of colors, or "fire," resulting from the dispersion of the refracted light (Fig. 10.17).

Dispersion is a cause of chromatic aberration in lenses. Optical systems in cameras often consist of several lenses to minimize this problem.

Another dramatic example of dispersion is the production of a rainbow, as discussed in the Insight on this page.

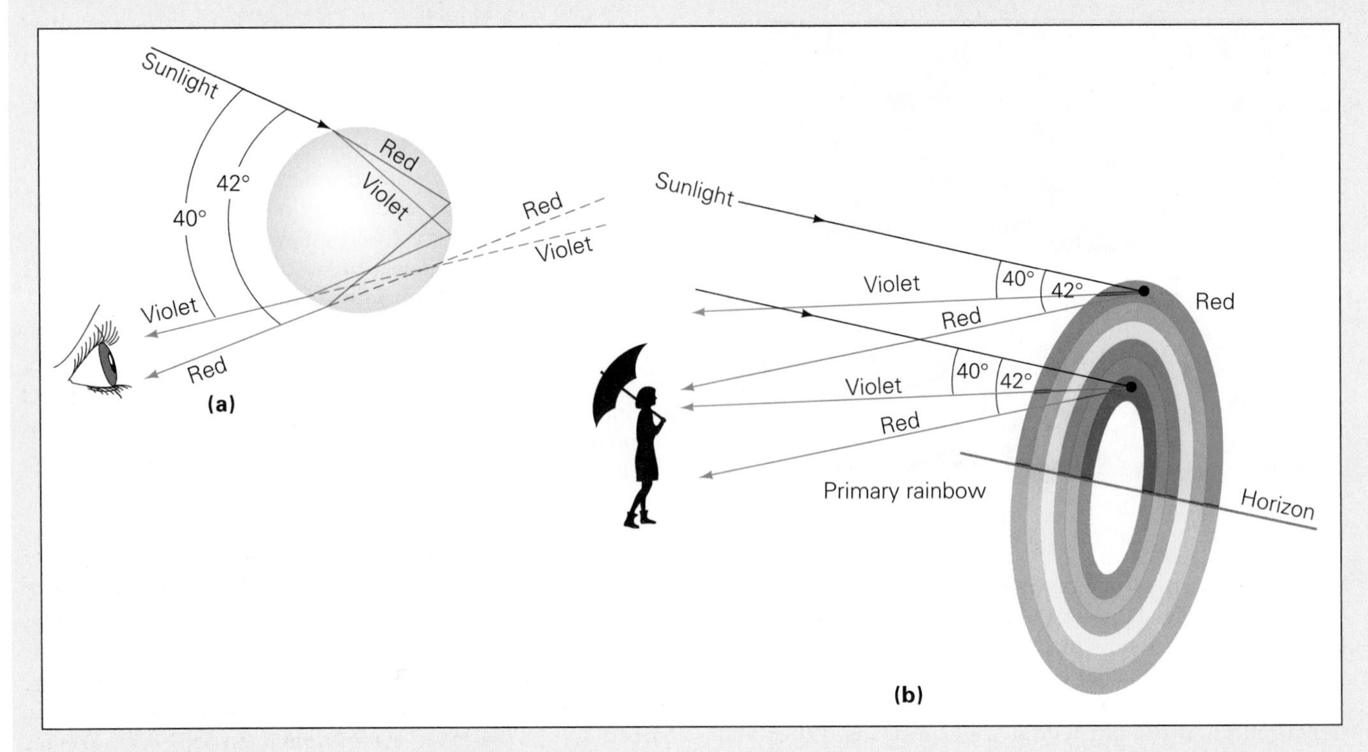

FIGURE 2 The rainbow Rainbows are created by the refraction, dispersion, and internal reflection of sunlight. **(a)** Light of different color emerges from the water droplet in different directions. **(b)** An observer sees red light at the top of the bow and violet or blue at the bottom.

Chapter Review

Important Concepts and Equations

- **Law of reflection:** The angle of incidence equals the angle of reflection (as measured from the normal to the reflecting surface):

$$\theta_i = \theta_r \qquad (10.1)$$

- The **index of refraction** of any medium is the ratio of the speed of light in a vacuum to its speed in that medium:

$$n = \frac{c}{v} = \frac{\lambda}{\lambda_m} \qquad (10.3, 10.4)$$

- The angle of refraction as a ray of light moves from one medium to another is given by **Snell's law**. If the second medium is more optically dense, the ray is refracted toward the normal; if the medium is less dense, the ray is refracted away from the normal. Snell's law is

$$\frac{\sin\theta_1}{\sin\theta_2} = \frac{v_1}{v_2} \quad \text{or} \quad n_1 \sin\theta_1 = n_2 \sin\theta_2 \qquad (10.2, 10.5)$$

- **Total internal reflection** occurs if the second medium is less dense that the first and the angle of incidence exceeds the critical angle:

$$\sin\theta_c = \frac{n_2}{n_1} \quad (n_1 > n_2) \qquad (10.6)$$

- The refractive **dispersion** of light occurs in some media because different wavelengths have slightly different indices of refraction and hence different speeds.

Exercises*

10.1 Wave Fronts and Rays *and* 10.2 Reflection

1. A wave front is (a) always circular, (b) parallel to a ray, (c) described by a surface of equal phase, or (d) none of these.

2. A ray (a) is perpendicular to the direction of energy flow, (b) is always parallel to other rays, (c) is perpendicular to a series of wave fronts, or (d) illustrates the wave nature of light.

3. For regular, or specular, reflection, (a) the angle of incidence equals the angle of reflection, (b) the rays of a reflected beam are parallel, (c) the incident ray, the reflected ray, and the normal lie in the same plane, or (d) all of the above.

4. For irregular, or diffuse, reflection, (a) the angle of incidence equals the angle of reflection, (b) the rays of a reflected beam are not parallel, (c) the incident ray, the reflected ray, and the local normal lie in the same plane, or (d) all of these.

5. CQ When you see the Sun over a lake or the ocean, you often observe a long swath of light (▼Fig. 10.21). What causes this effect, sometimes called a "glitter path?"

▲ **FIGURE 10.21 A glitter path** See Exercise 5.

6. CQ Under what circumstances will the angle of reflection be smaller than the angle of incidence?

7. CQ If a mirror is perfect (reflecting 100%), can you see its surface?

8. CQ The book you are reading does not have a light source, so it must be reflecting light from other sources. What type of reflection is this?

9. CQ It is difficult to drive during the night after a rain because of the glare. Instead of seeing the road, you see the images of buildings, trees, and so on. What causes this glare? Why is there no such glare when the road is dry? (See Insight on p. 326.)

10. ■ The angle of incidence of a light ray on a mirrored surface is 35°. What is the angle between the incident and reflected rays?

11. ■ A beam of light is incident on a plane mirror at an angle of 32° relative to the normal. What is the angle between the reflected rays and the surface of the mirror?

12. IE ■ A beam of light is incident on a plane mirror at an angle α relative to the surface of the mirror. (a) Will the angle between the reflected ray and the normal be (1) α, (2) $90° - \alpha$, or (3) 2α? (b) If $\alpha = 43°$, what is the angle between the reflected ray and the normal?

13. ■ A light ray incident on a plane mirror is at an angle of 55° relative to the surface of the mirror. At what angle of reflection is the reflected ray?

14. IE ■■ Two upright plane mirrors touch along one edge, where their planes make an angle of α. A beam of light is directed onto one of the mirrors at an angle of incidence $\beta < \alpha$ and is reflected onto the other mirror. (a) Will the angle of reflection of the beam from the second mirror be (1) α, (2) β, (3) $\alpha + \beta$, or (4) $\alpha - \beta$? (b) If $\alpha = 60°$ and $\beta = 40°$, what will be the angle of reflection of the beam from the second mirror?

15. IE ■■ Two identical plane mirrors of width w are placed a distance d apart with their mirrored surfaces parallel and facing each other. (a) A beam of light is incident at one end of one mirror so that the light just strikes the far end of the other mirror after reflection. Will the angle of incidence be (1) $\sin^{-1} w/d$, (2) $\cos^{-1} w/d$, or (3) $\tan^{-1} w/d$? (b) If $d = 50$ cm and $w = 25$ cm, what is the angle of incidence?

16. ■■ Two people stand 3.0 m away from a large plane mirror and spaced 5.0 m apart in a dark room. At what angle of incidence should one of them shine a flashlight on the mirror so that the reflected beam directly strikes the other person?

17. ■■ If you hold a 900-cm^2 square plane mirror 45 cm from your eyes and can just see the full length of an 8.5-m flagpole behind you, how far are you from the pole? [*Hint*: A diagram is helpful here.].

18. ■■■ Two plane mirrors, M_1 and M_2, are placed together as illustrated in ▶Fig. 10.22. (a) If the angle α between the mirrors is 70° and the angle of incidence, θ_{i_1}, of a light ray

*Assume angles to be exact.

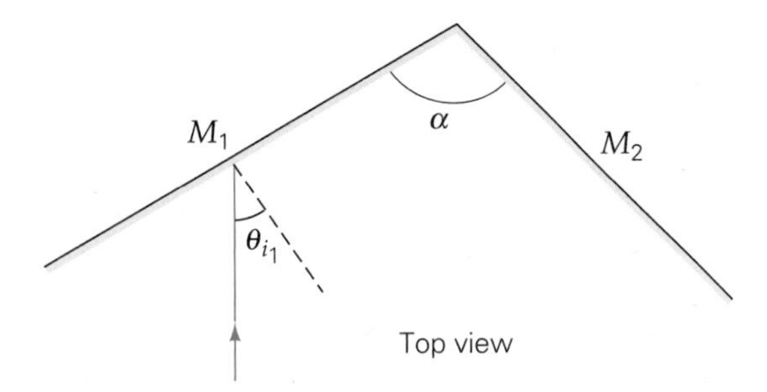

▲ **FIGURE 10.22 Plane mirrors together** See Exercises 18 and 19.

incident on M_1 is 35°, what is the angle of reflection, θ_{r_2}, from M_2? (b) If $\alpha = 115°$ and $\theta_{i_1} = 60°$, what is θ_{r_2}?

19. ■■■ For the plane mirrors in Fig. 10.22, what angles α and θ_{i_1} would allow a ray to be reflected back in the direction from which it came (parallel to the incident ray)?

10.3 Refraction *and* 10.4 Total Internal Reflection and Fiber Optics

20. Light refracted at the boundary of two different media (a) is bent toward the normal when $n_1 > n_2$, (b) is bent away from the normal when $n_1 > n_2$, (c) has the same angle of refraction as the angle of incidence, or (d) always decreases in speed.

21. The index of refraction (a) is always greater than or equal to 1, (b) is inversely proportional to the speed of light in a medium, (c) is inversely proportional to the wavelength of light in the medium, or (d) all of these.

22. CQ What is the fundamental physical reason for refraction?

23. CQ As light travels from one medium to another, does its wavelength change? its frequency? its speed?

24. CQ Ice has an index of reflection of 1.31, smaller than the value for water at 1.33. Why?

25. The critical angle for total internal reflection at a medium–air boundary (a) is independent of the wavelength of the light in the medium, (b) is greater for a medium with a smaller index of refraction, (c) may be greater than 90°, or (d) none of these.

26. CQ Under what conditions will total internal reflection occur?

27. CQ Explain why the pencil in ▸Fig. 10.23 appears almost severed. Also, compare this figure with Fig. 10.12b.

28. CQ The photos in ▸Fig. 10.24 were taken with a camera on a tripod at a fixed angle. There is a penny in the container, but only its tip is seen initially. However, when water is added, more of the coin is seen. Why? Use a diagram to explain.

◂ **FIGURE 10.23 Refraction effect** See Exercise 27.

▲ **FIGURE 10.24 You barely see it, but then you do** See Exercises 28 and 74.

29. CQ Two hunters, one with bow and arrow and the other with a laser gun, see a fish under water. They both aim directly where they see it. Which one, the arrow or the laser beam, has a better chance of hitting the fish? Explain.

30. CQ Will total internal reflection occur if light is traveling from air to glass?

31. CQ Why is fiber optics so useful in medicine?

32. ■ The speed of light in the core of the crystalline lens in a human eye is 2.13×10^8 m/s. What is the index of refraction of the core?

33. ■ Is the speed of light greater in diamond or in zircon? Express the difference as a percentage.

34. IE ■ A beam of light enters water. (a) Will the angle of refraction be (1) greater than, (2) equal to, or (3) less than the angle of incidence? Why? (b) If the beam enters the water at an angle of 60° relative to the normal of the surface, find the angle of refraction.

35. ■ Light passes from air into water. If the angle of refraction is 20°, what is the angle of incidence?

36. ■ A beam of light traveling in air is incident on a transparent plastic material at an angle of incidence of 50°. The angle of refraction is 35°. What is the index of refraction of the plastic?

37. IE ■ (a) For total internal reflection to occur, should the light be directed from air to a diamond or from a diamond to air? Why? (b) What is the critical angle of the diamond in air?

38. ■ The critical angle for a certain type of glass in air is 41.8°. What is the index of refraction of the glass?

39. ■■ A beam of light in air is incident on the surface of a slab of fused quartz. Part of the beam is transmitted into the quartz at an angle of refraction of 30° relative to a normal to the surface, and part is reflected. What is the angle of reflection?

40. ■■ A beam of light is incident on a flat piece of polystyrene at an angle of 55° relative to a normal to the surface. What angle does the refracted ray make with the plane of the surface?

41. ■■ Monochromatic blue light that has a frequency of 6.5×10^{14} Hz enters a piece of flint glass. What are the frequency and wavelength of the light in the glass?

42. ■■ Light passes from material A, which has an index of refraction of $\frac{4}{3}$, into material B, which has an index of refraction of $\frac{5}{4}$. Find the ratio of the speed of light in material B to the speed of light in material A.

43. ■■ In Exercise 42, what is the ratio of the light's wavelength in material B to that in material A?

44. ■■ The laser used in cornea surgery to treat corneal disease is the excimer laser, which emits ultraviolet light with a wavelength of 193 nm in air. The index of refraction of the cornea is 1.376. What are the wavelength and frequency of the light in the cornea?

45. IE ■■ (a) An object immersed in water appears closer to the surface than it actually is. What is the cause of this illusion? (b) Using ▼Fig. 10.25, show that the apparent depth for small angles of refraction is d/n, where n is the index of refraction of the water. [*Hint*: Recall that for small angles, $\tan \theta \approx \sin \theta$.]

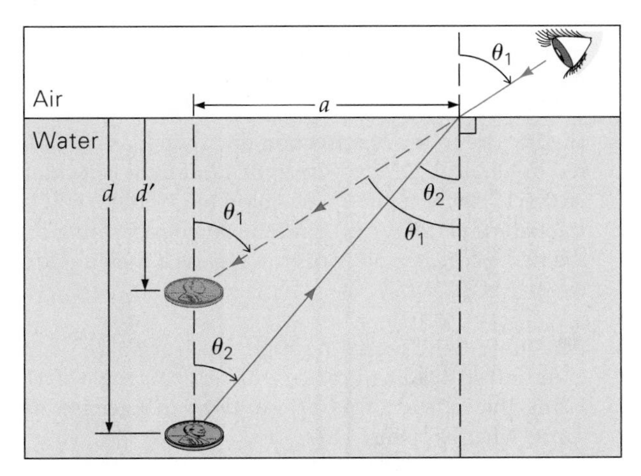

▲ **FIGURE 10.25** Apparent depth? See Exercise 45. (For small angles only; angles enlarged for clarity.)

46. ■■ A fish tank is made of glass with an index of refraction of 1.50. A person shines a light beam on the glass at an incident angle of 40° to see a fish inside. Is the fish illuminated? Justify your answer.

47. IE ■■ (a) A beam of light is to undergo total internal reflection through a 45°–90°–45° prism (▼Fig. 10.26). Will this arrangement depend on (1) the index of refraction of the prism, (2) the index of refraction of the surrounding medium, or (3) the indices of refraction of both? Why? (b) Calculate the index of refraction of the prism if the surrounding medium is air or water.

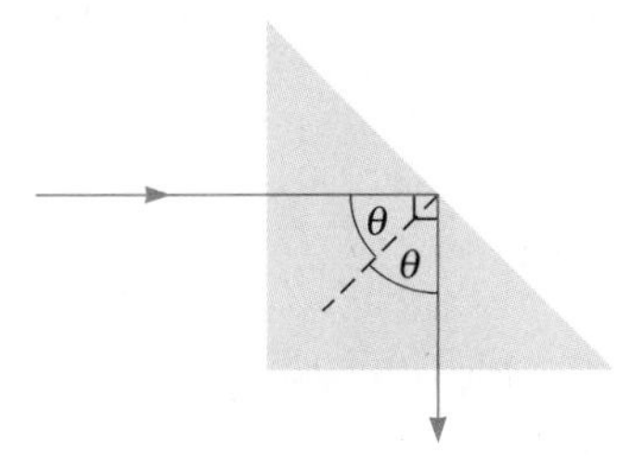

▲ **FIGURE 10.26 Total internal reflection in a prism** See Exercises 47 and 48.

48. ■■ A 45°–90°–45° prism (Fig. 10.26) is made of a material with an index of refraction of 1.85. Can the prism be used to deflect a beam of light by 90° (a) in air or (b) in water?

49. ■■ A light ray in air is incident on a glass plate 10.0 cm thick at an angle of incidence of 40°. The glass has an index of refraction of 1.65. The emerging ray on the other side of the plate is parallel to the incident ray, but is laterally displaced. What is the perpendicular distance between the original direction of the ray and the direction of the emerging ray? [*Hint*: See Example 10.4.]

50. ■■ A person lying at poolside looks over the edge of the pool and sees a bottle cap on the bottom directly below, where the depth is 3.2 m. How far below the water surface does the bottle cap appear to be? (See Exercise 45b.)

51. ■■ What percentage of the actual depth is the apparent depth of an object submerged in water if the observer is looking almost straight downward. (See Exercise 45b.)

52. ■■ At what angle to the surface must a diver submerged in a lake look toward the surface to see the setting Sun?

53. ■■ A submerged diver shines a light toward the surface of a body of water at angles of incidence of 40° and 50°. Can a person on the shore see a beam of light emerging from the surface in either case? Justify your answer mathematically.

54. IE ■■ To a submerged diver looking upward through the water, the altitude of the Sun (the angle between the Sun and the horizon) appears to be 45°. (a) Is 45° the actual altitude of the Sun? (b) If not, what is the Sun's actual altitude?

55. ■■ A coin lies on the bottom of a pool under 1.5 m of water and 0.90 m from the sidewall (▼Fig. 10.27). If a light beam is incident on the water surface at the wall, at what angle θ relative to the wall must the beam be directed so that it will illuminate the coin?

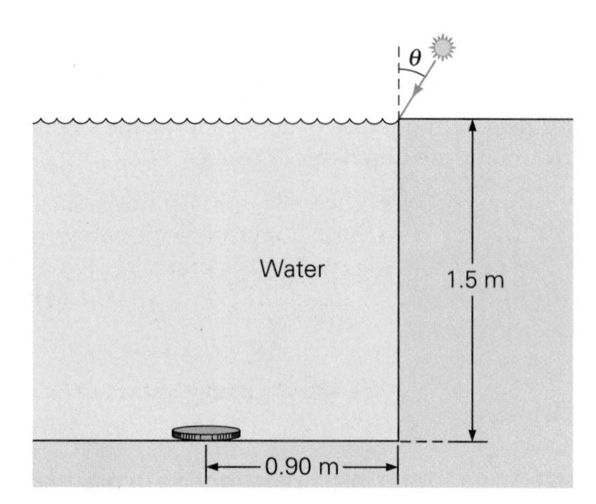

▲ **FIGURE 10.27 Find the coin** See Exercise 55 (not drawn to scale).

56. ■■ Describe a method for measuring the index of refraction of the fluid in Fig. 10.8a. Determine the index of refraction of the liquid.

57. IE ■■ A light beam traveling upward in a plastic material with an index of refraction of 1.60 is incident on an upper horizontal air interface at an angle of 45°. (a) Is the beam transmitted? (b) Suppose the upper surface of the plastic material is covered with a layer of liquid with an index of refraction of 1.20. What happens in this case?

58. ■■ A crown-glass plate 2.5 cm thick is placed over a newspaper. How far beneath the top surface of the plate would the print appear to be if you were looking almost vertically downward through the plate? (See Exercise 45b.)

59. ■■■ An outdoor circular fish pond has a diameter of 4.0 m and a uniform full depth of 1.50 m. A fish halfway down in the pond and 0.50 m from the near side can just see the full height of a 1.8-m-tall person. How far away from the edge of the pond is the person?

60. ■■■ A cube of flint glass sits on a newspaper on a table. By looking into one of the vertical sides of the cube, is it possible to see the portion of the newspaper covered by the glass?

61. ■■■ Two glass prisms are placed together (▶Fig. 10.28). (a) If a beam of light strikes the face of one of the prisms at normal incidence as shown, at what angle θ does the beam emerge from the other prism? (b) At what angle of incidence would the beam be refracted along the interface of the prisms?

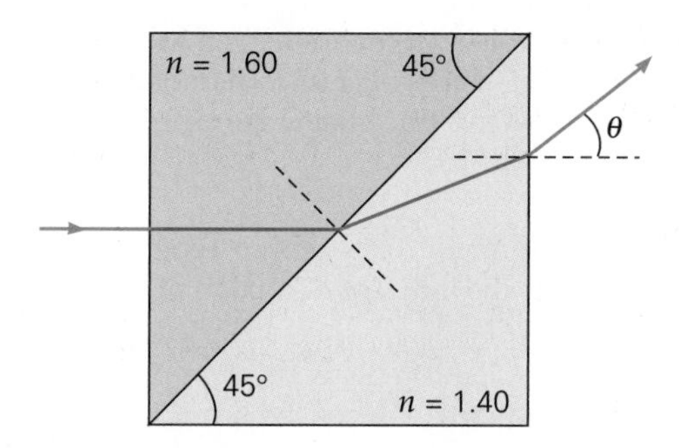

▲ **FIGURE 10.28 Joined prisms** See Exercise 61.

10.5 Dispersion

62. Dispersion can occur only if the light is (a) monochromatic, (b) polychromatic, (c) white light, or (d) both (b) and (c).

63. Dispersion can occur only in (a) reflection, (b) refraction, (c) total internal reflection, or (d) all of the above.

64. CQ What causes light of different frequencies to separate upon being refracted?

65. CQ Why is dispersion more prominent in a triangular-shaped prism than a square block?

66. CQ A glass prism disperses white light into a spectrum. Can a second glass prism be used to recombine the spectral components? Explain.

67. CQ You can never walk under a rainbow. Explain why.

68. CQ A light beam consisting of two colors, A and B, is sent through a prism. Color A is refracted more than color B. Which color has a longer wavelength? Explain.

69. CQ (a) If glass is dispersive, why don't we see a spectrum of colors when sunlight passes through a windowpane? (b) Does dispersion occur for polychromatic light incident on a dispersive medium at an angle of 0°? Explain. (Are the speeds of each color of light the same in the medium?)

70. IE ■■ The index of refraction of crown glass is 1.515 for red light and 1.523 for blue light. (a) If light is incident on crown class from air, which color, red or blue, will be refracted more? Why? (b) Find the angle separating rays of the two colors in a piece of crown glass if their angle of incidence is 37°.

71. ■■ White light passes through a prism made of crown glass and strikes an interface with air at an angle of 41.15°. Using the indices of refraction given in Exercise 70, describe what happens.

72. ■■ A beam of light with red and blue components of wavelengths 670 nm and 425 nm, respectively, strikes a slab of fused quartz at an incident angle of 30°. On refraction, the different components are separated by an angle of 0.001 31 rad. If the index of refraction of the red light is 1.4925, what is the index of refraction of the blue light?

73. ■■■ A beam of red light is incident on an equilateral prism as shown in ▼Fig. 10.29. (a) If the index of refraction of red light on the prism is 1.400, at what angle θ does the beam emerge from the other face of the prism? (b) Suppose the incident beam were white light. What would be the angular separation of the red and blue components in the emergent beam if the index of refraction of blue light were 1.403? (c) If the index of refraction of blue light were 1.405?

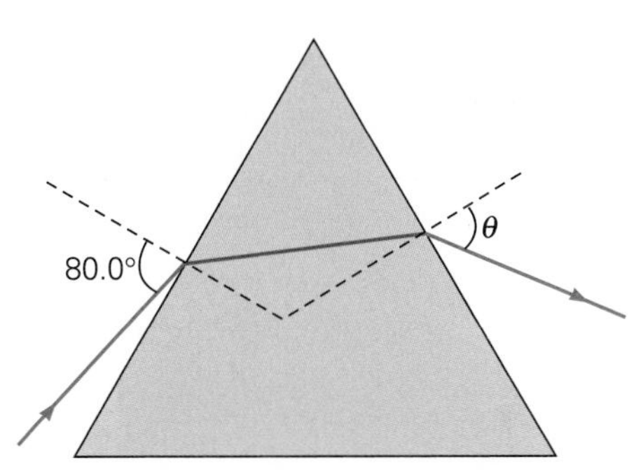

▲ **FIGURE 10.29 Prism revisited** See Exercise 73.

Additional Exercises

74. An opaque container that is empty except for a single coin is 15 cm deep. When looking into the container at a viewing angle of 50° relative to the vertical side of the container, you see nothing on the bottom. When the container is filled with water, you see the coin (from the same viewing angle) on the bottom of, and just beyond, the side of the container. (See Fig. 10.24.) How far is the coin from the side of the container?

75. Light travels from a material whose index of refraction is $n_1 = 2.0$ into another material whose index of refraction is $n_2 = 1.7$. The opposite parallel surface of the second material is exposed to the air. (a) Find the critical angle at which the light will be reflected at the interface of the materials. (b) Find the angle at which the light will pass through the interface and then be reflected at the opposite surface of the second material.

76. Light strikes a surface at an angle of 50° relative to the surface. What is the angle of reflection?

77. A beam of light traveling in water strikes a surface of a transparent material at an angle of incidence of 45°. If the angle of refraction in the material is 35°, what is the index of refraction of the material?

78. Yellow-green light of wavelength 550 nm is incident on the surface of a flat piece of crown glass at an angle of 40°. What is (a) the angle of refraction of the light? (b) the speed of the light in the glass? (c) the wavelength of the light in the glass?

79. Light strikes water perpendicularly to the surface. What is the angle of refraction?

80. In Fig. 10.20b, if the glass prism has an index of refraction of 1.5 and the experiment is done in water rather than in air, what happens to the spectrum emerging from the prism? How about in a liquid that also has an index of refraction of 1.5? Explain.

81. Light passes from medium A into medium B at an angle of incidence of 30°. The index of refraction of A is 1.5 times that of B. (a) What is the angle of refraction? (b) What is the ratio of the speed of light in B to the speed of light in A? (c) What is the ratio of the frequency of the light in B to the frequency of light in A? (d) At what angle of incidence would the light be internally reflected?

Appendices

Appendix I Mathematical Relationships

Algebraic Relationships

$(a + b)^2 = a^2 + 2ab + b^2$
$(a - b)^2 = a^2 - 2ab + b^2$
$(a^2 - b^2) = (a + b)(a - b)$

Quadratic Formula

If $ax^2 + bx + c = 0$, then $x = \dfrac{-b \pm \sqrt{b^2 - 4ac}}{2a}$

Powers and Exponents

$x^0 = 1$

$x^1 = x$	$x^{-1} = \dfrac{1}{x}$	
$x^2 = x \cdot x$	$x^{-2} = \dfrac{1}{x^2}$	$x^{\frac{1}{2}} = \sqrt{x}$
$x^3 = x \cdot x \cdot x$	$x^{-3} = \dfrac{1}{x^3}$	$x^{\frac{1}{3}} = \sqrt[3]{x}$
etc.	etc.	etc.

$x^a \cdot x^b = x^{(a+b)}$
$x^a/x^b = x^{(a-b)}$
$(x^a)^b = x^{ab}$

Logarithms

If $x = a^n$, then $n = \log_a x$.

common logarithms: base 10
(assumed when abbreviation "log" is used, unless another base is specified)

$\log 10^x = x$
$\log xy = \log x + \log y$
$\log x/y = \log x - \log y$
$\log x^y = y \log x$

natural logarithms: base $e = 2.71828\ldots$ (abbreviated "ln")

$\ln e^x = x$
$\log x = 0.43429 \ln x$
$\ln x = 2.3026 \log x$

Geometric and Trigonometric Relationships

Areas and Volumes of Some Common Shapes

Circle: $A = \pi r^2 = \dfrac{\pi d^2}{4}$ (area)
$c = 2\pi r = \pi d$ (circumference)

Triangle: $A = \frac{1}{2}ab$

Sphere: $A = 4\pi r^2$
$V = \frac{4}{3}\pi r^3$

Cylinder: $A = \pi r^2$ (end)
$A = 2\pi rh$ (body)
$A = 2(\pi r^2) + 2\pi rh$ (total)
$V = \pi r^2 h$

Definitions of Trigonometric Functions

$\sin\theta = \dfrac{y}{r}$ $\cos\theta = \dfrac{x}{r}$ $\tan\theta = \dfrac{\sin\theta}{\cos\theta} = \dfrac{y}{x}$

$\theta°$ (rad)	$\sin\theta$	$\cos\theta$	$\tan\theta$
0° (0)	0	1	0
30° ($\pi/6$)	0.500	0.866	0.577
45° ($\pi/4$)	0.707	0.707	1.00
60° ($\pi/3$)	0.866	0.500	1.73
90° ($\pi/2$)	1	0	$\rightarrow\infty$

For very small angles,

$\cos\theta \approx 1$ $\sin\theta \approx \theta$ (radians)

$\tan\theta = \dfrac{\sin\theta}{\cos\theta} \approx \theta$ (radians)

The sign of a trigonometric function depends on the quadrant, or the signs of x and y; for example, in the second quadrant

$(-x, y)$, $-x/r = \cos\theta$ and $y/r = \sin\theta$. The sign can also be assigned by using the reduction formulas.

Reduction Formulas

	(θ in second quadrant)	(θ in third quadrant)	(θ in fourth quadrant)
$\sin\theta =$	$\cos(\theta - 90°) =$	$-\sin(\theta - 180°) =$	$-\cos(\theta - 270°)$
$\cos\theta =$	$-\sin(\theta - 90°) =$	$-\cos(\theta - 180°) =$	$\sin(\theta - 270°)$

Fundamental Identities

$\sin^2\theta + \cos^2\theta = 1$

$\sin 2\theta = 2\sin\theta\cos\theta$

$\cos 2\theta = \cos^2\theta - \sin^2\theta = 2\cos^2\theta - 1 = 1 - 2\sin^2\theta$

$\sin^2\theta = \frac{1}{2}(1 - \cos 2\theta)$

$\cos^2\theta = \frac{1}{2}(1 + \cos 2\theta)$

For half-angle ($\theta/2$) identities, replace θ with $\theta/2$; for example,

$\sin^2\theta/2 = \frac{1}{2}(1 - \cos\theta)$

$\cos^2\theta/2 = \frac{1}{2}(1 + \cos\theta)$

$\sin(\alpha \pm \beta) = \sin\alpha\cos\beta \pm \cos\alpha\sin\beta$

$\cos(\alpha \pm \beta) = \cos\alpha\cos\beta \mp \sin\alpha\sin\beta$

$$\tan(\alpha \mp \beta) = \frac{\tan\alpha \pm \tan\beta}{1 \mp \tan\alpha\tan\beta}$$

Law of Cosines

For a triangle with angles A, B, and C with opposite sides a, b, and c, respectively:

$a^2 = b^2 + c^2 - 2bc\cos A$

(with similar results for $b^2 = \cdots$ and for $c^2 = \cdots$).

If $A = 90°$, this equation reduces to the Pythagorean theorem:
$a^2 = b^2 + c^2$ (of the form $r^2 = x^2 + y^2$)

Law of Sines

For a triangle with angles A, B, and C with opposite sides a, b, and c, respectively:

$$\frac{a}{\sin A} = \frac{b}{\sin B} = \frac{c}{\sin C}$$

Powers-of-10 (Scientific) Notation

In physics, many numbers are very big or very small. To express them, **powers-of-10 (scientific) notation** is frequently used. When the number 10 is squared or cubed, we get

$10^2 = 10 \times 10 = 100$

$10^3 = 10 \times 10 \times 10 = 1000$

You can see that the number of zeros is just equal to the power of 10. As an example, 10^{23} is a 1 followed by 23 zeros.

Negative powers of 10 also can be used. For example,

$$10^{-2} = \frac{1}{10^2} = \frac{1}{100} = 0.01$$

Thus, if a power of ten has a negative exponent, we shift the decimal place to the left once for each power of 10. For example, 1 centimeter (cm) is $1/100$ m, or 10^{-2} m, which is 0.01 m.

A number can be represented in powers-of-10 notation in many different ways—all correct. For example, the distance from Earth to the Sun is 93 million miles. This value can be represented as 93 000 000 miles, 93×10^6 miles, 9.3×10^7 miles, or 0.93×10^8 miles. Any of the given representations of 93 million miles is correct, although 9.3×10^7 is preferred. (In expressing powers-of-10 notation, it is customary to have one digit to the left of the decimal point, unless significant figures are involved.)

Thus it can be seen that the exponent, or power of 10, changes when the decimal point of the prefix number is shifted. General rules for this notation are as follows:

Rules for Using Powers-of-10 Notation

1. The exponent, or power of 10, is *increased* by 1 for every place the decimal point is shifted to the *left*.
2. The exponent, or power of 10, is *decreased* by 1 for every place the decimal point is shifted to the *right*.

This is simply a way of saying that if the coefficient (prefix number) gets smaller, the exponent gets correspondingly larger, and vice versa. Overall, the number is the same.

Example 1. ■ Expressing Numbers in Powers-of-10 Notation

Express the following numbers in powers-of-10 notation.

(a) 360 000 **(b)** 246.7 **(c)** 0.0694 **(d)** 0.000 011

Solution. Applying the preceding rules, we obtain the following:

(a) 360 000 = 3.6×10^5 (shift to left, rule 1)
54 321

(b) 246.7 = 2.467×10^2 (shift to left, rule 1)
21

(c) 0.0694 = 6.94×10^{-2} (shift to right, rule 2)
21

(d) 0.000011 = 1.1×10^{-5} (shift to right, rule 2)
12345

Powers-of-10 notation is useful in expressing the results of mathematical operations with the proper number of significant figures. For example, consider the operation

$$325 \times 45 = 14\,625$$

Expressing the result with two significant figures, we obtain

$$325 \times 45 = 1.5 \times 10^4$$

Example 2. ■ Using Powers-of-10 Notation to Express Calculation Results

Perform the following mathematical operation on a calculator, and express the result properly, using significant figures and scientific notation:

$$\frac{0.0024}{8.05} = ?$$

Solution. Doing this operation on a calculator gives

$$\frac{0.0024}{8.05} = 0.000\,298\,136$$

(*Note*: The number of digits in the result may vary with different calculators.)

The number 0.0024 has two significant figures, so

$$\frac{0.0024}{8.05} = 3.0 \times 10^{-4}$$

Arithmetic procedures of multiplication and division, as well as addition and subtraction, can be done in powers-of-10 notation.

Multiplication of Powers of 10

In multiplication, the exponents are added.

Example 3. ■

$$(2 \times 10^4)(4 \times 10^3) = 8 \times 10^7$$

and

$$(1.2 \times 10^{-2})(3 \times 10^6) = 3.6 \times 10^4$$

Division of Powers of 10

In division, the denominator exponent is subtracted from the numerator for exponent.

Example 4. ■

$$\frac{4.8 \times 10^8}{2.4 \times 10^2} = 2.0 \times 10^6$$

and

$$\frac{3.4 \times 10^{-8}}{1.7 \times 10^{-2}} = 2.0 \times 10^{-6}$$

An alternative method for division is to transfer all powers of 10 from the denominator to the numerator by changing the sign of the exponent. Then, the exponents of the powers of 10 may be added, because they are now being multiplied. The decimal parts are not transferred; they are divided in the usual manner. This method requires an additional step, but many students find that it leads to the correct answer more consistently. Thus,

$$\frac{4.8 \times 10^8}{2.4 \times 10^2} = \frac{4.8 \times 10^8 \times 10^{-2}}{2.4} = 2.0 \times 10^6$$

Squaring Powers of 10

When squaring exponential numbers, multiply the exponent by 2. The decimal part is multiplied by itself.

Example 5. ■

$$(3 \times 10^4)^2 = 9 \times 10^8$$

$$(4 \times 10^{-7})^2 = 16 \times 10^{-14}$$

Finding the Square Root of Powers of 10

To find the square root of an exponential number, follow the rule $\sqrt{10^a} = 10^{(\frac{a}{2})}$. Then, $10^{(\frac{a}{2})}$ is easily found with a calculator (using a 10^x function). At times you may want to get an idea of the order of magnitude by doing the square root in your head. In this case, express the $\sqrt{10^a}$ such that the power of ten is an even number so it can be evenly divided by 2, and $10^{(\frac{a}{2})}$ is the square root. The square root of a prefix of the power of ten can be estimated. Here are a couple of examples where the square roots of the prefixes are evident.

Example 6. ■

$$\sqrt{9 \times 10^8} = 3 \times 10^4$$

$$\sqrt{2.5 \times 10^{-17}} = \sqrt{25 \times 10^{-18}} = 5 \times 10^{-9}$$

Addition and Subtraction of Powers of 10

In addition or subtraction, the exponents of 10 must be the same value.

Example 7. ■

$$\begin{array}{r} 4.6 \times 10^{-8} \\ +\ 1.2 \times 10^{-8} \\ \hline 5.8 \times 10^{-8} \end{array}$$

and

$$\begin{array}{r} 4.8 \times 10^{7} \\ -\ 2.5 \times 10^{7} \\ \hline 2.3 \times 10^{7} \end{array}$$

Appendix II Kinetic Theory of Gases

The basic assumptions are as follows:

1. All the molecules of a pure gas have the same mass (m) and are in continuous and completely random motion. (The mass of each molecule is so small that the effect of gravity on it is negligible.)
2. The gas molecules are separated by large distances and occupy a volume that is negligible compared with these distances.
3. The molecules exert no forces on each other except when they collide.

4. Collisions of the molecules with one another and with the walls of the container are perfectly elastic.

The magnitude of the force exerted on the wall of the container by a gas molecule colliding with it is $F = \Delta p/\Delta t$. Assuming that the direction of the velocity (v_x) is normal to the wall, the magnitude of the average force is

$$F = \frac{\Delta(mv)}{\Delta t} = \frac{mv_x - (-mv_x)}{\Delta t} = \frac{2mv_x}{\Delta t} \tag{1}$$

After striking one wall of the container, which, for convenience, is assumed to be a cube with sides of dimensions L, the molecule recoils in a straight line. Suppose that the molecule reaches the opposite wall without colliding with any other molecules along the way. The molecule then travels the distance L in a time equal to L/v_x. After the collision with that wall, again assuming no collisions on the return trip, the round trip will take $\Delta t = 2L/v_x$. Thus, the number of collisions per unit time a molecule makes with a particular wall is $v_x/2L$, and the average force of the wall from successive collisions is

$$F = \frac{2mv_x}{\Delta t} = \frac{2mv_x}{2L/v_x} = \frac{mv_x^2}{L} \tag{2}$$

The random motions of the many molecules produce a relatively constant force on the walls, and the pressure (p) is the total force on a wall divided by the wall's area:

$$p = \frac{\Sigma F_i}{L^2} = \frac{m(v_{x_1}^2 + v_{x_2}^2 + v_{x_3}^2 + \cdots)}{L^3} \tag{3}$$

The subscripts refer to individual molecules.

The average of the squares of the speeds is given by

$$\overline{v_x^2} = \frac{v_{x_1}^2 + v_{x_2}^2 + v_{x_3}^2 + \cdots}{N}$$

where N is the number of molecules in the container. In terms of this average, Eq. 3 can be written as

$$p = \frac{Nm\overline{v_x^2}}{L^3} \tag{4}$$

However, the molecules' motions occur with equal frequency along any one of the three axes, so $\overline{v_x^2} = \overline{v_y^2} = \overline{v_z^2}$ and $\overline{v^2} = \overline{v_x^2} + \overline{v_y^2} + \overline{v_z^2} = 3\overline{v_x^2}$. Then

$$\sqrt{\overline{v^2}} = v_{\text{rms}}$$

where v_{rms} is called the root-mean-square (rms) speed. Substituting this result into Eq. 4 and replacing L^3 with V (since L^3 is the volume of the cubical container) gives

$$pV = \tfrac{1}{3}Nmv_{\text{rms}}^2 \tag{5}$$

This result is correct even though collisions between molecules were ignored. Statistically, these collisions average out, so the number of collisions with each wall is as described. This result is also independent of the shape of the container. A cube merely simplifies the derivation.

We now combine this result with the empirical perfect gas law:

$$pV = Nk_BT = \tfrac{1}{3}Nmv_{\text{rms}}^2$$

The average kinetic energy per gas molecule is thus proportional to the absolute temperature of the gas:

$$\overline{K} = \tfrac{1}{2}mv_{\text{rms}}^2 = \tfrac{3}{2}k_BT \tag{6}$$

The collision time is negligible compared with the time between collisions. Some kinetic energy will be momentarily converted to potential energy during a collision; however, this potential energy can be ignored, because each molecule spends a negligible amount of time in collisions. Therefore, by this approximation, the total kinetic energy is the internal energy of the gas, and the internal energy of a perfect gas is directly proportional to its absolute temperature.

Appendix III Planetary Data

Name	Equatorial Radius (km)	Mass (Compared with Earth's)*	Mean Density ($\times 10^3$ kg/m^3)	Surface Gravity (Compared with Earth's)	Semimajor Axis $\times 10^6$ km	Semimajor Axis AU†	Orbital Period Years	Orbital Period Days	Eccentricity	Inclination to Ecliptic
Mercury	2439	0.0553	5.43	0.378	57.9	0.3871	0.24084	87.96	0.2056	7°00′26″
Venus	6052	0.8150	5.24	0.894	108.2	0.7233	0.61515	224.68	0.0068	3°23′40″
Earth	6378.140	1	5.515	1	149.6	1	1.00004	365.25	0.0167	0°00′14″
Mars	3397.2	0.1074	3.93	0.379	227.9	1.5237	1.8808	686.95	0.0934	1°51′09″
Jupiter	71398	317.89	1.36	2.54	778.3	5.2028	11.862	4337	0.0483	1°18′29″
Saturn	60000	95.17	0.71	1.07	1427.0	9.5388	29.456	10760	0.0560	2°29′17″
Uranus	26145	14.56	1.30	0.8	2871.0	19.1914	84.07	30700	0.0461	0°48′26″
Neptune	24300	17.24	1.8	1.2	4497.1	30.0611	164.81	60200	0.0100	1°46′27″
Pluto	1500–1800	0.02	0.5–0.8	~0.03	5913.5	39.5294	248.53	90780	0.2484	17°09′03″

*Planet's mass/Earth's mass, where $M_E = 6.0 \times 10^{24}$ kg.

†Astronomical unit: 1 AU = 1.5×10^8 km, the average distance between the Earth and the Sun.

Appendix IV Alphabetical Listing of the Chemical Elements (The perodic table is provided inside the back cover.)

Element	Symbol	Atomic Number (Proton Number)	Atomic Mass
Actinium	Ac	89	227.0278
Aluminum	Al	13	26.98154
Americium	Am	95	(243)
Antimony	Sb	51	121.757
Argon	Ar	18	39.948
Arsenic	As	33	74.9216
Astatine	At	85	(210)
Barium	Ba	56	137.33
Berkelium	Bk	97	(247)
Beryllium	Be	4	9.01218
Bismuth	Bi	83	208.9804
Bohrium	Bh	107	(264)
Boron	B	5	10.81
Bromine	Br	35	79.904
Cadmium	Cd	48	112.41
Calcium	Ca	20	40.078
Californium	Cf	98	(251)
Carbon	C	6	12.011
Cerium	Ce	58	140.12
Cesium	Cs	55	132.9054
Chlorine	Cl	17	35.453
Chromium	Cr	24	51.996
Cobalt	Co	27	58.9332
Copper	Cu	29	63.546
Curium	Cm	96	(247)
Dubnium	Db	105	(262)
Dysprosium	Dy	66	162.50
Einsteinium	Es	99	(252)
Erbium	Er	68	167.26
Europium	Eu	63	151.96
Fermium	Fm	100	(257)
Fluorine	F	9	18.998403
Francium	Fr	87	(223)
Gadolinium	Gd	64	157.25
Gallium	Ga	31	69.72
Germanium	Ge	32	72.561
Gold	Au	79	196.9665
Hafnium	Hf	72	178.49
Hahnium	Ha	105	(262)
Hassium	Hs	108	(265)
Helium	He	2	4.00260
Holmium	Ho	67	164.9304
Hydrogen	H	1	1.00794
Indium	In	49	114.82
Iodine	I	53	126.9045
Iridium	Ir	77	192.22
Iron	Fe	26	55.847
Krypton	Kr	36	83.80
Lanthanum	La	57	138.9055
Lawrencium	Lr	103	(260)
Lead	Pb	82	207.2
Lithium	Li	3	6.941
Lutetium	Lu	71	174.967
Magnesium	Mg	12	24.305
Manganese	Mn	25	54.9380
Meitnerium	Mt	109	(268)
Mendelevium	Md	101	(258)
Mercury	Hg	80	200.59
Molybdenum	Mo	42	95.94
Neodymium	Nd	60	144.24
Neon	Ne	10	20.1797
Neptunium	Np	93	237.048
Nickel	Ni	28	58.69
Niobium	Nb	41	92.9064
Nitrogen	N	7	14.0067
Nobelium	No	102	(259)
Osmium	Os	76	190.2
Oxygen	O	8	15.9994
Palladium	Pd	46	106.42
Phosphorus	P	15	30.97376
Platinum	Pt	78	195.08
Plutonium	Pu	94	(244)
Polonium	Po	84	(209)
Potassium	K	19	39.0983
Praseodymium	Pr	159	140.9077
Promethium	Pm	61	(145)
Protactinium	Pa	91	231.0359
Radium	Ra	88	226.0254
Radon	Rn	86	(222)
Rhenium	Re	75	186.207
Rhodium	Rh	45	102.9055
Rubidium	Rb	37	85.4678
Ruthenium	Ru	44	101.07
Rutherfordium	Rf	104	(261)
Samarium	Sm	62	150.36
Scandium	Sc	21	44.9559
Seaborgium	Sg	106	(263)
Selenium	Se	34	78.96
Silicon	Si	14	28.0855
Silver	Ag	47	107.8682
Sodium	Na	11	22.98977
Strontium	Sr	38	87.62
Sulfur	S	16	32.066
Tantalum	Ta	73	180.9479
Technetium	Tc	43	(98)
Tellurium	Te	52	127.60
Terbium	Tb	65	158.9254
Thallium	Tl	81	204.383
Thorium	Th	90	232.0381
Thulium	Tm	69	168.9342
Tin	Sn	50	118.710
Titanium	Ti	22	47.88
Tungsten	W	74	183.85
Uranium	U	92	238.0289
Vanadium	V	23	50.9415
Xenon	Xe	54	131.29
Ytterbium	Yb	70	173.04
Yttrium	Y	39	88.9059
Zinc	Zn	30	65.39
Zirconium	Zr	40	91.22

Appendix V Properties of Selected Isotopes

Atomic Number (Z)	Element	Symbol	Mass Number (A)	Atomic Mass*	Abundance (%) or Decay Mode† (if radioactive)	Half-life (if radioactive)
0	(Neutron)	n	1	1.008665	β^-	10.6 min
1	Hydrogen	H	1	1.007825	99.985	
	Deuterium	D	2	2.014102	0.015	
	Tritium	T	3	3.016049	β^-	12.33 y
2	Helium	He	3	3.016029	0.00014	
			4	4.002603	$\approx$100	
3	Lithium	Li	6	6.015123	7.5	
			7	7.016005	92.5	
4	Beryllium	Be	7	7.016930	EC, γ	53.3 d

Atomic Number (Z)	Element	Symbol	Mass Number (A)	Atomic Mass*	Abundance (%) or Decay Mode† (if radioactive)	Half-life (if radioactive)
			8	8.005 305	2α	6.7×10^{-17} s
			9	9.012 183	100	
5	Boron	B	10	10.012 938	19.8	
			11	11.009 305	80.2	
			12	12.014 353	β^-	20.4 ms
6	Carbon	C	11	11.011 433	β^+, EC	20.4 ms
			12	12.000 000	98.89	
			13	13.003 355	1.11	
			14	14.003 242	β^-	5730 y
7	Nitrogen	N	13	13.005 739	β^-	9.96 min
			14	14.003 074	99.63	
			15	15.000 109	0.37	
8	Oxygen	O	15	15.003 065	β^+, EC	122 s
			16	15.994 915	99.76	
			18	17.999 159	0.204	
9	Fluorine	F	19	18.998 403	100	
10	Neon	Ne	20	19.992 439	90.51	
			22	21.991 384	9.22	
11	Sodium	Na	22	21.994 435	β^+, EC, γ	2.602 y
			23	22.989 770	100	
			24	23.990 964	β^-, γ	15.0 h
12	Magnesium	Mg	24	23.985 045	78.99	
13	Aluminum	Al	27	26.981 541	100	
14	Silicon	Si	28	27.976 928	92.23	
			31	30.975 364	β^-, γ	2.62 h
15	Phosphorus	P	31	30.973 763	100	
			32	31.973 908	β^-	14.28 d
16	Sulfur	S	32	31.972 072	95.0	
			35	34.969 033	β^-	87.4 d
17	Chlorine	Cl	35	34.968 853	75.77	
			37	36.965 903	24.23	
18	Argon	Ar	40	39.962 383	99.60	
19	Potassium	K	39	38.963 708	93.26	
			40	39.964 000	β^-, EC, γ, β^+	1.28×10^9 y
20	Calcium	Ca	30	39.962 591	96.94	
24	Chromium	Cr	52	51.940 510	83.79	
25	Manganese	Mn	55	54.938 046	100	
26	Iron	Fe	56	55.934 939	91.8	
27	Cobalt	Co	59	58.933 198	100	
			60	59.933 820	β^-, γ	5.271 y
28	Nickel	Ni	58	57.935 347	68.3	
			60	59.930 789	26.1	
			64	63.927 968	0.91	
29	Copper	Cu	63	62.929 599	69.2	
			64	63.929 766	β^-, β^+	12.7 h
			65	64.927 792	30.8	
30	Zinc	Zn	64	63.929 145	48.6	
			66	65.926 035	27.9	
33	Arsenic	As	75	74.921 596	100	
35	Bromine	Br	79	78.918 336	50.69	
36	Krypton	Kr	84	83.911 506	57.0	
			89	88.917 563	β^-	3.2 min
38	Strontium	Sr	86	85.909 273	9.8	
			88	87.905 625	82.6	
			90	89.907 746	β^-	28.8 y
39	Yttrium	Y	89	89.905 856	100	
43	Technetium	Tc	98	97.907 210	β^-, γ	4.2×10^6 y
47	Silver	Ag	107	106.905 095	51.83	

Atomic Number (Z)	Element	Symbol	Mass Number (A)	Atomic Mass*	Abundance (%) or Decay Mode† (if radioactive)	Half-life (if radioactive)
			109	108.904754	48.17	
48	Cadmium	Cd	114	113.903361	28.7	
49	Indium	In	115	114.90388	95.7; β^-	5.1×10^{14} y
50	Tin	Sn	120	119.902199	32.4	
53	Iodine	I	127	126.904477	100	
			131	130.906118	β^-, γ	8.04 d
54	Xenon	Xe	132	131.90415	26.9	
			136	135.90722	8.9	
55	Cesium	Cs	133	132.90543	100	
56	Barium	Ba	137	136.90582	11.2	
			138	137.90524	71.7	
			144	143.92273	β^-	11.9 s
61	Promethium	Pm	145	144.91275	EC, α, γ	17.7 y
74	Tungsten (Wolfram)	W	184	183.95095	30.7	
76	Osmium	Os	191	190.96094	β^-, γ	15.4 d
			192	191.96149	41.0	
78	Platinum	Pt	195	194.96479	33.8	
79	Gold	Au	197	196.96656	100	
80	Mercury	Hg	202	201.97063	29.8	
81	Thallium	Tl	205	204.97441	70.5	
			210	209.990069	β^-	1.3 min
82	Lead	Pb	204	203.973044	β^-, 1.48	1.4×10^{17} y
			206	205.97446	24.1	
			207	206.97589	22.1	
			208	207.97664	52.3	
			210	209.98418	α, β^-, γ	22.3 y
			211	210.98874	β^-, γ	36.1 min
			212	211.99188	β^-, γ	10.64 h
			214	213.99980	β^-, γ	26.8 min
83	Bismuth	Bi	209	208.98039	100	
			211	210.98726	α, β^-, γ	2.15 min
84	Polonium	Po	210	209.98286	α, γ	138.38 d
			214	213.99519	α, γ	164 μs
86	Radon	Rn	222	222.017574	α, β	3.8235 d
87	Francium	Fr	223	223.019734	α, β^-, γ	21.8 min
88	Radium	Ra	226	226.025406	α, γ	1.60×10^3 y
			228	228.031069	β^-	5.76 y
89	Actinium	Ac	227	227.027751	α, β^-, γ	21.773 y
90	Thorium	Th	228	228.02873	α, γ	1.9131 y
			232	232.038054	100; α, γ	1.41×10^{10} y
92	Uranium	U	232	232.03714	α, γ	72 y
			233	233.039629	α, γ	1.592×10^5 y
			235	235.043925	0.72; α, γ	7.038×10^8 y
			236	236.045563	α, γ	2.342×10^7 y
			238	238.050786	99.275; α, γ	4.468×10^9 y
			239	239.054291	β^-, γ	23.5 min
93	Neptunium	Np	239	239.052932	β^-, γ	2.35 d
94	Plutonium	Pu	239	239.052158	α, γ	2.41×10^4 y
95	Americium	Am	243	243.061374	α, γ	7.37×10^3 y
96	Curium	Cm	245	245.065487	α, γ	8.5×10^3 y
97	Berkelium	Bk	247	247.07003	α, γ	1.4×10^3 y
98	Californium	Cf	249	249.074849	α, γ	351 y
99	Einsteinium	Es	254	254.08802	α, γ, β^-	276 d
100	Fermium	Fm	253	253.08518	EC, α, γ	3.0 d

*The masses given throughout this table are those for the neutral atom, including the Z electrons.
†"EC" stands for electron capture.

Answers to Follow-up Exercises

Chapter 1

1.1 A mass of 1000 kg has a weight of 2200 lb. The weight of a metric ton is equivalent to the British *long* ton (2200 lb), or 200 lb greater than the British *short* ton (2000 lb).
1.2 Yes, [L] = [L], or m = m.
1.3 (a) 50 mi/h $[(0.447\text{ m/s})/(\text{mi/h})] = 22\text{ m/s}$.
(b) $(1\text{ mi/h})(1609\text{ km/mi})(1\text{ h}/3600\text{ s}) = 0.477\text{ m/s}$.
1.4 13.3 times.
1.5 $1\text{ m}^3 = 10^6\text{ cm}^3$.
1.6 European. 10 mi/gal $\approx$ 16 km/4L = 4 km/L, as compared with 10 km/L.
1.7 (a) $7.0 \times 10^5\text{ kg}^2$. (b) 3.02×10^2 (no units).
1.8 (a) 23.70. (b) 22.09.
1.9 $2.3 \times 10^{-3}\text{ m}^3$, or $2.3 \times 10^3\text{ cm}^3$.
1.10 16.9 m.
1.11 23.5 N or 23.5 S (Tropic of Cancer and Tropic of Capricorn, respectively).
1.12 $750\text{ cm}^3 = 7.50 \times 10^{-4}\text{ m}^3 \approx 10^{-3}\text{ m}^3$, $m = \rho V \approx (10^3\text{ kg/m}^3)(10^{-3}\text{ m}^3) = 1\text{ kg}$. (By direct calculation, $m = 0.79$ kg.)
1.13 $V \approx 10^{-2}\text{ m}^3$, cells/vol $\approx 10^4\text{ cells/mm}^3\,(10^9\text{ mm}^3/\text{m}^3) = 10^{13}\text{ cells/m}^3$, and (cells/vol)(vol) $\approx 10^{11}$ white cells.

Chapter 2

2.1 (a) No. If meters per minute is used, the answer will be in minutes. (b) 0.200 m/min (or 0.00333 m/s).
2.2 (a) $s_1 = 2.00$ m/s; $s_2 = 1.52$ m/s; $s_3 = 1.72\text{ m/s} \neq 0$, although the velocity is zero.
2.3 No. If the velocity is also in the negative direction, the object will speed up.
2.4 9.0 m/s in the direction of the original motion.
2.5 Yes, 96 m. (A lot quicker, isn't it?)
2.6 No, changes x_o positions, but the separation distance is the same.
2.7 $v_B = 2v_A$.
2.8 $x = v^2/2a$, $x_B = 48.6$ m, and $x_C = 39.6$ m; the Blazer should not tailgate within at least 9.0 m.
2.9 1.16 s longer.
2.10 Time for bill to fall its length = 0.179 s. This time is less than the average reaction time (0.192 s) computed in the Example, so most people cannot catch the bill.
2.11 $y_u = y_d = 5.12$ m, as measured from reference $y = 0$ at the release point.
2.12 Eq. 2.8′, $t = 4.6$ s; Eq. 2.10′, $t = 4.6$ s.

Chapter 3

3.1 $v_x = -0.40$ m/s, $v_y = +0.30$ m/s; the distance is unchanged.
3.2 $x = 9.00$ m, $y = 12.6$ m (same).
3.3 $\mathbf{v} = (0)\hat{\mathbf{x}} + (3.7\text{ m/s})\hat{\mathbf{y}}$.
3.4 No, the boat would curve back and forth, with both components acting.
3.5 $\mathbf{C} = (-7.7\text{ m})\hat{\mathbf{x}} + (-4.3\text{ m})\hat{\mathbf{y}}$.
3.6 $d = 524.976\text{ m} = 525$ m (rounding differences).
3.7 14.5° W of N.
3.8 (a) $y_o = +25$ m and $y = 0$; the equation is the same.
(b) $\mathbf{v} = (8.25\text{ m/s})\hat{\mathbf{x}} + (-22.1\text{ m/s})\hat{\mathbf{y}}$.
3.9 Both increase sixfold.
3.10 (a) If not, the stone would hit to the side of the block. (b) Eq. 3.11 does not apply; the initial and final heights are not the same. $R = 15$ m, which is way off the 27-m answer.
3.11 The ball thrown at 45°. It would have a greater initial velocity.
3.12 At the top of the parabolic arc, the player's vertical motion is zero and is very small on either side of this maximum height. Here, the player's horizontal velocity component dominates, and he moves horizontally, with little motion in the vertical direction. This gives the illusion of "hanging" in the air.
3.13 4.15 m from the net.

Chapter 4

4.1 6.0 m/s in the direction of the net force.
4.2 (a) 11 lb. (b) Weight in pounds $\approx$ 2.2 lb/kg.
4.3 8.3 N
4.4 (a) 50° above the $+x$-axis. (b) x- and y-components reversed: $\mathbf{v} = (9.8\text{ m/s})\hat{\mathbf{x}} + (4.5\text{ m/s})\hat{\mathbf{y}}$.
4.5 2000 N.
4.6 (a) $m_2 > 1.7$ kg. (b) $\theta < 17.5°$.
4.7 (a) 7.35 N. (b) Neglecting air resistance, 7.35 N, downward.
4.8 $T_1 = 25$ N.
4.9 (a) $F_1 = 3.5w$. Even greater than F_2. (b) $\Sigma F_y = ma$, and F_1 and F_2 would both increase.
4.10 $\mu_s = 1.41\mu_k$ (for three cases in Table 4.1).
4.11 No. F varies with angle, with the angle for minimum applied force being around 33° in this case. (Greater forces are required for 20° and 50°.) In general, the optimum angle depends on the coefficient of friction.
4.12 The deceleration of the crate would be less than that of the truck. That is, the truck slows down more than the crate, and the crate slides forward.
4.13 Air resistance depends not only on speed, but also on size and shape. If the heavier ball were larger, it would have more exposed area to collide with air molecules, and the retarding force would increase faster. Depending on the size difference, the heavier ball might reach terminal velocity first, and the lighter ball would strike the ground first. Alternatively, the balls might reach terminal velocity together.

Chapter 5

5.1 −2.0 J
5.2 Work is done initially in lifting the handles and load. But when you move the wheelbarrow forward at a constant height, no work is done by the vertical component because that component is perpendicular to the motion.
5.3 No, speed would decrease and it would stop moving.
5.4 $W_{x_1} = 0.034$ J, $W_x = 0.64$ J (measured from x_o)
5.5 No, $W_2/W_1 = 4$, or 4 times as much
5.6 Here we have $m_s = m_g/2$ as before. However, $v_s/v_g = (6.0\text{ m/s})/(4.0\text{ m/s}) = \frac{3}{2}$. Using a ratio, $K_s/K_g = \frac{9}{8}$, and the safety still has more kinetic energy than the guard. (Answer could also be obtained from direct calculations of kinetic energies, but for a relative comparison, a ratio is usually quicker.)

5.7 $W_3/W_2 = 1.4$, or 40% larger. More work, but a smaller percentage increase.
5.8 $\Delta K_{\text{total}} = 0$, $\Delta U_{\text{total}} = 0$
5.9 9.9 m/s
5.10 No. $E_o = E$ or $\frac{1}{2}mv_o^2 + mgh = \frac{1}{2}mv^2$. The mass cancels and the speed is independent of mass. (Recall that in free fall, all objects or projectiles fall with the same vertical acceleration g—see Section 2.5.)
5.11 0.025 m
5.12 (a) 59% (b) $E_{\text{loss}}/t = mg(y/t) = mgv = (60\ mg)$ J/s
5.13 Block would stop in rough area.
5.14 52%
5.15 (a) Same work in twice the time. (b) Same work in half the time.
5.16 (a) No. (b) Creation of energy.

Chapter 6

6.1 5.0 m/s. Yes, this is 18 km/h or 11 mi/h, a speed at which humans can run.
6.2 (1) Ship the greatest KE. (2) Bullet the least KE.
6.3 $(-3.0\ \text{kg}\cdot\text{m/s})\,\hat{\mathbf{x}} + (4.0\ \text{kg}\cdot\text{m/s})\,\hat{\mathbf{y}}$
6.4 It would increase to 60 m/s: greater speed, longer drive, ideally. (There is also a directional consideration.)
6.5 (a) No, for the m_1/m_2 system, external force on block. Yes, for the m_1/m_2 Earth system. But with m_2 attached to the Earth, the mass of this part of the system would be vastly greater than that of m_2, so its change in velocity would be negligible. (b) Assuming the ball is tossed in the + direction: for the tosser, $v_t = -0.50$ m/s; for the catcher, $v_c = 0.48$ m/s. For the ball: $p = 0$, +25 kg · m/s, +1.2 kg · m/s.
6.6 No. Energy went into work of breaking the brick, and some lost as heat and sound.
6.7 No.
6.8 No; all of the kinetic energy cannot be lost to make the dent. The momentum after the collision cannot be zero, since it was not zero initially. Thus, the balls must be moving and have kinetic energy. This can also be seen from Eq. 6.11: $K_f/K_i = m_1/(m_1 + m_2)$, and K_f cannot be zero (unless m_1 is zero, which is not possible).
6.9 5.0 m
6.10 No. If $v_1 = v_2$, then $m_1 - m_2 = 2m_1$, which requires that $m_2 = -m_1$. Negative mass is not possible, so m_1m_2 is always less than $2m_1$ and the velocities cannot be equal.
6.11 Same as reverse collision, 0.0022.
6.12 All of the balls swing out, but to different degrees. With $m_1 > m_2$, the stationary ball (m_2) moves off with a greater speed after collision than the incoming, heavier ball (m_1), and the heavier ball's speed is reduced after collision, in accordance with Eq. 6.16 (see Fig. 6.14b). Hence, a "shot" of momentum is passed along the row of balls with equal mass (see Fig. 6.14a), and the end ball swings out with the same speed as was imparted to m_2. Then, the process is repeated: m_1, *now moving more slowly*, collides again with the initial ball in the row (m_2), and another, but smaller, shot of momentum is passed down the row. The new end ball in the row receives less kinetic energy than the one that swung out just a moment previously, and so doesn't swing as high. This process repeats itself instantaneously for each ball, with the observed result that all of the balls swing out to different degrees.
6.13 $M = 11$ kg, initially at origin
6.14 $(X_{\text{CM}}, Y_{\text{CM}}) = (0.47\ \text{m}, 0.10\ \text{m})$; same location as in Example, two-thirds of the length of the bar from m_1. Note: The location of the CM does not depend on the frame of reference.
6.15 Yes, the CM does not move.

Chapter 7

7.1 (a) +0.10% (b) 39 kg
7.2 2.3×10^{-4} L, or 2.3×10^{-7} m^3
7.3 (1) Having enough nails, and (2) having them all of equal height and not so sharp a point. This could be achieved by filing off the tips of the nails so as to have a "uniform" surface. Also, this would increase the effective area.
7.4 3.03×10^4 N (or 6.82×10^3 lb—about 3.4 tons!) This is roughly the force on your back right now. Our bodies don't collapse under atmospheric pressure because cells are filled with incompressible fluids (mostly water), bone, and muscle, which react with an equal outward pressure (equal and opposite forces). As with forces, it is a pressure *difference* that gives rise to dynamic effects.
7.5 $d_o = \sqrt{\dfrac{F_o}{F_i}}\,d_i = \sqrt{\dfrac{1}{10}}\,(8.0\ \text{cm}) = 2.5\ \text{cm}$
7.6 10.3 m (about 34 ft). You can see why we don't use water barometers.
7.7 Pressure in veins is lower than that in arteries (120/80).
7.8 greater, by 7.75×10^2
7.9 (a) The object would sink, so the buoyant force is less than the object's weight. Hence, the scale would have a reading greater than 40 N. Note that with a greater density, the object would not be as large and less water would be displaced. (b) 41.8 N.
7.10 11%
7.11 −18%
7.12 69%
7.13 As the water falls, speed (v) increases and area (A) must decrease to have Av = a constant.
7.14 0.38 m

Chapter 8

8.1 (a) 40°C (b) You should immediately know the answer—this is the temperature at which the Fahrenheit and Celsius temperatures are numerically equal.
8.2 (a) $T_R = T_F + 460$ (b) $T_R = \frac{9}{5}T_C + 492$ (c) $T_R = \frac{9}{5}T_K$
8.3 96°C
8.4 273°C; no, not on Earth
8.5 50 C°
8.6 It depends on the metal of the bar. If the thermal expansion coefficient (α) of the bar is less than that of iron, it will not expand as much and not be as long as the diameter of the circular ring after heating. However, if the bar's α is greater than that of iron, the bar will expand more than the ring and the ring will be distorted.
8.7 Basically, the situations would be reversed. Faster cooling would be achieved by submerging the ice in Example 8.7—the cooler water would be less dense and would rise, promoting mixing. For a lake with cooling at the surface, cooler, less-dense water would remain at the surface until minimum density was achieved. With further cooling, the denser water would sink and freezing would occur from the bottom up.
8.8 v_{rms}, 1.69%; K, 3.41%

8.9 The rotational kinetic energy for oxygen is the difference between the total energies, 2.44×10^3 J. The oxygen is less massive and so has the higher v_{rms}.

Chapter 9

9.1 (a) 2.3 (b) 10.2
9.2 (a) 858 m (b) $\Delta t = 0.05$ s
9.3 It would be greatest in He, because it has the smallest molecular mass. (It would be lowest in oxygen, which has the largest molecular mass.)
9.4 (a) The dB scale is logarithmic, not linear.
(b) 3.16×10^{-6} W/m^2
9.5 No, $I_2 = (316)I_1$
9.6 65 dB
9.7 destructive interference: $\Delta L = 2.5\lambda = 5(\lambda/2)$, and $m = 5$. No sound would be heard if the waves from the speakers had equal amplitudes. Of course, during a concert the sound would not be single-frequency tones but would have a variety of frequencies and amplitudes. Listeners at certain locations might not hear certain parts of the audible spectrum, but this probably wouldn't be noticed.
9.8 toward, 431 Hz; past, 369 Hz
9.9 With the source and the observer traveling in the same direction at the same speed, their relative velocity would be zero. That is, the observer would consider the source to be stationary. Since the speed of the source and observer is subsonic, the sound from the source would overtake the observer without a shift in frequency. Generally, for motions involved in a Doppler shift, the word *toward* is associated with an *increase* in frequency and *away* with a *decrease* in frequency. Here, the source and observer remain a constant distance apart. (What would be the case if the speeds were supersonic?)
9.10 768 Hz; yes

Chapter 10

10.1 Light travels in straight lines and is reversible. If you can see someone in a mirror, that person can see you. Conversely, if you can't see the trucker's mirror, then he or she can't see your image in that mirror and won't know that your car is behind the truck.
10.2 $n = 1.25$
10.3 By Snell's law, $n_2 = 1.25$, so $v = c/n_2 = 2.40 \times 10^8$ m/s.
10.4 With a greater n, θ_2 is smaller so the refracted light inside the glass is toward the lower-left. Therefore the lateral displacement is larger. 0.72 cm.
10.5 (a) The frequency of the light is unchanged in the different media, so the emerging light has the same frequency as that of the source. (b) The wavelength in air is independent of the water and glass media, as can be shown by adding another step (medium) to the Example solution. By reverse analysis, $\lambda_{air} = n_{water}\lambda_{water} = (c/v_{water})\lambda_{water} = c/f$. Thus, the wavelength in air is c/f.
10.6 Because of total internal reflections, the diver could not see anything above water. Instead, he would see the reflection of something on the sides and/or bottom of the pool. (Use reverse ray tracing.)
10.7 $n = 1.4574$. Green light will be refracted more than red light as green has a shorter wavelength, thus greater n than red light. By Snell's law, green will have a smaller angle of refraction so it is refracted more.

Answers to Odd-Numbered Exercises

Chapter 1

1. **(b)**
3. **(c)**
5. **(b)**
7. Decimal (base 10) has a dime worth 10¢ and a dollar worth 10 dimes or 100¢. By analogy a duodecimal system would have a dime worth 12¢ and a dollar worth 12 "dimes" or $1.44 in current dollars.
9. 1 nautical mile = 6076 ft
11. **(c)**
13. **(c)**
15. Dimensional analysis uses the fundamental dimensions of physical quantities such as length ([L]), mass ([M]), time ([T]), etc. Unit analysis uses a specific system of units. For example, if the mks system is used, then meter (m), kilogram (kg), and second (s) are used in unit analysis.
17. **(d)**
19. $m^2 = m^2$
21. no; $V = \pi d^3/6$
23. no; $m/s \neq m/s - m$
25. yes; $[L]^2 = [L]^2 + [L]^2$
27. 1/s, or s^{-1}
29. **(a)** $kg \cdot m^2/s^2$ **(b)** yes
31. **(a)**
33. **(a)** cm as it is the smallest unit among the ones listed **(b)** 183 cm
35. 37 000 000 times
37. 73.0 m, 79.8 m, 24.1 m
39. 68 L
41. metric; $9.4 \times 10^2\ m^2$
43. **(a)** 341 m/s **(b)** 0.268 s
45. **(a)** 16 km/h for each 10 mi/h **(b)** 113 km/h
47. **(a)** 59.1 mL **(b)** 3.53 oz
49. 6.1 cm
51. **(a)** $26\ m^3$ **(b)** $9.2 \times 10^2\ ft^3$
53. **(a)** $62.3\ lb/ft^3$ **(b)** 8.34 lb
55. **(a)**
57. 5.05 cm; 5.05×10^{-1} dm; 5.05×10^{-2} m
59. no; only one doubtful digit; best 25.48 cm
61. **(a)** 1.0 m **(b)** 8.0 cm **(c)** 16 kg **(d)** $1.5 \times 10^{-2}\ \mu s$
63. **(a)** 10.1 m **(b)** 775 km **(c)** 2.55×10^{-3} kg **(d)** 9.30×10^7 mi
65. $1.1 \times 10^{-2}\ m^2$
67. **(a)** three, since the height has only 3 significant figures **(b)** $470\ cm^2$
69. **(a)** $2.0\ kg \cdot m/s$ **(b)** $2.1\ kg \cdot m/s$ **(c)** no, rounding difference
71. **(c)**
73. 56 m
75. 100 kg
77. **(a)** 52% **(b)** 64 g, 20 g
79. 9.47×10^{15} m
81. 0.87 m
83. same area for both, $1.3\ cm^2$
85. 25 min
87. 17 m
89. $0.32, $0.32/L = $1.21/gal
91. $42\ cm^2$
93. about $10^2\ cm^3$
95. 0.60 L
97. not reasonable (56 mi/h)
99. **(a)** Since $d = (13\ mi) \tan 25°$ and $\tan 25° < 1(\tan 45° = 1)$, d is less than 13 mi. **(b)** 6.1 mi
101. 7.2 kg

Chapter 2

1. **(a)** scalar, **(b)** vector, **(c)** scalar, **(d)** vector
3. **(a)**
5. Yes, for a round trip. No; distance is always greater than or equal to the magnitude of displacement.
7. Speed is the magnitude of the velocity.
9. The distance traveled is greater than or equal to 300 m.
11. 1.65 m down
13. 30 km, no
15. **(a)** 0.50 m/s **(b)** 8.3 min
17. **(a)** between 40 m and 60 m, as any side of a triangle cannot be greater than the sum of the other two sides. The magnitude of the displacement is the hypotenuse of the right triangle so it cannot be smaller than the longer of the sides perpendicular to each other. **(b)** 45 m at 27° west of north
19. **(a)** 2.7 cm/s **(b)** 1.9 cm/s
21. **(a)** 7.35 s **(b)** no
23. **(a)** $\bar{s}_{0-2.0\,s} = 1.0\ m/s$; $\bar{s}_{2.0\,s-3.0\,s} = 0$; $\bar{s}_{3.0\,s-4.5\,s} = 1.3\ m/s$; $\bar{s}_{4.5\,s-6.5\,s} = 2.8\ m/s$; $\bar{s}_{6.5\,s-7.5\,s} = 0$; $\bar{s}_{7.5\,s-9.0\,s} = 1.0\ m/s$ **(b)** $\bar{v}_{0-2.0\,s} = 1.0\ m/s$; $\bar{v}_{2.0\,s-3.0\,s} = 0$; $\bar{v}_{3.0\,s-4.5\,s} = 1.3\ m/s$; $\bar{v}_{4.5\,s-6.5\,s} = -2.8\ m/s$; $\bar{v}_{6.5\,s-7.5\,s} = 0$; $\bar{v}_{7.5\,s-9.0\,s} = 1.0\ m/s$ **(c)** $v_{1.0\,s} = s_{0-2.0\,s} = 1.0\ m/s$; $v_{2.5\,s} = s_{2.0\,s-3.0\,s} = 0$; $v_{4.5\,s} = 0$; $v_{6.0\,s} = \bar{s}_{4.5\,s-6.5\,s} = -2.8\ m/s$ **(d)** $v_{4.5\,s-9.0\,s} = -0.89\ m/s$
25. 8.7×10^2 km
27. 59.9 mi/h; no
29. impossible, because the average speed to home would have to be infinity
31. Yes, although the speed of the car is constant, its velocity is not because of the change in direction.
33. v_o
35. yes. For example, an object moving in the $+x$-axis (positive velocity) slows down (negative acceleration or acceleration in the $-x$-axis).
37. $1.85\ m/s^2$
39. 3.7 s
41. 36 m
43. $a_{0-4} = 2.0\ m/s^2$; $a_{4-10} = 0$; $a_{10-18} = -1.0\ m/s^2$
45. 150 s
47. **(d)**
49. **(a)**
51. no, $9.9\ m/s^2$
53. **(a)** $3.5\ m/s^2$ **(b)** 4.5 s
55. **(a)** 81.4 km/h **(b)** 0.794 s
57. 3.09 s and 13.7 s. After 3.09 s, it is 175 m from where the reverse thrust was applied. However, if the reverse thrust is continuously applied (possible, but not likely) it will reverse its direction and be back to 175 m from the point where the initial reverse thrust was applied, it had taken 13.7 s.
59. **(a)** travels in the $+x$ direction and then reverses. The object has initial velocity in the $+x$ direction and it takes time for the object to decelerate and stops, and then reverse direction. **(b)** 23 s **(c)** 40 m/s in $-x$
61. 1.43×10^{-4} s
63. **(a)** $30\ m/s^2$ **(b)** 75 m/s
65. no, $x = 13.3$ m
67. **(a)** −12 m/s; −4.0 m/s **(b)** −18 m **(c)** 50 m
69. **(a)** x_o—initial position, x—final position, v_o—initial velocity, v—final velocity, a—acceleration, t—time interval **(b)** The condition under which these equations hold is that the motion needs to be motion with constant acceleration.
71. **(d)**
73. zero and $9.8\ m/s^2$ downward
75. The ball moves with a constant velocity.
77. 78.4 m
79. **(a)** 4 times, as displacement is proportional to the time squared **(b)** 15.9 m and 4.0 m
81. no, not a good deal.
83. 67 m
85. slightly less than 8.0 m/s
87. **(a)** 48 m **(b)** 38 m/s downward
89. **(a)** same, 1.14 s **(b)** 11.2 m/s, −11.2 m/s (equal but opposite)
91. **(a)** less than 95%, as the height depends on the velocity squared **(b)** 3.61 m
93. hits 14 cm in front of the prof
95. **(a)** $\sqrt{6}$, as time interval depends on the square root of acceleration **(b)** Earth: 16.5 m, 3.67 s; Moon: 99.2 m, 22.0 s
97. **(a)** −20.9 m/s **(b)** 2.87 s
99. **(a)** 21 m/s **(b)** 19 m
101. 45 mi/h
103. **(a)** greater than R but less than $2R$. For any right triangle, the hypotenuse is always greater than any one of the two sides that are perpendicular to each other (R) and less than the sum of the two sides perpendicular to each other ($R + R = 2R$). **(b)** 71 m
105. 16.6 m/s
107. 1.2×10^2 m
109. **(a)** 27 m/s **(b)** 4.3 s
111. **(a)** It takes sound time to travel from the bottom of the well to the person. **(b)** 51.7 m
113. **(a)** $5.0\ m/s^2$ **(b)** 13 m/s **(c)**

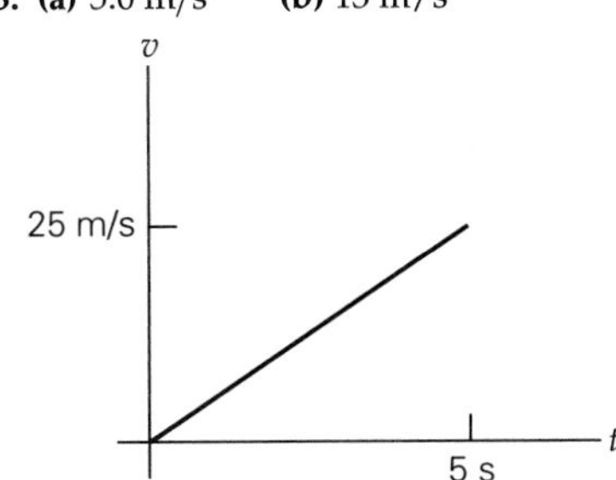

(d)

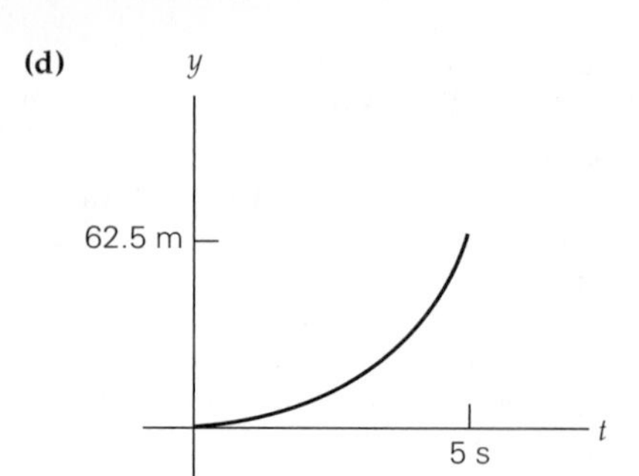

115. 12 km/h

Chapter 3

1. **(a)**
3. yes, e.g. circular motion
5. **(a)** Linear velocity increases or decreases in magnitude only. **(b)** parabolic path **(c)** circle
7. **(a)** between 4.0 m/s^2 and 7.0 m/s^2 as the hypotenuse of a right triangle can never be smaller than either of the two sides perpendicular to each other (so it must be greater than 4.0 m/s^2) and greater than the sum of the two sides perpendicular to each other (so it must be less than 7.0 m/s^2) **(b)** 5.0 m/s^2, 53° above $+x$-axis
9. **(a)** 6.0 m/s **(b)** 3.6 m/s
11. **(a)** 70 m **(b)** 0.57 min, 0.43 min
13. $x = 1.75$ m; $y = -1.75$ m
15. **(a)** $x = 6.56$ m; $y = 3.25$ m **(b)** 5.41 m/s at 13.9° above $+x$-axis
17. 1.0 m/s
19. **(a)** 1.5 m/s **(b)** 70 m
21. opposite direction, same direction, at right angle
23. yes when the vector is in the y-direction
25. $v_x = 8.66$ m/s; $v_y = 5.00$ m/s
27. **(a)** Yes, vector addition is associative.
(b)

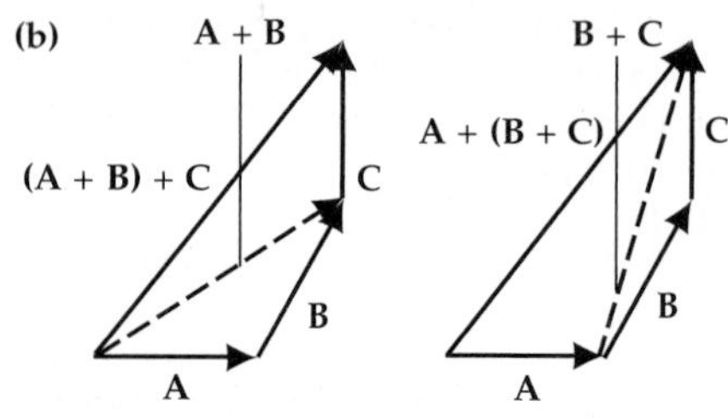

29. **(a)** +15 km/h **(b)** −75 km/h
31. 109 mi/h
33. **(a)**

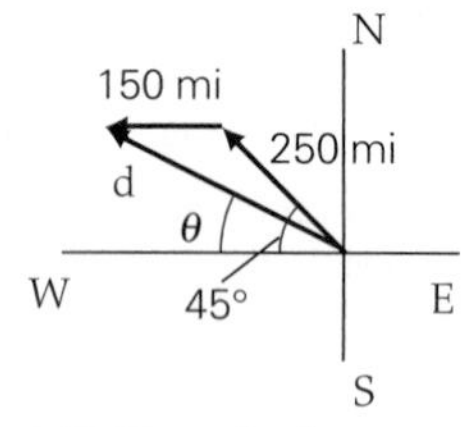

(b) 372 mi at 28.4° north of west
35. **(a)** $(-3.4\text{ cm})\,\hat{\mathbf{x}} + (-2.9\text{ cm})\,\hat{\mathbf{y}}$ **(b)** 4.5 cm, 63° above $-x$-axis **(c)** $(4.0\text{ cm})\,\hat{\mathbf{x}} + (-6.9\text{ cm})\,\hat{\mathbf{y}}$
37. **(a)** $(14.4\text{ N})\,\hat{\mathbf{y}}$ **(b)** 12.7 N at 85.0° above $+x$-axis
39. 16 m/s at 79° above the $-x$-axis
41. opposite
43. 8.5 N at 21° below $-x$-axis
45. parallel 30 N, perpendicular 40 N
47. 27 m at 72° above $-x$-axis
49. **(a)** west of north **(b)** 102 mi/h at 61.1° north of west
51. 242 N at 48° below $-x$-axis
53. Since the rain is coming down at an angle relative to you, you should hold the umbrella so it is tilted forward (perpendicular to the velocity of the rain relative to you).

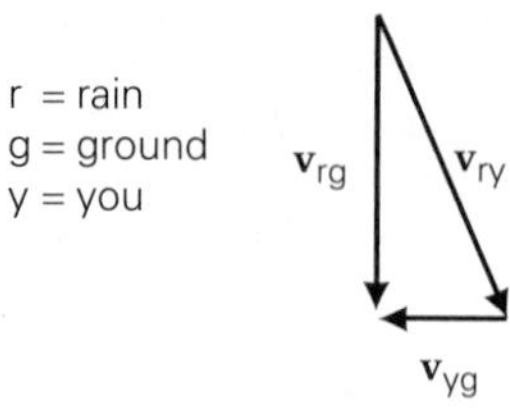

55. straight up. Both you and the ball has the same horizontal velocity relative to the ground or they have zero horizontal velocity relative to each other so the object returns to your hand.
57. 13 s
59. **(a)** +85 km/h **(b)** −5 km/h
61. 4.0 min
63. 146 s = 2.43 min
65. **(a)** 68 m **(b)** 0.76 m/s, 11° relative to shore
67. **(a)** also increases **(b)** 4.7 m/s
69. **(a)** 24° east of south **(b)** 1.5 h
71. 45°
73. The vertical motion does not affect the horizontal motion.
75. 2.7×10^{-13} m; no
77. 40 m
79. horizontal: 26 m/s, vertical: 15 m/s
81. **(a)** Ball B collides with ball A because they have the same horizontal velocity. **(b)** 0.11 m, 0.11 m
83. **(a)** 0.77 m **(b)** The ball would not fall back in.
85. **(a)** 1.15 km **(b)** 30.7 s **(c)** 6.13 km
87. 35° or 55°
89. **(a)** 26 m **(b)** 23 m/s at 68° below horizontal
91. 40.9 m/s, 11.9° above horizontal
93. The pass is short.
95. **(a)**

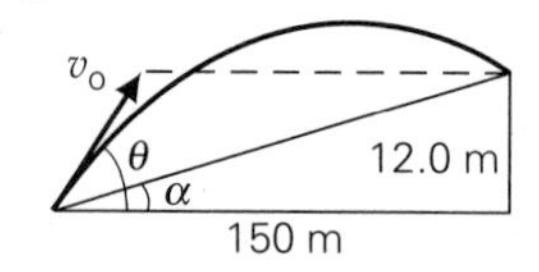

(b) 66.0 m/s **(c)** too long
97. $(4.0\text{ m/s})\,\hat{\mathbf{x}} + (2.0\text{ m/s})\,\hat{\mathbf{y}}$; 4.5 m/s at 27° above $+x$-axis
99. 90 miles at 45° north of east
101. 6.02 m/s
103. 63°
105. **(a)** 30.3° or 59.7° **(b)** no
107. **(a)** 21.7 m/s **(b)** 33.3 m/s, 49.3° below horizontal
109. **(a)** 53° above or below $+x$-axis **(b)** ±8.0 m/s
111. 6.1×10^2 km

Chapter 4

1. no. If an object remains at rest, the *net force* is zero. There could still be forces acting on it as long as the net force is zero.
3. Your tendency is to remain at rest or move with constant velocity. However, the plane is accelerating to a velocity faster than yours so you are "behind" and feel being "pushed" into the seat. The seat actually supplies a forward force to accelerate you to the same velocity as the plane.
5. **(c)**
7. no, same mass, same inertia
9. balloon moves **(a)** forward **(b)** backward
11. The dishes at rest tend to remain at rest.
13. $m_{Al} = 1.35 m_{water}$
15. $\mathbf{F}_3 = (-7.6\text{ N})\,\hat{\mathbf{x}}$
17. **(b)**
19. No, both mass and gravity decrease.
21. "Soft hands" here result in longer contact time between the ball and the hands. The increase in contact time decreases the magnitude of acceleration. From Newton's second law, this in turn decreases the force required to stop the ball and its reaction force, the force on the hands.
23. 1.7 kg
25. 7.0×10^5 N
27. 75.5 kg
29. 78 N, 18 lb
31. **(a)** on the Earth **(b)** 5.4 kg (2 lb)
33. **(a)** 1.2 m/s^2 **(b)** same
35. 2.40 m/s^2
37. **(a)** 0.133 m/s^2 **(b)** Only 300 N needed to maintain constant v.
39. 8.9×10^4 N
41. **(c)**
43. The forces on different objects (one on horse, one on cart) cannot cancel.
45. Yes, the forces on different objects (one on ball, one on bat) cannot cancel.
47. brick hits the fist hard with a force of 800 N, no
49. 1.5 m/s^2, opposite to hers
51.

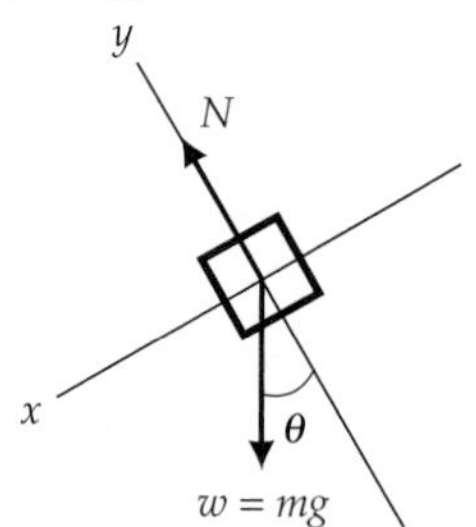

mg-gravitational force
N-normal force by ramp on car

53. **(a)** all of the preceding, depends on the acceleration **(b)** $a = 1.8$ m/s^2 downward
55. **(a)** 735 N **(b)** 735 N **(c)** 585 N
57. **(a)** 2.0 m/s^2, 19° north of east **(b)** 1.3 m/s^2 30° south of east
59. **(a)** 0.96 m/s^2 **(b)** 2.6×10^2 N
61. 64 m
63. **(a)** both the tree separation and sag **(b)** 6.1×10^2 N
65. **(a)** 0.711 m/s^2 **(b)** 1067 N

67. **(a)** 2.5 m/s^2 right **(b)** 2.0 m/s^2 left
69. 1.1 m/s^2, up
71. 3.9×10^2 N
73. 1.2 m/s^2, m_1 up and m_2 down **(b)** 21 N
75. **(a)** no friction **(b)** opposite its direction of velocity **(c)** sideways **(d)** forward, in direction of velocity
77. Kinetic friction (sliding) is less than static friction (rolling).
79. increasing normal force, therefore friction; yes; more difficult to accelerate
81. The treads are designed to displace water so cars with regular tires can drive in the rain. However, the wide and smooth drag race tires increase friction because it uses a softer compound therefore large coefficient of friction.
83. 2.7×10^2 N
85. **(a)** zero **(b)** 3.1 m/s^2
87. 0.064
89. 0.44 m/s^2
91. **(a)** 30° **(b)** 22°
93. 0.73
95. **(a)** 26 N **(b)** 21 N
97. 0.33
99. **(a)** between 0.72 kg and 1.7 kg **(b)** between 0.88 kg and 1.5 kg
101. 1.50×10^3 N
103. no
105. **(a)** 75 N **(b)** 0.097
107. 0.32 N
109. 5.2 m
111. no; 24.6 m $<$ 26 m

Chapter 5

1. **(d)**
3. negative, as force and displacement are opposite
5. **(a)** No, the weight is not moving, so there is no displacement and therefore, no work. **(b)** Yes, positive work is done by the force exerted by the weightlifter. **(c)** No, as in (a), no work is done. **(d)** Yes, but the positive work is done by gravity, not the weightlifter.
7. Positive on the way down and negative on the way up. No, it is not constant. Maximum at points B and D ($\theta = 0°$ or $180°$) and minimum at points A and C ($\theta = 90°$).

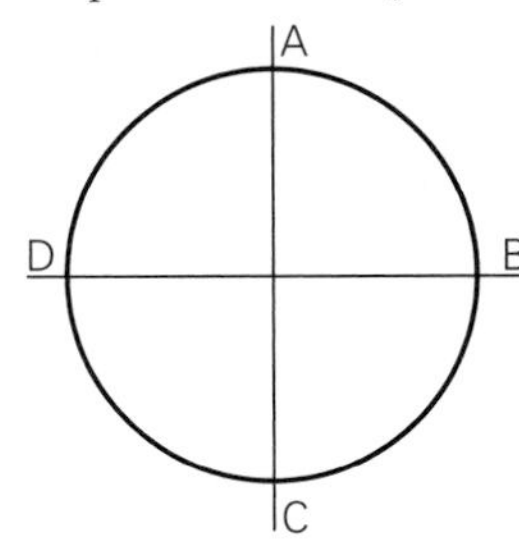

9. −98 J
11. 6.65 m
13. 3.7 J
15. **(a)** negative because the direction of force is opposite (180°) to the displacement (up). **(b)** 1.47×10^5 J
17. 2.3×10^3 J
19. **(a)** 1.48×10^5 J **(b)** -1.23×10^5 J **(c)** 2.50×10^4 J
21. **(c)**
23. three times as much
25. 2.5 cm
27. 1.25×10^5 N/m
29. 0.21 J
31. **(a)** 15 kg **(b)** 5.1 kg more
33. −3.0 J
35. Because the heel can lift from the blade, the blade will be in contact with the ice longer. This will make the displacement a bit greater (longer stride) so that the work done is greater. Greater work translates to faster speed according to the work-energy theorem.
37. reducing speed. Reducing the speed by half will reduce K by $\frac{3}{4}$ while reducing the mass by half will only reduce K by half.
39. $\sqrt{2}\, v$
41. **(a)** 75% **(b)** 7.5 J
43. **(a)** 45 J **(b)** 21 m/s
45.

$$W_{net} = -fd = \tfrac{1}{2}mv^2 - \tfrac{1}{2}mv_o^2 = 0 - \tfrac{1}{2}mv_o^2.$$

$$d = \frac{v_o^2}{2f} \propto v_o^2;\ 200\ \text{m}$$

47. 8.3×10^3 J
49. $x^2 - x_o^2$
51. 4.9×10^2 J
53. 5.9 J
55. **(a)** 8.0 J **(b)** 5.6 J
57. **(a)** all the same as the change in potential energy is independent of the reference level **(b)** $U_b = -44$ J; $U_a = 66$ J **(c)** -1.1×10^2 J
59. (d)
61. final height = initial height
63. Each time you land on the trampoline, you coil your legs on the way down, then push down on the trampoline as you land, thereby compressing it more; storing more energy, you rebound and go higher. The limit is determined by the "spring constant" of the trampoline and how much you can compress it.
65. no
67. **(a)** 15.0 J, zero, 15.0 J **(b)** 7.65 J, 7.35 J, 15.0 J **(c)** zero, 15.0 J, 15.0 J
69. **(a)** 20 J; 60 J **(b)** 8.9 m/s **(c)** 80 J
71. **(a)** 1.03 m **(b)** 0.841 m **(c)** 2.32 m/s
73. **(a)** 11 m/s **(b)** no **(c)** 7.7 m/s
75. **(a)** 2.7 m/s **(b)** 0.38 m **(c)** 29°
77. -7.4×10^2 J
79. 12 m/s
81. no, energy; 9.0×10^6 J
83. They are doing the same amount of work (same mass, same height). So the one that arrives first will have expended more power due to shorter time interval.
85. 97 W
87. 5.7×10^{-5} W
89. 6.7×10^2 J
91. 2.3×10^6 J
93. **(a)** 2.3 hp **(b)** 10 hp
95. $0.36
97. **(a)** more **(b)** 0 − 10 cm: 0.25 J; 10 − 20 cm: 0.75 J
99. **(a)** 4.9 m **(b)** independent of mass
101. **(a)** 8.17×10^5 J **(b)** 3.90×10^3 W
103. **(a)** 0.166 m **(b)** 4.70 m/s
105. **(a)** 5.5×10^2 W **(b)** 0.74 hp

Chapter 6

1. **(b)**
3. no, mass is also a factor
5. not necessarily; different mass can still have different kinetic energies
7. 75 kg
9. **(a)** no, as velocity is also a factor in calculating momentum **(b)** the running back, 38 kg·m/s more
11. 24 J
13. 4.05 kg·m/s in direction opposite to initial velocity
15. **(a)** 3.7 kg·m/s down **(b)** 7.0 kg·m/s down
17. 3.5 m/s in the same direction or 8.2 m/s in opposite direction
19.

$$\Delta \mathbf{p} = (-1.1\ \text{kg}\cdot\text{m/s})\,\hat{\mathbf{x}} + (-2.8\ \text{kg}\cdot\text{m/s})\,\hat{\mathbf{y}}$$

21. 6.5×10^3 N
23. **(a)** 491 kg·m/s downward **(b)** yes; 519 kg·m/s downward
25. increase contact time so to increase impulse
27. **(a)** Drive: large impulse (large $\bar{F}$ and Δt); chip shot: small impulse (small $\bar{F}$ and Δt). **(b)** Jab: small impulse (small $\bar{F}$ and Δt); knock-out punch: large impulse (large $\bar{F}$ and Δt). **(c)** Bunting: small impulse (small $\bar{F}$ and Δt); home-run swing: large impulse (large $\bar{F}$ and Δt).
29. Not necessarily, contact time is also important.
31. 6.0×10^3 N
33. **(a)** 1.2×10^3 N **(b)** 1.2×10^4 N
35. **(a)** hitting it back. When a ball changes its direction, the change in momentum is greater. **(b)** 1.2×10^2 N in direction opposite to v_o
37. 1.1×10^3 N and 4.7×10^2 N
39. 8.2 N upward
41. 0.057 s
43. **(a)**
45. Throw something or even blow breath (there is no friction so you cannot walk).
47. Golf ball has a much smaller mass.
49. 1.0 m/s westward
51. 1.67 m/s in original direction of bullet
53. 7.6 m/s, 12° above the $+x$-axis
55. **(a)** 11 m/s to the right **(b)** 22 m/s to the right **(c)** at rest
57. 0.78 m/s
59. 0.61 m/s, 0.73 m/s
61. **(c)**
63. Momentum is a vector and kinetic energy is a scalar.
65. elastic, as the kinetic energy is conserved
67. $v_1 = -0.48$ m/s; $v_2 = +0.020$ m/s
69. $v_p = -1.8 \times 10^6$ m/s; $v_a = 1.2 \times 10^6$ m/s
71. **(a)** completely inelastic, because the fish and the bird are combined after the "collision" (catch) **(b)** 5.6 m/s

73. **(a)** south of east **(b)** 13.9 m/s, 53.1° south of east

75. no, 1.1 kg · m/s at 69° below x-axis or 249°

77. **(a)** $m_1/m_2 = 1/2$ **(b)** $v_2 = (2/3)v_{1o}$

79. **(a)** $v = v_o/90$ **(b)** 2.5×10^2 m/s **(c)** no, 99%

81. **(b)** $e_{elastic} = 1.0$; $e_{inelastic} = 0$

83. **(d)**

85. directly above the foot on the ground

87. **(a)** (0, −0.45 m) **(b)** no, only that they are equidistant from CM

89. **(a)** 4.6×10^6 m from the center of Earth **(b)** 1.8×10^6 m below the surface of Earth

91. 82.8 m

93. still at center of sheet

97. **(a)** the 65 kg travels 3.3 m and the 45 kg travels 4.7 m **(b)** same distances as in part (a).

99. **(a)** no **(b)** in the same direction

101. 2.1×10^5 J

103. $v_1 = v_2 = 2.0$ m/s

105. **(a)** 36 km/h, 56° north of east **(b)** 49% lost

107. **(a)** inelastic **(b)** 2.1 N · s **(c)** 21 N

109. **(a)** no **(b)** 4.5 m/s

111. 7.7×10^{-23} m/s

Chapter 7

1. **(c)**

3. steel wire

5. N/m

7. 0.020

9. 1.1×10^{11} N/m^2

11. 47 N

13. 3.92×10^{-5} m

15. 2.0×10^{-7} m

17. 6.7×10^3 N/m^2

19. **(a)** ethyl alcohol as it has the smallest bulk modulus **(b)** $\Delta p_w/\Delta p_{ea} = 2.2$

21. 5.4×10^{-5}

23. **(c)**

25. When the bowl is full, the atmospheric pressure on the water does not allow any water out of the bottle. When the water level in the bowl decreases below the neck of the bottle, air bubbles in and water flows out until the pressures are equalized again. No, the height does not depend on the surface area.

27. Bicycle tires have a much smaller contact area with the ground so they need a higher pressure to balance the weight of the bicycle and the rider.

29. Pressure inside balances pressure outside.

31. **(a)** higher due to its low density **(b)** 10 m

33. **(a)** higher as it has a lower density **(b)** 22 cm

35. 6.39×10^{-4} m^2

37. **(a)** a lower pressure inside the can as stream condenses **(b)** 1.6×10^4 N = 3600 lb

39. Air density decreases rapidly with altitude.

41. 2.2×10^5 N (about 50 000 lb)

43. **(a)** 1.1×10^8 Pa **(b)** 1.9×10^6 N

45. 470 N; 1.2×10^6 Pa

47. 2.6 mm

49. **(a)**

51. The level does not change. As the ice melts, the volume of the newly converted water decreases; however, the ice, which was initially above the water surface, is now under the water. This compensated for the decrease in volume. It does not matter whether the ice is hollow or not. Both can be proved mathematically.

53. They will receive the same buoyant force as it depends only on the volume of the fluids displaced and independent of the mass of the object.

55. Yes, reading increases due to the reaction force of the buoyant force.

57. **(a)** water displacement **(b)** no; 18.8×10^3 kg/m^3 $< \rho_g = 19.3 \times 10^3$ kg/m^3

59. 33 N, same

61. no, 14.5×10^3 kg/m^3 $< \rho_g = 19.3 \times 10^3$ kg/m^3

63. 0.33 m

65. 17.7 m

67. 2.3 m/s^2

69. There are more capillaries than arteries.

71. **(c)**

73. The concave bottom makes the air travel faster under the car. This increase in speed will reduce the pressure under the car. The pressure difference forces the car more on the ground to provide a greater normal force and friction for traction.

75. the side facing the batter spinning downward so to generate the extra downward force caused by the pressure difference between the top and bottom of the ball

77. **(a)** increase by a factor of 4 from the equation of contunity **(b)** decrease by a factor of 9.

79. **(a)** 3.5 cm^3/s **(b)** 0.031% **(c)** It is a physiological need. The slow speed is needed to give time for the exchange of substances such as oxygen between the blood and the tissues.

81. **(a)** 0.99 m/s; 1.7 m/s; 2.2 m/s; 2.6 m/s **(b)** 0.44 m, from y = 20 cm

83. 2.2 Pa

85. **(b)**

87. **(a)**

89. 3.5×10^2 Pa

91. 99.99 cm

93. **(a)** 0.09 m **(b)** 8.1 kg

95. 1.32×10^5 N or 2.96×10^4 lb

97. 8.5×10^2 kg/m^3

99. 0.45 m

101. 2.2 m/s

103. **(a)** v_s = 11 cm/s; v_n = 66 cm/s **(b)** 1.2×10^3 Pa

105. **(a)** 3.3×10^4 N **(b)** 3.8×10^4 N

107. **(a)** 9.8×10^{-4} m^3 **(b)** 1.5×10^3 kg/m^3 **(c)** Yes, but less precisely—the sphere would float, and you would have to estimate the portion of its volume that was submerged.

Chapter 8

1. **(d)**

3. not necessarily. Internal energy does not solely depend on temperature. It also depends on mass.

5. Air has water and it may freeze, potentially at high altitudes.

7. **(a)** 538°C **(b)** −18°C **(c)** −29°C **(d)** −40°C

9. −70°C

11. 56.7°C and −62°C

13. 136°F; −128°F

15. **(a)** −101 F° **(b)** 558 F°

17. **(c)**

19. **(a)** increases **(b)** constant

21. The pressure of the gas is held constant. So if the temperature increases, so does the volume and vice versa, according to the ideal gas law. Therefore temperature is determined from volume.

23. The balloons collapsed. Due to the decrease in temperature, the volume also decreases.

25. a higher atmospheric pressure at lower altitude, which causes the bag not to inflate as its pressure is lower.

27. **(a)** −273°C **(b)** −23°C **(c)** 0°C **(d)** 52°C

29. 300K

31. **(a)** 2.2 mol **(b)** 2.5 mol **(c)** 3.0 mol **(d)** 2.5 mol

33. 1.2×10^5 Pa

35. 0.0247 m^3

37. **(a)** increase from the ideal gas law **(b)** $p_2 = 4p_1$

39. 33.4 lb/in^2

41. **(a)** increase from the ideal gas law **(b)** 10.6%

43. **(d)**

45. **(a)** Ice moves upward. **(b)** Ice moves downward. **(c)** copper

47. Volume increases.

49. No, it will not be distorted because both the ring and the bar are made of iron so they will expand at the same rate as one single piece. Yes, the circular ring will be distorted, if the bar is made of aluminum.

51. Lid expands more than glass.

53. **(a)** high because the tape shrinks **(b)** 0.06%

55. 0.0027 cm

57. **(a)** 60.07 cm **(b)** 3.91×10^{-3} cm^2; yes

59. **(a)** The ring, so it expands and then the ball can go through. **(b)** 353°C

61. **(a)** spill because the coefficient of volume expansion is greater for gasoline than steel. **(b)** 0.48 gal

63. 13.4×10^3 kg/m^3

65. **(a)** 1.54×10^4 °C **(b)** no

67. **(c)**

69. The gases diffuse through the porous membrane, but the helium gas diffuses faster because its atoms have a smaller mass. Eventually there will be equal concentrations of gases on both sides of the container.

71. **(a)** 6.1×10^{-21} J **(b)** 7.7×10^{-21} J

73. **(a)** 6.21×10^{-21} J **(b)** 1.37×10^3 m/s

75. increases by a factor of $\sqrt{2}$

77. 1.12 times

79. **(a)**

81. it has more degrees of freedom

83. 6.1×10^3 J

85. 0.46 gal

87. 6.8×10^{-4} m
89. 7.8 cm
91. 33 C°
93. **(a)** 3.3×10^{-2} mol **(b)** 2.0×10^{22} molecules **(c)** 0.94 g
95. **(a)** 18 F° **(b)** 5.6 C°
97. 9.9×10^{20}
101. 3.3 cm
103. 2.026×10^5 Pa

Chapter 9

1. **(b)**
3. **(a)**
5. sounds not all in our audible range
7. same time
9. Sound travels considerably faster in solids than in air. Dogs can hear better by putting their ear on the floor. Yes, it is related to people putting their ears on railroad tracks.
11. 32°C
13. 1.5×10^3 m
15. **(a)** increases as the speed of sound increases with temperature and $v = \lambda f$. So if v increases and f remains the same, λ increases **(b)** +0.047 m
17. **(a)** 7.5×10^{-5} m **(b)** 1.5×10^{-2} m
19. **(a)** 0.81 s **(b)** 0.78 s
21. −1.75%
23. 90 m
25. **(a)** less than double because the total time is the sum of the time it takes for the stone to hit the ground (free fall motion) and the time it takes sound to travel back that distance **(b)** 1.0×10^2 m **(c)** 8.7 s
27. **(c)**
29. to compress a large physical range into a smaller scale
31. **(a)** 8×10^{-17} W **(b)** 8×10^{-5} W
33. **(a)** 1/9 as I is inversely proportional to the square of R. Tripling R will reduce I to $1/3^2 = 1/9$ **(b)** 1.4 times
35. **(a)** 100 dB **(b)** 60 dB **(c)** −30 dB
37. **(a)** increases but will not double. Doubling the power will double the intensity but not the intensity level. **(b)** 96 dB; 99 dB
39. **(a)** 3.72×10^{-4} W/m^2; 1.00×10^{-1} W/m^2 **(b)** 9.55×10^{-3} W/m^2; 6.03×10^{-2} W/m^2
41. **(a)** 63 dB **(b)** 83 dB **(c)** 113 dB
43. **(a)** 10^{-3} W/m^2, 10^{-8} W/m^2 **(b)** $I_M/I_L = 10^5$
45. 10 bands
47. $I_B = 0.56I_A$, $I_C = 0.25I_A$, $I_D = 0.17I_A$
49. **(a)** 3.2×10^{-3} W/m^2 **(b)** 16
51. 10^5 bees
53. **(b)**
55. **(a)** no **(b)** increasing frequency
57. The varying sound intensity is caused by the interference effect. At certain locations there is constructive interference and at other locations, there are destructive interference.
59. moving away from us
61. 0.172 m
63. **(a)** both (1) and (3) because the beat frequency only measure the frequency difference between the two and it does not specify which frequency is higher. So the frequency of the violin can be either higher or lower than that of the instrument. **(b)** 267 Hz and 261 Hz
65. **(a)** Since the heard frequency is higher than the siren frequency, the person is moving toward the siren. **(b)** 13.7 m/s
67. 3.3 Hz
69. 90°
71. **(a)** 1.74 **(b)** 555 m/s
73. 28 m/s
75. **(b)**
77. **(a)** The snow absorbs sound so there is little reflection. **(b)** In an empty room, there is less absorption. So the reflections die out more slowly and therefore the sound sounds hollow and echoing. **(c)** Sound is reflected by the shower walls and standing waves are set up, giving rise to more harmonics and therefore richer sound quality.
79. no
81. the closed end must be a node
83. 510 Hz
85. **(a)** does not exist, only odd harmonics **(b)** 0.30 m
87. **(a)** The position at the mouthpiece is an antinode because it has the maximum vibration. **(b)** 0.655 m **(c)** 0.390 m
89. 1.92×10^3 Hz
91. $I_2 = 1.44I_1$
93. speed of sound
95. 3.9×10^{-7} J
97. 38 vibrations
99. 755 Hz approaching and 652 moving away
101. 1.1 m
103. **(a)** 566 Hz **(b)** 443 Hz

Chapter 10

1. **(c)**
3. **(d)**
5. Water surface has waves, only certain segments of the surface are oriented so as to reflect the Sun's image toward us at any instant. It is like reflections from a series of little mirrors oriented in different directions. The reflecting facets change almost randomly from moment to moment as the water surface undulates.
7. No; if it is reflecting 100%, then you cannot see its surface but the reflections of other objects.
9. After rain, water fills the unevenness of the road and the reflection off the road is specular so images of buildings, trees, and so on are formed. When the road is dry, the unevenness of the road cause diffuse reflection so there are no images of buildings, tree, etc.
11. 58°
13. 35°
15. **(a)** $\tan^{-1} w/d$ **(b)** 27°
17. 12 m
19. 90°, any θ_{i1}
21. **(d)**
23. yes, no, yes
25. **(b)**
27. This severed look is because the angle of refraction is different for air-glass interface than the angle of refraction for water-glass interface. The top portion refracts from air to glass and the bottom portion refracts from water to glass. This is different from what's on Fig. 10.12b. In that figure, we see the top portion directly in air and the bottom portion in water through refraction from water to air. The angle of refraction made the pencil appears to be bent.
29. The laser beam has a better chance to hit the fish. The fish appears to the hunter at a location different from its true location due to refraction. The laser beam obeys the same law of refraction and retraces the light the hunter sees to the fish. The arrow goes into the water in a near-straight line path.
31. It is so useful due to some of its unique properties. An fiber optic is very flexible, small in size, and can be inserted in almost everywhere, compared to the old mechanical based devices with mirrors and lenses.
33. 26% greater in zircon
35. 27°
37. **(a)** diamond to air, because diamond has a higher index of refraction **(b)** 24°
39. 47°
41. 6.5×10^{14} Hz; 2.8×10^{-7} m
43. $\frac{16}{15}$
45. **(a)** This is caused by refraction of light in the water-air interface. The angle of refraction in air is greater than the angle of incidence in water so the object immersed in water appears closer to the surface.
47. **(a)** both, because $\theta_c \geq \sin^{-1}(n_2/n_1)$ **(b)** 1.41; 1.88
49. 3.2 cm
51. 75%
53. seen for 40° but not for 50°; $\theta_c = 49°$
55. 43°
57. **(a)** no, $\theta_c = 38.7°$ **(b)** transmitted, $\theta_c = 48.6°$
59. 2.0 m
61. **(a)** 12.5° **(b)** 26.2°
63. **(b)**
65. two refractions and two dispersions in a prism
67. To see a rainbow, the light has to be behind you. Actually, you won't see a primary rainbow if the Sun's angle above the horizon is greater than 42°. Therefore you cannot look up to find a rainbow thus you cannot walk under a rainbow.
69. **(a)** $\theta \approx 0°$ **(b)** No (no); the speeds are different.
71. Red is transmitted and blue is internally reflected.
73. **(a)** 21.7° **(b)** 0.22° **(c)** 0.37°
75. **(b)** 58° **(c)** 30°
77. 1.64
79. 0°: no direction change
81. **(a)** 49° **(b)** 1.5 **(c)** 1 **(d)** 42°

Photo Credits

Chapter 1—CO.1 Jonathan Daniel/Getty Images Sport Services **Fig. 1.2b** International Bureau of Weights and Measures, Sevres, France **Fig. 1.3b** National Institute of Standards and Technology (NIST) **Fig. 1.5** Frank Labua/Pearson Education/PH College **Fig. 1.5.1** IBM Research, Almaden Research Center **Fig. 1.5.2** Dr. Harold G. Craighead and Dustin Carr, Cornell University **Fig. 1.7a** Jerry Wilson/Lander University **Fig. 1.7b** Kip Peticolas/Fundamental Photographs **Fig. 1.8.1** JPL/NASA **Fig. 1.8** T. Kuwabara/Don W. Fawcett/Visuals Unlimited **Fig. 1.9** John Smith/Jerry Wilson **Fig. 1.15** Peter Brock/Getty Images, Inc, **Fig. 1.18** Dennis Kunkel/Dennis Kunkel Microscopy, Inc. © Dennis Kunkel Microscopy, Inc. **Fig. 1.18a** Frank Labua/Pearson Education/PH College

Chapter 2—CO.2 David A. Northcott/CORBIS **Fig. 2.2** John Smith/Jerry Wilson **Fig. 2.3** JPL/NASA/Getty Images, Inc. **Fig. 2.5** Corbis Digital Stock **Fig. 2.14.2** AP/Wide World Photos **Fig. 2.14** James Sugar/Black Star **Fig. 2.15a** Frank Labua/Pearson Education/PH College **Fig. 2.15b** Frank Labua/Pearson Education/PH College **Fig. 2.14.1** North Wind Picture Archives

Chapter 3—CO.3 C. E. Nagele/Getty Images, Inc. **Fig. 3.12** David Madison/Getty Images Inc. **Fig. 3.13b** Photri-Microstock, Inc. **Fig. 3.16b** Richard Megna/Educational Development Center/ Fundamental Photographs **Fig. 3.18** © Paul Thompson; Ecoscene/CORBIS **Fig. 3.23** AP/Wide World Photos

Chapter 4—CO.4 T.J. Florian/Rainbow **Fig. 4.1** The Granger Collection **Fig. 4.4** John Smith/Jerry Wilson **Fig. 4.15a** Ronald Brown/Arnold & Brown **Fig. 4.15b** Ronald Brown/Arnold & Brown **Fig. 4.19a** Patrick Behar/Photo Researchers, Inc. **Fig. 4.19b** Charles Krebs/Corbis/Stock **Fig. 04.4 M. Ferguson/PhotoEdit.** Market **Fig. 4.25** M. Ferguson/PhotoEdit **Fig. 4.26** Vandystadt/Photo Researchers, Inc. **Fig. 4.28** Ronald Brown/Arnold & Brown **Fig. 4.30** Otto Creule/Getty Images Sport Services **Fig. 4.39** Michael Dunn/Corbis/Stock Market **Fig. 4.40L** The Goodyear Tire & Rubber Company **Fig. 4.40R** The Goodyear Tire & Rubber Company **Fig. 4.41** Sean Thompson/Getty Images, Inc. **Fig. 4.12.3a** Michael Freeman **Fig. 4.12.3b** Michael Freeman **Fig. 4.12.3c** Michael Freeman **Fig. 4.14.2** AP/Wide World Photos

Chapter 5—CO.5 © Dimitri Iundt; TempSport/CORBIS **Fig. 5.9** Guntram Gerst/Peter Arnold, Inc. **Fig. 5.11a** Ken Straiton/Photo Researchers, Inc. **Fig. 5.11b** Vince Streano/The Image Works **Fig. 5.19** The Image Works **Fig. 5.22** SuperStock, Inc. **Fig. 5.23a** Bob Daemmrich/Stock Boston **Fig. 5.23b** Bob Daemmrich/Stock Boston **Fig. 5.26** Bont Skates Pty Ltd **Fig. 5.28** © Harold & Esther Edgerton Foundation, 2002, Courtesy of Palm Press, Inc. **Fig. 5.22.1** AP/Wide World Photos

Chapter 6—CO.6 AP/Wide World Photos **Fig. 6.1a** Gary S. Settles/Photo Researchers, Inc. **Fig. 6.1b** David G. Curran/Rainbow **Fig. 6.1c** Tom & Susan Bean, Inc. **Fig. 6.5a** Omikron/Science Scource/Photo Researchers, Inc. **Fig.6.7.1Liewellyn/Pictor/ImageState International Stock Photography Ltd.** **Fig. 6.8a** M. Hans/Vandystadt/Photo Researchers, Inc. **Fig. 6.8b** Globus Brothers/Corbis/Stock Market **Fig. 6.11a** Ann Purcell/Photo Researchers, Inc. **Fig. 6.11b** H.P. Merten/Corbis/Stock Market **Fig. 6.15a** Richard Megna/Fundamental Photographs **Fig. 6.15b** Richard Megna/Fundamental Photographs **Fig. 6.16** Richard Megna/ Fundamental Photographs **Fig. 6.20a** Paul Silverman/ Fundamental Photographs **Fig. 6.20b** Paul Silverman/Fundamental Photographs **Fig. 6.20c** Paul Silverman/Fundamental Photographs **Fig. 6.22** John McDermott/Getty Images, Inc **Fig. 6.24b** NASA Headquarters **Fig. 6.24c** NASA Headquarters **Fig. 6.27** Jonathan Watts/Science Photo Library/Photo Researchers, Inc. **Fig. 6.29** Runk/Schoenberger/Grant Heilman Photography, Inc. **Fig. 6.33** Fritz Polking/Peter Arnold, Inc. **Fig. 6.35a** Addison Geary/Stock Boston **Fig. 6.36** Charles Krebs/Getty Images Inc **Fig. 6.7.1** Llewellyn/Pictor, New York

Chapter 7—CO.7 Sunstar/Photo Researchers, Inc. **Fig. 7.11** James Holmes/Reed Nurse/Science Photo Library/Photo Researchers, Inc. **Fig. 7.12** REUTERS/Alexander Demianchuk/Getty Images, Inc. **Fig. 7.14** Compliments of Clearly Canadian Beverage Corporation **Fig. 7.15** Ralph A. Clevenger/CORBIS **Fig. 7.16** Tom Pantages **Fig. 7.22b** Hermann Eisenbeiss/Photo Researchers, Inc. **Fig. 7.23a** David Spears/Science Photo Library/Photo Researchers, Inc. **Fig. 7.23b** Richard Steedman/Corbis/Stock Market **Fig. 7.25** Patrick Watson/Medichrome/The Stock Shop, Inc. **Fig. 7.26** Patrick Watson/Medichrome/The Stock Shop, Inc. **Fig. 7.27** Underwood & Underwood/CORBIS **Fig. 7.28** Frank LaBua/Pearson Education/PH College **Fig. 7.29a** Charles D. Winters/Photo Researchers, Inc. **Fig. 7.29b** Charles D. Winters/Photo Researchers, Inc. **Fig. 7.33** Michael J. Howell/Stock Boston **Fig. 7.34a** Stephen T. Thornton **Fig. 7.34b** John Smith/Jerry Wilson **Fig. 7.35** Stephen T. Thornton **Fig. 7.38a** Stephen T. Thornton **Fig. 7.38b** Stephen T. Thornton **Fig. 7.5.1** Jonathan Watts/ Science Photo Library/Photo Researchers, Inc. **Fig. 7.5.2** Blair Seitz/ Photo Researchers, Inc.

Chapter 8—CO.8 Jim Corwin/Photo Researchers, Inc. **Fig. 8.2c** Frank LaBua/Pearson Education/PH College **Fig. 8.3b** Richard Megna/ Fundamental Photographs **Fig. 8.3a** Leonard Lessin/Peter Arnold, Inc. **Fig. 8.6a** Sinclair Stammers/Science Photo Library/Photo Researchers, Inc. **Fig. 8.6b** Sinclair Stammers/Science Photo Library/Photo Researchers, Inc. **Fig. 8.11a** Richard Choy/Peter Arnold, Inc. **Fig. 8.11b** Joe Sohm/ The Image Works **Fig. 8.15a** Paul Silverman/Fundamental Photographs **Fig. 8.15b** Paul Silverman/Fundamental Photographs **Fig. 8.15c** Paul Silverman/Fundamental Photographs **Fig. 8.20** Stephen T. Thornton **Fig. 8.5.1** Maximilian Stock Ltd./Science Photo Library/Photo Researchers, Inc.

Chapter 9—CO.9 Susan McCartney/Photo Researchers, Inc. **Fig. 9.1b** Leonard Lessin/Peter Arnold, Inc. **Fig. 9.6** Reed Kaestner/CORBIS **Fig. 9.12.1** Matt Meadows/Science Photo Library/Photo Researchers, Inc. **Fig. 9.12b** Philippe Plailly/Science Photo Library/Photo Researchers, Inc. **Fig. 9.14** Jeff Greenberg/Visuals Unlimited **Fig. 9.15c** Jerry Wilson **Fig. 9.16b** Photo by George De Sota/Getty Images **Fig. 9.18b** Richard Megna/Fundamental Photographs

Chapter 10—CO.10 Martin Harvey/Peter Arnold, Inc. **Fig. 10.4b** Peter M. Fisher/Corbis/Stock Market **Fig. 10.5.1** E. R. Degginger/Color-Pic, Inc. **Fig. 10.21** Photri/Corbis/Stock Market **Fig. 10.7** Richard Megna/ Fundamental Photographs **Fig. 10.9** Richard Megna/Fundamental Photographs **Fig. 10.11a** Kent Wood/Photo Researchers, Inc. **Fig. 10.12b** Jerry Wilson **Fig. 10.14b** Ken Kay/Fundamental Photographs **Fig. 10.16** Stuart Westmorland/CORBIS **Fig. 10.17a** © Gemological Institute of America **Fig. 10.18a** Courtesy of Cenco **Fig. 10.19a** Nick Koudis/Getty Images, Inc. **Fig. 10.19b** Hank Morgan/Photo Researchers, Inc. **Fig. 10.20a** David Parker/Photo Researchers, Inc. **Fig. 10.23a** SIU/Photo Researchers, Inc. **Fig. 10.24a** Frank LaBua/Pearson Education/PH College **Fig. 10.24b** Frank LaBua/Pearson Education/PH College **Fig. 10.13.1a** © Edward Pascuzzi **Fig. 10.19.1a** Southern Illinois University/Photo Researchers, Inc. **Fig. 10.19.1b** Charles Lightdale/ Photo Researchers, Inc. **Fig. 10.20.1** Doug Johnson/Photo Researchers, Inc.

Index

The Periodic Table of Elements

PERIODS	s: GROUP I	GROUP II	d: Transition elements										p: GROUP III	GROUP IV	GROUP V	GROUP VI	GROUP VII	GROUP VIII
1	1 **H** 1.01 $1s^1$																	2 **He** 4.00 $1s^2$
2	3 **Li** 6.94 $2s^1$	4 **Be** 9.01 $2s^2$											5 **B** 10.81 $2p^1$	6 **C** 12.01 $2p^2$	7 **N** 14.01 $2p^3$	8 **O** 16.00 $2p^4$	9 **F** 19.00 $2p^5$	10 **Ne** 20.18 $2p^6$
3	11 **Na** 22.99 $3s^1$	12 **Mg** 24.31 $3s^2$											13 **Al** 26.98 $3p^1$	14 **Si** 28.09 $3p^2$	15 **P** 30.97 $3p^3$	16 **S** 32.07 $3p^4$	17 **Cl** 35.45 $3p^5$	18 **Ar** 39.95 $3p^6$
4	19 **K** 39.10 $4s^1$	20 **Ca** 40.08 $4s^2$	21 **Sc** 44.96 $3d^14s^2$	22 **Ti** 47.88 $3d^24s^2$	23 **V** 50.94 $3d^34s^2$	24 **Cr** 52.00 $3d^54s^1$	25 **Mn** 54.94 $3d^54s^2$	26 **Fe** 55.85 $3d^64s^2$	27 **Co** 58.93 $3d^74s^2$	28 **Ni** 58.69 $3d^84s^2$	29 **Cu** 63.55 $3d^{10}4s^1$	30 **Zn** 65.39 $3d^{10}4s^2$	31 **Ga** 69.72 $4p^1$	32 **Ge** 72.61 $4p^2$	33 **As** 74.92 $4p^3$	34 **Se** 78.96 $4p^4$	35 **Br** 79.90 $4p^5$	36 **Kr** 83.80 $4p^6$
5	37 **Rb** 85.47 $5s^1$	38 **Sr** 87.62 $5s^2$	39 **Y** 88.96 $4d^15s^2$	40 **Zr** 91.22 $4d^25s^2$	41 **Nb** 92.91 $4d^45s^1$	42 **Mo** 95.94 $4d^55s^1$	43 **Tc** (98) $4d^55s^2$	44 **Ru** 101.07 $4d^75s^1$	45 **Rh** 102.91 $4d^85s^1$	46 **Pd** 106.42 $4d^{10}5s^6$	47 **Ag** 107.87 $4d^{10}5s^1$	48 **Cd** 112.41 $4d^{10}5s^2$	49 **In** 114.82 $5p^1$	50 **Sn** 118.71 $5p^2$	51 **Sb** 121.76 $5p^3$	52 **Te** 127.60 $5p^4$	53 **I** 126.90 $5p^5$	54 **Xe** 131.29 $5p^6$
6	55 **Cs** 132.91 $6s^1$	56 **Ba** 137.33 $6s^2$	57 **La** 138.91 $5d^16s^2$ *	72 **Hf** 178.49 $5d^26s^2$	73 **Ta** 180.95 $5d^36s^2$	74 **W** 183.85 $5d^46s^2$	75 **Re** 186.21 $5d^56s^2$	76 **Os** 190.2 $5d^66s^2$	77 **Ir** 192.22 $5d^76s^2$	78 **Pt** 195.08 $5d^96s^1$	79 **Au** 196.97 $5d^{10}6s^1$	80 **Hg** 200.59 $5d^{10}6s^2$	81 **Tl** 204.36 $6p^1$	82 **Pb** 207.2 $6p^2$	83 **Bi** 208.98 $6p^3$	84 **Po** (209) $6p^4$	85 **At** (210) $6p^5$	86 **Rn** (222) $6p^6$
7	87 **Fr** (223) $7s^1$	88 **Ra** 226.03 $7s^2$	89 **Ac** 227.03 $6d^17s^2$ †	104 **Rf** (261) $6d^27s^2$	105 **Db** (262) $6d^37s^2$	106 **Sg** (263) $6d^47s^2$	107 **Bh** (264) $6d^57s^2$	108 **Hs** (265) $6d^67s^2$	109 **Mt** (268) $6d^77s^2$	110 (269)	111 (272)	112 (277)						

Key: Atomic number — 26; Symbol — **Fe**; Atomic mass — 58.85; Outer electron configuration — $3d^64s^2$

f

*	58 **Ce** 140.12 $5d^14f^16s^2$	59 **Pr** 140.91 $4f^36s^2$	60 **Nd** 144.24 $4f^46s^2$	61 **Pm** (145) $4f^56s^2$	62 **Sm** 150.36 $4f^66s^2$	63 **Eu** 151.96 $4f^76s^2$	64 **Gd** 157.25 $5d^14f^76s^2$	65 **Tb** 158.93 $5d^14f^86s$	66 **Dy** 162.50 $4f^{10}6s^2$	67 **Ho** 164.93 $4f^{11}6s^2$	68 **Er** 167.26 $4f^{12}6s^2$	69 **Tm** 168.93 $4f^{13}6s^2$	70 **Yb** 173.04 $4f^{14}6s^2$	71 **Lu** 174.97 $5d^14f^{14}6s^2$	(Lanthanides)
†	90 **Th** 232.04 $6d^27s^2$	91 **Pa** 231.04 $5f^26d^17s^2$	92 **U** 238.03 $5f^36d^17s^2$	93 **Np** 237.05 $5f^46d^17s^2$	94 **Pu** (244) $5f^66d^07s^2$	95 **Am** (243) $5f^76d^07s^2$	96 **Cm** (247) $5f^76d^17s^2$	97 **Bk** (247) $5f^86d^17s^2$	98 **Cf** (251) $5f^{10}6d^07s^2$	99 **Es** (252) $5s^{11}6d^07s^2$	100 **Fm** (257) $5f^{12}6d^07s^2$	101 **Md** (258) $5f^{13}6d^07s^2$	102 **No** (259) $5f^{14}6d^07s^2$	103 **Lr** (260) $5f^{14}6d^17s^2$	(Actinides)